CONSTANTS

(*See also* Appendix I)

ELEMENTARY CLASSICAL PHYSICS

VOLUME I

ELEMENTARY
CLASSICAL PHYSICS

VOLUME I

(MECHANICS, KINETIC THEORY, THERMODYNAMICS)

RICHARD T. WEIDNER
PROFESSOR OF PHYSICS
RUTGERS UNIVERSITY
NEW BRUNSWICK, NEW JERSEY

ROBERT L. SELLS
PROFESSOR OF PHYSICS
STATE UNIVERSITY COLLEGE
GENESEO, NEW YORK

ALLYN AND BACON, INC. BOSTON

PREFACE

This is the first of two volumes in elementary classical physics. This volume treats mechanics, kinetic theory, and thermodynamics; the second volume treats electromagnetism and wave motion. Together with the authors' *Elementary Modern Physics*, these volumes constitute a series of introductory texts in college physics for students of science and engineering.

Our aim, above all, has been to be clear and to be rigorous. The approach of this text, as reflected in the sequence of topics and their relative emphasis, represents a departure, but not a radical departure, from that of traditional physics texts. Primary emphasis is given to the basic conservation laws, particularly as they relate to contemporary physics. Many traditional but secondary topics and applications have been omitted or relegated to problems. For example, we concentrate on linear-momentum conservation, but de-emphasize statics; we treat heat and thermodynamics from the point of view of the kinetic theory of gases, and de-emphasize calorimetry. The historical development of physics, an interesting study in itself, has been largely omitted, although a brief chronology of important discoveries in classical mechanics and heat is given in Appendix IV.

We have tried to give thorough and complete expositions, so that the beginning student may, hopefully, be able to read with understanding, not only those topics which are presented formally in a course, but other topics as well. In particular, the first several chapters on kinematics are developed in considerable detail, not because we expect that instructors will wish to spend a large amount of time on these chapters, but rather because we have found that students in the early stages of a course require extremely careful exposition. Indeed, our attitude throughout has been to begin at the beginning and to give thorough explanations in detail. Although recent curriculum revisions in high-school physics now permit college physics to be taught at a somewhat more sophisticated level than heretofore, we believe that most science and engineering students still require a text which presents the fundamental ideas of classical physics at a realistic conceptual and analytical level.

The title of the text is accurate. Although many applications of modern physics are used as examples, we stop short of quantum and relativity physics. Our motivation is simply that, insofar as their everyday physical experiences are concerned, students live in a classical world; to introduce relativistic and quantum physics into the introductory physics course at too early a stage not only may result in fundamental topics of classical physics being poorly understood, or not learned at all, but also may result in a rather superficial understanding of the ideas of relativity and quantum physics.

We assume that students using this book are concurrently studying the calculus. Derivatives are first invoked seriously in Chapter 4. Vector algebra is treated in Chapter 3 and is used extensively thereafter. The dot and cross products of vectors are defined when required for the development of physical ideas (in the definition of work and of torque, respectively).

The sequence of topics is somewhat unconventional. After treating translational kinematics, frames of reference, and the law of inertia, we begin dynamics with the law of linear-momentum conservation and its experimental confirmation in collisions. Following this, force is *defined* as the time rate of linear momentum, the superposition principle for forces is discussed, and then Newton's second law of motion is treated. This procedure is, we believe, logically and pedagogically justified, not only because of certain difficulties inherent in using the Newtonian laws as the foundation of mechanics, but especially because of the dominant role played by linear momentum and its conservation in modern physics.

Then follow chapters on work, kinetic energy, and the conservation of energy principle. These topics—difficult ones for the beginning student—are given more attention than is typical in an introductory text. We hope thereby to avoid misconceptions to be unlearned later.

The emphasis throughout is on the atomic point of view. This is evident in the chapters on hydrodynamics and elasticity. It is even more crucial in the discussion of heat, which is introduced through the kinetic theory of gases. Indeed, the meaning of the first and second laws of thermodynamics is first illustrated in the molecular behavior of gas molecules. Considerable emphasis is given to the ideas of (if not the mathematical apparatus of) statistical mechanics. The thermal behavior of solids and liquids comes later; here again we concentrate on the ideas of order and disorder, rather than on calorimetry and mechanical equivalence. The elements of formal thermodynamics follow. A word on usage: We use the term *heat* to denote the energy transfer process arising from a temperature difference; the term *thermal energy* (rather than heat) is used to denote disordered internal energy.

We have deferred the topic of wave motion to Volume II, where the discussion of mechanical waves is integrated into the treatment of other types of waves, notably electromagnetic waves and light, and of wave phenomena generally. Chapters 39 and 40 of Volume II, which deal exclusively with mechanical waves, may, however, be introduced earlier without serious discontinuities. One might say that this volume is concerned mostly with particles; the second volume treats wave behavior, and the interaction of particles with fields.

Sections set in small type contain secondary and optional topics, or detailed mathematical proofs that instructors may wish to omit. For the most part, those topics which might well be omitted in a short course are either placed near the chapter ends (as in the case of the general proof of the parallel-axis theorem) or are grouped together in a separate chapter (as in the case of hydrodynamics, or the second chapter on the kinetic theory).

The mks absolute system of units is given primary emphasis. We also include, however, the English gravitational and cgs absolute systems. Comprehensive conversion factors are given in Appendix II.

There are numerous illustrative examples. We have not skimped in giving full explanations, particularly where these examples lend themselves to alternative interpretations or to interesting extensions. Many examples concern classical physics as applied to atomic and nuclear physics. Most chapters conclude with a brief, but carefully selected, summary of the principal ideas introduced therein. There are many problems, numerical and non-numerical, at the chapter ends. Those of more than average difficulty are identified with an asterisk. Answers to odd-numbered problems are given in the back of the book. Since we wish students working numerical problems to concentrate on physical principles rather than computations, answers to problems involve two, or at most three, significant figures.

Our thanks go to Mr. John S. Brown, who checked the answers to all problems and examples; to Mrs. Patricia Kinder, who typed the manuscript with great efficiency; to Mrs. Anita Gala and Miss Bette R. MacIntyre, who assisted the authors in proofreading; and to the editorial and production staffs of Allyn and Bacon, who facilitated our efforts throughout.

Richard T. Weidner
Robert L. Sells

New Brunswick, New Jersey
Geneseo, New York

CONTENTS

FOUR
KINEMATICS IN TWO DIMENSIONS

FIVE
UNIFORM CIRCULAR MOTION AND SIMPLE HARMONIC MOTION

SIX
REFERENCE FRAMES

SEVEN
THE LAW OF INERTIA AND THE CONSERVATION OF MASS

EIGHT
LINEAR MOMENTUM AND ITS CONSERVATION

NINE
FORCE

TEN
NEWTONIAN MECHANICS AND ITS APPLICATIONS

ELEVEN
ENERGY

TWELVE
POTENTIAL ENERGY AND THE CONSERVATION OF ENERGY

THIRTEEN
ROTATIONAL KINEMATICS

FOURTEEN
ROTATIONAL DYNAMICS

FIFTEEN
ANGULAR MOMENTUM

CONTENTS

SIXTEEN
GRAVITATION

SEVENTEEN
ELASTICITY AND SIMPLE HARMONIC MOTION

EIGHTEEN
FLUIDS

NINETEEN
TEMPERATURE AND THERMAL EXPANSION

TWENTY
IDEAL GASES: MACROSCOPIC PROPERTIES

TWENTY-ONE
IDEAL GASES: MICROSCOPIC PROPERTIES AND THE KINETIC THEORY OF GASES

TWENTY-TWO
FURTHER ASPECTS OF THE KINETIC THEORY

TWENTY-THREE
THERMAL PROPERTIES OF SOLIDS AND LIQUIDS

TWENTY-FOUR
THE SECOND LAW OF THERMODYNAMICS AND HEAT ENGINES

APPENDICES

ELEMENTARY CLASSICAL PHYSICS

VOLUME I

O N E

INTRODUCTION

Physics is *the* fundamental experimental science. Its purpose is to make sense out of the behavior of the physical universe. Physics begins with controlled observation, or experiment, in which some one phenomenon is examined quantitatively through measurements. The relations among the physical quantities observed in experimentation are expressed with precision and economy, in the language of mathematics. When a relation summarizes many experiments with a reliability so great that it can be said to reflect universal behavior in nature, then it is said to be a "law" of physics. Happily, the laws of physics are few, and the whole variety of physical phenomena is comprehended in a remarkably small number of fundamental laws.

Theory and experiment both play essential roles in the development of physics. Experiment discloses the facts of nature; theory makes sense out of them. Theory, moreover, suggests still further experiments as tests of the laws of physics, and experiment reveals points at which a theory may be defective.

Physics is not complete—and probably will never be. As contemporary physicists probe the nucleus of the atom and its constituent particles, they find phenomena unaccounted for in present-day laws of physics. Presumably, if one knew completely the "elementary" particles of physics and the ways in which they interact with one another, all other physical phenomena—atomic and nuclear structure, the behavior and properties of ordinary materials, and even the collisions of galaxies—would be explainable. But that day has not arrived.

Although all "laws" in physics must be regarded as incomplete and tentative to a greater or lesser degree and although there is no single theory of physics, there is one body of knowledge in physics that can be regarded as essentially complete and correct: this is *classical physics*. So-called classical physics deals with the behavior of bodies of ordinary size (greater than that of the atom, which is 10^{-10} m) moving at speeds much less than that of light, (3×10^8 m/sec). It had its origins in mechanics, in the work of Galileo and Newton. Its last chapters were written at the end of the nineteenth century, when the theories of thermodynamics and electromagnetism reached their full classical development.

Classical mechanics and electromagnetism can be said to be "right" because their theories adequately describe the behavior of all bodies of ordinary size. But classical physics fails when applied to the motions of bodies of atomic or nuclear size (for which the quantum theory must be invoked) or to high-speed particles (for which the theory of relativity must be used). We study classical physics, not only because it is correct over a broad domain, but also because the same concepts and language of classical physics appear in the modern physics of high-speed atomic particles.

I-I Events The birth of Galileo took place at latitude 43.7° north, longitude 10.4° east of Greenwich, altitude 1500 feet above sea level, in the year A.D. 1564. Four numbers are required in the specification of this historical event—three for its location in space and one for its location in time. Classical physics also deals with events in space and time. An event in physics may be nothing more than the appearance of a particle, but it is distinct from an historical event in that it represents a universal behavior illustrating the simple and general laws of physics.

An event in physics also is completely described by three quantities giving the location relative to some arbitrarily chosen origin (not necessarily the Earth's center or the town of Greenwich) and a single quantity giving the time relative to some arbitrarily chosen zero of time. That is to say, the events in physics, like ordinary events, are described in terms of position and time.

I-2 Length Measurement of position requires a measurement of length, and a length measurement requires the choice of a universally agreed upon standard of length, relative to which all distance measurements are ultimately related. In the metric systems—the *meter-kilogram-second*, or mks, and the *centimeter-gram-second*, or cgs—the standard of length is the *meter*. The meter was first chosen such that the distance from the Earth's pole to its equator along the meridian line through Paris would be 10,000,000 meters. Later the meter was defined as the distance between two fine scratches on a carefully preserved bar of platinum-iridium, the original of which is kept at the International Bureau of Weights and Measures in France. Secondary standards, or near replicas, are distributed to such agencies as the National Bureau of Standards in Washington. At present the meter is defined in terms of the wavelength of orange light of the visible spectrum, emitted by atoms of isotope-86 of krypton. By definition,

$$1 \text{ m} = 1,650,763.73 \text{ wavelengths of krypton-86 light}$$

A standard of length must meet the requirements of easy accessibility and high accuracy, unappreciably influenced by such disturbances as changes in temperature or pressure. The platinum-iridium bar, which was the standard of length before 1960, can expand with a temperature rise or shrink with a pressure rise. This leads to ambiguities compounded by the width of the scratches. And, worst of all, the bar can be lost or destroyed!

The krypton-86 spectral line overcomes these difficulties in large measure. The wave length of this electromagnetic radiation is (nearly) independent of external changes and depends only on the structure of the atoms of krypton-86, which is, of course, identical for all such atoms.

The standard of length in the English (or engineering) system of units is the *foot*. It is, by definition, exactly one third of a yard where, by legal agreement,

$$1 \text{ yd} = 0.9144 \text{ m}$$

For the conversion factors between other length units see Appendix II.

In its simplest form a measurement of the length of an object consists simply of counting the number of times the standard of length—for example, an ordinary meter stick—is contained in the object to be measured. *All* measurements in physics are characterized by the same steps: the choice of a standard, and a counting of the multiples (or submultiples) of the standard in the measured quantity.

I-3 Time Just as one can describe the length of an object as that which one measures with a meter stick, time can best be defined as the physical quantity which one reads from a clock. But what is a clock, and especially, what is a reliable clock? Any object or collection of objects showing regular repetitive motion may be used as a clock. The heart beat, the pulse, may be used as a very crude clock. A swinging pendulum or an oscillating spring are better clocks. The daily rotation of the Earth about its axis provides a still better basis for measurements of time intervals. Indeed, the *second*, the standard unit for time both in the metric and in the English system of units, is presently defined in terms of the Earth's motion. The second is so chosen that there are 86,400 seconds (60 × 60 × 24) in one day.

There are other repetitive motions in our solar system, which can be measured accurately enough to serve as clocks: for example, the motion of the Earth (and the inner planets Mercury and Venus) about the Sun, the motion of the Moon about the Earth, and the motion of some moons of Jupiter about that planet. All of these motions are almost completely frictionless and, when treated as clocks, they are all found to remain in synchronism with one another.

Unfortunately, the rotational motion of the Earth about its axis does *not* remain in synchronism with the other astronomical clocks. With respect to these other, more nearly frictionless, clocks, the Earth's rotational motion is slowing down such that the length of a day (one rotation of the Earth) is increased by 0.001 sec per century. Therefore, if the second is to be defined by international agreement in terms of the Earth's rotation, one must choose a particular period of time, and this has been done: the solar year 1900. Then, by definition,

$$\text{the solar year } 1900 = 31,556,925.9747 \text{ sec}$$

By the *solar* year is meant the interval of time required for the Earth to make one complete trip *relative* to the Sun.

It can be expected that the second will, before many more years, be redefined, as is the meter, in terms of the invariable properties of atoms. That is, the second and other time standards will eventually be specified in terms of an *atomic clock*. The atomic clock has the advantages of ready accessibility and reliability. Roughly speaking, the number of oscillations per unit time of electrons relative to the nucleus of an atom, or of an atom of a molecule relative to other atoms of the same molecule, is independent of external influence.

The ranges of length and time measurements encountered in human observation are: *Length:* from 10^{-15} m, the size of an atom's nucleus, to 10^{25} m, the size of the universe. *Time:* from 10^{-23} sec, nuclear time, to 10^{17} sec, the age of the universe. Man—in space and in time—seems to lie between the microscopic and macroscopic limits.

1-4 Systems of units The metric system is used almost universally in scientific work because it is simple. Unlike the English system, in which the several units of length are related to one another by nonsimple multiples (the mile is 5280 feet, the foot is 12 inches) the metric units are always related by multiples of 10. For example, the kilometer is 1000 meters.

Listed in Table 1-1 are the prefixes which are commonly used to change the size of units by multiples of ten.

Table 1-1

Prefix	Meaning
pico-	10^{-12}
nano-	10^{-9}
micro-	10^{-6}
milli-	10^{-3}
centi-	10^{-2}
deci-	10^{-1}
deka-	10^{1}
hekto-	10^{2}
kilo-	10^{3}
mega-	10^{6}
giga-	10^{9}

Thus, a kilometer is a thousand meters, and a nanosecond is a billionth of a second.

Length and time, represented by the meter and second, are two of the three fundamental units of measurement in the metric system. The third fundamental unit is mass, for which the standard is the kilogram in the metric system. The mass standard will be discussed in Section 7-3; we merely note here that *all* physical quantities in mechanics can be expressed in terms of these fundamental and independent quantities: length (L), time (T), and mass (M). That is, a given physical quantity is described by its *dimensions*, by a certain combination of M, L, and T only. Clearly, a distance has the dimension length (L), and the dimension of speed is length divided by time (L/T). As we shall see, the dimensions of force are (ML/T^2) and the dimensions of energy are (ML^2/T^2). Here we follow the usual convention of writing the dimensions of a physical quantity in parentheses.

T W O

STRAIGHT-LINE KINEMATICS

Classical physics begins with dynamics, and dynamics begins with kinematics. Dynamics is concerned with the motions of objects as they are related to the physical concepts of mass, force, momentum, and energy, and with the general laws unifying these concepts. Kinematics, on the other hand, has a more modest program. Combining the ideas of geometry and time, it describes motion without giving attention to its causes. Thus, kinematics is a necessary preliminary to the study of dynamics and the search for physical laws. In this chapter we explore the kinematics of a particle moving along a straight line, the meaning of the terms "displacement," "velocity," and "acceleration," and the mathematical relations that apply to the special case of motion with constant acceleration.

2-1 The meaning of a particle What is a particle? It is not, necessarily, a tiny, hard sphere as commonly imagined; rather, we define a particle simply as an object that is small enough for its size to be unimportant for the scale of our observations. It has no internal structure with which we need be concerned. Thus, a star may properly be regarded as a particle when viewed as one part of a galaxy, but an atom is too large to be considered a particle when we examine its component parts. It is all a matter of scale. The particle is the physical counterpart of the "point" in mathematics; it has not only the property of precise localizability but also the physical attributes of mass and motion. Kinematics is concerned, however, only with the motion of a particle, not its mass.

If, on the scale of our observation, an object has a finite size, it is not a particle. However, if the body has a symmetrical shape—for example, a sphere or disk—it is proper to represent the whole object as a particle located at the center of symmetry (later to be identified with the center of mass). The procedure of treating an extended body as if it were a particle will be justified later in our discussion of dynamics; here we merely accept it as a reasonable proposition.

2-2 Coordinates, displacement, and distance We restrict our discussion in this chapter to a particle having *rectilinear motion*, or motion along a straight line. A straight line is defined by the physicist as the path of a beam of light through a vacuum. The particle's *location* along the straight line, here called the X-axis, is designated the *coordinate x*. The coordinate x has some appropriate unit of length. Locations to the right of the origin are labeled "plus"; those to the left, "minus."

The *displacement* of the particle is defined as the *change* in its *position* (in its coordinate). We represent the displacement by the symbol Δx (where the symbol delta,† means "the change in"). If x_i is the *i*nitial coordinate and x_f is the "*f*inal" coordinate at some later time, then

$$\Delta x = x_f - x_i \qquad [2\text{-}1]$$

When the displacement is to the right, Δx is positive; when the particle's final position is to the left of its initial position, Δx is negative.

The displacement must be carefully distinguished from the *distance* traveled. The distance is the *total length of path traversed* by the particle and is, by definition, always positive.

The relations among coordinates, displacement, and distance are illustrated in Figure 2-1. Here a particle began at a, then traveled to b and, finally, to the position c. If these measures are in meters, the respective coordinates are $x_a = -3$ m, $x_b = +4$ m, and $x_c = -1$ m. The over-all displacement of the particle, from a to c, is

$$x_{ac} = x_c - x_a = (-1 \text{ m}) - (-3 \text{ m}) = +2 \text{ m}$$

† For the Greek alphabet see Appendix VI.

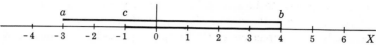

Figure 2-1. Relations among coordinates, displacement, and distance for a particle going from a to b to c.

The total distance traveled by the particle is 12 m: 7 m from a to b plus 5 m from b to c.

2-3   Motion at constant speed   To analyze the motion of a particle one must have a record of its positions at various instants of time. A simple way of making such a record is to photograph the moving object with a motion-picture camera. Then each frame of film shows the position of the

Figure 2-2. Representation of multiflash photograph.

object relative to the reference frame of the camera at the time that the picture was taken. Each frame shows one event in the history of the particle. A still simpler photographic method may be used, that of the multiflash photograph. In this method the lens of the camera is kept open and the moving object is illuminated at regular intervals by a flashing (stroboscopic) light source. The duration of each light flash is extremely short. The photograph, many times exposed, then shows a succession of images, a record of events in the body's motion: its coordinates as a function of time. By including a meter stick and a clock in the multiflash photograph, one has in a single picture all the information required for analyzing the motion. A representation of how a disc in a multiflash photograph would move is shown in Figure. 2-2.

In this chapter we analyze only rectilinear motion, beginning with the

Figure 2-3

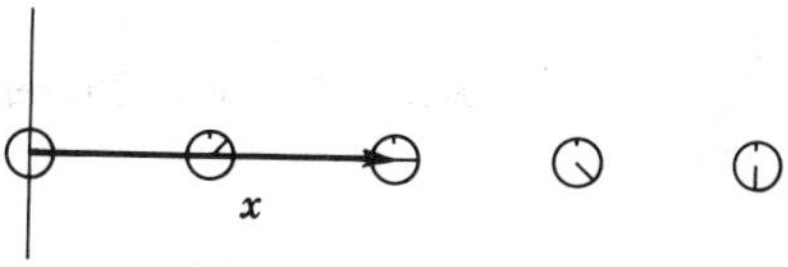

simple case shown in Figure 2-3. The images are seen to be equally spaced; therefore, the body covers equal distances in equal times. For convenience, the origin is chosen to be that point at which the particle is located when the clock reads zero; that is, we choose $x_i = 0$ when $t = 0$.

The displacement (relative to the origin) is plotted as a function of time in Figure 2-4. A straight line has been drawn through the points representing the data. This implies that the particle has traveled continuously between the points registered on the photograph; such an interpretation† would be

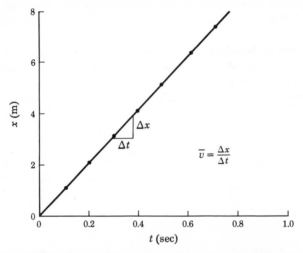

Figure 2-4. Displacement-time graph for the motion shown in Figure 2-3.

reasonable, but its correctness could only be ascertained by further multi-flash photographs taken with smaller time intervals. To extend the straight line beyond the observed points—to extrapolate the motion—is, of course, even more hazardous.

The *average velocity* $\bar{v}$ is defined as the *displacement* a particle undergoes *divided by the elapsed time* for this displacement. In symbols,

$$\bar{v} = \frac{\Delta x}{\Delta t} \qquad [2\text{-}2]$$

where $\Delta t = t_f - t_i$ and Δx is the corresponding displacement. From its definition, velocity has the dimensions of length divided by time (L/T), as in the examples m/sec, feet/sec, miles/hour, light-years/year.

† It is possible to make serious errors in interpreting a multiflash photograph. Suppose, for example, that only one image is registered: one could conclude that the object had not moved at all. But there are other possibilities: the object may have moved so fast that only one picture with the body in the field of view was taken, or the object may have moved back and forth with such timing that it was always at the same position when the light flashed.

We see from Figure 2-4 that, over the interval $t = 0.30$ sec to $t = 0.40$ sec, the average velocity is

$$\bar{v} = \frac{\Delta x}{\Delta t} = \frac{(4.0 - 3.0)\text{ m}}{(0.40 - 0.30)\text{ sec}} = 10\text{ m/sec}$$

Because this displacement-time curve, as it is called, is a straight line, any pair of points on the line would yield the same result for $\bar{v}$. Thus, the motion indicated in Figure 2-3, represented by the displacement-time graph of Figure 2-4, is that of *constant velocity* (sometimes called *uniform velocity*).

If, as will be recalled, the slope of any line is the change in the ordinate (x) over the corresponding change in the abscissa (t), it follows that the *velocity* is the *slope* of the *displacement-time line*. The steeper the slope, the greater the velocity and the larger the Δx for a given Δt. A horizontal line, which has a slope of zero, indicates the state of rest, and a line inclined downward and to the right denotes a negative velocity, or motion to the left.

The term *average speed* means the total *distance* of path traveled divided by the elapsed time, and is not to be confused with average velocity.

Example 1   An automobile travels east at a constant speed of 20 miles/hour, and, immediately upon reaching a point a distance d away, returns at the constant speed of 40 miles/hour. What are (a) the average velocity, and (b) the average speed, both over the entire trip? (Neither is 30 miles/hour!)

(a) The total displacement is zero; consequently, the average velocity is *zero* (by Equation 2-2). (b) We compute the average speed by dividing the total distance traveled, $2d$, by the total time elapsed: $d/20$ miles/hour going plus $d/40$ miles/hour on return. Thus, the average speed is

$$\frac{2d}{(d/20) + (d/40)}\text{ mi/hr} = 26.7\text{ mi/hr}$$

Rectilinear motion at constant velocity is described by the mathematical relation

$$v = x/t$$

$$[2\text{-}3]$$

or
$$x = vt$$

where $\Delta x = x$ and $\Delta t = t$ because $x_i = 0$ when $t_i = 0$.

Equation 2-3 is the *equation of motion* for constant velocity along the X-direction. For the motion of Figure 2-3 the equation of motion is

$$x = (10\text{ m/sec})t, \qquad \text{for} \qquad 0 < t < 1.0\text{ sec}$$

and we are able to give the position of the particle for any time t within the one-second interval.

A velocity-time graph corresponding to the motion in Figure 2-3 is shown

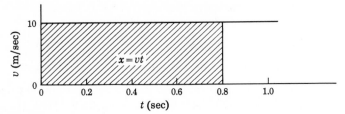

Figure 2-5. Velocity-time graph. The distance traveled is equal to the area under the curve.

in Figure 2-5. The horizontal straight line indicates that the velocity is positive and constant. The displacement x of the body from the starting point is represented by the total area under the velocity-time curve. For a velocity-time graph the term "area" has the units of length (*not* length squared), inasmuch as the area here is the product of velocity and time.

Figure 2-6. Representation of a multiflash photograph of rectilinear motion at nonconstant velocity.

2-4 Instantaneous velocity We turn now to a rectilinear motion in which the velocity is *not* constant, illustrated by the "multiflash photograph" of Figure 2-6. The corresponding displacement-time graph is shown in Figure 2-7. The body moves slowly at first, picks up speed, and then slows

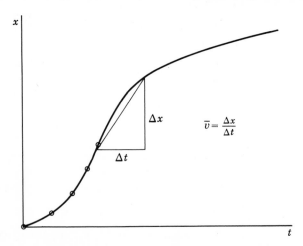

Figure 2-7. Displacement-time graph for the motion shown in Figure 2-6. The average velocity over the time interval shown is $\bar{v} = \Delta x/\Delta t$.

down. As before, the average velocity $\bar{v}$ over any time interval Δt is the ratio $\Delta x / \Delta t$ of the displacement Δx to the corresponding time interval Δt; that is, $\bar{v}$ is the slope of the straight line connecting two points on the displacement-time curve. But, unlike the displacement-time graph of Figure 2-4, the constant slope of which characterizes motion at *constant* velocity, the curve of Figure 2-7 does *not* yield the same value for $\bar{v}$ for different pairs of points. What is needed here is the *instantaneous velocity*, the velocity at an instant of time, which we will take to be the *average velocity* computed *over an infinitesimally small time interval*.

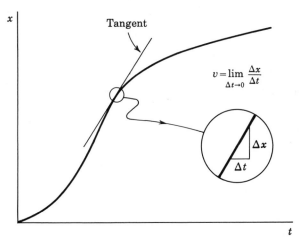

Figure 2-8. The instantaneous velocity is the tangent of the displacement-time graph, which is the limit of the average velocity for a vanishingly small time interval.

The computation of the instantaneous velocity from the displacement-time curve is illustrated in Figure 2-8. The interval chosen for Δt must be very small, so small that the actual curve over the chosen Δt cannot be distinguished from a straight line drawn between the two end points. Now, a line drawn tangent to the displacement-time curve will be identical with the curve over a small region at the point of contact. Therefore, the instantaneous velocity is the slope of the curve. In formal terms: the instantaneous velocity v at time t is the limit, as the time interval Δt approaches zero duration, of the displacement Δx divided by the corresponding time interval Δt, the interval Δt being centered at time t. In symbols,

$$\text{instantaneous velocity} = v = \lim_{\Delta t \to 0} \frac{\Delta x}{\Delta t} = \frac{dx}{dt} \qquad \text{[2-4]}$$

(Especially important formulas shall be printed in boxes). In the notation of the calculus, v is dx/dt, which is called the derivative of x with respect to t, or the time rate of the displacement. (Although we give in this chapter some calculus definitions, we shall not require the mathematical apparatus of the calculus in the next several chapters.)

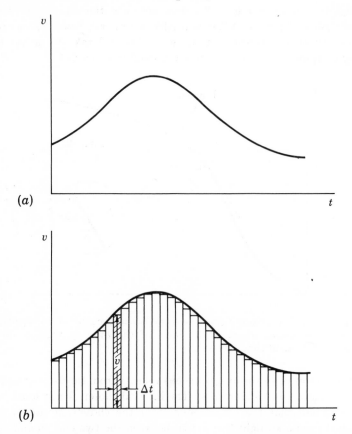

Figure 2-9. (a) Instantaneous velocity as a function of time. (b) The displacement is equal to the area under the velocity-time graph.

Hereinafter, the symbol v will be used to represent the instantaneous velocity, and so will the term "velocity" unless otherwise specified.

The term *instantaneous speed* is used to designate the magnitude of the instantaneous velocity; speed is always positive. In addition, velocity indicates the direction of motion (plus if to the right, minus if to the left).

Figure 2-9a gives the instantaneous velocity as a function of time. It was derived from the displacement-time curve of Figure 2-8 by the procedure of taking slopes. We see that the particle first moved with a relatively small, positive velocity (a low speed to the right), and that its velocity later increased, reached a maximum, and then decreased.

One derives a velocity-time curve from the slope of a displacement-time curve; conversely, one can arrive at a displacement-time curve given first the velocity-time curve. We found that for *constant* velocity the displacement is simply the area under the velocity-time line (see Figure 2-5). We can extend this to the case of nonconstant velocity to show that here again the displacement is the area between the velocity-time curve and the time axis. Consider Figure 2-9b. A number of narrow rectangles, each of width Δt, are fitted under the curve. Over a small time interval Δt the velocity may be regarded as essentially constant. The corresponding displacement Δx is $v \Delta t$ which is, as we see from the figure, the area of the shaded rectangle. Then, if the entire displacement x (from the start to the time t) is to be found, we add all the elementary rectangles, the contributions that are made to the displacement as Δt approaches zero, which is to say that the displacement is equal to the entire area under the velocity-time curve. If the velocity is negative and the velocity-time curve lies below the time axis, the contribution of the area "under" the curve is negative. In the language of integral calculus,

$$x_f - x_i = \lim_{\Delta t \to 0} \Sigma v \, \Delta t = \int_{t_i}^{t_f} v \, dt$$

2-5 Acceleration The velocity gives the time rate of the displacement. It is also useful to define a quantity which is the time rate of the velocity. This quantity is called "acceleration." The *average acceleration* $\bar{a}$ is defined as the change in velocity Δv divided by the corresponding elapsed time interval Δt:

$$\bar{a} = \frac{\Delta v}{\Delta t} \qquad [2\text{-}5]$$

Thus, the average acceleration is the slope of the straight line drawn between two points on a velocity-time curve. The *instantaneous acceleration a* is the average acceleration over an infinitesimally small time interval (see Figure 2-10). Equivalently, a is the slope of the velocity-time curve, or the time rate of velocity. In symbols:

$$\text{instantaneous acceleration} = a = \lim_{\Delta t \to 0} \frac{\Delta v}{\Delta t} = \frac{dv}{dt} \qquad [2\text{-}6]$$

The term "acceleration" shall be used hereinafter to denote the instantaneous acceleration.

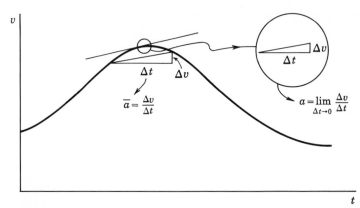

Figure 2-10. The instantaneous acceleration is the tangent of the velocity-time graph, which is the limit of the average acceleration for a vanishingly small time interval.

Acceleration has the units of velocity divided by time. Its dimensions are length/time^2 (L/T^2). Examples are: (miles/hour)/sec, (m/sec)/sec, (ft/sec)/sec, knots/sec. It is customary to write (m/sec)/sec as m/sec^2. Thus, a body having a constant acceleration of $+10$ m/sec^2 has velocity increasing, to the right, by 10 m/sec during each one-second interval.

Figure 2-11 is a graph of the instantaneous acceleration as a function of time, derived from the velocity-time curve of Figure 2-9. Note that the acceleration is at first positive, later zero, then negative, and finally zero again. Thus, Figure 2-11 indicates that, respectively, first the velocity of the body was increasing to the right, later the velocity was momentarily unchanged, then the velocity to the right decreased, and finally the velocity was constant.

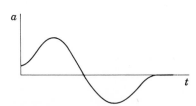

Figure 2-11. Instantaneous acceleration as a function of time.

The procedure we have followed, in defining the velocity as the time rate of the displacement and the acceleration as the time rate of the velocity, could be extended to yield a quantity giving the time rate of the acceleration (which would give a measure of the "jerkiness" of the motion); but this is not usually necessary. The terms velocity and acceleration are sufficient to describe motion adequately, and in our discussion of kinematics we need go no further than describing the time rate of the velocity. The reasons for this lie in the physics, or dynamics, of the motion, not in the mathematics or kinematics of the motion—as we shall see later.

Let us examine the displacement-time, velocity-time, and acceleration-time curves of another motion, as displayed in Figure 2-12. The body was first at rest in region A, then (positively) accelerated in region B. It coasted with constant velocity during C. In region D the body slowed down, came to rest momentarily, and reversed the direction of its motion. In region E the body moved with a constant speed to the left, approached and finally passed its starting point. This is a familiar motion. It is exemplified by a body set into motion by a push to the right and later returned by a push to the left. It must be emphasized, however, that in our study of kinematics we are not concerned with the causes of the motion, but only with its description.

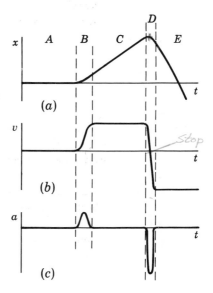

Note also that the velocity in Figure 2-12 is the slope of the displacement-time curve and the acceleration is the slope of the velocity-time curve. Conversely, the displacement is the area under the velocity-time curve and the velocity is the area under the acceleration-time curve.

Figure 2-12. (a) Displacement-time graph. (b) Velocity-time graph derived from (a). (c) Acceleration-time graph derived from (b).

2-6 Rectilinear motion at constant acceleration A simple, special, but important, type of rectilinear motion is that in which the acceleration is constant, or uniform. Of course, if the acceleration is *constantly zero*, the particle has a *constant velocity*: it is either moving with unchanging speed in a straight line or remaining at rest.

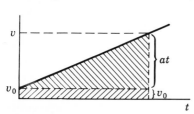

Figure 2-13. Velocity-time graph for constant acceleration.

Consider Figure 2-13, a velocity-time graph for constant acceleration a. Here the slope is unchanged. The velocity increases by equal amounts in equal time intervals, the change in the velocity being proportional to the time interval. We label the velocity at $t = 0$ the *initial velocity* v_0. The velocity at any other time t is simply v.

Because the acceleration is assumed constant, the average acceleration over a finite time interval and the instantaneous acceleration over a vanishingly small time interval are equal. We may choose any two points on the velocity-time curve to find the slope, or acceleration. For convenience, we choose the time interval running from time 0 to time t, during which the velocity has changed from v_0 to v. Thus,

$$a = \frac{\Delta v}{\Delta t} = \frac{v - v_0}{t - 0}$$

or

$$\boxed{v = v_0 + at}$$ [2-7]

Equation 2-7 gives the velocity at time t in terms of the initial velocity, the acceleration, and the elapsed time. The final velocity v is comprised of two parts: the initial velocity v_0 and the change in velocity at, as shown in Figure 2-13.

Let us express the displacement x in terms of the time t and the constants v_0 and a. We find the displacement from the velocity-time curve by computing the area under the curve. It is clear that the total area under the straight line in Figure 2-13 is a rectangle of width t and height v_0 plus a right triangle of sides t and at. Thus, the displacement x is the sum of $v_0 t$ and $\frac{1}{2}(at)(t)$, or

$$\boxed{x = v_0 t + \tfrac{1}{2}at^2}$$ [2-8]

The two terms in Equation 2-8 have a simple interpretation: the first gives the displacement that would occur if the velocity were to remain v_0, and the second is the additional displacement resulting from the acceleration.

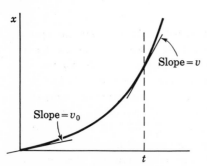

Figure 2-14. Displacement-time graph for constant acceleration.

Figure 2-14 is a displacement-time curve for constant acceleration. Equation 2-8 shows that it is a parabola. The slope increases uniformly, corresponding to the constant acceleration.

The kinematic formulas Equations 2-7 and 2-8 are particularly useful because they permit the future (and past) history of a particle to be projected; that is, they give the displacement and velocity for any future time when the initial displacement (zero), the initial velocity (v_0), and the constant acceleration (a) are known.

We can arrive at another useful kinematic formula by noting that the average velocity $\bar{v}$, defined as the total displacement divided by the elapsed time, is, for constant acceleration, simply the (algebraic) average of the initial and final velocities:

$$\bar{v} = (v_0 + v)/2 \qquad\qquad [2\text{-}9]$$

This follows from the fact that the area of the trapezoid under the velocity-time curve, which gives the displacement, is identical with the area of the rectangle under a velocity-time curve for a constant velocity equal to $\bar{v}$, as given by Equation 2-9. See Figure 2-15. Since $x = \bar{v}t$, we have

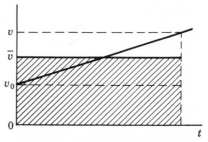

$$x = \frac{(v_0 + v)}{2} t \qquad\qquad [2\text{-}10]$$

Figure 2-15. Graph for constant acceleration: the area under the average velocity $\bar{v}$ *versus* time is equal to the area under the trapezoid in Figure 2-13.

A fourth kinematic formula is easily obtained by solving for t from Equation 2-7 and substituting in Equation 2-10:

$$x = \frac{(v + v_0)}{2} \frac{(v - v_0)}{a}$$

Rearranging yields

$$v^2 = v_0{}^2 + 2ax \qquad\qquad [2\text{-}11]$$

The four kinematic formulas, Equations 2-7, 2-8, 2-10, and 2-11, relate five quantities: the constants v_0 and a and the variables x, v, and t. Equation 2-7 contains v, v_0, a, and t, but not x. Similarly, Equations 2-8, 2-10, and 2-11 do not contain v, a, and t, respectively. These relations are the basis of solving all problems in motion at constant acceleration along a line. They express in mathematical language nothing more than the logical and algebraic consequences of the definitions of velocity and constant acceleration.

The kinematic relations for constant acceleration are easily verified by the differential calculus:

$$x = v_0 t + \tfrac{1}{2}at^2$$

$$v = \frac{dx}{dt} = v_0 + at$$

$$a = \frac{dv}{dt} = a$$

Conversely, by integrating we can obtain the velocity-time and displacement-time formulas directly from the definitions:

$$a = \frac{dv}{dt}$$

or

$$dv = a\,dt$$

We integrate velocity from the initial value v_0 to the final value v, the corresponding limits on time being zero and t:

$$\int_{v_0}^{v} dv = a \int_{0}^{t} dt$$

$$v - v_0 = at$$

[2-7]

$$v = v_0 + at$$

We integrate once more to find x:

$$\frac{dx}{dt} = v_0 + at$$

or

$$dx = v_0\,dt + at\,dt.$$

The displacement is zero when the time is zero and is x when the time is t. Thus, the definite integrals are

$$\int_{0}^{x} dx = v_0 \int_{0}^{t} dt + a \int_{0}^{t} t\,dt$$

[2-8]

$$x = v_0 t + \tfrac{1}{2}at^2$$

Note that the assumed constancies of v_0 and a were an essential part of the analysis.

Example 2   A car starting from rest travels one quarter of a mile in 24.1 sec. (a) What is the acceleration, assuming it to be constant? (b) What is the car's final speed?

(a) We know v_0, x, and t, and are to find a. Equation 2-8 is useful here:

$$x = v_0 t + \tfrac{1}{2}at^2 = \tfrac{1}{2}at^2, \qquad \text{since } v_0 = 0$$

Solving for a we have

$$a = \frac{2x}{t^2} = \frac{2 \times \tfrac{1}{4}\,\text{mi}}{(24.1\,\text{sec})^2} \times \frac{5280\,\text{ft}}{1\,\text{mi}}$$

$$a = 4.55\,\text{ft/sec}^2$$

(b) We are to compute v, knowing v_0, a, and t. Equation 2-7, $v = v_0 + at$, is applicable:

$$v = 0 + (4.55\,\text{ft/sec}^2)(24.1\,\text{sec})$$

$$v = 110\,\text{ft/sec}$$

or, in the units miles per hour,

$$v = \frac{110 \text{ ft}}{\text{sec}} \times \frac{3600 \text{ sec}}{1 \text{ hr}} \times \frac{1 \text{ mi}}{5280 \text{ ft}}$$

$$v = 74.8 \text{ mi/hr}$$

Note two points, illustrated in this example and applicable to all problems in kinematics—indeed, applicable to all problems in physics:

(1) We solve algebraically for the unknown *before* substituting numerical values for symbols.

(2) The units are always carried along with the numbers, and treated algebraically. One necessary (but not sufficient) test of the correctness of the solution is whether the dimensions are appropriate. Any formula *in physics* must be dimensionally consistent: that is, all of its terms must have the same dimensions. For example, the terms x, $v_0 t$, and $\frac{1}{2}at^2$ in the equation $x = v_0 t + \frac{1}{2}at^2$ all have the same *dimension*, namely, length. Furthermore, the terms must have the same *units*; for example, the lengths must be all in feet. Of course, no answer is complete if it does not specify the units.

Example 3 A car starts from rest when a traffic light turns green, and it accelerates at 4.0 feet/sec². A truck moving at a constant speed of 60 feet/sec in the same direction passes the car at the instant the automobile starts moving. (a) At what later time will the car catch up with the truck? (b) At that time what distance will it be from the traffic light? (c) What is the speed of the automobile as it overtakes the truck?

(a) Here we must consider the simultaneous motion of two objects. We make the displacement and velocity of the *truck* x_t and v_{0t} respectively; the truck's equation of motion is then

$$x_t = v_{0t}t = (60 \text{ ft/sec})t$$

where the acceleration of the truck is zero. Using the subscript a to denote the *automobile*, its equation of motion is

$$x_a = v_{0a}t + \tfrac{1}{2}a_a t^2 = \tfrac{1}{2}(4.0 \text{ ft/sec}^2)t^2$$

Note that the time t is the *same* for both. We wish to find when the two vehicles are at the same place (strictly, side by side) at the same time; that is, we ask "At what time t is $x_t = x_a$"? Equating x_t and x_a, we have

$$(60 \text{ ft/sec})t = (2.0 \text{ ft/sec}^2)t^2$$

$$t = 0 \text{ sec} \quad \text{or} \quad t = 30 \text{ sec}$$

There are *two* answers. And there should be two, inasmuch as the truck and car were side by side at the start and then again 30 sec later.

(b) Knowing that $t = 30$ sec, we can substitute this value in either of the equations of motion:

$$x_t = (60 \text{ ft/sec})t = (60 \text{ ft/sec})(30 \text{ sec})$$

$$x_a = x_t = 1.8 \times 10^3 \text{ ft}$$

Note that, since only two significant figures are given for any of the known quantities, the displacement here can properly be written with only two significant figures.

(c) What is v_a when $t = 30$ sec?

$$v_a = v_{0a} + a_a t = 0 + (4.0 \text{ ft/sec}^2)(30 \text{ sec})$$
$$v_a = 1.2 \times 10^2 \text{ ft/sec}$$

The car's speed at the time it passes the truck is twice the constant speed of the truck. This follows also from Equation 2-9, $\bar{v} = (v_0 + v)/2$. The truck must have the same average velocity over the entire trip as the automobile, for they both have equal displacements in equal times. Therefore, $v = 2\bar{v}$ when $v_0 = 0$. A kinematics problem may often be solved in a variety of ways, using the four kinematic relations. This is hardly surprising: the four kinematic formulas all have their origin in the definitions of velocity and acceleration.

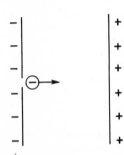

Figure 2-16. An electron undergoing motion at constant acceleration between two oppositely-charged, parallel plates.

Example 4 An electron traveling at 4.0×10^6 m/sec to the right enters the region between vertical, parallel, electrically charged, metal plates separated by 2.0 cm; see Figure 2-16. Within this region the electron undergoes a constant acceleration of 7.9×10^{14} m/sec^2 to the right. (The electron has a negative electric charge; the left and right plates carry minus and plus electric charges, respectively, by virtue of their connection to the terminals of a battery. The constant acceleration here has its origin in electric charges.)

(a) With what velocity does the electron strike the right plate? (b) How long does it take to reach this plate?

(a) We know that $v_0 = 4.0 \times 10^6$ m/sec and that $a = 7.9 \times 10^{14}$ m/sec^2; we ask for v when $x = 2.0 \times 10^{-2}$ m. Equation 2-11, $v^2 = v_0^2 + 2ax$, is useful:

$$v^2 = (4.0 \times 10^6 \text{ m/sec})^2 + 2(7.9 \times 10^{14} \text{ m/sec}^2)(2.0 \times 10^{-2} \text{ m})$$
$$v = 6.9 \times 10^6 \text{ m/sec}$$

(b) We compute t from Equation 2-10, $x = (v_0 + v)t/2$, knowing v_0, v, and x:

$$t = \frac{2x}{v_0 + v} = \frac{2(2.0 \times 10^{-2} \text{ m})}{(4.0 + 6.9) \times 10^6 \text{ m/sec}}$$
$$t = 3.7 \times 10^{-9} \text{ sec}$$

The electron undergoes an extraordinarily large acceleration, but for only a very short time.

Now suppose that the connections to the metal plates are reversed, such that the electron has a constant acceleration of 7.9×10^{14} m/sec^2 to the *left*. Again the electron enters the region between the plates from the left with a speed of 4.0×10^6 m/sec.

(c) How far from the left plate does the electron move before being turned back?

We know that $v_0 = 4.0 \times 10^6$ m/sec and $a = -7.9 \times 10^{14}$ m/sec^2. The electron stops moving to the right and starts moving to the left when its velocity goes from plus to minus, that is, when $v = 0$. From Equation 2-11, $v^2 = v_0^2 + 2ax$, we have

$$x = -\frac{v_0^2}{2a} = -\frac{(4.0 \times 10^6 \text{ m/sec})^2}{2(-7.9 \times 10^{14} \text{ m/sec}^2)}$$

$$x = 1.0 \times 10^{-2} \text{ m} = +1.0 \text{ cm}$$

(d) How long does it take for the electron to return to the left plate?

The electron has a zero displacement at the left plate. We seek t for $x = 0$. Equation 2-8, $x = v_0 t + \frac{1}{2}at^2$, gives

$$0 = (4.0 \times 10^6 \text{ m/sec})t + \frac{1}{2}(-7.9 \times 10^{16} \text{ m/sec}^2)t^2$$

$$t = 0 \quad \text{or} \quad t = 1.0 \times 10^{-8} \text{ sec}$$

Note that the kinematic formulas for constant acceleration are applicable in this instance only to the region between the plates ($0 < x < 2.0 \times 10^{-2}$ m), the only region in which the acceleration is known.

2-7 Freely falling bodies All freely falling bodies close to the Earth's surface have a nearly constant magnitude of acceleration toward the center of the Earth. By a "falling" body is meant not only one dropped from rest, but also a thrown object, in the vicinity of the Earth's surface. Such a body is truly *freely* falling only when it moves through a vacuum but, for relatively low speeds and for smooth, compact, dense objects, the resistance of the air is nearly negligible and their motion closely approximates the motion of free fall. Thus, descending parachutes, flying birds, and falling leaves do not qualify as freely falling objects. Unless it is stated otherwise, we shall hereinafter ignore the effects of air resistance.

The acceleration of a freely falling body does not depend on the mass or weight of the object. Experiments show that an apple, a neutron (a small, electrically neutral particle with a mass of only 1.7×10^{-27} kg), or any other object near the Earth's surface, falls with a constant acceleration of 32.2 feet/sec^2 = 9.80 m/sec^2 = 980 cm/sec^2. This acceleration plays so important a rôle in physics that it is designated by a special symbol, g, and is referred to as the *acceleration due to gravity* (*not* as "gravity" and especially not as the "force of gravity"). How g is related to the general phenomenon of gravitation will be dealt with later; here we treat only of falling-body kinematics.†

We must qualify slightly some of our assertions. Strictly, g is not constant. The value of g differs (no more than 0.4 per cent) at various places on the Earth's surface. Moreover, g decreases with increasing distance from the

† The fundamental theoretical and experimental discoveries in the motion of falling bodies and the kinematics of accelerated motion were made by Galileo Galilei (1564–1642), the first physicist of the modern era and one of the great physicists of all time. Galileo's contributions to science are sketched in Chapter 7.

Earth's center (the Moon "falls" around the Earth, but with an acceleration of only 2.7×10^{-3} m/sec^2). For altitudes of up to 40 miles above sea level, g is constant to within 2 per cent.

For convenience in computation in this chapter and in Chapter 4 we shall use rounded-off, approximate, values for g:

$$g \simeq 32 \text{ ft/sec}^2 \simeq 10 \text{ m/sec}^2 \simeq 1000 \text{ cm/sec}^2$$

Falling-body motion is one of the very few situations in physics illustrating motion at constant acceleration (another example is a charged particle between parallel, charged plates), and the four kinematic formulas, Equations 2-7, 2-8, 2-10, and 2-11, apply. The direction of motion is along the vertical, and it is appropriate to label the displacement y, rather than x, the positive direction of the Y-axis customarily being chosen as vertically upward. The velocities v_0 and v are now the instantaneous initial and final velocities, respectively, along the Y-direction, and the acceleration along the vertical direction is $a = -g$. We treat only rectilinear falling-body motion here; the more general case of motion in two dimensions is discussed in Chapter 4.

Example 5 An object is thrown vertically upward at 30 m/sec. (a) What is its displacement after 4 sec? (b) What is its velocity after 4 sec? (c) What is the maximum height it attains? (d) How long does it take for the object to return to the ground? (e) What is its velocity upon striking the ground?

(a) We know that $v_0 = +30$ m/sec and $a = -10$ m/sec^2; we are to find y for $t = 4$ sec. Equation 2-8, $y = v_0 t + \frac{1}{2}at^2$, becomes

$$y = (30 \text{ m/sec})(4 \text{ sec}) + \frac{1}{2}(-10 \text{ m/sec}^2)(4 \text{ sec})^2$$

$$y = +40 \text{ m}$$

(b) What is v after 4 sec? Equation 2-7, $v = v_0 + at$, is useful here:

$$v = (30 \text{ m/sec}) + (-10 \text{ m/sec}^2)(4 \text{ sec})$$

$$v = -10 \text{ m/sec}$$

Four seconds after the object is thrown it is 40 m above the ground and traveling downward with an instantaneous speed of 10 m/sec. The total *distance* traveled is, however, *not* 40 m.

(c) At its maximum height, where the object is changing direction of motion, its velocity is zero. Therefore, we want y when $v = 0$, using Equation 2-11, $v^2 = v_0^2 + 2ay$:

$$y = \frac{v^2 - v_0^2}{2a} = \frac{0 - (30 \text{ m/sec})^2}{2(-10 \text{ m/sec}^2)}$$

$$y = +45 \text{ m}$$

(d) The displacement y is zero when the object strikes the ground (the total *distance* over the trip is, in magnitude, twice the maximum height). We wish to find the corresponding time of flight. Using Equation 2-8, $y = v_0 t + \frac{1}{2}at^2$, to find t for $y = 0$, we have:

$$0 = (v_0 + \tfrac{1}{2}at)t$$

$$t = 0, \quad \text{or} \quad -\frac{2v_0}{a} = -\frac{2(30 \text{ m/sec})}{(-10 \text{ m/sec}^2)}$$

$$t = 0 \quad \text{or} \quad t = 6.0 \text{ sec}$$

The time of flight is 6.0 seconds.

(e) The average velocity $\bar{v}$ of the entire motion is zero, inasmuch as the over-all displacement y is zero. Therefore, Equation 2-9, $\bar{v} = (v_0 + v)/2$, gives

$$v = 2\bar{v} - v_0 = 0 - 30 \text{ m/sec}$$

$$v = -30 \text{ m/sec}$$

(Alternatively, we can find v for $t = 6.0$ sec by using Equation 2-7.) The body strikes the ground with the same speed as that with which it was thrown. The entire motion is, in fact, symmetrical in time about the midtime. Stated differently, it is the same motion with time running backwards; one cannot distinguish between motion pictures of a thrown object, one with the film run forwards and the other backwards.

The displacement-time, velocity-time, and acceleration-time curves in Figure 2-17 display all of the information we have computed here (and more). Note that the displacement is zero at 6.0 sec, as is indicated not only on the displacement-time curve but also by the net area, shaded, on the velocity-time graph.

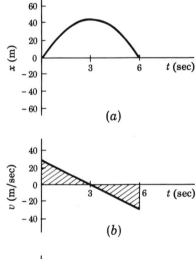

Figure 2-17. (a) Displacement-time, (b) velocity-time, and (c) acceleration-time graphs for a projectile thrown vertically upward at 30 m/sec.

Example 6 A man drops a baseball from the window of a tall building, and then 0.80 sec later throws a second baseball vertically downward with an initial speed of 40 ft/sec. How long after the second ball is thrown does it pass the first, and how far down?

For this problem it is convenient to choose the positive Y-direction as downward, thereby making the initial velocity of the second baseball positive and avoiding a cluster of minus signs in the kinematic equations. The equations of motion for the two baseballs, labeled with subscripts 1 and 2, are

$$y_1 = v_{01}t_1 + \tfrac{1}{2}at_1^2$$

$$y_1 = 16t_1^2$$

and

$$y_2 = v_{02}t_2 + \tfrac{1}{2}at_2^2$$

$$y_2 = 40t_2 + 16t_2^2$$

Note that the times t_1 and t_2 are *not* identical; in fact, t_2 is zero when t_1 is 0.80 sec. Therefore,

$$t_1 = t_2 + 0.80 \text{ sec}$$

The equation for the first ball may be rewritten:

$$y_1 = 16(t_2 + 0.80)^2$$

We are interested in t_2 for $y_1 = y_2$:

$$16(t_2 + 0.80)^2 = 40t_2 + 16t_2^2$$

A little algebra gives

$$t_2 = 0.72 \text{ sec}$$

and

$$y_1 = y_2 = 370 \text{ ft}$$

2-8   Summary   For rectilinear motion along x, the instantaneous velocity v is the time rate of displacement:

[2-4]
$$v = \lim_{\Delta t \to 0} \frac{\Delta x}{\Delta t} = \frac{dx}{dt}$$

The instantaneous acceleration a is the time rate of velocity:

[2-6]
$$a = \lim_{\Delta t \to 0} \frac{\Delta v}{\Delta t} = \frac{dv}{dt}$$

The kinematic relations describing rectilinear motion at the *constant* acceleration a are:

[2-7]
$$v = v_0 + at$$

[2-8]
$$x = v_0 t + \tfrac{1}{2}at^2$$

[2-10]
$$x = \tfrac{1}{2}(v_0 + v)t$$

[2-11]
$$v^2 = v_0^2 + 2ax$$

where x is the displacement and v is the velocity at time t, x being zero and v being v_0 at $t = 0$.

All freely falling bodies near the Earth's surface have a constant downward acceleration $g = 9.80 \text{ m/sec}^2 = 980 \text{ cm/sec}^2 = 32 \text{ feet/sec}^2$.

PROBLEMS

(Answers to problems in this chapter assume that $g \simeq 32$ ft/sec$^2 \simeq$ 10 m/sec$^2 \simeq 1000$ cm/sec^2.)

2-1 When in motion, an automobile has an essentially constant speed of 50 miles/hour. How many 10-minute stops can the automobile make during an 8.0-hour trip if it is to cover 350 miles?

2-2 An automobile travels east for 10 minutes at 40 miles/hour, west at 30 miles/hour for 20 minutes, and finally east at 50 miles/hour for 15 minutes. For the entire trip, what are (a) the average speed, (b) the average velocity, (c) the displacement, and (d) the distance traveled?

2-3 An airplane flies from New York (latitude 41° north, longitude 74° west of Greenwich) to Melbourne (latitude 38° south, longitude 145° east of Greenwich) along a great circle in a time of 32 hours. The Earth's radius is 3960 miles. What are (a) the displacement, (b) distance traveled, (c) average speed, and (d) average velocity for this trip?

2-4 An automobile travels at a constant speed of 40 miles/hour in a straight line for 2.0 hours and then immediately returns to the starting point at a constant speed of 60 miles/hour. What are (a) the average speed for the entire trip, (b) the average velocity over the entire trip, (c) the average speed over the first 75 per cent of the entire trip in distance, (d) the corresponding average velocity, (e) the average speed over the first 75 per cent of the entire trip in time, and (f) the corresponding average velocity?

2-5 Listed below are a set of odometer readings and clock readings taken from a moving automobile. Plot displacement-time, velocity-time, and acceleration-time graphs from these data.

Odometer (mi)	Clock (sec)
12,400.12	10.0
12,400.20	11.0
12,400.30	12.0
12,400.45	13.0
12,400.70	14.0
12,400.79	15.0
12,400.82	16.0
12,400.85	17.0
12,400.88	18.0

2-6 The following are automobile speedometer readings (in miles per hour) taken at 10 sec intervals: 40, 47, 52, 50, 42, and 32. If the odometer read 15,407.8 miles when the first reading was taken, what should it read when the last reading is taken? Plot displacement-time, velocity-time, and acceleration-time graphs for this motion.

2-7 The displacement (in meters) of a body is given as a function of time (in seconds) by the expression $x = (6.00 \text{ m/sec}^3)t^3$. Compute the average velocity centered (in time) at $t = 2.00$ sec for the time intervals (a) 2.00 sec, (b) 0.200 sec, and (c) 0.020 sec. (d) What is the instantaneous velocity at $t = 2.00$ sec? (e) Confirm your result by measuring the slope at $t = 2.00$ sec on a displacement-time graph.

2-8 An automobile originally has a velocity of $+20$ m/sec, and 100 sec later has a velocity of -20 m/sec. What is the average acceleration over the 100 sec interval?

2-9 ★ The following relations give the displacement of a body, x, as a function of the time t; the other symbols represent constants. Find the velocity and acceleration in each instance as a function of time by taking derivatives, and give the appropriate dimensions of the constants: (a) $x = At^3$, (b) $x = B \sin Ct$, (c) $x = De^{-kt}$, (d) $x = Et + Ft^2 + Gt^3$.

2-10 ★ The following relations give the acceleration of a body, a, as a function of the time t; the other symbols represent constants. Assume $x = 0$ and $v = v_0$ when $t = 0$. Find the velocity and displacement in each instance as a function of time by integrating and give the appropriate dimensions of the constants: (a) $a = -At$, (b) $a = B \cos Ct$, (c) $a = D + Et$.

2-11 Draw approximate velocity-time and acceleration-time graphs corresponding to the motions portrayed in the displacement-time graphs of Figure 2-18.

2-12 Draw approximate displacement-time and acceleration-time graphs corresponding to the motions portrayed in the velocity-time graphs of Figure 2-19.

2-13 ★ A simple method of measuring the speed of high-speed particles, or of light, is the *time-of-flight* method. In this method particles are sent toward two discs rotating at the same (rotational) speed on a common axis, the discs being separated by a known distance. Each disc has a slot, but the slot in one disc has an angular displacement of θ with respect to the second disc; see Figure 2-20.

(a) Suppose that a time-of-flight machine, sometimes also called a *velocity selector*, is devised to measure the speed of neutrons. If the discs are separated by 1.0 m, rotated at 32,000 rotations/minute, and the disc slots separated by 180°, what are the speeds (note!) of neutrons passing through the velocity selector?

(b) The device may be used with a single disc for measuring the speed of light by having the light pass through an opening in the same disc a second time. To reduce the usually extraordinarily high rotational speed, a number of equally spaced openings (or teeth) may be used rather than a single slot. Suppose that the distance between the rotating disc and the mirror is 22.9 km and that the disc has a diameter of 4.00 cm and 180 teeth. What is the minimal angular speed of the disc, in rotations per minute, that will permit light to pass through the disc on the return trip? The speed of light is 3.00×10^8 m/sec. (The first accurate terrestrial determinations of the speed of light were made by A. H. L. Fizeau in 1849, who used this method.)

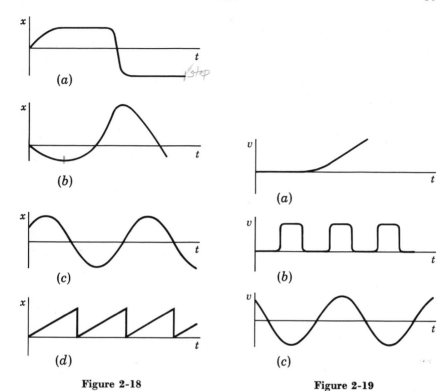

Figure 2-18

Figure 2-19

2-14 A body has an initial velocity of $+20$ feet/sec. Its acceleration is a constant -4.0 feet/sec². (a) What are the body's displacement and velocity at $t = 3.0$ sec? (b) What are the body's displacement and velocity at $t = 8.0$ sec? (c) At what time is the body's average velocity zero? (d) How long does it take the body to attain zero displacement? (e) At what time is the velocity -20 feet/sec?

2-15 An automobile traveling at 60.0 miles/hour can decelerate at 7.00 feet/sec². (a) How long does it take to come to rest? (b) How far has it traveled, assuming the acceleration to remain constant?

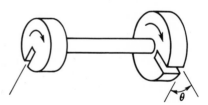

Figure 2-20. Simple type of velocity selector.

2-16 A body starting from rest increases in speed, from 20 m/sec to 40 m/sec, over a distance of 80 m. If the acceleration is constant throughout, what is the distance traveled before reaching 20 m/sec?

2-17   An object originally at rest is subject to a constant acceleration of 3.0 m/sec^2 from $t = 0$ to $t = 2.5$ sec; the acceleration is zero from $t = 2.5$ sec to $t = 4.5$ sec; the acceleration is -4.0 m/sec^2 from $t = 4.5$ sec to $t = 6.0$ sec. What are the displacement and velocity of the object at (a) $t = 3.0$ sec and (b) $t = 6.0$ sec?

2-18   In three different runs a Volkswagon goes from 0 to 50 miles/hour in 19.3 sec; it covers one quarter-mile from a standing start in 24.5 sec, and accelerates from 35 to 55 miles/hour in 15.0 sec. Compute the acceleration, assumed constant, in these three runs. In which does the car display the greatest "pick-up"?

2-19   A Rolls Royce reaches 60 miles/hour in less than 12 sec from a standing start. The Dusenberg can stop in 30 feet from 30 miles/hour. Which automobile has the larger acceleration magnitude (assumed constant)? (Notice that the first acceleration gives a measure of engine performance whereas the second acceleration is related to brake performance.)

2-20   An object originally at rest is subject to a constant acceleration of 15 m/sec^2 for 0.50 sec and then is allowed to "coast" for 2.00 sec. Then the constant acceleration is again "turned on" for 0.50 sec, and is again followed by motion without acceleration for another 2.00 sec. If this pattern is continued, what are (a) the velocity and (b) the displacement 10.0 sec after the start?

2-21   A car starts from rest with a constant acceleration of 0.80 m/sec^2 at the moment a traffic light turns green. At this same moment a truck is traveling at the constant speed of 20 m/sec but is at a distance of 25 m from the traffic light. (a) Will the car and truck pass? (b) If so, where and when? Draw a displacement-time graph for both vehicles on the same diagram.

2-22   A man's left and right palms are moving toward each other at velocities of 10 m/sec and -10 m/sec, respectively. A fast-flying insect originally on the left palm flies to the right palm at 30 m/sec; when it arrives there, it immediately turns back to the left palm, flying at the same speed. It continues to fly between the approaching palms, originally separated by 0.40 m. What is the total distance traveled by the insect?

2-23 ★ Train A is traveling east at a constant speed of 40 miles/hour. Train B on the same track, and originally east of train A by 1700 feet, is traveling west at an initial speed of 15 miles/hour and has a constant acceleration of 1.2 (miles/hour)/sec to the east. (a) At what point relative to the starting position of train A do the trains collide? (b) At what time do they collide? (c) What is the velocity of B relative to A at the instant of collision?

2-24   With a velocity of 8.0×10^5 m/sec an electron enters the region between two electrically charged, parallel, metal plates separated by 3.5 cm, as in Figure 2-16. In the region between the plates the electron has a constant acceleration to the right of 4.0×10^{14} m/sec^2. (a) With what velocity does it strike the distant plate? (b) How long does it take to traverse the distance between the plates?

2-25 Assume the same situation given in Problem 2-24, except for an acceleration to the left. (a) Does the electron strike the right plate, or return to
the left plate? (b) At what time?

2-26 It is found by experiment that the time taken for an electron starting
from rest at the left plate, Figure 2-16, to reach the right plate varies
inversely as the square root of the number of batteries (connected in series)
attached to the parallel metal plates. How does the acceleration of an
electron in the region between the plates depend upon the number of
batteries?

2-27 A boy throws a ball upward. It strikes the ground 4.0 sec later.
(a) With what speed was the ball thrown? (b) What height did it achieve?

2-28 An automobile is pushed off a cliff 100 feet high. With what velocity
does it strike the ground below?

2-29 With what muzzle velocity must a bullet be fired vertically upward to
achieve a maximum height of 20,000 feet?

2-30 Show that the following assertion of Galileo, taken from *Two New
Sciences* (1683), is correct: ". . . so far as I know no one has yet pointed
out that the distances traversed during equal intervals of time, by a
body falling from rest, stand to one another in the same ratio as the odd
numbers beginning with unity."

2-31 A man standing on a tower 150 feet high throws a ball upward at 30
feet/sec. He clocks the time elapsed before the ball strikes the ground
and finds it to be 4.40 sec. Was the ball's motion influenced importantly
by the resistance of the air?

2-32 A body is dropped from rest. What distance does it traverse over the
interval $t = 6.0$ sec to $t = 8.0$ sec?

2-33 A juggler throws each of three knives upward at 16 feet/sec. With what
speed must he throw each knife when juggling four knives, assuming the
same interval between the throwing of each knife?

2-34 ★ An apartment-dweller sees a flowerpot (originally on a window sill
above) pass the 4.0-foot-high window of his fifth-floor apartment in 0.12
sec. The distance between floors is 10 feet. From what floor did the
flowerpot fall?

2-35 ★ A man throws a baseball upward and then 2.00 sec later throws a second
baseball upward with the same speed as the first. The balls are seen
to collide 0.400 sec after the second one was thrown. (a) What was the
initial speed of both? (b) Where did they collide?

2-36 A rocket ascends vertically with a constant acceleration of 35 m/sec²
while the fuel is burning. The fuel is exhausted after 100 sec. (a) What
is the maximum height achieved? (b) What is the total time the rocket
is in the air?

2-37 A parachutist jumps from an airplane at an altitude of 5000 feet. For
the first 10 sec he falls freely; then he pulls the ripcord, the parachute
opens, and he falls with an *upward* acceleration of 60 feet/sec² until the
downward speed reaches 16 feet/sec. Thereafter, he falls at a constant
velocity. How long does the entire trip to the ground take?

2-38   An elevator 3.0 m from floor to ceiling descends at the constant speed of 2.0 m/sec. An object becomes detached from the ceiling and falls to the elevator floor. How long does it take for the object to strike the floor?

2-39   A balloon ascends at 30 feet/sec. A sandbag is dropped when the balloon is 200 feet above the ground. (a) How long does it take for the sandbag to strike the ground? (b) What is its velocity then?

2-40 ★ A number of stones are attached to a string in such a way that the distance between adjacent stones increases by a constant amount from one pair of stones to the next. The string is held at the large-spacing end, the lowest stone touching the ground. Show that, if the string is dropped from rest, the stones strike the ground at equally spaced time intervals.

2-41 ★ A man standing on a bridge above the ground holds one end of a 25-foot string in his hand. A stone is attached to the other end, and a second stone is attached 10 feet above the lower end. If the man drops the string from rest and finds the time interval between the striking of the two stones against the ground to be 0.15 sec, what is the vertical distance between the man and the ground?

2-42 ★ Show that the acceleration due to gravity, of the Moon "falling" toward the Earth, is 2.7×10^{-3} m/sec^2. The Moon is at a distance of 3.8×10^5 km from the Earth's center and its period is 27.3 days. The Moon "falls" toward the Earth in the sense that it departs from straight-line motion in such a manner that it always remains the same distance from the Earth, moving in a circular path. (This analysis was first made by Sir Isaac Newton for the purpose of comparing g at the site of the Moon and g at the Earth's surface.)

2-43 ★ Galileo showed by experiment that when a ball rolls from rest down a smooth incline, its displacement is directly proportional to the square of the time elapsed; thus, the motion is that of uniform acceleration. Experiment shows, furthermore, that with an incline of fixed length but adjustable in angle, the time for a ball to roll from rest to the bottom varies inversely as the square root of the height of the upper end of the incline above the lower. According to this information, how does the acceleration down the incline depend on the angle of the incline?

T H R E E

VECTORS

Our discussion of kinematics thus far has been restricted to motion along a line. But motion in general occurs in two or three dimensions, in a plane or in space. The same terms used to describe one-dimensional motion— *displacement, velocity,* and *acceleration*—are used also in two- and three-dimensional kinematics, but here they have a new significance: displacement, velocity, and acceleration in two or more dimensions are *vector* quantities.

3-1 Scalars and vectors In elementary physics we encounter two types of physical quantities, *vector quantities* and *scalar quantities* (or simply *vectors* and *scalars*). A scalar quantity has magnitude only and it obeys the usual laws of algebra. Examples of scalars are the pure numbers of arithmetic and such physical quantities as time, volume, and mass. A scalar physical quantity is fully specified by giving a number together with an appropriate unit, as in 10.4 sec, 10^4 m^3, or 9.11×10^{-31} kg.

A vector quantity, on the other hand, has (1) direction, as well as (2) magnitude, and (3) it obeys the rules of *vector algebra* which are found to hold for displacement vectors. We shall be concerned only with the vector properties of displacement in this chapter, because displacement serves as a prototype for other vector quantities, such as velocity and acceleration. We shall find that the use of vectors will permit us to treat two- or three-dimensional kinematics with generality and simplicity; indeed, we shall see that such fundamental physical quantities as momentum, force, angular momentum, and torque are also vectors.

3-2   Displacement as a vector

We shall first discuss displacements in a plane. Consider Figure 3-1, which shows the position in the plane of a small disc at three different times. Initially the object was at point a, later at b, and finally at c. The *displacement* is defined as the *change* in the *position* of the object. We can represent the displacement from a to b by drawing a directed line segment between the two points, locating the arrowhead at the terminus b and indicating thereby that the displacement was from a to b. The length of the line segment represents, in any appropriate scale, the distance along the straight line from a to b. Note particularly that we do *not* say (or know) whether the object has traveled along a *straight* line from a to b—its path between the two end points may, in fact, have been quite tortuous; all we know is that b is the final *position* and a the initial one.

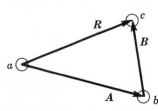

Figure 3-1. An object at positions a, b, and c.

We represent the vector a to b by the bold-faced symbol A. Because it is difficult to write boldface symbols on paper or on the blackboard, a vector quantity such as A is commonly distinguished from a scalar quantity by an arrow above the symbol, $\vec{A}$, or by using a wavy underscore, A. The magnitude of the vector A is a scalar quantity and is symbolized by light-faced type, as A. Thus, if b is 10 m distant from a, $A = 10$ m.

The displacement from point b to point c in Figure 3-1 is written B, and R represents the vector displacement from a to c. It is clear from the geometry of the figure that if an object is first displaced from a to b, and then from b to c, the over-all, or *resultant*, displacement is equivalent to a single displacement directly from a to c. In the symbolism of vector algebra we write the *vector equation*

$$A + B = R \qquad [3\text{-}1]$$

This implies that the single displacement R gives the same change in position as the two successive displacements, A and B. See Figure 3-2.

Equation 3-1 represents a very special sort of algebra, vector algebra, and the plus sign has a special meaning. The resultant R is the *vector sum* of A and B. Unless A and B point in the same direction, the scalar equation

$A + B = R$ is *not* true. Indeed, if A is fixed in both magnitude and direction whereas B is fixed in magnitude only, the *magnitude* of R can assume any value ranging from $A + B$, when A and B are aligned, to the magnitude of $A - B$ when they are in opposite directions.

Let us restate the definition of a vector. *It is a quantity*, such as displacement, *that has magnitude and direction and which follows the law of vector addition illustrated in Figure 3-2 and symbolized by Equation 3-1.* Conversely, a quantity having magnitude and direction is *not* a vector *unless* it obeys the law of vector addition. Therefore, we shall later have to test such quantities as velocity, acceleration, momentum, and force by the laws of vector algebra, to determine whether they qualify as vectors.

Now we establish certain basic operations in vector algebra: the equality of two vectors, the negative of a vector, the commutative and associative laws of vector addition, the subtraction of vectors, and the multiplication of

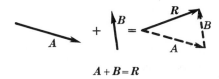

$$A + B = R$$

Figure 3-2. Graphical representation of the vector sum $A + B = R$.

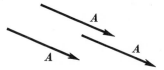

Figure 3-3. All three vectors are the same vector A.

a vector by a scalar. Some of these operations have their counterpart in ordinary algebra, and it is useful to recall first these seemingly obvious, yet fundamental, operations as they apply to ordinary numbers. The negative of 3 is such that $(3) + (-3) = 0$. The commutative law holds because $3 + 2 = 2 + 3$. The associative law holds because $(2 + 3) + 4 = 2 + (3 + 4)$. Multiplication is simply iterative addition, as in $3 \times 2 = 2 + 2 + 2$. Subtraction of 2 from 5 is simply the addition of -2 to 5, that is, $5 - 2 = 5 + (-2)$.

EQUALITY OF TWO VECTORS   Two displacement vectors are equal when they are of the same magnitude and point in the same direction, even when they are located at different points in space. Remembering that displacement is the *change* in position, it follows that any two displacements of, say, 10 m north are identical although they have different starting points. Thus, all the vectors shown in Figure 3-3 are, in fact, the same vector. This property of vectors is important because it allows us to move a vector from one location to another in a diagram without changing the vector in any way, so long as the magnitude and direction are unchanged. (This assertion does not contradict our usage in Chapter 2, where the displacement along a line was designated x. The quantity x there represented *both* the displacement and the coordinate position because all displacements were measured relative to the origin as starting point.)

NEGATIVE OF A VECTOR   If A represents the displacement from a to b, then $-A$ is the displacement from b to a, inasmuch as $A + (-A) = 0$, as shown in Figure 3-4. The vectors A and $-A$ have the same magnitude but are oppositely directed. To find the negative of A we merely reverse the direction of its arrow. For example, if the displacement A is 5.0 m northeast, $-A$ is 5.0 m southwest.

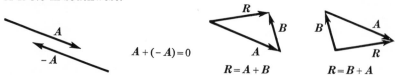

Figure 3-4. To find the negative of a vector one merely reverses the direction of the arrow.

Figure 3-5. The commutative law of vector addition illustrated: $A + B = B + A$.

COMMUTATIVE LAW IN VECTOR ADDITION   The resultant vector R can be written either as $A + B$ or as $B + A$. See Figure 3-5. Because the order is of no consequence, we may add B to A, or A to B, to yield R:

$$R = A + B = B + A$$

ASSOCIATIVE LAW IN VECTOR ADDITION   The vector sum of three or more successive displacements does not depend on the order in which we add the displacements. Therefore $(A + B) + C = A + (B + C)$, as shown in Figure 3-6.

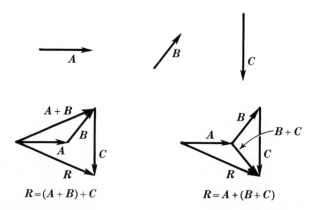

Figure 3-6. The associative law of vector addition illustrated: $(A + B) + C = A + (B + C)$.

SUBTRACTION OF VECTORS   To subtract B from A we add the two vectors A and $-B$. The vector difference D is $D = A - B = A + (-B)$. See Figure 3-7.

We can look at this differently. Add B to both sides of $D = A + (-B)$ to obtain $D + B = A$. Then the vector difference D is that vector which must be added to B to yield A.

MULTIPLICATION OF A VECTOR BY A SCALAR   The vector $2A$ is defined as the sum of A and A, inasmuch as two successive and identical displacements, A and A, yield a resultant vector of the same direction as A but with twice the magnitude of A. Thus, $2A = A + A$.

In general, the multiplication of vector A by the scalar s yields another vector having the direction of A but a magnitude sA. Moreover, if s is negative, the direction of sA is opposite to the direction of A. See Figure 3-8.

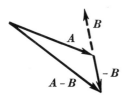

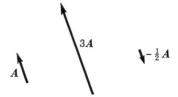

Figure 3-7. The vector difference $D = A - B$.

Figure 3-8. Multiplication of a vector by a scalar changes the length and/or sense of the vector, but not its direction.

Scalar quantities may be added together only if they represent the same physical quantity in appropriate units. For example, we may add 3.0 m and 4.0 m to yield 7.0 m, but to try to add 3.0 m and 4.0 m/sec is senseless. Likewise, we may add together only similar vector quantities; that is, displacement A and displacement B may be added, but it is meaningless to add displacement A and velocity v.

Just as it is permissible to multiply one scalar quantity by a second scalar quantity, it is permissible to multiply a vector quantity A carrying one set of units by a scalar s with another set of units, the units of sA being the product of the units of s and of A. For example, if v is the velocity vector 10 m/sec north and Δt is the scalar 2.0 sec, their product $v\Delta t$ is, we shall see, a displacement vector of 20 m north. Thus, multiplying a vector by a scalar may transform it into a different kind of vector.

The scalar (or dot) product of two vectors is treated in Section 11-4, the vector (or cross) product in Section 14-2.

3-3 Component representation of vectors Vectors have a simple meaning in terms of their graphical representation and geometrical interpretation, and it is possible to find the magnitude and direction of the sum of several vectors simply by drawing the vectors to scale, head-to-tail fashion, with a ruler and protractor. Figure 3-9 illustrates such a construction. The graphical method for solving problems in vector algebra is, however, often inconvenient and limited in accuracy, and the computation of vector sums is best made through the analytical method based on the components of a vector.

First, we define the component of a vector A along any line as the orthogonal projection of A along the line. For the vector A shown in Figure 3-10

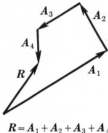

$$R = A_1 + A_2 + A_3 + A_4$$

Figure 3-9. One can find graphically the resultant R of the several vectors A_1, A_2, A_3, and A_4 by arranging the vectors in a polygon in head-to-tail fashion.

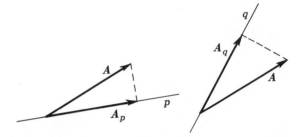

Figure 3-10. The component of the vector A along two different directions.

the component of A along the line p is the vector A_p. The component along the line q is A_q, and the component along a line perpendicular to A is zero. It follows that the magnitude of the component of A along any direction is $A \cos \theta$, where θ is the angle between the vector A and the chosen line (or direction).

The components of the vector A along two arbitrary directions p and q are shown in Figure 3-11a. Notice that the sum of these two vector components, A_p and A_q, is *not* equal to the original vector A. On the other hand, if we find the components of A along any two mutually perpendicular directions, then the vector sum of these two component vectors *is* equal to the original vector A (Figure 3-11b). This follows from the fact that the components along two mutually perpendicular directions are independent of one another; that is, a vector along X has no component along Y, and conversely.

Any vector (in the plane) can always be represented by, or resolved into, two mutually perpendicular vector components. Such a coordinate system is called a rectangular Cartesian coordinate system, the two perpendicular coordinate axes usually being identified as the X- and Y-axes. The location of the origin and the orientation of the axes are, of course, arbitrary. By assigning positive and negative directions to the coordinate axes it is possible

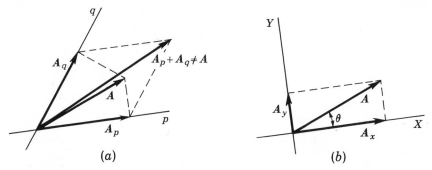

Figure 3-11. (a) The vector sum of the components (A_p and A_q) of a vector A is *not* in general equal to A. (b) The vector sum of the *rectangular* components (A_x and A_y) of a vector A is equal to A.

to specify any vector in a plane completely by giving its X- and Y-components, the signs $+$ or $-$ signifying the direction of the component (left or right, up or down). In the coordinate system of Figure 3-11b the vector A has the rectangular components

$$A_x = A \cos \theta$$
$$A_y = A \sin \theta$$

[3-2]

where, following the usual convention, we measure the angle θ counterclockwise from the positive X-axis. Conversely, the two components of a vector (in a plane) uniquely determine the vector. That is, if we know A_x and A_y then we know the vector A,

its magnitude being given by:

$$A = \sqrt{A_x{}^2 + A_y{}^2}$$

and its direction by:

$$\tan \theta = A_y/A_x$$

[3-3]

Two numbers are required to describe the vector A in a plane: either A and θ, or A_x and A_y.

Example 1 Consider the displacement whose length is 10.0 feet and whose direction is 30° north of east. Find the components of this vector along the north-south and east-west lines.

We identify $+X$ as east, $-X$ as west, $+Y$ as north, and $-Y$ as south. From Equation 3-2:

$$A_x = A \cos 30° = (10.0 \text{ ft})(0.866) = +8.66 \text{ ft east}$$

$$A_y = A \sin 30° = (10.0 \text{ ft})(0.500) = +5.00 \text{ ft north}$$

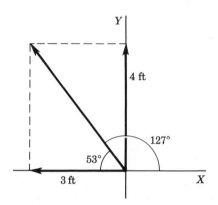

Figure 3-12

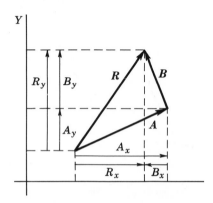

Figure 3-13. The rectangular component of the resultant equals the algebraic sum of the components of the vectors along the same axis:
$$R_y = A_y + B_y; \quad R_x = A_x - B_x.$$

Example 2   Given the components of the displacement R as $R_x = -3.0$ feet and $R_y = +4.0$ feet, find the direction and magnitude of R.

By Equation 3-3, the magnitude of R is

$$R = \sqrt{(R_x{}^2 + R_y{}^2)} = \sqrt{(-3.0 \text{ ft})^2 + (4.0 \text{ ft})^2} = 5.0 \text{ ft}$$

and the angle with respect to the positive X-axis is

$$\tan \theta = R_y/R_x = (4 \text{ ft})/(-3 \text{ ft}) = -1.3$$

$$\text{(counterclockwise from } +X)$$

or $\theta = 127°$, or $53°$ above the negative X-axis; see Figure 3-12.

3-4   Vector addition by the component method   The rectangular components of vectors are useful for finding the sum of several vectors by the analytical method. For example, let us find the sum of the two vectors A and B by the component method. See Figure 3-13.

If the resultant of two vectors A and B is $R = A + B$, then from the geometry of Figure 3-13 we see that the component of the vector R is equal to the sum of the components of the vectors A and B along any line in the plane. Thus, along the X-axis we have

$$R_x = A_x + B_x$$

and along the Y-axis we have

$$R_y = A_y + B_y$$

The magnitude and direction of the resultant vector are then found easily:

$$R = \sqrt{R_x{}^2 + R_y{}^2} \qquad \text{and} \qquad \tan\theta = R_y/R_x$$

The procedure of finding vector sums by the analytical method of components can, of course, be extended to problems involving more than two vectors. The general procedure is this:

(1) Choose conveniently oriented rectangular coordinate axes (such that as many vectors as possible lie along X or Y).

(2) Resolve each vector into its X- and Y-components.

(3) Sum (algebraically) the X-components of the vectors to find the X-component of the resultant, and do similarly for the Y-components.

(4) Find the magnitude and direction of the resultant from its X- and Y-components.

(5) Sketch the vectors roughly in head-to-tail fashion to find the approximate resultant by geometrical construction, and check this result against that obtained analytically to detect gross errors in computation.

Example 3   A man walks 7.00 miles 30° north of east, 3.46 miles 60° north of west, 3.00 miles 30° south of west, and finally 2.00 miles south. Find the man's final distance and direction relative to his starting point by the analytical method.

These four displacements and their sum were shown in Figure 3-9, which illustrates the geometrical method as applied to this problem. For convenience in finding components we locate the tails of all four displacements at the origin; see Figure 3-14a. (Recall that any vector may be relocated without its value being changed, as long as the magnitude and direction are unchanged.) We have labeled the four displacements respectively A_1, A_2, A_3, and A_4. Because of the orientation of the X- and Y-axes shown in Figure 3-14a, all but one of the vectors lie along the coordinate axes.

Next, we find the rectangular components of each vector. For example, the components of A_4 (2.00 miles south) are:

$$A_{4x} = (2.00 \text{ mi}) \cos 240° = -(2.00 \text{ mi}) \cos 60° = -1.00 \text{ mi}$$

$$A_{4y} = (2.00 \text{ mi}) \sin 240° = -(2.00 \text{ mi}) \sin 60° = -1.73 \text{ mi}$$

The components of all vectors are shown in the table below (such a table is a useful device for keeping one's information organized).

VECTOR	X-COMPONENT	Y-COMPONENT
$A_1 = 7.00$ mi $30°$ N of E	$+7.00$ mi	0 mi
$A_2 = 3.46$ mi $60°$ N of W	0	$+3.46$
$A_3 = 3.00$ mi $30°$ S of W	-3.00	0
$A_4 = 2.00$ mi S	-1.00	-1.73
	$R_x = +3.00$ mi	$R_y = +1.73$ mi

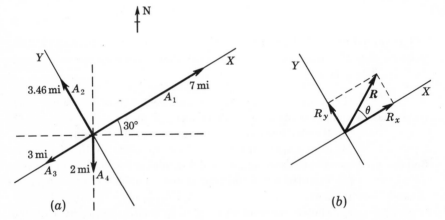

Figure 3-14. (a) Four displacement vectors whose resultant is to be computed. Note that the rectangular components are easily computed by choosing X- and Y-axes as shown. (b) The resultant and its components along the chosen X- and Y-axes.

The resultant R has components $R_x = 3.00$ mi and $R_y = 1.73$ mi. The magnitude R and direction θ of the resultant then is

$$R = \sqrt{R_x{}^2 + R_y{}^2} = \sqrt{(3.00)^2 + (1.73)^2} \text{ mi} = 3.46 \text{ mi}$$

$$\tan \theta = R_y/R_x = (1.73 \text{ mi})/(3.00 \text{ mi}) = 0.578$$

$$\theta = 30°$$

The resultant is 3.46 miles $30°$ east of north, as shown in Figure 3-14b.

Example 4 Find the displacement A_3 which, when added to the displacements $A_1 = 3.00$ feet east and $A_2 = 4.00$ feet $60°$ north of east, gives a resultant of zero.

We are to find A_3 where $A_1 + A_2 + A_3 = 0$, or $A_3 = -(A_1 + A_2)$. We choose east as the X-axis, north as the Y-axis; see Figure 3-15. In terms of components:

$$A_{3x} = -A_{1x} - A_{2x}$$

$$A_{3x} = -(3 \text{ ft}) - (4 \text{ ft cos } 60°)$$

$$A_{3x} = -5.00 \text{ ft}$$

and

$$A_{3y} = -A_{1y} - A_{2y}$$

$$A_{3y} = 0 - (4 \text{ ft sin } 60°)$$

$$A_{3y} = -3.46 \text{ ft}$$

Therefore, the magnitude of A_3 is

$$A_3 = \sqrt{(-5.00)^2 + (-3.46)^2} \text{ ft } = 6.09 \text{ ft}$$

and the direction of A_3 is

$$\tan \theta = \frac{A_{3y}}{A_{3x}} = \frac{(-3.46)}{(-5.00)} = 0.692$$

$$\theta = 215°, \text{ that is, } 35° \text{ south of west}$$

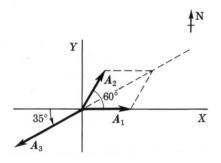

Figure 3-15

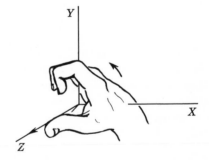

Figure 3-16. The X-, Y-, and Z-axes shown form a right-handed set.

3-5 Vectors in three dimensions We have discussed displacement vectors that lie in the plane of the X- and Y-axes. Any two (noncollinear) vectors A and B define a plane, and when $R = A + B$ the resultant lies in this plane. However, we need not restrict displacements to a plane with rectangular components along only the X- and Y-axes. In general, a displacement vector has components along the three mutually perpendicular coordinate axes, X, Y, and Z, in three dimensions.

The coordinate axes shown in Figure 3-16 form a *right*-handed set. If one imagines the $+X$-axis to be turned into the $+Y$-axis through the smaller

(90°) angle with the fingers of the *right* hand, the direction of the $+Z$-axis, which is perpendicular to the X-Y-plane, is given by the direction of the right-hand thumb. Thus, in a right-hand set of axes, $+X$ points to the right, $+Y$ points upward, and $+Z$ points out of the paper.

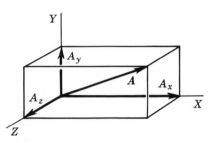

Because the three directions are mutually perpendicular, a vector along one axis (such as X) has *no* components along the other two axes (such as Y and Z). The rectangular components of a vector in three dimensions are the orthogonal projections of that vector along the axes

Figure 3-17. The rectangular components of a vector in three dimensions.

X, Y, and Z. The components A_x, A_y, and A_z of vector A are shown in Figure 3-17. From the geometry of Figure 3-17 it follows that

$$A^2 = A_x{}^2 + A_y{}^2 + A_z{}^2$$

Therefore, the magnitude of A is

$$A = \sqrt{A_x{}^2 + A_y{}^2 + A_z{}^2} \qquad [3\text{-}4]$$

The analytical method of adding vectors is easily extended to three dimensions. One resolves each vector into its X-, Y-, and Z-components. Then one adds algebraically all X-components to obtain the X-component of the resultant, and likewise for Y and Z. Finally, the magnitude of the resultant is found from Equation 3-4.

To such a *vector* equation as

$$\boldsymbol{R} = \boldsymbol{A} + \boldsymbol{B} + \boldsymbol{C}$$

there correspond *three* component *scalar* equations:

$$R_x = A_x + B_x + C_x$$

$$R_y = A_y + B_y + C_y$$

$$R_z = A_z + B_z + C_z$$

Herein lie the economy, generality, and elegance of the vector algebra. A single vector equation replaces three scalar equations. Moreover, the vector equation expresses a relationship which is independent of the particular choice of coordinate axes.

Example 5   Find the magnitude of $A + B + C$, where the respective components are

$$A_x = 10 \text{ m} \qquad A_y = 12 \text{ m} \qquad A_z = -3 \text{ m}$$
$$B_x = -5 \text{ m} \qquad B_y = 7 \text{ m} \qquad B_z = 13 \text{ m}$$
$$C_x = 5 \text{ m} \qquad C_y = -11 \text{ m} \qquad C_z = -4 \text{ m}$$

Note that A, B, and C do *not* lie in a single plane.

The components of the resultant are:

$$R_x = A_x + B_x + C_x = (10 - 5 + 5) \text{ m} = 10 \text{ m}$$
$$R_y = A_y + B_y + C_y = (12 + 7 - 11) \text{ m} = 8 \text{ m}$$
$$R_z = A_z + B_z + C_z = (-3 + 13 - 4) \text{ m} = 6 \text{ m}$$

and the magnitude of the resultant is

$$R = \sqrt{R_x{}^2 + R_y{}^2 + R_z{}^2} = \sqrt{10^2 + 8^2 + 6^2} \text{ m} = 14.1 \text{ m}$$

PROBLEMS

3-1   Find the vector sum of the following displacements: 10.0 miles east, 6.00 miles 30° north of west, and 6.50 miles southwest.

3-2   The vector A is a displacement of 4.0 m north. What are (a) $3A$, (b) $-2A$, (c) $A/10$?

3-3   The vector A is a displacement of 10.0 feet at 150°. What are the X- and Y-components of (a) $5A$, (b) $-A/2$, (c) $-2A$?

3-4   What is the resultant of the displacements 2.0 miles north and 2.0 km east?

3-5   Find the rectangular components of (a) 20 feet at 150°, (b) 30 feet at 270°, and (c) 50 feet at 307°.

3-6   A body falls 20 m vertically downward from the top of an incline. (a) What is the displacement? What are the components of this displacement (b) along, and (c) perpendicular to, the incline, which makes an angle of 30° with respect to the horizontal?

3-7   A body is displaced 10 feet horizontally. What are the components of this displacement (a) along and (b) perpendicular to an incline making an angle of 37° with respect to the horizontal?

3-8   Find (a) the vector sum $A + B$, and (b) the vector difference $A - B$, of the vectors $A = 10.0$ m east and $B = 20.0$ m north.

3-9   Find the resultant of the following displacements: 10.0 m northeast, 20.0 m northwest, 15.0 m south, and 10.0 m southeast.

3-10   Vector A is 5.0 m at 30°, B is 10.0 m at 225°, C is 15.0 m at 270°, and $A + B + C + D = 0$. What is D?

3-11   Vector A makes an angle θ with vector B. Show that the magnitude of $A + B$ is $(A^2 + B^2 + 2AB \cos \theta)^{\frac{1}{2}}$.

3-12   (a) Find the resultant of the following displacements by taking components along the directions north, south, east, and west: 15 miles northeast, 10 miles south, and 20 miles southwest. (b) Find the resultant of the same three displacements by now taking components along the directions northeast, northwest, southwest, and southeast. (That the resultant is the same in both instances illustrates, for this special case, the independence of the vector sum of the particular choice of coordinate axes.

3-13   The vector A is 12.0 feet at 45°. What is the vector B if the magnitude of $A + B$ equals the magnitude of $A - B$?

3-14   It is known that $A + B + C = 0$ and that $A = B = C$. What is the angle between A and B?

3-15   Vector A has a magnitude which is much greater than that of vector B. Show that (a) if A and B are nearly aligned, the magnitude of their vector sum is close to $A + B$, and that (b) if A and B are nearly at right angles, the magnitude of their vector sum or difference is close to A.

3-16   One can trace out an ellipse by putting a loop of string over two fixed pins and moving a pencil in the loop while keeping the string taut. Show that if $A + B = C$ and $A + B = k$, where C and k are constants, the locus of points traced out by the tail of vector B is an ellipse.

3-17 ★   The rectangular components of a vector along the X- and Y-axes are x and y respectively. A second set of mutually perpendicular axes, X' and Y', have their origin at the origin of X and Y, but the X'-axis is at an angle of θ with respect to X. (a) Show that the components x' and y' along X' and Y', respectively, are given by $x' = x \cos \theta + y \sin \theta$ and $y' = y \cos \theta - x \sin \theta$. (These equations are known as the coordinate transformation equations for pure rotation.) (b) Prove that the magnitude of a vector is independent of the choice of coordinate axes by showing that $x^2 + y^2 = x'^2 + y'^2$.

3-18   A man walks 1000 feet east, then 500 feet north, and finally he ascends 200 feet in an elevator. What is the magnitude of the man's displacement relative to his starting point?

3-19   Vector A is perpendicular to vector B, and A is also perpendicular to C. Yet B and C do *not* lie in the same direction. Explain.

3-20   Find the magnitude of the vector sum $A + B + C$, where the respective components are: $A_x = 5.0$ m, $A_y = -10.0$ m, $A_z = 8.0$ m, $B_x = 0.0$ m, $B_y = 20.0$ m, $B_z = 12.0$ m, $C_x = 15.0$ m, $C_y = -10.0$ m, and $C_z = 5.0$ m.

3-21   Vectors A and B have magnitudes of 10 m and 3 m respectively. How must A and B be oriented to give a resultant which has a magnitude of (a) 13 m, (b) 7 m, (c) 8 m, and (d) 10 m?

3-22   A displacement A of 10.0 feet in magnitude followed by a displacement of 5.0 feet in magnitude yields a resultant with a magnitude of 7.0 feet. What is the angle between vectors A and B?

3-23   The cosines of the respective angles between the vector A and the X-, Y-, and Z-axes are α, β, and γ. The quantities α, β, and γ are known as the *direction cosines* of A. Show that the components of A are (a) $A_x = \alpha A$, $A_y = \beta A$, and $A_z = \gamma A$, and (b) $\alpha^2 + \beta^2 + \gamma^2 = 1$.

F O U R

KINEMATICS IN TWO DIMENSIONS

In this chapter we extend our discussion of kinematics to motion in a plane. We shall find that velocity and acceleration behave as vector quantities. The special case of motion with constant acceleration is treated analytically.

4-1 Velocity and acceleration as vector quantities The definitions of the average and instantaneous velocities and accelerations—all vector quantities with direction as well as magnitude, as we shall see—are similar to the definitions of the corresponding scalars in one-dimensional motion.

Consider the simulated multiflash photograph, Figure 4-1. The position of the body relative to some arbitrary origin, here chosen as the starting point a, is specified by the displacement vector r. If we designate the displacement from point g to point k by Δr, then, as seen from Figure 4-1,

$$r_g + \Delta r = r_k$$

(Note that Δr does *not* depend on the origin chosen for the vectors r_g and r_k.) The time interval elapsing between the appearance of the body at g, and later at k, is Δt. Then the average velocity $\bar{v}$ over the interval Δt is defined as the displacement $\Delta \boldsymbol{r}$ (a vector) divided by the elapsed time Δt (a scalar):

$$\bar{\boldsymbol{v}} = \frac{\Delta \boldsymbol{r}}{\Delta t} \qquad [4\text{-}1]$$

The average velocity is, of course, a vector quantity, inasmuch as it represents the vector quantity $\Delta \boldsymbol{r}$ multiplied by the scalar quantity $1/\Delta t$.

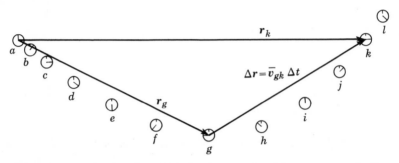

Figure 4-1. A simulated multiflash photograph. The average velocity from k to p is $\bar{\boldsymbol{v}}_{kp}$.

Because Δt is always positive, the direction of the vector $\bar{\boldsymbol{v}}$ is the same as the direction of the vector $\Delta \boldsymbol{r}$. The motion from g to k in Figure 4-1 is clearly not one of constant velocity, but the average velocity from g to k gives that *constant velocity* which the particle must have if it is to undergo the same displacement in the same time interval as it has undergone during its actual displacement from g to k.

The instantaneous velocity $\boldsymbol{v}$, the time rate of displacement, is the limit of the average velocity as the time interval becomes indefinitely small:

$$\boldsymbol{v} = \lim_{\Delta t \to 0} \frac{\Delta \boldsymbol{r}}{\Delta t} = \frac{d\boldsymbol{r}}{dt} \qquad [4\text{-}2]$$

The time interval is sufficiently small to give the instantaneous velocity when the displacement $\Delta \boldsymbol{r}$ cannot be distinguished from the actual path of the particle over the interval Δt. Therefore, the instantaneous velocity of a particle is always tangent to the particle's path, pointing in the direction of the motion. It follows from Equation 4-2 that, if Δt is small enough, the velocity $\boldsymbol{v}$ will be essentially constant in direction and magnitude over this time interval, and the incremental displacement $\Delta \boldsymbol{r}$ will be $\boldsymbol{v}\Delta t$. See Figure 4-2. The dimensions of velocity are, of course, length divided by time.

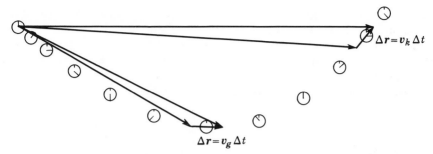

Figure 4-2. The instantaneous velocities at g and k are $\boldsymbol{v}_g$ and $\boldsymbol{v}_k$, respectively.

Vectors showing the instantaneous velocity at several points along the path are shown in Figure 4-3a. Note that the velocity vectors are all tangent to the path; their lengths represent (on an arbitrarily chosen scale for velocity) the distance covered per unit time over infinitesimal time intervals. The magnitude of the instantaneous velocity is called the instantaneous speed.

Note further that a diagram such as that of Figure 4-3a, in which velocity vectors are shown superimposed on the path of the particle, is a combination,

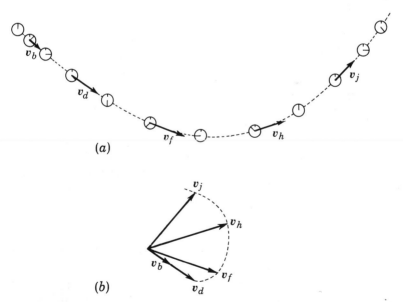

Figure 4-3. (a) Instantaneous velocity vectors at several points. The tails of the velocity vectors are here placed at the corresponding positions of the moving particle. (b) The instantaneous velocity vectors of (a) drawn from a common origin.

as it were, of two diagrams: one giving the location of the particle (according to an arbitrarily chosen scale of distances) and the second showing the instantaneous velocity vectors (with a different scale), each velocity vector being located for convenience with its tail at the position of the particle at that instant. We may relocate any vector without changing its value, and we may equally well display the velocity vectors together, as in Figure 4-3b,

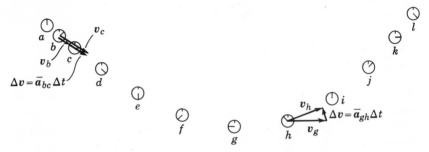

Figure 4-4. Average acceleration vectors a_{ab} and a_{kl}.

with all tails at the same origin in what may appropriately be termed "velocity space."

The average acceleration $\bar{a}$ is defined as the change in (instantaneous) velocity per unit time:

$$\bar{a} = \frac{\Delta v}{\Delta t} \qquad [4\text{-}3]$$

The average acceleration is a vector by virtue of being the product of the vector Δv and a scalar $1/\Delta t$. It has the dimensions of velocity divided by time. Equation 4-3 shows that the change in the velocity Δv over the interval Δt is $\bar{a}\Delta t$. See Figure 4-4. Note that the direction of Δv, and hence of $\bar{a}$, is *not* necessarily along v, the direction of motion. An acceleration occurs if the velocity changes magnitude, or direction, or both magnitude and direction.

The instantaneous acceleration is simply the average acceleration over an infinitesimal time interval, that is, the time rate of the velocity:

$$a = \lim_{\Delta t \to 0} \frac{\Delta v}{\Delta t} = \frac{dv}{dt} \qquad [4\text{-}4]$$

Figure 4-5a shows instantaneous-acceleration vectors superimposed on a diagram of the particle's path. The scale of the acceleration vectors is arbitrary (but different from the scales for displacement and velocity). The same acceleration vectors are shown in "acceleration space" in Figure 4-5b. At the start of the motion (a, b, c, d) the acceleration is constant in direction and magnitude and lies along the direction of the motion. In the

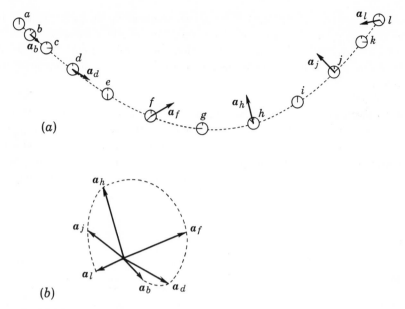

(a)

(b)

Figure 4-5. (a) Instantaneous acceleration vectors at several points. The tails of the acceleration vectors are here placed at the corresponding positions of the moving particle. (b) The instantaneous acceleration vectors of (a) drawn as from a common origin.

vicinity of points g, h, i, and j, where the body moves with constant speed but changes direction of motion, the acceleration vectors are at right angles to the path. At such points as f and l the acceleration is neither along nor perpendicular to the path. In every case the instantaneous acceleration vector gives the magnitude and direction of the *change* in the *velocity vector* per unit time.

It is often convenient to show different types of vectors on the same diagram. Figure 4-6 shows the displacement, instantaneous velocity, and

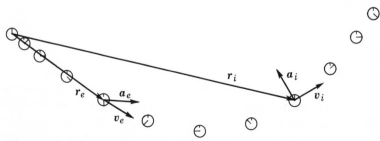

Figure 4-6. Displacement, instantaneous velocity, and instantaneous acceleration vectors for different positions of a moving particle.

instantaneous acceleration vectors for two points along the path. It must be emphasized that displacements may properly be added to displacements, velocities to velocities, and accelerations to accelerations. We cannot, however, add together unlike vector quantities, such as displacement and velocity.

4-2 Motion at constant acceleration A special and important type of motion in two dimensions is that in which the acceleration is constant both in magnitude and direction. We recall that in one-dimensional kinematics the velocity v and displacement x of a particle having an initial velocity v_0 and a constant acceleration a are given in terms of the time t by

[2-7] $$v = v_0 + at$$

[2-8] $$x = v_0 t + \tfrac{1}{2} a t^2$$

The corresponding relations in two (or three) dimensions are easily shown to be

For constant $\boldsymbol{a}$:
$$\boldsymbol{v} = \boldsymbol{v}_0 + \boldsymbol{a}t \qquad \text{[4-5]}$$
$$\boldsymbol{r} = \boldsymbol{v}_0 t + \tfrac{1}{2}\boldsymbol{a}t^2 \qquad \text{[4-6]}$$

Here $\boldsymbol{r}$ is the *displacement* relative to the origin ($\boldsymbol{r} = 0$ when $t = 0$), $\boldsymbol{v}_0$ and $\boldsymbol{v}$ are the instantaneous vector velocities at the times 0 and t, respectively, and $\boldsymbol{a}$ is the constant vector acceleration. It is important to recognize that $\boldsymbol{r}$ does *not* represent the distance traveled by the particle.

Equation 4-5 follows directly from the definition of average acceleration; for, if the acceleration is constant, the instantaneous acceleration $\boldsymbol{a}$ is identical with the average acceleration $\bar{\boldsymbol{a}}$. The (vector) difference in velocity $\Delta\boldsymbol{v}$ is $\boldsymbol{v} - \boldsymbol{v}_0$, and the time interval Δt is the time elapsed after $t = 0$. Therefore, Equation 4-3 becomes

$$\bar{\boldsymbol{a}} = \boldsymbol{a} = \frac{\Delta\boldsymbol{v}}{\Delta t} = \frac{\boldsymbol{v} - \boldsymbol{v}_0}{t}$$

[4-5] $$\boldsymbol{v} = \boldsymbol{v}_0 + \boldsymbol{a}t$$

Equation 4-6 is also easily arrived at. Suppose that the acceleration is zero; then the displacement $\boldsymbol{r}$ is along the direction of the constant velocity $\boldsymbol{v}_0$ and $\boldsymbol{r} = \boldsymbol{v}_0 t$. Now suppose that the initial velocity is zero, but not the acceleration; the displacement x along a line is given by $x = \tfrac{1}{2}at^2$, where the acceleration a is along the X-axis. This relation may be written in vector form as $r = \frac{1}{2}at^2$, where the vectors r and a are along the same direction. Inasmuch as displacements follow the rules of the vector algebra, the displacement r will, in general, be equal to the vector sum of the displacement v_0t at constant velocity and the displacement $\frac{1}{2}at^2$ arising from a uniformly changing velocity:

[4-6] $$r = v_0t + \tfrac{1}{2}at^2$$

The vector equations 4-5 and 4-6 are illustrated in Figure 4-7. In general, the velocity v is not necessarily along the direction of v_0, and the displacement r not necessarily along the direction of v_0t or of $\frac{1}{2}at^2$. Furthermore, the displacement vector r and the velocity vector v are *not*, in general, parallel.

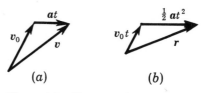

The origin of the vector r is usually chosen as the origin of the X- and Y-axes, and we may write the vector equations 4-5 and 4-6 equivalently in

Figure 4-7. Vector relations giving (a) the displacement and (b) the velocity, for motion at constant acceleration.

scalar form by using the components of the displacement, velocity, and acceleration along the X- and Y-directions, as shown in Figure 4-8. These scalar equations are:

$$v_x = v_{0x} + a_x t$$ [4-7]

$$v_y = v_{0y} + a_y t$$

$$x = v_{0x}t + \tfrac{1}{2}a_x t^2$$ [4-8]

$$y = v_{0y}t + \tfrac{1}{2}a_y t^2$$

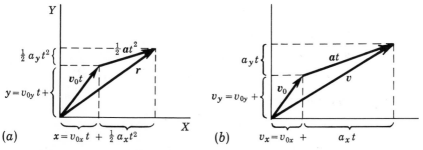

Figure 4-8. Scalar kinematic relations giving the rectangular components of (a) the displacement and (b) the velocity, as derived from the vector kinematic relations.

The motion of a particle at constant acceleration in a plane is described completely by two independent and simultaneous motions along the X- and Y-axes. The X- and Y-motions both are rectilinear motions at the constant accelerations a_x and a_y, respectively.

The strategy for solving kinematic problems in two dimensions with constant acceleration is this:

We resolve the vector displacements, velocities, and accelerations into components along the X- and Y-axes, and use Equations 4-7 and 4-8 for the components of the velocities and displacements along X and Y. The link between these equations is the common time t.

Example 1 An object is projected along a horizontal surface with an initial velocity of 20 m/sec in a direction 37° above the positive X-axis. The object has a constant acceleration of 4.0 m/sec² in a direction opposite to the initial velocity. Find the X- and Y-components of (a) the displacement and (b) the velocity, 6.0 sec after the start.

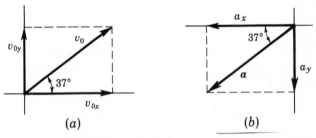

(a)   *(b)*

Figure 4-9. The rectangular components of (a) the initial velocity and (b) the constant acceleration.

The components of the initial velocity and of the acceleration are seen from Figure 4-9 to be

$$v_{0x} = v_0 \cos \theta = (20 \text{ m/sec}) \cos 37° = 16 \text{ m/sec}$$

$$v_{0y} = v_0 \sin \theta = (20 \text{ m/sec}) \sin 37° = 12 \text{ m/sec}$$

$$a_x = a \cos \theta = (-4.0 \text{ m/sec}^2) \cos 37° = -3.2 \text{ m/sec}^2$$

$$a_y = a \sin \theta = (-4.0 \text{ m/sec}^2) \sin 37° = -2.4 \text{ m/sec}^2$$

Equations 4-7 and 4-8 yield

$$v_x = v_{0x} + a_x t = (16 \text{ m/sec}) + (-3.2 \text{ m/sec}^2)(6.0 \text{ sec})$$

$$= -3.2 \text{ m/sec}$$

$$v_y = v_{0y} + a_y t = (12 \text{ m/sec}) + (-2.4 \text{ m/sec}^2)(6.0 \text{ sec})$$

$$= -2.4 \text{ m/sec}$$

and

$$x = v_{0x}t + \tfrac{1}{2}a_x t^2 = (16 \text{ m/sec})(6.0 \text{ sec}) + \tfrac{1}{2}(-3.2 \text{ m/sec}^2)(6.0 \text{ sec})^2$$

$$= 36.4 \text{ m}$$

$$y = v_{0y}t + \tfrac{1}{2}a_y t^2 = (12 \text{ m/sec})(6.0 \text{ sec}) + \tfrac{1}{2}(-2.4 \text{ m/sec}^2)(6.0 \text{ sec})^2$$

$$= 28.8 \text{ m}$$

When the *initial velocity* and the constant *acceleration* are along the *same direction*, the path of the motion is a *straight line* along the direction of v_0 or a. This is simply the case of rectilinear motion at constant acceleration, as treated in Chapter 2.

4-3 Projectile motion Now suppose that v_0 and a have *different* directions. Figure 4-10 shows displacement and velocity vector diagrams

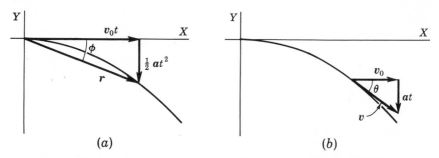

(a)   (b)

Figure 4-10. A projectile thrown horizontally: (a) the displacement vectors and (b) the velocity vectors.

(superimposed on the X- and Y-axes and the trajectory of the particle) for the simple case in which v_0 is horizontal and a is vertically downward. This situation is exemplified by an object, or projectile, thrown horizontally and falling under the influence of gravity. The velocity is initially along the X-direction; thus, $v_{0y} = 0$. In addition, the acceleration is in the vertical direction, and $a_x = 0$. Choosing the positive Y-axis as upward, we write a_y as $-g$, where g is 32 feet/sec², or 10 m/sec². Equations 4-7 and 4-8 become

$$v_x = v_{0x} \qquad v_y = -gt$$

$$x = v_{0x}t \qquad y = -\tfrac{1}{2}gt^2$$

The body coasts along the horizontal while it accelerates from rest along the vertical. By eliminating t between the equations for x and y, we can find the equation of the path, giving y in terms of x and of the constants v_{0x} and g:

$$y = -\left(\frac{g}{2v_{0x}{}^2}\right)x^2 \qquad\qquad [4\text{-}9]$$

The path is a parabola whose axis of symmetry is parallel to the direction of the constant acceleration; the instantaneous velocity vector v is tangent to the path at all points, as shown in Figure 4-10b.

A simulated multiflash photograph of this motion is shown in Figure 4-11, together with the projections of the motion along the X- and Y-axes.

Because the vertical and horizontal components of the motion are completely independent of one another, the *vertical* motion of an object thrown horizontally is identical with that of an object dropped from rest. Therefore, if one throws an object horizontally and simultaneously drops a second body from rest, the two objects strike a horizontal plane at the same instant. The thrown object strikes the surface with a larger velocity (it has both horizontal and vertical velocity components), but the *vertical components* of the horizontally thrown and the dropped objects are identical at any given time.

Figure 4-11. Simulated multiflash photograph corresponding to Figure 4-10.

Example 2 An airplane traveling horizontally at 150 feet/sec and at an altitude of 600 feet is going to drop a package on a target that is at ground level. (a) At what horizontal distance from the target must the package be released? (b) How long is the package in flight? (c) With what velocity does it strike the ground? (d) What is the displacement of the target area relative to the airplane at the moment the package is released? We assume (unrealistically) that there is no air resistance.

(a) (b) A package dropped from an airplane traveling at 150 feet/sec along X is, in effect, thrown along X at 150 feet/sec with respect to the ground. The equations of motion, giving the X- and Y-components of the velocity and displacement, are written

$$v_x = v_{0x} = 150 \text{ ft/sec}$$

$$v_y = -gt = -(32 \text{ ft/sec}^2)t$$

$$x = v_{0x}t = (150 \text{ ft/sec})t$$

$$y = -\tfrac{1}{2}gt^2 = -(16 \text{ ft/sec}^2)t^2$$

These equations apply for an observer at rest with respect to the ground, the origin of the coordinates being at the point where the package is released. When the package has descended 600 feet, $y = -600$ feet, and the corresponding time t is the time of flight. Therefore,

$$-600 \text{ ft} = -(16 \text{ ft/sec}^2)t^2$$

$$\text{time of flight} = t = 6.12 \text{ sec}$$

The package is in motion for 6.12 sec along the vertical direction, and it is, therefore, also in motion for 6.12 sec along the horizontal direction. We wish to find x for $t = 6.12$ sec:

$$x = (150 \text{ ft/sec})(6.12 \text{ sec}) = 920 \text{ ft}$$

The package must be released when the airplane is 920 feet horizontally from the target.

(c) We find the velocity at $t = 6.12$ sec, the time at which the package strikes the ground, by finding first the velocity components v_x and v_y:

$$v_x = 150 \text{ ft/sec}$$

$$v_y = -(32 \text{ ft/sec}^2)(6.12 \text{ sec}) = -196 \text{ ft/sec}$$

The magnitude of the velocity v at $t = 6.12$ sec is

$$v = \sqrt{v_x{}^2 + v_y{}^2} = \sqrt{(150)^2 + (196)^2} \text{ ft/sec}$$

$$v = 249 \text{ ft/sec}$$

The direction θ of v with respect to the X-axis is found from

$$\tan \theta = v_y/v_x = (-196 \text{ ft/sec})/(150 \text{ ft/sec}) = -1.31$$

$$\theta = 53° \text{ below the horizontal}$$

(d) The magnitude of the displacement r of the target relative to the airplane at the moment the package was released is

$$r = \sqrt{x^2 + y^2} = \sqrt{(920)^2 + (600)^2} \text{ ft}$$

$$r = 1100 \text{ ft}$$

The direction φ of r with respect to the horizontal is found from

$$\tan \varphi = y/x = (-600 \text{ ft})/(920 \text{ ft}) = -0.652$$

$$\varphi = 33° \text{ below the horizontal}$$

Note that the directions θ and φ of the velocity and displacement, respectively, are *not* the same.

We now consider the more general case in which the initial velocity v_0 is *not* at right angles to the constant acceleration a. The vector a is assumed to be vertically downward and the vector v_0 at some oblique angle with respect to the X-axis. The displacement and velocity diagrams are shown in Figure 4-12, together with the path of the particle. Again, the displacement r and velocity v are *not* parallel. Figure 4-12a shows that the displacement is comprised of two contributions: the displacement $v_0 t$ along the original direction of motion, which would be the entire displacement if there were no acceleration, and the displacement $\frac{1}{2}at^2$ vertically downward, which arises from the constant acceleration. Figure 4-12b shows the two contributions to the velocity v: the constant initial velocity v_0 and the change in velocity at arising from the constant acceleration a. Figure 4-13 shows that the horizontal component of v is unchanged throughout the motion, but that the vertical component (downward) of v increases steadily in time.

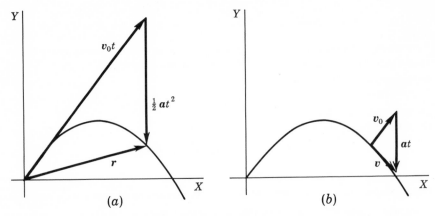

Figure 4-12. A projectile thrown obliquely: (a) the displacement vectors and (b) the velocity vectors.

The motion illustrated in Figure 4-13 is a general projectile motion over ranges small compared with the Earth's radius; for these ranges the acceleration is constant and has a magnitude g. When a body is thrown obliquely into the air it changes from its otherwise straight-line motion because of the acceleration due to gravity. Consider a bullet shot from a gun aimed directly at a distant object; this object is held above the ground and released from rest at the instant the bullet is fired. If one could, so to speak, "turn off gravity," the bullet would travel a straight-line path, the object would not fall when released, and the bullet would hit the object.

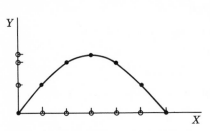

Figure 4-13. Simulated multiflash photograph corresponding to Figure 4-12.

Now suppose that bullet and object fall, as do all objects close to the Earth, with the same constant vertical acceleration. The object falls a distance of $\frac{1}{2}gt^2$ from rest, and during this same time the bullet "falls" the same vertical distance $\frac{1}{2}gt^2$ from its straight-line motion. Consequently, the bullet always strikes the target, quite apart from the magnitude or direction of the initial velocity, or even of the magnitude of g.

The equations of motion, giving the X- and Y-components of displacement and velocity as a function of time, are easily written from Equations 4-7 and 4-8 as follows:

$$v_x = v_{0x} \qquad v_y = v_{0y} - gt$$

$$x = v_{0x}t \qquad y = v_{0y}t - \tfrac{1}{2}gt^2$$

(Here again the positive direction of the Y-axis is up.) These relations differ from those used earlier to describe an object thrown horizontally in that we now have a nonzero value for v_{0y}. They are the general relations for projectile motion.

We arrive at the equation of the path of a projectile by eliminating t between the equations for x and y:

$$y = \left(\frac{v_{0y}}{v_{0x}}\right)x - \left(\frac{g}{2v_{0x}{}^2}\right)x^2$$

The vertical displacement y is a quadratic function of x and the projectile traces out a parabolic path. The instantaneous velocity v is, of course, tangent to the path at all times, as shown in Figure 4-12b.

Example 3   A projectile leaves the barrel of a cannon with a speed of 248 feet/sec at an angle of 40° above the horizontal. Ignoring the effects of air resistance, find (a) the maximum altitude achieved by the projectile, (b) the horizontal range (the horizontal distance traversed when the projectile is again at its initial elevation), and (c) the displacement and velocity of the projectile 15 sec after firing.

The components of v_0 are given in terms of θ_0, the angle between v_0 and the X-axis, and v_0:

$$v_{0x} = v_0 \cos \theta_0 = (248 \text{ ft/sec}) \cos 40° = 190 \text{ ft/sec}$$

$$v_{0y} = v_0 \sin \theta_0 = (248 \text{ ft/sec}) \sin 40° = 159 \text{ ft/sec}$$

The equations of motion become

$$v_x = 190 \text{ ft/sec} \qquad v_y = (159 \text{ ft/sec}) - (32 \text{ ft/sec}^2)t$$

$$x = (190 \text{ ft/sec})t \qquad y = (159 \text{ ft/sec})t - (16 \text{ ft/sec}^2)t^2$$

These equations give the position and velocity of the projectile, in terms of their respective components, at any time t. All questions concerning the motion are answered by applying these equations.

(a) The maximum height y is obtained by first finding the time t at which the projectile is at the highest point, and then substituting this t into the equation for y. At the point of maximum altitude the projectile travels horizontally, and $v_y = 0$. Thus, with $v_y = 0$, we obtain

$$v_y = 0 = 159 \text{ ft/sec} - (32 \text{ ft/sec}^2)t$$

$$t = (159/32) \text{ sec} = 5.0 \text{ sec}$$

$$y = (159 \text{ ft/sec})t - (16 \text{ ft/sec}^2)t^2$$

$$= (159 \text{ ft/sec})(5.0 \text{ sec}) - (16 \text{ ft/sec}^2)(5.0 \text{ sec})^2$$

$$\text{Maximum height:} \quad y = 395 \text{ ft}$$

(b) If we are to compute the horizontal range we must first find the time at which the projectile is again on the X-axis; that is, we compute t for $y = 0$ and substitute this time of flight into the equation for x:

$$y = 0 = (159 \text{ ft/sec})t - (16 \text{ ft/sec}^2)t^2$$

$$t = 0, \quad \text{and } 10.0 \text{ sec}$$

This quadratic equation has two solutions; the projectile was at $y = 0$ both at $t = 0$ and at $t = 10.0$ sec, the time of flight. The horizontal range is then

Range: $\qquad x = (190 \text{ ft/sec})t = (190 \text{ ft/sec})(10.0 \text{ sec}) = 1900 \text{ ft}$

(c) Now we are to find the displacement and velocity of the projectile after it has been in flight for 15 sec. Because the projectile takes only 10 sec to return to the X-axis, it will not move with the constant acceleration g for the entire 15 sec if the ground is at the same level as the X-axis. But, of course, the equations of motion do not "know" this: they give the component displacements and velocities at *any* time for which the acceleration remains constant. Thus, the computed displacement and velocity at $t = 15$ sec are those which the projectile would have had if it had continued in free fall under the influence of gravity—as would be the case if the projectile were fired from a high cliff.

$$v_x = 190 \text{ ft/sec}$$

$$v_y = (159 \text{ ft/sec}) - (32 \text{ ft/sec}^2)t$$

$$= (159 \text{ ft/sec}) - (32 \text{ ft/sec}^2)(15 \text{ sec}) = -321 \text{ ft/sec}$$

The magnitude of v and direction φ of the velocity at $t = 15$ sec are

$$v = \sqrt{v_x{}^2 + v_y{}^2} = \sqrt{(190)^2 + (-321)^2} \text{ ft/sec} = 372 \text{ ft/sec}$$

$$\tan \varphi = v_y/v_x = (-321 \text{ ft/sec})/(190 \text{ ft/sec}) = -1.69$$

$$\varphi = 59° \text{ below the horizontal}$$

The component displacements at $t = 15$ sec are

$$x = (190 \text{ ft/sec})t = (190 \text{ ft/sec})(15 \text{ sec}) = 2850 \text{ ft}$$

$$y = (159 \text{ ft/sec})t - (16 \text{ ft/sec}^2)t^2$$

$$= (159 \text{ ft/sec})(15 \text{ sec}) - (16 \text{ ft/sec}^2)(15 \text{ sec})^2 = -1215 \text{ ft}$$

Fifteen seconds after firing, the projectile is 2850 feet to the right and 1215 feet below the starting point, and at this time its velocity is 372 feet/sec at 59° below the horizontal.

The motion of a projectile, or of any freely falling body, over short ranges close to the Earth's surface is most conveniently treated by choosing the Y-axis as the vertical direction with the constant downward acceleration of magnitude g. Projectile motion, however, is just one familiar example of two-dimensional motion at constant acceleration. Another example is that of an electrically charged particle moving in the region between two parallel, plane, oppositely charged, metal plates. (Later we shall identify such a situation as one of an electric charge in a uniform electric field; similarly, a body falling freely near the Earth can be described as a gravitational mass in a uniform gravitational field.)

Suppose that a particle moves with constant acceleration to the right, as would an electron moving between two vertical, parallel, metal plates on which charges of opposite sign have been placed. The displacement and velocity vectors would be related as shown in Figure 4-14. Now the *vertical*

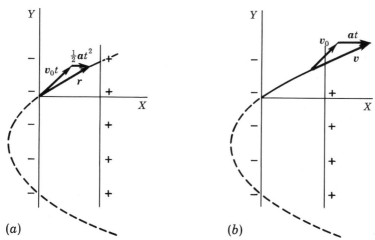

Figure 4-14. An electrically charged particle, between two oppositely charged, parallel plates, which has a constant acceleration to the right. (a) The vector displacement. (b) The vector velocity.

component of the velocity is unchanged (neglecting the trivial effect of gravity), while the horizontal component of the velocity increases in the direction of the acceleration. The component Equations 4-7 and 4-8 become

$$v_x = v_{0x} + a_x t \qquad v_y = v_{0y}$$
$$x = v_{0x}t + \tfrac{1}{2}a_x t^2 \qquad y = v_{0y}t$$

where a_y is zero because the acceleration a is now along the X-axis. The path is again parabolic, but now the parabola's axis of symmetry is horizontal.

Example 4 An electron traveling initially at 5.0×10^6 m/sec enters the region between two vertical, parallel, electrically charged, metal plates separated by 2.0 cm. The electron enters at an angle of 37° with respect to the horizontal, as shown in Figure 4-15. Within the region between the plates the electron has a constant acceleration of 7.9×10^{14} m/sec² to the right. (a) Where does the electron strike the right plate? (b) With what velocity does it strike? (c) Where does the electron strike a plate when the electric charges on the plates are interchanged? (The acceleration is then of the same magnitude but to the left.)

We have the following constants:

$$a_x = 7.9 \times 10^{14} \text{ m/sec}^2$$

$$a_y = 0$$

$$v_{0x} = v_0 \cos \theta = (5.0 \times 10^6 \text{ m/sec}) \cos 37° = 4.0 \times 10^6 \text{ m/sec}$$

$$v_{0y} = v_0 \sin \theta = (5.0 \times 10^6 \text{ m/sec}) \sin 37° = 3.0 \times 10^6 \text{ m/sec}$$

The equations of motion are written:

$$v_x = (4.0 \times 10^6 \text{ m/sec}) + (7.9 \times 10^{14} \text{ m/sec}^2)t$$

$$v_y = (3.0 \times 10^6 \text{ m/sec})$$

$$x = (4.0 \times 10^6 \text{ m/sec})t + (\tfrac{1}{2})(7.9 \times 10^{14} \text{ m/sec}^2)t^2$$

$$y = (3.0 \times 10^6 \text{ m/sec})t$$

(a) The electron has an initial velocity component to the right and its acceleration is also to the right. Clearly, the electron strikes the right, rather than the

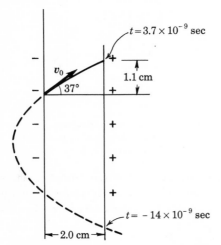

Figure 4-15. An electron enters the region between the plates with a velocity of 5.0×10^6 m/sec at an angle of 37°; it has a constant acceleration to the right. The dotted line shows the parabola of which the actual path is but a portion.

Figure 4-16. The situation shown in Figure 4-15, but with the charges, and the direction of the acceleration, reversed.

left, plate. Its horizontal displacement upon striking the plate is $x = 2.0$ cm $= 2.0 \times 10^{-2}$ m. We must find the corresponding vertical displacement y. Our procedure is this: We first find t for $x = 2.0 \times 10^{-2}$ m, and then we use the computed value of t in the equation for y.

$$x = 2.0 \times 10^{-2} \text{ m} = (4.0 \times 10^6 \text{ m/sec})t + (\tfrac{1}{2})(7.9 \times 10^{14} \text{ m/sec})t^2$$

Solving this quadratic equation for t we find

$$t = -14 \times 10^{-9} \text{ sec}, \quad \text{or } 3.7 \times 10^{-9} \text{ sec}$$

It is the second solution that we wish. (The first solution has no physical significance in this problem. It gives the time when the electron would have departed from the right plate, traveling with constant acceleration to the right *all the while*, so that its motion 14×10^{-9} sec later would be identical with that of the electron leaving the left plate. See Figure 4-15.)

(b) From the time of flight we can compute the vertical displacement, as well as the horizontal and vertical components of the electron's velocity upon striking the right plate.

$$y = (3.0 \times 10^6 \text{ m/sec})(3.7 \times 10^{-9} \text{ sec}) = 1.1 \text{ cm}$$

$$v_x = (4.0 \times 10^6 \text{ m/sec}) + (7.9 \times 10^{14} \text{ m/sec}^2)(3.7 \times 10^{-9} \text{ sec}) = 6.9 \times 10^6 \text{ m/sec}$$

$$v_y = 3.0 \times 10^6 \text{ m/sec} \quad \text{(always)}$$

The motion of the electron consists of the superposition of two independent motions: vertical motion at constant speed and horizontal motion at constant acceleration. (The *horizontal* motion is identical with that of the electron in Example 4c, Chapter 2.)

(c) Now consider the electron's motion when the electric charges on the plates are reversed. The electron consequently experiences the same magnitude of acceleration, but to the left rather than to the right. See Figure 4-16. We are to find the position of the electron as it strikes a plate, the initial velocity still being 5.0×10^6 m/sec at $37°$ above the horizontal. The vertical displacement y is found by determining first the time t at which the electron has returned to $x = 0$:

$$x = 0 = (4.0 \times 10^6 \text{ m/sec})t + (\tfrac{1}{2})(-7.9 \times 10^{14} \text{ m/sec}^2)t^2$$

or $\qquad\qquad t = 0 \text{ (start)}, \ 1.0 \times 10^{-8} \text{ sec (finish)}$

and $\qquad\qquad y = (3.0 \times 10^6 \text{ m/sec})(1.0 \times 10^{-8} \text{ sec})$

$$= 3.0 \times 10^{-2} \text{ m} = 3.0 \text{ cm}$$

An important assumption was made here. It was assumed that the electron, originally traveling to the right but accelerated to the left, does *not* strike the right plate but, rather, is turned back to the left before its displacement to the right is as large as the separation between the plates. We can be sure that the electron misses the right plate only when we compute the maximum positive value of x and find it to be less than 2.0 cm. We leave it as an exercise for the student to show that $x < 2.0 \times 10^{-2}$ m when $v_x = 0$.

4-4 Summary In two and three dimensions, displacements, velocities, and accelerations are vectors.

The instantaneous velocity v is the time rate of the vector displacement:

[4-2] $$\boldsymbol{v} = \lim_{\Delta t \to 0} \frac{\Delta \boldsymbol{r}}{\Delta t} = \frac{d\boldsymbol{r}}{dt}$$

The instantaneous acceleration a is the time rate of the vector velocity:

[4-4] $$a = \lim_{\Delta t \to 0} \frac{\Delta v}{\Delta t} = \frac{dv}{dt}$$

For the constant acceleration a, the velocity and displacement are given by

[4-5] $$v = v_0 + at$$

[4-6] $$r = v_0 t + \tfrac{1}{2}at^2$$

where r is the displacement and v is the velocity at time t, r being zero and v being v_0 at $t = 0$. Problems involving an acceleration of constant magnitude and direction are conveniently solved by writing the corresponding scalar equations giving the displacement and velocity components parallel and perpendicular to a.

Two important examples of motion at constant acceleration are projectile motion, for which $a = g$, the acceleration due to gravity, and the motion of an (electrically) charged particle between two plane, parallel, oppositely electrically charged, metal plates.

PROBLEMS

(Answers to problems in this chapter assume that $g \simeq 32$ ft/sec$^2 \simeq$ 10 m/sec$^2 \simeq 1000$ cm/sec^2.

4-1   A particle undergoes a constant acceleration of 4.0 feet/sec^2 along the negative X-axis, starting with an initial velocity of 12 feet/sec at an angle of 37° below the positive X-axis. After 10 sec, what are the X- and Y-components of the displacement and velocity?

4-2   A particle has an initial velocity of 20 m/sec at a counterclockwise angle of 150° with respect to the positive X-axis. It moves with a constant acceleration of 10 m/sec^2 along the positive Y-axis. What are (a) the velocity v and (b) the displacement r, both 4.0 sec after the start?

4-3   The equations of motion of a particle moving with constant acceleration are $x = -10t + 30t^2$ and $y = 15t - 20t^2$, where x and y are in meters and t is in seconds. What are the magnitudes and directions of (a) the initial velocity and (b) the acceleration? (c) Sketch roughly the path of the particle.

4-4   In Figure 4-2 the displacement vector traces out a path, tangents to which give the direction of the velocity. What is indicated by the path traced out by velocity vectors in Figure 4-3b in velocity space?

4-5   In the simulated multiflash photograph of Figure 4-1, the body is imagined to have started at point a and moved to b, c, etc. Suppose, now, that the motion is reversed (or that time is reversed), and the body starts at q, moves to p, o, etc., and comes finally to point a. How do (a) the velocity and (b) the acceleration vectors compare with those shown in Figures 4-3 and 4-5? The reversal of the velocity direction and the nonreversal of the acceleration direction arise from the fact that the velocity is the *first* time derivative of the displacement and the acceleration is the *second* time derivative of the displacement. (c) How does the time derivative of the acceleration behave under time reversal?

4-6 A ball rolls off the edge of a 30-inch-high table with a speed of 12 feet/sec. How far horizontally from the edge of the table does the ball strike the floor?

4-7 A baseball pitcher throws a baseball horizontally at a speed of 100 feet/sec toward home plate, 60 feet from the pitcher's mound. Through what vertical distance will the baseball have fallen when passing over the home plate?

4-8 A stone is thrown horizontally with a speed of 35 feet/sec from the edge of a cliff 150 feet high. (a) Where does the stone strike, relative to the base of the cliff? (b) With what speed? (c) With what velocity?

4-9 As neutrons go, one with a speed of 2200 m/sec (a thermal neutron) is a slow neutron. How far must such a neutron travel horizontally to fall vertically 1.0 cm?

4-10 A bomb, dropped from a plane flying horizontally at an altitude of 6400 feet, is observed to strike the ground at an angle of 37° below the horizontal. (a) At what speed was the plane traveling when it released the bomb? (b) Assuming that the plane continues to fly at this same velocity, how far apart are the plane and the bomb when the bomb hits the ground?

4-11 A projectile is thrown with an initial speed v_0 at an angle of θ_0 with respect to a horizontal surface. (a) What is the maximum height the projectile achieves (in terms of v_0, θ_0, and g)? (b) What is the time of flight for the entire motion? (c) Show that the horizontal range is given by $(v_0^2/g) \sin 2\theta$. (d) Show that any two complementary angles θ_0 (such as 20° and 70°) give the same range. (This was first proved by Galileo Galilei.) (e) Show that the range is a maximum for $\theta_0 = 45°$.

4-12 (a) At what *two* angles relative to the horizontal must a gun be aimed so that the horizontal range of the projectile is 10,000 feet, the muzzle velocity being 800 feet/sec? (b) Calculate the time of flight for each of the two trajectories in part (a).

4-13 The world record for the javelin throw is 86.04 m. Presumably, the javelin was thrown at an angle of 45°, the angle for which the range is a maximum (Problem 4-11). (a) By what amount would the range be reduced if the javelin were thrown with the same speed but at an angle of 43°? (b) Records for athletic events (improperly) do not take into account the fact that g is not the same at all points on the Earth; for example, at 30° latitude g is about 979.3 cm/sec², and at 60° latitude it is about 981.9 cm/sec², both at sea level. By how much would the javelin range be changed in going from 30° to 60° latitude?

4-14 It is confidently expected that freely falling bodies on the Moon will have an acceleration, due to the Moon's gravity, of 1.6 m/sec². How would (a) the maximum height, (b) the time of flight, and (c) the range of a projectile thrown from the Moon's surface compare with the corresponding quantities on Earth?

4-15   A gun shoots a bullet with a maximum horizontal range of 3000 feet. What is the maximum height to which the gun can shoot a similar bullet?

4-16   With what initial speed must a football leave a punter's foot if it is to land 60 yards away and is kicked at an angle of 45°?

4-17   A skier leaves a slope at 20° above the horizontal with a speed of 30 feet/sec. The horizontal landing surface is 10 feet below the slope. (a) At what horizontal distance from the launching point does he land? (b) At what speed does he land?

4-18   A hoop in a vertical plane is located 12 feet from the floor. A man is 10 feet horizontally from the hoop and throws a ball from 4.0 feet above the floor. With what speed and at what angle must the ball be thrown so that it passes through the hoop horizontally?

4-19 ★ A projectile fired over a horizontal surface has the displacement components $x = 40$ feet and $y = 60$ feet at one instant of time, and the components $x' = 80$ feet and $y' = 60$ feet at a later time. What is the initial velocity?

4-20   A batter hits a baseball with a speed of 100 feet/sec at an angle of 45°. If he begins running around the bases at 20 feet/sec, 0.2 sec after hitting the ball, where will he be relative to the bases when the ball strikes the ground? The distance between bases is 90 feet.

4-21   A projectile fired over a horizontal surface achieves a maximum height of 200 feet and has a range of 600 feet. With what speed and at what angle with respect to the horizontal was the projectile fired?

4-22   A rocket, starting from rest, constantly accelerates at 100 m/sec² in a direction of 60° to the Earth's surface. The fuel burns out in 10 sec. Find (a) the maximum height the rocket rises and (b) the flight time and range of the rocket.

4-23   Calculate the rise, flight time, and range of the rocket in Problem 4-22, supposing it was aimed at 45° instead of 60° to the horizontal.

4-24   A rifle has its gunsight adjusted for targets 1500 yards distant. The muzzle velocity of bullets used in the rifle is 4000 feet/sec. Assuming that the gun is shot when the barrel is essentially horizontal, give the angle between the gunsight and the rifle barrel.

4-25   A ball is thrown at an angle of 70° with a speed of 54 feet/sec in a room whose ceiling is 30 feet above the throwing point. Where does the ball first strike?

4-26   A certain ball has the magnitude of the vertical component of its velocity reduced by 20 per cent when it strikes a hard surface; the horizontal component is unchanged. If the ball is thrown horizontally at a speed of 4.0 feet/sec from a height of 3.2 feet above the surface, at what horizontal distance from the starting point will the ball make its second bounce?

4-27 A player "shoots" a basketball at a hoop which is 12 feet above the floor and 20 feet horizontally from the player. The ball leaves the player's hands 6.0 feet above the floor at an angle of 60° to the horizontal. (a) What must be the initial speed of the ball if it is to go through the hoop? (b) What is the maximum height the ball rises above the floor?

4-28 ★ An object sliding freely on an inclined plane of angle φ (with respect to the horizontal) has a constant acceleration of $g \sin \varphi$ down the incline. An object projected obliquely upward on the incline with initial speed v_0 traces out a parabolic path and returns to the base in 1.5 sec. With respect to the base line, what are the possible angles of projection?

4-29 It is found that a ball rolling on an inclined plane has a constant acceleration of 12 feet/sec² down the incline. The ball is given an initial speed of 4 feet/sec in a direction parallel to the base of the incline at a distance of 6.0 feet from the lower edge of the incline. (a) At what point will the ball come to the base of the incline? (b) With what speed?

4-30 A particle moving over an inclined plane of 30° has a constant acceleration of 5.0 m/sec² down the incline. If the particle is projected with an initial velocity of 20 m/sec at an angle of 60° with respect to the base line, how far from its starting point does the particle return to the base line?

4-31 An elevator has a light source at one side that shines a beam of light horizontally across to the opposite wall 2.0 m away. The light source may be thought to emit particles of light which travel at a speed of 3.0×10^8 m/sec. At what constant acceleration upward must the elevator move so that the spot of light on the distant wall is displaced downward by 1.0 mm, as viewed by an observer in the elevator?

Actually, an observer in a closed elevator would not be able to distinguish between the upward accelerated motion just described and a downward motion caused by some gravitational attraction. He could conclude that the light beam is bent downward because it is accelerated downward and has weight. The equivalence of accelerated motion and gravitational attraction is the basic assumption of the general theory of relativity; the bending of light when it passes close to a sun, predicted by the general theory, has been observed.

4-32 The acceleration of a proton in the region between two vertical, parallel, electrically charged, metal plates is 4.0×10^{11} m/sec² to the right. The proton leaves the left (positively charged) plate with a speed of 4.0×10^4 m/sec and at an angle of 30° with respect to the left plate. The negatively charged plate is 4.0 cm to the right. (a) Where does the proton strike? (b) What is the time of flight?

4-33 An electron is accelerated from rest by a constant acceleration of 6.0×10^{12} m/sec² to the right. It strikes a plate 4.0 cm to the right of the starting point. How far down does the electron fall under the influence of gravity in traveling to the plate?

4-34 ★ The left plate of two vertical, parallel, metal plates carries a negative electric charge. The right plate is positively charged. An electron is released from rest at the left plate, and a proton (carrying a positive electric charge) is simultaneously released from rest at the right plate.

The particles move in opposite directions with constant, but different, acceleration magnitudes. They collide at a point close to the right plate. In fact, the point of collision is $\frac{1}{1837}$ of the plate separation from the right plate. What is the ratio of the electron's acceleration to the proton's acceleration?

4-35 ★ Consider Figure 4-17. Electrically charged particles are accelerated horizontally from rest between the two vertical plates. The particles

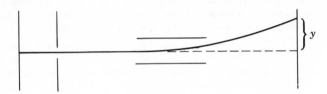

Figure 4-17

then enter the region between horizontal plates, where they are accelerated vertically. When the particles finally strike the screen, their vertical displacement is y. Show that y is unchanged if the *ratio* of the accelerations between the vertical and horizontal plates, respectively, is not changed. Because the acceleration of a charged particle between a pair of parallel charged plates is directly proportional to the electric charge of the particle, *any* charged particle will strike at the same point y (neglecting free fall due to gravity, of course).

4-36 ★ An electron moving horizontally at a speed of 3.0×10^6 m/sec enters midway between two horizontal, electrically charged, metal plates separated by 1.5 cm. While traveling between the plates, the electron has an upward acceleration of 5.0×10^{13} m/sec². The horizontal length of the two plates is 5.0 cm. (a) What distance is the electron from the upper plate when it emerges? (b) What is the velocity of the electron upon emerging from the plates? (c) Assuming that after the electron emerges from the plates it has a constant downward acceleration equal to that due to gravity, what are the horizontal and vertical displacements (in kilometers) of the electron relative to the plates when it achieves its maximum height? (Electrons, to be sure, fall with an acceleration g, but this acceleration is ordinarily so small compared with the acceleration arising from electric charges that one may properly assume that charged particles travel at constant velocity unless influenced by other electric charges.

4-37 An electron moving horizontally to the right at a speed v_0 enters the region between two horizontal, electrically charged, metal plates, as shown at the center of Figure 4-17. The acceleration is constant and vertical in the region between the parallel plates, and zero outside this region. Show that the vertical displacement y of electrons on the distant screen (relative to their position on the screen when the acceleration is zero) is directly proportional to the acceleration between the plates.

The arrangement described here is used in the cathode-ray oscilloscope or television picture tube. The displacement y is proportional to the acceleration between the plates, which is, in turn, proportional to the potential difference, or voltage, between the plates. Thus, the displacement y is a measure of the applied voltage, and the device may be used as a voltmeter.

4-38 ★ Consider the arrangement shown in Figure 4-17. Electrons having an initial horizontal velocity of 4.0×10^6 m/sec enter the region between the horizontal plates, where the acceleration is 5.0×10^{13} m/sec^2 upward. The plates have a horizontal dimension of 3.0 cm. The screen is 25 cm to the right of the right ends of the plates. (a) Compute the magnitude and direction of the electrons' velocity as they leave the parallel plates. (b) Compute the vertical displacement y of the electron beam at the screen. (c) What is the time of flight from the moment an electron enters the horizontal plates until it strikes the screen?

F I V E

UNIFORM CIRCULAR MOTION AND SIMPLE HARMONIC MOTION

The kinematics of uniform circular motion and of the closely related simple harmonic motion along a line are developed analytically in this chapter.

5-1 Uniform circular motion A particle moving in a circular arc at constant speed is said to be in uniform circular motion. It covers equal distances along the circumference in equal times, while continuously changing its direction of motion. The velocity, although constant in magnitude, continuously changes in direction, and there is, consequently, an acceleration. We wish to find the magnitude and direction of this acceleration.

It is convenient (but not necessary) to indicate the location of a particle traveling in a circle by means of a displacement vector, or *radius vector*, r, whose tail is at the center of the circle. Then, if the speed of the body is constant, the radius vector sweeps through equal angles in equal times, the magnitude of the radius vector remaining unchanged. Consider the small displacement $\Delta \boldsymbol{r}$ occurring in a very small time interval Δt. The vector displacement $\Delta \boldsymbol{r}$ cannot be distinguished from the true path of the particle along a short segment of circular arc; see Figure 5-1. The two radius

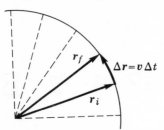

vectors $\boldsymbol{r}_i$ and $\boldsymbol{r}_f$, giving the initial and final displacements over the small interval Δt and being both of magnitude r, are related to $\Delta \boldsymbol{r}$ by

$$\boldsymbol{r}_f - \boldsymbol{r}_i = \Delta \boldsymbol{r} = \boldsymbol{v}\Delta t$$

where $\boldsymbol{v}$ is the velocity over the interval Δt.

Figure 5-1. The displacement $\Delta \boldsymbol{r}$ over the time interval Δt of a particle moving in uniform circular motion.

The velocity vector is always at right angles to the radius vector. As the radius vector rotates, so does the associated velocity vector. See Figure 5-2a, where the velocity vectors, all of the same magnitude, are shown with their tails on the circumference of the circle, and Figure 5-2b, where the same velocity vectors are displayed with their tails at a common point.

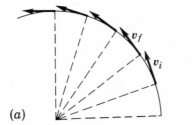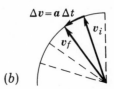

(a)   (b)

Figure 5-2. (a) Instantaneous velocity vectors arranged with their tails at the corresponding positions of the particle. (b) The same velocity vectors arranged with their tails at a common origin.

The initial and final velocities, $\boldsymbol{v}_i$ and $\boldsymbol{v}_f$, both of magnitude v, differ only in direction, and their vector difference $\Delta \boldsymbol{v}$ is given by

$$\boldsymbol{v}_f - \boldsymbol{v}_i = \Delta \boldsymbol{v} = \boldsymbol{a}\Delta t$$

where $\boldsymbol{a}$ is the acceleration occurring in the time interval Δt during which the velocity has changed from $\boldsymbol{v}_i$ to $\boldsymbol{v}_f$. Now, the radius vectors $\boldsymbol{r}_i$, $\boldsymbol{r}_f$, and $\Delta \boldsymbol{r}$ form an isosceles triangle which is similar to the triangle formed by the corresponding velocity vectors $\boldsymbol{v}_i$, $\boldsymbol{v}_f$, and $\Delta \boldsymbol{v}$. This is so because the displacement vector sweeps through the same angle as does the velocity vector during the time Δt. Consequently, the magnitudes of corresponding sides are in the same ratio:

$$\frac{\Delta r}{r} = \frac{\Delta v}{v}$$

or

$$\frac{v\Delta t}{r} = \frac{a\Delta t}{v}$$

Thus:

$$a = \frac{v^2}{r}$$ [5-1]

The acceleration of a particle moving at constant speed v in a circle of radius r has a constant magnitude of v^2/r. Now let us find the direction of the acceleration.

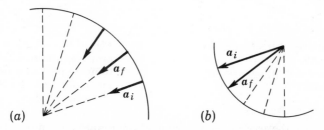

Figure 5-3. (a) Instantaneous acceleration vectors arranged with their tails at the corresponding positions of the particle. (b) The same acceleration vectors arranged with their tails at a common origin.

The vector $\Delta r = v\Delta t$ is perpendicular to r, and the vector $\Delta v = a\Delta t$ is perpendicular to v, as seen from Figures 5-1 and 5-2. Therefore, the acceleration has a direction always opposite to that of the displacement r: that is, it is directed toward the center of the circle. Uniform circular motion is, then, characterized by an acceleration that is constant in magnitude, changing in direction, and always radially inward. See Figures 5-3 and 5-4. The term *radial*, or *centripetal* ("center-seeking"), *acceleration* is used to designate such an acceleration.

The converse is true. When a body moves with an acceleration which is always perpendicular to the direction of motion and constant in magnitude, the body executes circular motion at constant speed. We may write a vector equation for the centripetal acceleration as follows:

$$\boldsymbol{a} = -\left(\frac{v}{r}\right)^2 \boldsymbol{r}$$ [5-2]

The minus sign indicates that the direction of a is opposite to that of r. The magnitude of a is $(v/r)^2$ multiplied by the magnitude of r; thus, $a = (v/r)^2 r = v^2/r$, in agreement with Equation 5-1.

Example 1   An ice skater skating at 10 feet/sec turns in a circle of 15 feet in radius. What is the centripetal acceleration?

From Equation 5-1 we have

$$a = v^2/r = (10 \text{ ft/sec})^2/(15 \text{ ft}) = 6.7 \text{ ft/sec}^2$$

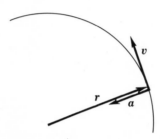

Figure 5-4. Instantaneous velocity and acceleration vectors for a particle in uniform circular motion.

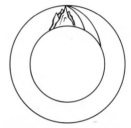

Figure 5-5. A body is projected horizontally from the peak of a high mountain at several different speeds.

The direction of the acceleration is horizontal and toward the center of the circle.

Example 2   Suppose that an object is projected horizontally from the peak of an imaginary high mountain extending well above most of the Earth's atmosphere, but still within an approximate range so that the acceleration due to gravity can be taken as 32 ft/sec² (Figure 5-5). We know that any body moving through space close to the Earth's surface has an acceleration toward the center of the Earth of a constant magnitude of 32 feet/sec². Over distances along the Earth's surface that are small compared with the Earth's radius, it is proper to assume that the acceleration due to gravity is constant in direction as well as in magnitude. Therefore, if the object is thrown from the mountain peak with a moderate speed, its path is a parabola and it strikes the Earth after traveling for much less than several hundred miles.

If the object is thrown with a higher speed, so that it travels a distance comparable to the Earth's radius before striking the Earth, the acceleration can *not* be regarded as constant in direction (although the magnitude of g is still 32 feet/sec², a value accurate to within 2 per cent, for altitudes of less than 40 miles). Consequently, the path is not a parabola. On the other hand, if the initial speed is sufficiently great, the object flies out into space, where both the magnitude and direction of g change, and it either orbits the Earth in an elliptical path or, if the speed is very great, leaves the Earth, never to return. There is one particular speed at which an object will always fall the same distance toward the Earth that it curves away from its straight-line motion; which is to say, there is one particular speed for which the object will travel in a circle. For this circular path the acceleration **g** is always at right angles to the object's velocity, and the object is in a circular orbit at constant speed. The argument developed here was first put forth by Sir Isaac Newton (1642–1727).

Let us compute the speed and the period (the time for one complete revolution) of a satellite in circular orbit close to the Earth's surface (we assume, as always, that there is no atmospheric drag). The Earth's mean radius is 3960 miles $= 2.1 \times 10^7$ feet.

The centripetal acceleration has the magnitude 32 feet/sec^2, and the radius of the orbit is 2.1×10^7 feet. From Equation 5-1 we have

$$a = v^2/r$$
$$v = \sqrt{ar} = \sqrt{(32 \text{ ft/sec}^2)(2.1 \times 10^7 \text{ ft})}$$
$$v = 2.6 \times 10^4 \text{ ft/sec} = 1.8 \times 10^4 \text{ mi/hr}$$

The time for one revolution T is the circumference divided by the speed:

$$T = 2\pi(2.1 \times 10^7 \text{ ft})/(2.6 \times 10^4 \text{ ft/sec})$$
$$T = 5.0 \times 10^3 \text{ sec} = 84 \text{ min}$$

The scientific foundations of satellite motion were established by Newton; technological advances in rocketry made possible the first artificial satellite in 1957. We are now in a position to understand the simpler kinematical aspects of satellite launching and recovery. After firing, the rocket first follows a nearly parabolic path. At its highest point, when the velocity is parallel to the Earth's surface, a booster rocket is fired to increase the speed of the released satellite to the value required for orbital motion (1.8×10^4 miles/hr for orbits near the Earth's surface). If the satellite is well above the Earth's atmosphere, so that atmospheric drag is indeed negligible, the speed remains constant and the satellite orbits indefinitely; on the other hand, if the drag of the atmosphere is appreciable, the speed is reduced and the satellite moves in a smaller radius ($a = g$ is constant, while $r = v^2/g$), spiralling toward the Earth. Even in the absence of atmospheric drag, the satellite can be recovered by firing a retrograde rocket to reduce the speed; see Figure 5-6.

5-2 Angular speed It is often useful to describe uniform circular motion in terms of the rate at which the radius vector sweeps through angles, rather than in terms of the tangential speed v.

We first define the *radian* as a measure of angles. In the two concentric circles in Figure 5-7, the ratio of the arc length to the radius, $s/r = s'/r'$, is the same for both circles because both arcs are subtended by the same angle θ. Thus, the ratio s/r is determined solely by the angle, and this ratio can be considered a measure of the angle itself. By definition:

$$\boxed{\theta \text{ in radians} = \frac{s}{r}} \qquad [5\text{-}3]$$

The angle θ, in radians, is equal to the arc subtended by θ divided by the corresponding radius. (If θ is measured in degrees, the corresponding relation is $\theta = (360°/2\pi)(s/r)$, as is easily confirmed by choosing s for the circumference $2\pi r$.) An angle of 1 radian, therefore, subtends an arc equal to the radius and, around the entire circle for which $s = 2\pi r$, the angle θ is 2π radians:

$$2\pi \text{ radians} = 360°$$

$$1 \text{ radian} = \frac{360°}{2\pi} = 57.3 \dots °$$

Note that the radian measure is a pure number having no dimensions. If an angle is given as, say, $\theta = \pi/2$, this means that θ is $\pi/2$ radians, or 90°.

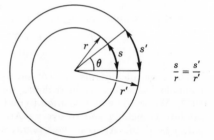

$$\frac{s}{r} = \frac{s'}{r'}$$

Figure 5-6. A satellite follows a parabolic path in free flight upon leaving and entering the Earth's atmosphere. The satellite's orbital motion is, in the most simple case, uniform circular motion.

Figure 5-7. The radian defined: θ (in radian) = $s/r = s'/r'$.

Just as a constant linear speed v is defined as the distance traveled divided by the elapsed time ($v = s/t$), a constant *angular* speed ω is defined as the *angle* swept through by the radius vector *divided by the elapsed time.* Taking θ to be zero when time t is zero, we have

$$\omega = \frac{\theta}{t} \qquad [5\text{-}4]$$

Thus, uniform circular motion lends itself to a simple description in terms of the polar coordinates r and θ: r is constant, and the angle θ increases linearly with time according to $\theta = \omega t$.

We wish to relate the circumferential speed v to the corresponding angular speed ω of the radius vector. By definition,

$$s = r\theta$$

Dividing by the time t,

$$\left(\frac{s}{t}\right) = r\left(\frac{\theta}{t}\right)$$

Therefore,

$$\boxed{v = r\omega} \qquad\qquad [5\text{-}5]$$

It must be emphasized that Equation 5-5 applies only when ω is measured in units of radians per time; for example, $\omega = 20$ radians/sec. A reason for measuring angles in radians is that relations such as Equation 5-3 and 5-5 then take on a particularly simple form. Equation 5-5 shows, for example, that, if a rod is rotated about one end, the points of the rod have speeds directly proportional to their respective distances from the axis of rotation, although all points have, of course, the same angular speed. See Figure 5-8.

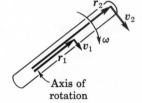

Figure 5-8. The speeds of points on a rotating body are proportional to their respective distances from the axis of rotation.

We found earlier that the magnitude of the centripetal acceleration is

$$a = \frac{v^2}{r} = \left(\frac{v}{r}\right)^2 r$$

Using Equation 5-5 we may rewrite this as

$$a = \omega^2 r \qquad\qquad [5\text{-}6]$$

A point at a fixed distance r from the center of a circle has a radial acceleration that is proportional to the square of the angular speed. We may write Equation 5-6 in vector form also, recalling that the direction of $\boldsymbol{a}$ is opposite to that of the radius vector $\boldsymbol{r}$:

$$\boxed{\boldsymbol{a} = -\omega^2 \boldsymbol{r}} \qquad\qquad [5\text{-}7]$$

Example 3 A 12-inch (diameter) phonograph record turns at $33\frac{1}{3}$ revolutions/minute. What is the magnitude of the centripetal acceleration of a point at the edge?

The record makes $33\frac{1}{3}$ rotations/minute, or 33.3×60 rotations/sec. Each rotation corresponds to 2π radians. Therefore, the angular speed is

$$\omega = \left(33.3\,\frac{\text{rot}}{\text{min}}\right)\left(\frac{1\ \text{min}}{60\ \text{sec}}\right)\left(\frac{2\pi\ \text{rad}}{1\ \text{rot}}\right) = 3.5\ \text{rad/sec}$$

and

$$a = \omega^2 r = (3.5\ \text{sec}^{-1})^2(0.50\ \text{ft}) = 6.1\ \text{ft/sec}^2$$

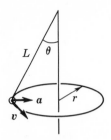

Figure 5-9. A stone on a string which sweeps out a cone about the vertical at constant speed. Note that the acceleration lies in the plane of the horizontal circle.

Example 4 A stone is attached to the lower end of a string 1.0 m long and swung in a horizontal circle, as shown in Figure 5-9. When the string makes a constant angle of 30° with the vertical, it is found that the stone executes 32 revolutions in one minute. What is the direction and magnitude of the radial acceleration of the stone?

The angular speed is

$$\omega = \left(32\,\frac{\text{rot}}{\text{min}}\right)\left(\frac{1\,\text{min}}{60\,\text{sec}}\right)\left(\frac{2\pi\,\text{rad}}{1\,\text{rot}}\right) = 3.35\,\text{rad/sec}$$

The radius of the stone's circular path is (1.0 m) sin 30°, and the centripetal acceleration has the magnitude

$$a = \omega^2 r = (3.35\,\text{sec}^{-1})^2(1.0\,\text{m})\sin 30° = 5.6\,\text{m/sec}^2$$

The direction of the centripetal acceleration is toward the center of the horizontal circle.

5-3 Radial and tangential components of acceleration When a particle moves in a straight-line path, the direction of its velocity is constant along the path, and changes in speed occur by virtue of an acceleration which also must always lie along the path. On the other hand, when a particle moves in a circular arc at constant speed, the direction of its velocity changes continuously while the magnitude of the velocity is constant, and the acceleration (constant in magnitude) now points at right angles to the path and is radially inward toward the center of curvature of the circular arc. Thus, an acceleration *along* the path is identified with a change in the *magnitude* of the velocity, while an acceleration *perpendicular* to the path is identified with a change in the *direction* of the velocity.

In general, of course, a particle may follow a more complicated path, and both the magnitude and the direction of the velocity may change. Consider Figure 5-10, which shows a particle moving in a curved path at a non-constant speed. (This is the situation at point f of Figure 4-5a.) It is useful to resolve the acceleration, which here lies neither along the path nor perpendicular to it, into components: a *tangential* component a_t and a *radial* component a_r. The component a_t corresponds to a change in the speed, but not the direction, of the velocity; the component a_r corresponds to a change in the direction, but not the speed, of the velocity. The radial acceleration a_r points toward the *instantaneous center of curvature* of the path; its magnitude is v^2/r, where v is the instantaneous speed of the particle and r is the instantaneous radius of curvature of the path, that is, the radius of the circle which can be best fitted to the curved path at that point. The components a_t and a_r are, of course, related to the magnitude of the acceleration a by

$$a = \sqrt{a_t{}^2 + a_r{}^2}$$

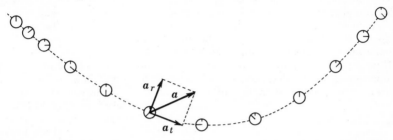

Figure 5-10. The instantaneous acceleration resolved into tangential and radial components.

Example 5 A body in free flight near the Earth's surface has a velocity of 40 feet/sec at an angle of 60° above the horizontal. (a) What are the tangential and radial components of the body's acceleration at this time? (b) What is the radius of curvature of the body's path at this time?

(a) The tangential component of the acceleration is parallel to the velocity,

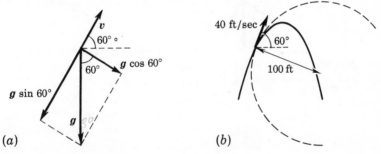

(a)   (b)

Figure 5-11. (a) Tangential and radial components of the acceleration g along the direction of the instantaneous velocity. (b) The projectile is moving instantaneously in a vertical circle 100 feet in radius.

namely, at 60° with respect to the horizontal. The radial component is at right angles to the velocity. We are then to find the components of g, the acceleration due to gravity, along the direction of the velocity and perpendicular to it. From the geometry of Figure 5-11a it follows that

$$a_t = g \sin 60° = 28 \text{ ft/sec}^2$$

$$a_r = g \cos 60° = 16 \text{ ft/sec}^2$$

(b) The radial component of the acceleration, the instantaneous speed, and the instantaneous radius of curvature are related by $a_r = v^2/r$. Therefore,

$$r = v^2/a_r = (40 \text{ ft/sec})^2/(16 \text{ ft/sec}^2)$$

$$r = 100 \text{ ft}$$

The meanings of the tangential and radial components of the acceleration in this example are these: At the instant that the velocity is 40 feet/sec at 60°, (a) the speed is being reduced along the direction of motion at the rate of 28 feet/sec², and at this same time (b) the body is moving instantaneously along a circular arc of 100 feet in radius; see Figure 5-11b.

If we wish, we can analyze any motion in terms of the radial and tangential components of the acceleration. Consider, for example, the motion of a projectile thrown horizontally and falling, under the influence of gravity (Figure 5-12).

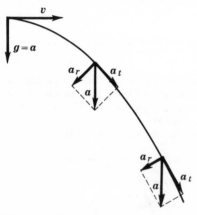

Initially, the body is moving horizontally while the acceleration of gravity is vertically downward. At first the body has only a radial component of acceleration (equal to g), and no tangential component, and the velocity changes direction only. Later, however, there is a component of **g** along the path. Therefore, both the speed and the direction of the velocity are changing. As time goes on, the body picks up speed and moves in a circle of larger instantaneous radius of curvature (v is larger, a_r is smaller, and $r = v^2/a_r$ must, therefore, be larger).

Figure 5-12. The acceleration components, tangential and radial to the parabolic path (and to the instantaneous velocity) for a projectile thrown horizontally.

5-4 Simple harmonic motion In discussing motion at constant acceleration (Section 4-2), as exemplified by projectile motion, we found it useful to describe the motion in terms of the equivalent simultaneous and independent motions along the X- and Y-axes. This procedure was a natural one inasmuch as the acceleration was constant both along the X- and Y-directions. On the other hand, it was found simpler to describe uniform circular motion in terms of r and $\omega = \theta/t$, both of these quantities being constant. Now let us describe uniform circular motions in terms of the rectangular coordinates, X and Y. This is not merely an interesting academic exercise; it will lead to a particularly important new type of motion, simple harmonic motion, examples of which are found in all branches of physics.

By definition, *simple harmonic motion is the projected motion along a diameter, of a particle moving in a circle at constant speed.*

Consider a particle moving counterclockwise at constant speed v in a circle of radius A. The constant angular speed of the radius vector is ω, where $v = A\omega$. The particle has a constant-acceleration magnitude of $a = v^2/A = \omega^2 A$, the direction of the acceleration being radially inward. We assume

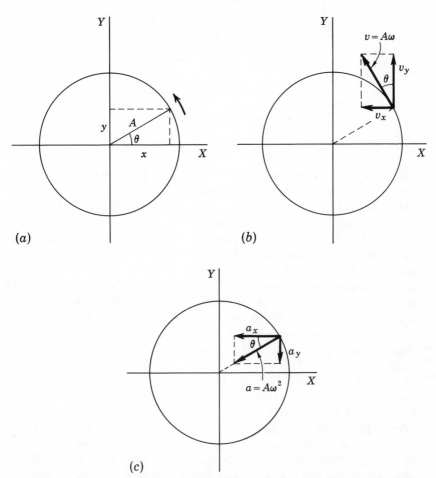

Figure 5-13. The rectangular components of (a) the displacement, (b) the velocity, and (c) the acceleration for a particle moving in a circle of radius A at the constant angular speed ω.

that at the time $t = 0$, the particle is on the positive X-axis, so that $\theta = \omega t$, where θ is the angle in radians made by the radius vector with respect to the positive X-axis. Figures 5-13a, b, and c show, respectively, the displacement, velocity, and acceleration of the uniform circular motion, and the corresponding components along the X- and Y-axes.

From the geometry of Figure 5-13 it follows that

$$
\begin{aligned}
x &= A \cos \theta = A \cos \omega t \\
v_x &= -\omega A \sin \theta = -\omega A \sin \omega t \\
a_x &= -\omega^2 A \cos \theta = -\omega^2 A \cos \omega t
\end{aligned}
\qquad [5\text{-}8]
$$

and

$$
y = A \sin \theta = A \sin \omega t
$$

$$
v_y = \omega A \cos \theta = \omega A \cos \omega t \qquad [5\text{-}9]
$$

$$
a_y = -\omega^2 A \sin \theta = -\omega^2 A \sin \omega t
$$

We first examine the dependence of x, v_x, and a_x on time. Later we will turn to the Y-components, which are similar.

Displacement-time, velocity-time, and acceleration-time graphs of the component motion along the X-axis of uniform circular motion are shown in Figures 5-14a, b, and c. The displacement, velocity, and acceleration components are all sinusoidal functions of the time; that is, the displacement, velocity, and acceleration components vary with time as the sine or cosine (or linear combinations thereof). The position along the X-axis oscillates between $+A$ and $-A$, the motion being confined, or *bound*, between these limits. The magnitude of the maximum displacement A is called the *amplitude* of the motion. Similarly, the velocity oscillates between the extreme values $+\omega A$ and $-\omega A$, and the acceleration between $+\omega^2 A$ and $-\omega^2 A$.

Inspection of Figure 5-14 shows that the velocity here is, as always, the slope of the displacement-time graph and that the acceleration is the slope of the velocity-time graph.†

When the particle moving at constant speed in a circle (frequently referred to as the *reference circle*) completes one revolution, its X-displacement goes through one cycle, tracing out one complete cosine curve (Figure 5-14). Calling the number of cycles per unit time the *frequency f*, and the time for one complete cycle the *period T*, we have

$$
f = \frac{1}{T} \qquad [5\text{-}10]
$$

---

† This result also follows directly from the definitions of velocity and acceleration in which the calculus is used:
$$
\begin{aligned}
v_x &= (d/dt)x = (d/dt)(A \cos \omega t) = -\omega A \sin \omega t \\
a_x &= (d/dt)v_x = (d/dt)(-\omega A \sin \omega t) = -\omega^2 A \cos \omega t
\end{aligned}
$$

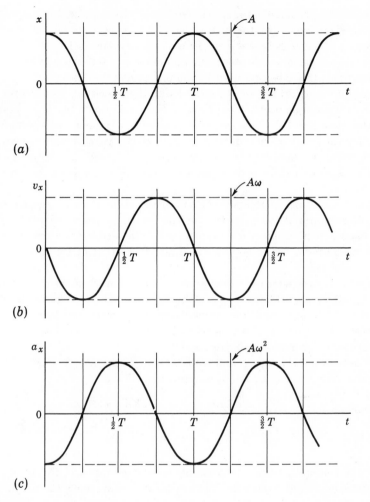

Figure 5-14. (a) Displacement-time, (b) velocity-time, and (c) accelera-tion-time graphs for the motion along the X-axis of uniform circular motion.

If the particle in the reference circle makes f rotations per unit time, going through 2π radians for each rotation, then the angular speed ω, which gives the number of radians turned through per unit time, is

$$\omega = 2\pi f = \frac{2\pi}{T} \qquad\qquad [5\text{-}11]$$

The quantity ω is sometimes referred to as the *angular frequency*. The angular *frequency* ω of the simple harmonic motion is the same as the corresponding angular *speed* ω of the uniform circular motion.

The displacement x is a positive maximum at $t = 0$ because of our choice of zero time. It will be a positive maximum again at the times $t = T, 2T, \ldots$, as seen in Figure 5-14a. On the other hand, the velocity v_x does not reach a positive maximum until $t = \frac{3}{4}T$, and the acceleration a_x is a positive maximum at $t = \frac{1}{2}T$. Thus, we see that the displacement lags behind the velocity (in time) by one quarter-cycle, and the velocity lags behind the acceleration (in time) by one quarter-cycle. As Figure 5-14 shows, a *lag* in time appears as a shift to the *right*, and a *lead* in time appears as a shift to the *left*.†

Now let us consider the velocity and acceleration when the displacement is a maximum and the particle is at the *amplitude position* $x = A$. Then the particle is momentarily at rest ($v_x = 0$); the acceleration has its maximum magnitude, but is opposite in direction to that of the displacement ($a_x = -\omega^2 A$).

Next let us consider the velocity and acceleration when the displacement is zero and the particle is at $x = 0$. At this position the body has its maximum speed ($v_x = -\omega A$) and the acceleration is momentarily zero ($a_x = 0$). (These conclusions can also be reached by examining the components of the uniform circular motion in Figure 5-13.)

Equations 5-8 give a_x, v_x, and x all in terms of the time t. If we wish, we can eliminate t to find a_x and v_x in terms of x. First,

$$a_x = -\omega^2 A \cos \omega t = -\omega^2 (A \cos \omega t)$$

$$\boxed{a_x = -\omega^2 x} \qquad [5\text{-}12]$$

The *acceleration* of a particle in simple harmonic motion is always directly *proportional* to the *displacement*, but opposite in direction: the proportionality constant is $\omega^2 = 4\pi^2 f^2 = 4\pi^2/T^2$.

We find v_x in terms of x as follows:

$$v_x = -A\omega \sin \omega t = \mp A\omega \sqrt{1 - \cos^2 \omega t} = \mp A\omega \sqrt{1 - \left(\frac{x}{A}\right)^2}$$

$$v_x = \mp \omega \sqrt{A^2 - x^2} \qquad [5\text{-}13]$$

We turn now to the Y-components of the uniform circular motion. Displacement-time, velocity-time, and acceleration-time graphs are shown

† We will later use (Section 17-3) the term *phase* to describe these relations.

in Figures 5-15a, b, c. The motion is again simple harmonic motion with amplitude A and frequency $f = \omega/2\pi$. However, in comparing Figures

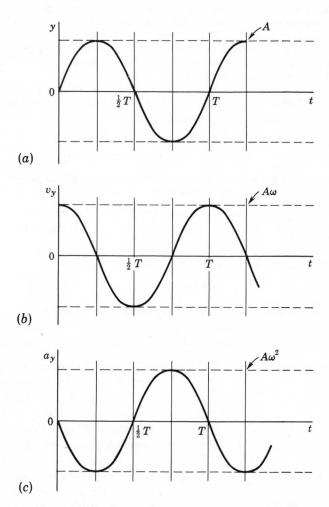

Figure 5-15. (a) Displacement-time, (b) velocity-time, and (c) acceleration-time graphs for the motion along the Y-axis of the uniform circular motion whose X-components are given in Figure 5-14.

5-14 and 5-15, or Equations 5-8 and 5-9, we see that y, v_y, and a_y all lag in time behind the corresponding x, v_x, and a_x by one quarter-cycle (or, equivalently, x, v_x, and a_x all lead y, v_y, and a_y, respectively, by one quarter-cycle).

Example 6 A particle executes simple harmonic motion at a frequency of 2.00 cycles/sec with an amplitude of 5.00 cm. The particle is at the amplitude position at time $t = 0$. Find (a) the period, (b) the angular frequency, (c) the maximum speed, (d) the maximum acceleration, and, at the time $t = \frac{1}{6}$ sec, (e) the displacement, (f) velocity, and (g) acceleration.

(a) The period T is $1/f = 1/(2.00 \text{ cycles/sec}) = 0.500$ sec/cycle.

(b) The angular frequency ω is $2\pi f = 2\pi(2.00 \text{ sec}^{-1}) = 4\pi$ radians/sec. (Note that the units of angular frequency are given as radians per second. The product $\omega t = \theta$ then has the units of radians.)

(c) (d) It is useful first to write down the equations giving the displacement, velocity, and acceleration at any time t. From Equations 5-8 we have

$$x = A \cos \omega t = (5.00 \text{ cm}) \cos \omega t$$
$$v_x = -\omega A \sin \omega t = -(4\pi \text{ rad/sec})(5.00 \text{ cm}) \sin \omega t$$
$$a_x = -\omega^2 A \cos \omega t = -(4\pi \text{ rad/sec})^2(5.00 \text{ cm}) \cos \omega t$$

The maximum magnitude of the sine or the cosine is 1.00; therefore, it follows that the maximum speed and acceleration are

$$v_x \text{ (max)} = (4\pi \text{ rad/sec})(5.00 \text{ cm}) = 62.8 \text{ cm/sec}$$
$$a_x \text{ (max)} = (4\pi \text{ rad/sec})^2(5.00 \text{ cm}) = 789 \text{ cm/sec}^2$$

(e) (f) (g) In order to find the displacement, velocity, and acceleration at $t = \frac{1}{6}$ sec, we must first compute the angle $\theta = \omega t$:

$$\theta = \omega t = (4\pi \text{ rad/sec})(\tfrac{1}{6} \text{ sec}) = 2\pi/3 \text{ rad} = 120°$$

Then,

$$x = (5.00 \text{ cm}) \cos \omega t = (5.00 \text{ cm}) \cos 120° = -4.33 \text{ cm}$$
$$v_x = -(\text{max } v_x) \sin \omega t = -(62.8 \text{ cm/sec}) \sin 120° = -31.4 \text{ cm/sec}$$
$$a_x = -(\text{max } a_x) \cos \omega t = -(789 \text{ cm/sec}^2) \cos 120° = +683 \text{ cm/sec}^2$$

We have here analyzed uniform circular motion by resolving it into the equivalent simultaneous and independent simple harmonic motions along two mutually perpendicular directions. Simple harmonic motions having the same amplitude and the same frequency along X and Y, but whose Y-motion lags behind the X-motion by one quarter-cycle, will, when superposed, yield uniform circular motion in the counterclockwise sense. Conversely, the projection of uniform circular motion along any diameter is simple harmonic motion. (The shadow of a particle in uniform circular motion illuminated by some distant light source moves in simple harmonic motion, as shown in Figure 5-16.)

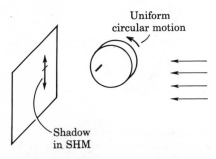

Figure 5-16. The projection of uniform circular motion along any diameter is simple harmonic motion.

Simple harmonic motion is one important example of *periodic motion*. By periodic motion is meant repetitive motion, an example of which is shown in the displacement-time curve of Figure 5-17.

The *period* T in periodic motion is defined as the smallest time interval such that, if the motion is known during any interval of duration T, we can find the motion for *all times* merely by shifting the displacement-time curve to the right or left an integral number of periods. The periodic motion illustrated by Figure 5-17 is clearly *not* simple harmonic motion. There is a general mathematical theorem (known as the *Fourier theorem*) which describes the following important property: any periodic motion can be obtained by the superposition, or summation, of a number of simple harmonic motions, which may differ in amplitude and frequency. This is why simple harmonic motion is so important.

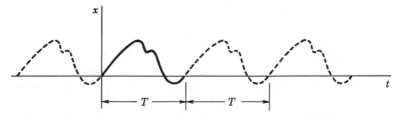

Figure 5-17. A displacement-time graph for one example of periodic motion with the period T.

We have treated the *kinematics* of simple harmonic motion. The *dynamics* of simple harmonic motion, in which one inquires into the physical situations for which the acceleration is indeed proportional to the displacement $(a_x = -\omega^2 x)$, is, of course, of still greater interest, and will be treated in Chapter 17. Some physical examples of simple harmonic motion are these: a pendulum swinging through small angles, a body vibrating while attached to a spring, atoms vibrating in a solid or in a molecule, the sinusoidally varying pressure in a sound wave, electric currents oscillating in the conductors of alternating-current circuits, and the oscillating electric and magnetic fields of an electromagnetic wave.

5-5 Review of two-dimensional kinematics We have discussed the kinematics of three important types of motion frequently encountered in physics. Let us set down the chief characteristics of each.

(1) *The acceleration is constant in magnitude and direction.* The path is a *parabola* whose axis of symmetry is parallel to the direction of the acceleration. The component of the velocity at *right angles* to the acceleration is *unchanged*, while the component of the velocity *along* the

direction of the acceleration *increases uniformly* with time. (In the special case in which there is no component of the velocity perpendicular to the acceleration, the parabola collapses and becomes a straight line, as is illustrated by a body thrown vertically upward.)

(2) *The acceleration is constant in magnitude but always perpendicular to the velocity.* The path is a *circle*, and the particle travels at *constant speed.* The acceleration is *radially inward* and has a magnitude of v^2/r or $\omega^2 r$, where v is the linear speed, ω the angular speed, and r the radius of curvature of the path.

(3) *The acceleration is proportional to the displacement, but opposite in direction, and the velocity is along the line of the displacement.* The path is a straight line, and the particle is bound between limits and oscillates *sinusoidally* in *simple harmonic motion.* The displacement, velocity, and acceleration all vary in time as the sine or cosine (or combinations thereof).

PROBLEMS

5-1   A car rounds a circular curve at a constant speed of 30 miles/hour. What must be the radius of the curve if the car is to have a centripetal acceleration equal in magnitude to the acceleration of gravity?

5-2   In a hydrogen atom in its normal state, an electron rotates in a circular orbit of radius 0.53×10^{-10} m about a proton. The electron's speed is $(\frac{1}{137})c$, where c is the speed of light, 3.0×10^8 m/sec. What is the magnitude of the acceleration of the electron?

5-3   In a typical betatron electron accelerator, an electron travels in a circular path of radius 2.0 m at, essentially, the speed of light, 3.0×10^8 m/sec. What is the radial acceleration?

5-4   A stone attached to a string 2.0 feet long is swung in a circle lying in a vertical plane. At the highest point the stone's speed is 3.0 feet/sec and at the lowest point it is 16.3 feet/sec. What are the magnitude and direction of the stone's acceleration at (a) the highest and (b) the lowest points?

5-5 ⋆ A projectile thrown horizontally will fall a vertical distance $\frac{1}{2}gt^2$ in the time t. If the projectile has a sufficiently high speed, it will become a satellite, and the distance it falls, $\frac{1}{2}gt^2$, will then be exactly the same as the distance that the earth curves away from a straight line by virtue of its spherical shape. Show, from the geometry of Figure 5-18, that the magnitude of the acceleration g is v^2/r, where v is the speed of the object and r is its radius of curvature. This is an alternative method of deriving the centripetal-acceleration relation; it was the method used by Sir Isaac Newton.

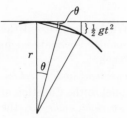

Figure 5-18.

5-6 At time $t = 0$ a particle begins at an origin to travel initially along the X-axis at a speed v. Its acceleration at $t = 0$ is a in the Y-direction. The acceleration remains constant in magnitude and remains perpendicular to the velocity until the particle has traced out one quarter of a circle. Then the acceleration is reduced to $a/4$, and it remains constant in magnitude and again perpendicular to the velocity until the particle completes another quarter-circle. Find the total vector displacement of the particle in terms of v and a.

5-7 An airplane flying at the constant speed of 300 miles/hour travels in a circle 1.15 miles in radius in pulling out of a dive: (a) what are the direction and magnitude of the centripetal acceleration of the airplane at its lowest point? Suppose, now, that the airplane, again traveling at 300 miles/hour initially climbs steeply and then turns downward in a circle 1.15 miles in radius: (b) what are the direction and magnitude of the centripetal acceleration at the highest point and (c) what would be the behavior of unattached objects inside the airplane when it passes through the highest point?

5-8 What is the acceleration of a man standing 20 feet from the axis of rotation of a merry-go-round making four turns a minute?

5-9 A flashlight is turned at an angular speed of 30°/sec. What is the speed with which the spot of light travels across (a) a wall 100 m distant and (b) the face of Jupiter when it is 10^7 km distant?

5-10 A wheel rotates at 10 revolutions/minute. What are the speed and acceleration of a point (a) 1.0 feet and (b) 2.0 feet from the axis of rotation?

5-11 Because the Earth rotates about its axis, objects at rest on the Earth's surface have a centripetal acceleration toward the axis of rotation. Compute the centripetal acceleration of an object at the latitudes (a) 0°, (b) 45°, and (c) 90°, and compare these values with g. The Earth's radius is 3960 miles.

5-12 The Moon is 240,000 miles from the Earth and revolves about it in 27.3 days. (a) What is the acceleration (in units of g) of the Moon relative to the Earth? (b) What is the acceleration due to gravity of any body at a point 240,000 miles from the Earth's center?

5-13 The Earth is 93 million miles from the Sun and revolves about it once a year. What is the acceleration (in units of g) of the Earth relative to the Sun?

5-14 ★ The planets orbit around the Sun in nearly circular paths. The radii and periods (to two significant figures) of some of the planets are:

	Radius (mi)	Period (days)
Mercury	3.6×10^7	88
Mars	15×10^7	690
Jupiter	48×10^7	4300
Saturn	89×10^7	11,000

(a) Compute the centripetal acceleration of each of these planets toward the Sun. (b) Show that the acceleration of any planet toward the Sun is inversely proportional to the square of its distance from the Sun, by plotting a graph of the acceleration versus $1/r^2$ for each of the four planets (a straight line shows that $a \propto 1/r^2$). (c) Determine from the graph made for part (b) the acceleration of the Earth toward the Sun; the Earth-to-Sun distance is 9.3×10^7 miles. (d) Compute the period of rotation of the Earth about the Sun from the acceleration given in part (c), and compare this with the known period (1 year.)

5-15 Show that if the centripetal acceleration of a particle in uniform circular motion is proportional to $1/r^2$, as it is in the case of planets about the Sun (see Problem 5-14), then the period of rotation is proportional to $r^{\frac{3}{2}}$.

5-16 A centrifuge is a device for separating materials according to their relative densities. Particles rotated in a high-speed centrifuge achieve extraordinarily high accelerations. What is the centripetal acceleration (in units of g) of a particle in a centrifuge at a distance of 3.0 mm from the axis of rotation and making 4000 turns/sec?

5-17 A ball is thrown horizontally at 120 feet/sec. Find the tangential and radial components of the acceleration 5.0 sec later.

5-18 An object in free flight near the Earth's surface has a velocity at an angle of 30° with respect to the horizontal. What are the (a) horizontal, (b) vertical, (c) tangential, and (d) radial components of the acceleration?

5-19 A ball is thrown at an angle of 60° above the horizontal. What are (a) the radial and (b) the tangential components of the acceleration at the instant the ball begins free flight?

5-20 A ball is thrown at 64 feet/sec at an angle of 70° above the horizontal. (a) What are the radial and tangential components of the ball's acceleration when it is at its maximum height? (b) What is the radius of curvature of the path at the highest point? (c) Draw the path of the ball, together with the circle along which the ball travels at the highest point.

5-21 Two particles, A and B, have the same magnitude of acceleration. Particle A has a radial acceleration and no tangential acceleration, and it moves in a circular orbit of radius r. Particle B, which starts from rest, has a tangential acceleration but no radial acceleration. (a) How far does particle B travel in the time that particle A has turned through a quarter-circle? (b) How far has B traveled (in terms of r) when its speed is equal to that of A?

5-22 The equation of motion for a particle in simple harmonic motion is written $x = 4.0 \cos 8.0t$, where x is in meters and t in seconds. What are (a) the amplitude, (b) the frequency, (c) the period, (d) the maximum speed, (e) the maximum acceleration, and (f) the displacement, velocity, and acceleration at $t = \pi/4$ sec?

5-23 The equation of motion of a particle undergoing simple harmonic motion is $y = 3.0 \sin (\pi/6)t$ where y is in feet and t is in seconds. What are (a) the amplitude, (b) the period, (c) the maximum speed, (d) the maximum acceleration, and (e) the displacement, velocity, and acceleration at $t = 1.00$ sec?

5-24 A particle is oscillating in simple harmonic motion between the limits $x = 5.0$ cm and $x = 12.0$ cm. Its maximum speed is 450 cm/sec. What are (a) the frequency and (b) the maximum acceleration?

5-25 A particle oscillating in simple harmonic motion travels a distance of 20 cm during the time of one complete cycle. The maximum acceleration is 4.0 cm/sec². What is the frequency of oscillation?

5-26 A particle moves in simple harmonic motion with an amplitude of 0.25 m and a period of 4.0 sec. What are (a) the maximum speed and (b) the maximum acceleration?

5-27 A particle moves clockwise in a circle of 6.0 cm in radius at a speed of 78 cm/sec. Write down the equations giving the X- and Y-components of the displacement, velocity, and acceleration, as a function of time. Assume that $x = 6.0$ cm and $y = 0$ at $t = 0$.

5-28 ★ One end, A, of a long rod is attached to a point on the circumference of a uniformly rotating wheel. The other end, B, is restricted to sliding along a straight line, as shown in Figure 5-19. Show that the end B executes simple harmonic motion if the length of the rod is large compared with the radius of the wheel. (*Hint:* See Problem 3-15.)

Figure 5-19.

5-29 A pendulum oscillating with an amplitude that is small compared with its length executes simple harmonic motion. A pen is attached to the lower end of the pendulum, and the pen writes on a sheet of paper drawn at constant speed along a horizontal plane at right angles to the plane of oscillation of the pendulum. Show the trace on the paper to be a sine or cosine curve. (Conversely, that the trace is sinusoidal is a demonstration that the motion is simple harmonic.)

5-30 A typical atom in a solid at ordinary temperatures undergoes simple harmonic motion with an amplitude of 10^{-10} m and a frequency of 10^{13} cycles/sec. What are (a) the maximum speed of the atom and (b) the maximum acceleration?

5-31 The shadow of a particle is observed to oscillate in simple harmonic motion with an amplitude of 0.75 feet and a period of 0.40 sec. What are (a) the radius of the path in which the particle moves and (b) its angular speed?

5-32 For a particle oscillating in simple harmonic motion, at what displacement relative to the amplitude is the speed one half of the maximum speed?

5-33 Describe the motion that is given by the following equations of motion: (a) $x = A \cos \omega t$ and $y = -A \sin \omega t$, (b) $x = A \cos \omega t$ and $y = A \cos \omega t$, (c) $x = A \cos \omega t$ and $y = -A \cos \omega t$.

5-34 Show that two uniform circular motions having the same radius and angular speed, one clockwise and the other counterclockwise, will, when superimposed, yield simple harmonic motion along a single straight line.

5-35 ★ Show that the superposition of two simple harmonic motions along the X- and Y-axes, respectively, having *unequal* amplitudes and one lagging behind the other by one quarter of a cycle, yields an elliptical path, rather than a circular path, whose axis of symmetry is along the X- or Y-axis.

5-36 A particle moves back and forth along the X-axis between $+20$ cm and -20 cm in simple harmonic motion. It makes one complete oscillation in 2.0 sec. (a) At what *constant* speed must a second particle move back and forth between the same limits such that it oscillates with the same frequency? (b) Find the fraction of time spent by each of these particles in the region between $x = +10$ cm and $x = -10$ cm.

5-37 ★ A particle, released from rest at the point $x = +20$ cm, has an acceleration that is always constant in magnitude. The direction of the acceleration is always opposite to that of the displacement of the particle from the origin; that is, when the particle is to the right of the origin the acceleration is to the left, and when the particle is to the left of the origin the acceleration is to the right. (a) What must be the magnitude of the acceleration if this particle is to oscillate back and forth between $x = +20$ cm and $x = -20$ cm with the same frequency as the two particles in Problem 5-36?

5-38 ★ The left end of a horizontal spring is held fixed and the right end is attached to a small block which rests on a smooth frictionless surface. It is found that, after the spring has been compressed or stretched and then released, the block executes simple harmonic motion with a frequency of 1.60 oscillations/sec for any amplitude. The block is now detached from the spring, pushed against the spring, thereby compressing the spring a distance of 4.00 cm, and then released. (a) At what point (relative to the equilibrium position of the right end of the spring) will the block no longer be in contact with the spring? (b) What is the speed of the block after parting from the spring?

5-39 ★ A platform supported by a spring is observed to oscillate vertically in simple harmonic motion with a period of 0.125 sec. A small object is now placed on the platform, the platform is pushed down a distance of 5.00 cm, and then released. (a) At what point (relative to the equilibrium position of the platform) will the small object leave the platform? (b) What is the separation distance between the object and the platform when the platform first reaches its highest point?

5-40 ★ A straight cane is held at the upper end while the lower end rests obliquely on a smooth horizontal surface. The upper end of the cane is made to execute vertical simple harmonic motion. Under what conditions does the motion of the lower end closely approximate simple harmonic motion?

5-41 A block sits on a platform that undergoes simple harmonic motion in the vertical direction with an amplitude of 5.00 mm. Assuming that the frequency is increased gradually from zero, at what frequency of oscillation of the platform will the block first lose contact with the platform?

5-42 A block sits on a platform undergoing simple harmonic motion in the vertical direction. It is noticed that it first becomes possible to slip a

thin sheet of paper between the block and the platform when the frequency of oscillation has been increased to 80 vibrations/sec. What is
the amplitude of the simple harmonic oscillation?

5-43 ★ A toy gun is pointed horizontally while attached o a platform that
undergoes simple harmonic motion in the vertical direction with an
amplitude of 6.0 cm and a period of 0.20 sec. The speed of the bullet
relative to the gun is 100 cm/sec. What is the velocity of the bullet
relative to the Earth if the gun is fired when the gun is (a) at the highest
point of its motion, and (b) at the midpoint?

5-44 ★ It can be shown (Section 16-8) that a particle moving through a tunnel
constructed diametrically through the Earth has an acceleration toward
the Earth's center whose magnitude is proportional to the distance to the
center of the Earth. (a) What would be the motion of a body dropped
from rest into such a tunnel from the Earth's surface? (b) With what
speed would the body pass the center of the Earth? (c) What is the
period of the motion? (It is interesting to compare the period and maximum speed of a body falling through an Earth tunnel with the period and
speed of a satellite traveling in a circular orbit close to the surface of
the Earth.)

REFERENCE FRAMES

The displacements, velocities, and accelerations of moving objects discussed heretofore were all implicitly assumed to have been measured relative to the reference frame of the Earth's surface. More specifically, it was assumed that the motion of an object was recorded by a multiflash camera at rest on Earth. In this chapter we treat the motion of an object as viewed from different reference frames, moving relative to one another. This will lead us to the rule for adding relative velocities, and the Galilean transformation equations.

6-1 Reference frames and relative velocities For simplicity, we first consider one-dimensional motion at constant speed. An object's motion will be supposed to be recorded by a camera fixed to the Earth and also by a second camera moving at a constant velocity with respect to the Earth. We label the reference system of the Earth S_1; the displacement, velocity, and acceleration of the object as measured by an observer at rest on Earth are written x_1, v_1, and a_1, where the subscript 1 informs us that these quantities are measured with respect to the system S_1. A second reference system, S_2, moves to the right with a constant velocity v relative to S_1. For convenience, we always assume that at time $t = 0$ the origins of S_1 and S_2 coincide. From the point of view of an observer in S_2, the displacement, velocity, and acceleration of the object are x_2, v_2, and a_2.

Because system S_2 moves to the right with a velocity $+v$ with respect to S_1, it follows that an observer in S_2 would say that S_1 and all bodies at rest in S_1 move to the left with a velocity $-v$. Strictly, we can speak *only* of the *relative motion* of any two systems, their relative speed v being simply the separation distance between the two origins divided by the elapsed time.

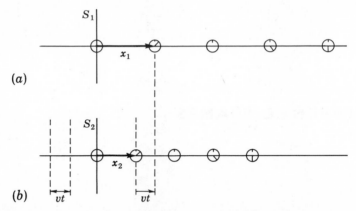

Figure 6-1. Simulated multiflash photographs giving the positions of a body in uniform motion to the right, as seen (a) by an observer in the reference frame S_1 and as seen (b) by an observer in reference frame S_2. S_2 has a velocity v to the right relative to S_1.

To choose a system labeled S_1 as one which is at rest on Earth is merely a matter of convenience; S_1 could, in fact, be any reference frame.

Figure 6-1a shows a simulated multiflash photograph taken with a camera fixed in S_1, the object moving to the right with a constant speed v_1. Figure 6-1b shows the *same* motion, but now as photographed with a camera at rest in S_2. We see that the displacement x_1 (as measured in S_1) exceeds the displacement x_2 (in S_2) by an amount vt, where vt is the distance separating the two origins at time t. Therefore,

$$x_2 = x_1 - vt$$

or
$$x_1 = x_2 + vt \qquad \text{[6-1]}$$

The second equation follows from the first, not only according to simple algebra but also from another consideration. The two reference frames are altogether equivalent. Consequently, S_1 has a velocity $-v$ with respect to

S_2 if S_2 has a velocity of $+v$ with respect to S_1, and we may interchange subscripts 1 and 2 while at the same time replacing v by $-v$ in the first equation to arrive at the second.

Dividing both sides of Equation 6-1 by t yields a relation among velocities:

$$v_2 = v_1 - v$$

or
$$v_1 = v_2 + v \qquad\qquad [6\text{-}2]$$

Equations 6-1 and 6-2 are said, in formal language, to be the coordinate and velocity transformations, respectively, for two reference frames moving at a constant relative velocity.

Example 1 A bicycle travels east at 15 feet/sec with respect to the Earth, and a train travels east at 25 feet/sec. (a) What is the cyclist's velocity relative to the train? (b) What is the train's velocity relative to the cyclist?

(a) Choosing the Earth as system S_1, the train as system S_2, and the cyclist as the object being observed, we have

$$v = 25 \text{ ft/sec}$$

and
$$v_1 = 15 \text{ ft/sec}$$

Therefore,
$$v_2 = v_1 - v = (15 \text{ ft/sec}) - (25 \text{ ft/sec})$$

$$v_2 = -10 \text{ ft/sec}$$

The cyclist moves *west* at 10 feet/sec relative to the train.

(b) It follows immediately that, if the cyclist has a velocity of 10 feet/sec west relative to the train, the train has a velocity of 10 feet/sec east relative to the cyclist. But let us reach this result in another way: we again choose the Earth as system S_1, but now S_2 is chosen to be the cyclist and the train is the object observed. Therefore,

$$v = 15 \text{ ft/sec}$$

$$v_1 = 25 \text{ ft/sec}$$

$$v_2 = v_1 - v = (25 \text{ ft/sec}) - (15 \text{ ft/sec})$$

$$v_2 = 10 \text{ ft/sec}$$

The train moves east at 10 feet/sec relative to the cyclist.

To extend the above transformations to two or three dimensions is straightforward. Again we are to find the relationship between the motion of an object as viewed in S_1 and as viewed in S_2. This time, however, the object moves in S_1 at a constant velocity v_1 which is *not* parallel to the relative velocity v. Again, for convenience, the positive X-axes are chosen in the direction of v, and the two origins coincide at $t = 0$. The motion of the particle as seen by S_1 is shown in the multiflash photograph of Figure 6-2a. The same motion is shown in Figure 6-2b, but here recorded with a camera at rest in S_2. The Y-components, y_1 and y_2, are the same, and the X-components differ, as before. Therefore,

$$x_2 = x_1 - vt$$
$$y_2 = y_1$$

or, vectorially: $r_2 = r_1 - vt$ [6-3]

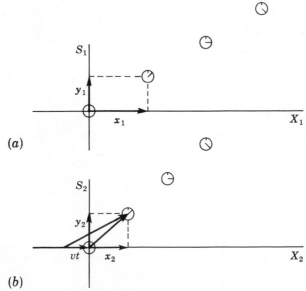

Figure 6-2. Simulated multiflash photographs of a body moving with constant velocity (a) as viewed in S_1 and (b) as viewed in S_2.

Dividing each of the displacement vectors in Equation 6-3 by the time t gives us a relationship among the velocities:

$$v_1 = v_2 + v \qquad [6\text{-}4]$$

where v is the velocity of S_2 with respect to S_1. Thus, Equation 6-4 says that the vector velocity of the particle as observed in system S_1 is equal to the vector velocity of the particle as observed in system S_2 plus the relative velocity of S_2 with respect to S_1. Equations 6-2 and 6-4 are the coordinate and velocity transformation equations, respectively, for two reference systems moving at a constant relative velocity. They are known as the

Galilean transformation equations. Although derived here for the special situation of a particle moving at a constant velocity with respect to either reference frame, these transformations hold, as we will prove shortly, for any motion of the particle.

The Galilean transformations are simple and (apparently) obvious. They express in formal mathematical language our everyday common-sense conceptions of space and time. These transformation equations are not, however, altogether correct. For speeds approaching the speed of light (3.0×10^8 m/sec) they must be supplanted by the more general *Lorentz transformation equations*, of the special theory of relativity. The Lorentz transformations

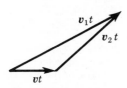

Figure 6-3. Vector relation showing that $v_1 = v_2 + v$.

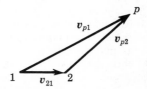

Figure 6-4. A mnemonic device for relative velocities. The heads and tails are labelled p, 1, and 2 to correspond respectively to the particle, reference frame 1, and reference frame 2; v_{p1} gives the velocity of the particle relative to 1, etc.

reduce, as they must, to the Galilean transformations for the moderate speeds with which we shall be concerned in this volume.†

There is a helpful mnemonic for keeping straight the meaning of the terms and their signs in Equation 6-4. If we represent the velocity of the *particle* relative to system 1 by v_{p1}, the velocity of the particle relative to 2 by v_{p2}, and the velocity of system 2 with respect to system 1 by v_{21}, Equation 6-4 becomes

$$v_{p1} = v_{p2} + v_{21} \qquad [6\text{-}5]$$

Notice that the "outside" subscripts on the right-hand side of the equation correspond to the subscripts of the term on the left-hand side of the equation. This is illustrated also in Figure 6-4. The head of each velocity vector is identified with the moving object (or reference frame), and the tail has the label of the reference frame with respect to which the velocity is measured.

A simple conclusion follows from Equation 6-4: if a body moves with a constant velocity in one reference frame, then its velocity relative to any

† See, for example, Weidner and Sells, *Elementary Modern Physics*, Allyn and Bacon, Inc., 1960, Chap. 2.

other reference frame is also constant (but different), provided the two reference frames have a constant relative velocity. Moreover, a reference frame can always be found in which the body's velocity is zero. For example, if a block moves to the right at 20 feet/sec relative to the Earth, then, with respect to a train traveling 20 feet/sec to the right, the block *is* (not merely appears to be) *at rest*. Thus, *the states of motion with constant velocity and of rest differ* from one another *only through the arbitrary choice of a reference frame*. We shall see that the choice of a suitable reference frame can often simplify considerably the analysis of motion.

Example 2   A man rows a boat at 3.00 miles/hour with respect to the water. He is to cross a river 1.00 mile wide, in which the current is 4.00 miles/hour.

(a) If the man continuously heads the boat up river at an angle of 15° to the river bank, how long will it take him to cross the river, and at what point down river will he reach the opposite bank?

If we are to find the time for the boat to cross the river, we need first the X-component of the boat's velocity relative to the ground. The velocity of the *boat* relative to the *ground*, v_{bg}, is the vector sum of the velocity of the *boat* relative to the *water*, v_{bw}, and the velocity of the *water* relative to the *ground*, v_{wg}: $v_{bg} = v_{bw} + v_{wg}$, as shown in Figure 6-5a. The X-component of v_{bg} is equal to the X-component of v_{bw}:

$$v_{bw} \sin 15° = (3.00 \text{ mi/hr}) \sin 15° = 0.776 \text{ mi/hr}$$

Therefore, the time for the boat to cross the 1.00-mile-wide river is

$$t = (1.00 \text{ mi})/(0.776 \text{ mi/hr}) = 1.29 \text{ hr}$$

Now we find the distance down river traveled by the boat in this time of 1.29 hours. The Y-component of the boat's velocity relative to the ground is seen from Figure 6-5 to be:

$$v_{wg} - v_{bw} \cos 15° = (4.00 \text{ mi/hr}) - (3.00 \text{ mi/hr}) \cos 15°$$
$$= 1.10 \text{ mi/hr down river}$$

Therefore, in the time of 1.29 hours, the boat moves down river a distance of

$$y = (1.10 \text{ mi/hr})(1.29 \text{ hr}) = 1.42 \text{ mi}$$

(b) How far down river will the rower be transported if he heads the boat to cross the river in the least time? Find the time of crossing.

If the boat is to cross in the least time the rower must *head* the boat directly across the river, so that the X-component of his velocity relative to the ground is a maximum. The vector v_{bw} must point directly cross-river as shown in Figure 6-5b. Then, the X-component of v_{bg} is equal to v_{bw} and the Y-component of v_{bg} is equal to v_{wg}. The time for crossing is simply

$$t = (1.00 \text{ mi})/(3.00 \text{ mi/hr}) = 0.333 \text{ hr}$$

and in this time the boat is transported down river a distance

$$y = (4.00 \text{ mi/hr})(0.333 \text{ hr}) = 1.33 \text{ mi}$$

(c) Find the time of crossing and the distance traveled down river if the rower heads the boat to move the least distance down river.

In order that the boat may travel a minimum distance down river, the angle, say θ, of the boat's velocity v_{bg} relative to the river bank must be a maximum,

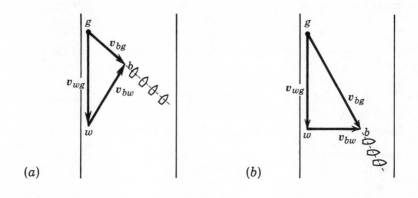

(a)   (b)

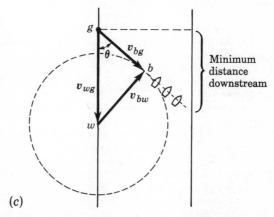

(c)

Figure 6-5. (a) The boat is headed up river at an angle of 15° relative to the bank. (b) The boat is headed cross-river to reach the opposite shore in the least time. (c) The boat is headed to move the least distance down river.

as shown in Figure 6-5c. We can see that the angle must be the maximum angle from the following consideration: the displacement of the boat relative to the ground is in the same direction as v_{bg}. It is apparent that, to have the minimum displacement (therefore, the minimum distance down river), the vector v_{bg} must make the largest possible angle with respect to the bank, and this occurs when v_{bg} is tangent to the circle representing the possible terminal points of the vector

v_{bg}. Thus, v_{bg} is perpendicular to v_{bw}, and the angle θ is determined by

$$\sin \theta = v_{bw}/v_{wg} = (3.00 \text{ mi/hr})/(4.00 \text{ mi/hr})$$

or $\theta = 48.5°$

The magnitude of v_{bg} is

$$v_{bg} = \sqrt{(4.00)^2 - (3.00)^2} \text{ mi/hr} = 2.65 \text{ mi/hr}$$

The X-component of v_{bg} is $(2.65 \text{ mi/hr}) \sin 48.5° = 1.98 \text{ mi/hr}$, and the crossing time is

$$t = (1.00 \text{ mi})/(1.98 \text{ mi/hr}) = 0.505 \text{ hr}$$

The Y-component of v_{bg} is $(2.65 \text{ mi/hr}) \cos 48.5° = 1.77 \text{ mi/hr}$ and, in the time 0.506 hours, the boat travels downstream

$$y = (1.77 \text{ mi/hr})(0.506 \text{ hr}) = 0.895 \text{ mi}$$

Example 3 A man wishes to catch raindrops falling vertically downward. If the drops are to be caught at the bottom of a long tube and the man is stationed (at rest) on Earth, he must point the tube along the vertical. If the man is in motion, the raindrops will strike the side of the tube before reaching the bottom. Therefore, if the drops are to reach the bottom and pass centrally through the tube, the tube must be inclined with respect to the vertical in the direction of the man's motion. What is this angle of inclination?

The velocity vectors are shown in Figure 6-6, where v_{de} is the velocity of the drops relative to the earth, v_{te} is the velocity of the tube relative to the earth, and v_{dt} is the velocity of the drops relative to the tube. The direction of the vector v_{dt} is, of course, also the direction, relative to the vertical, in which the tube must be pointed. Figure 6-6 shows that

$$\tan \theta = v_{te}/v_{de}$$

The speed of the drops v_{de} can be computed if the angle θ is measured and the speed v_{te} is known.

In similar fashion, light from a distant star at the zenith would pass centrally through a telescope pointed vertically upward if the Earth were at rest. But the Earth is *not* at rest relative to the distant (or "fixed") stars: it moves about the Sun at a speed of 3.0×10^4 m/sec. It is necessary, therefore, for an astronomer to tilt a telescope slightly, with respect to the vertical, to have light from an overhead star pass through the center of the telescope (the star must be in a plane perpendicular to the Earth's velocity). This phenomenon, known as the *stellar aberration of light*, was first recognized (1725) by J. Bradley. Bradley used the aberration effect to measure the speed of light. If the orbital speed of the Earth, 3.0×10^4 m/sec, is v and the speed of light relative to the distant star, 3.0×10^8 m/sec, is c, the angle of inclination θ of the telescope is given by

$$\tan \theta = v/c = (3.0 \times 10^4 \text{ m/sec})/(3.0 \times 10^8 \text{ m/sec}) = 10^{-4}$$

$$\theta = 20.5 \text{ sec of arc}$$

This very small angular displacement (5.7×10^{-3} degrees of arc) *is* observable. The velocity vectors as seen by an observer on Earth are shown in Figure 6-7a, and the relative velocities as seen by an observer at rest on a fixed star are shown in Figure 6-7b.

Actually, this analysis is not quite correct. Figure 6-7 shows the speed of light relative to the telescope to be *larger* than the speed of light relative to the stars, but experiment shows most emphatically (and paradoxically, from the point of view of the Galilean transformations of classical physics) that the speed of light is *exactly the same for all observers*, whatever their state of motion.† The Galilean transformations do *not* hold for bodies traveling at speeds close to that of light, and certainly not for light itself. These matters are resolved in the special theory of relativity, which gives, for the aberration angle, $\tan\theta = (v/c)/(1 - v^2/c^2)^{\frac{1}{2}}$. The computed angle differs from 20.5 sec of arc, however, by only 5×10^{-7} per cent!

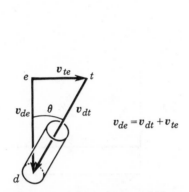

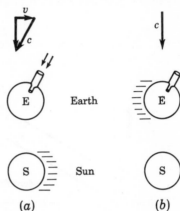

$$v_{de} = v_{dt} + v_{te}$$

Figure 6-6. Raindrops falling vertically are caught in the bottom of a tube moving horizontally. The *d*rops, *e*arth, and *t*ube are represented by *d*, *e*, and *t*.

Figure 6-7. (a) Stellar aberration as seen by an observer on Earth. (b) Stellar aberration as seen by an observer at rest on a fixed star.

6-2 Accelerated objects and reference frames We have arrived at the rule for adding relative velocities through the special situation in which the observed object's velocity is *constant* relative to one reference frame and, therefore, also constant relative to a second frame moving at a constant velocity relative to the first. The rule is a vector addition:

[6-4] $$v_1 = v_2 + v$$

where v is the constant velocity of system S_2 relative to S_1. It is easy to show that this same relationship holds when the body's velocity changes, the velocities v_1 and v_2 being the *instantaneous* velocities of the body as measured by observers in systems 1 and 2, respectively. We simply imagine the average velocities as being measured over a very short time interval: then the average velocity becomes equal to the instantaneous velocity. The

† Strictly, the observers must be in *inertial systems*, defined in Chapter 7.

relative velocity v between the two reference frames *must*, however, *remain constant*.

Now let us find how the acceleration a_1 of an object as measured by an observer at rest in system S_1 is related to the acceleration a_2 of the same object as measured by an observer at rest in S_2. We obtain the acceleration by finding the time rate of velocity, and Equation 6-4 yields

$$\Delta v_1 = \Delta v_2 + \Delta v = \Delta v_2$$

because v is constant and $\Delta v = 0$. Dividing by Δt gives

$$\frac{\Delta v_1}{\Delta t} = \frac{\Delta v_2}{\Delta t}$$

$$a_1 = a_2 \qquad\qquad [6\text{-}6]$$

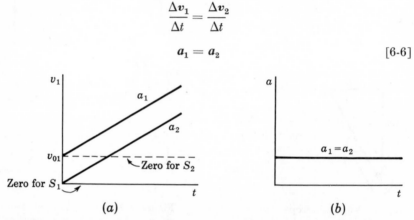

Figure 6-8. (a) Velocity-time graphs: motion at constant acceleration as viewed from two different reference frames. (b) Acceleration-time graph for motion at constant acceleration as viewed from two reference frames.

Thus, if an object has an acceleration (constant or changing) in one reference frame at a given instant, it has, at this same instant, exactly the *same* acceleration in any other reference frame which is moving with a *constant* velocity with respect to the first. Although the measured coordinates and velocities are different, as viewed from two such reference systems, the object's acceleration is the same.

Consider, for example, the simple case of a body moving with constant acceleration a_1 along the direction of relative motion in system S_1, the initial velocity being v_{01}. The velocity-time graph for this motion is shown in Figure 6-8a. The slope is constant, indicating a constant acceleration. Now consider the same motion from the point of view of an observer who is moving in system S_2 and whose velocity relative to S_1 is chosen as $v = v_{01}$. With respect to S_2 the body is initially at rest, but it gains velocity at precisely the same rate as does the body relative to S_1. This is indicated by the velocity-time graph of Figure 6-8a, for observer S_2; the velocity intercept is zero, but the slopes of the lines are identical. Both observers measure the same acceleration, as indicated in Figure 6-8b.

We see that by the proper choice of origin and reference frame it has been possible to have both $x = 0$ and $v = 0$ at $t = 0$. We can make the displacement x equal to zero at $t = 0$ by the appropriate choice of the zero of displacement origin. Likewise, we can make the initial velocity v_0 equal to zero by the appropriate choice of reference frame.

Can we find a reference system such that the acceleration will also be zero? Yes, but only if this reference frame is in *constant acceleration* with respect to S_1 and S_2, as described above. Therefore, if x, v, and a are all to be made zero at $t = 0$, the procedure is clear: choose a reference frame that has the same origin, initial velocity, and acceleration as the particle—or, in simpler language, if the body is never to move, ride with it.

Suppose that an apple falls from a tree; then an observer at rest on the ground, an observer at rest in the tree, and an observer having a constant velocity relative to the Earth will all agree that the acceleration of the apple is toward the ground and of magnitude g. Suppose further that a man drops from the tree at the same instant as the apple; then the apple and the man will have the same acceleration g and have identical motions as measured by an observer on Earth. However, the observer falling with the apple may claim (properly) that the apple is at rest and that the Earth falls toward him with a constant acceleration g.

From the point of view of the *kinematics* of the motion, there is no reason to prefer the description of motion given by an observer on Earth to the description given by another observer falling toward the Earth. There is, however, a profound difference when we consider the *dynamics* of the motion. We shall find that the laws of motion and the dynamical equations of motion become particularly simple in certain reference frames, those known as *inertial frames*, and not in others. Our intuitive choice of the Earth as reference frame over a reference frame attached to a falling object is justified because the Earth is, at least approximately, an inertial frame. More about this in Chapter 7.

Example 4 A boy, standing on a train traveling east at 90 feet/sec, throws a ball straight up at 32 feet/sec relative to the train at the moment the train passes a crossing. (a) How far from the crossing is the boy when he catches the ball? (b) What is the path of the ball as viewed by an observer on the ground?

(a) The motion of the ball is simplest when viewed from the reference frame which travels with the train. With respect to this frame the boy is at rest, and the ball is seen to rise and descend vertically. The time of flight of the ball can be computed from the equation of motion:

$$y = v_0 t + \tfrac{1}{2}at^2$$
$$0 = (32 \text{ ft/sec})t + \tfrac{1}{2}(-32 \text{ ft/sec}^2)t^2$$
$$t = 0, \quad \text{or } 2.0 \text{ sec}$$

Thus, two seconds elapse from the moment the ball leaves the boy's hand until it is caught.

An observer on the ground agrees that the ball is in the air for 2.0 sec. During this time, however, the train had advanced a distance of (90 feet/sec)(2.0 sec) = 180 feet.

(b) Figure 6-9 shows the path of the ball as viewed from the train and from the ground.

(a)

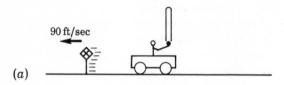

(b)

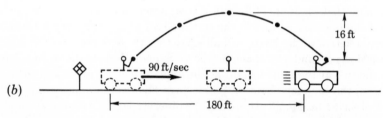

Figure 6-9. A boy riding in a train throws a ball vertically upward. The motion as seen (a) from a reference frame at rest with the train and (b) from a reference frame at rest with the Earth.

6-3   The kinematics of rolling bodies   We can most easily treat the kinematics of rolling bodies by considering first the simple situation in which a wheel rotates at constant angular speed about a fixed axis. Suppose that the wheel of radius r in Figure 6-10 is made to rotate uniformly in the clockwise sense by pressing a board against the bottom of the wheel and moving the board to the left with constant speed v. If the wheel turns without slipping, the point of the wheel touching the board must, at any instant, have the same velocity v as does the board. All points on the wheel's circumference have the same speed v, although it is only at the point of contact that a point on the circumference has a *velocity to the left.* As the wheel completes one turn, the board moves to the left a distance $2\pi r$, the circumference of the wheel.

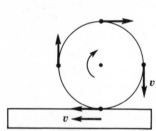

Figure 6-10. A wheel rotates at constant angular speed because a board pressed against it moves at constant velocity.

Now let us view the same motion from a different reference frame, that in which the *board* is *at rest*. The wheel now rolls to the right without slipping and the wheel's axle has a speed v with respect to the surface on which it rolls. The motion of the wheel can be considered as two superposed motions: rotation of the wheel about the axle at constant angular speed, and advance to the right of all points on the wheel at the speed v. Figures 6-11a, b, c

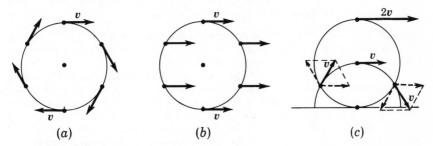

(a) $\qquad\qquad$ (b) $\qquad\qquad$ (c)

Figure 6-11. Vectors giving the velocities of several points on a rolling wheel. (a) The rotation of the wheel about its center, (b) the uniform translational motion of the wheel, and (c) a rolling wheel—rotation about an instantaneous axis. The motion in (c) is the superposition of the motions in parts (a) and (b).

show, respectively, the rotation of the wheel about its center, the advance to the right of all points at speed v, and the velocity vectors resulting from the superposition of the two motions in (a) and (b).

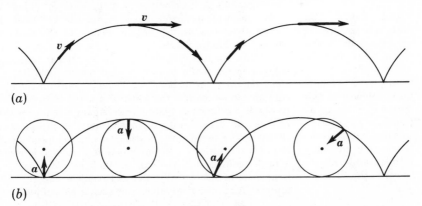

(a)

(b)

Figure 6-12. (a) The path, a cycloid, traced out by a point on the rim of a rolling wheel. The instantaneous velocity is always tangent to the path. (b) The instantaneous acceleration has a constant magnitude and always points toward the wheel's axle.

The point of contact has, at any instant, a *zero* speed. The axle has the velocity v to the right. Further, a point on the top of the wheel has the velocity $2v$. All three velocities are with respect to the surface. Moreover, the velocity vectors show that the wheel is *rotating* instantaneously *about the point of contact*, called the *instantaneous axis of rotation*. Thus a wheel which rolls without slipping can be thought of as rotating at each instant about an axis of rotation at the point of contact, this point of contact moving to the right at the same speed v as that of the axle.

Example 5 Discuss the path of a point on the rim of a wheel which (a) rolls without slipping on a horizontal surface and (b) advances along the direction of the axle. Both are viewed by an outside observer.

(a) We concentrate on the path of some one point on the rim of the rolling wheel, as shown in Figure 6-12a. Such a point moves in a circle at constant speed with respect to the axle, while the axle moves to the right at constant speed relative to the Earth. Relative to the horizontal surface, this path is a *cycloid*. The direction of the velocity of the point is, as always, indicated by a tangent to the path, and the velocity vector changes in a complicated way. The change in instantaneous velocity with time is, however, just the acceleration, and the acceleration here is really very simple. We recall that, if a body has an acceleration in one reference frame, then the body has exactly the *same* acceleration in a second reference frame moving at a constant velocity relative to the first. In the reference frame for which the wheel's axle is at *rest*, all points on the circumference have the centripetal acceleration v^2/r toward the fixed center of the circle. Therefore, a point on the circumference of a *rolling* wheel also has an acceleration of magnitude v^2/r (where v is the speed of the *axle*), where again the acceleration vector always points toward the center of the moving wheel; see Figure 6-12b.

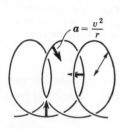

Figure 6-13. The path, a helix, traced out by a point on the rim of the uniformly rotating wheel which is displaced at uniform velocity in the direction of the rotation axis. The instantaneous acceleration is constant in magnitude and points toward the wheel's axle.

(b) Now we imagine that a wheel rotates at constant angular speed while it moves at constant velocity v_a *along the direction of the axle*. Then a point on the circumference traces out the path of a *helix*, with respect to Earth, as shown in Figure 6-13. Again a point on the rim has an acceleration of magnitude v^2/r (where v is the *tangential* speed of the particle; *not* v_a, the speed along the axis of rotation), and the direction of the acceleration is once again toward the axis of the helix. We shall see later that an electrically charged particle moving in a uniform magnetic field traces out such a helical path.

PROBLEMS

6-1 Billiard ball A, moving to the right at the speed v, approaches an identical billiard ball B initially at rest. Ball A hits ball B head on, and after the collision A is at rest and B moves to the right at speed v. Describe the collision (a) from a reference frame attached to ball A, (b) from a reference frame attached to ball B, and (c) from a reference frame moving to the right at speed $v/2$.

6-2 A train is traveling north at 40 feet/sec. A man on the train walks across the aisle from east to west at 10 feet/sec with respect to the train. What is the man's velocity with respect to the ground?

6-3 Two trains approach a railroad station, one from the north at 60 miles/hour, the other from the east at 80 miles/hour. Find the velocities of (a) the railroad station and (b) the south-bound train relative to an observer on the west-bound train.

6-4 In still air a man, at a distance of 680 m from a mountain lying to the east, fires a pistol and hears an echo after 4.00 sec. What must be the wind velocity (east or west) for the measured time interval to differ from 4.00 sec by 1.0 per cent?

6-5 An airplane flies with an air speed of 300 miles/hour heading north. There is a wind of 60 miles/hour blowing from the northeast. (a) What is the ground speed of the airplane? (b) In what direction is it heading relative to the ground?

6-6 ★ A man rows a boat in still water at 4.0 miles/hour. He is to cross a river in which the current is 3.0 miles/hour. In what direction should he head, relative to the downstream direction, to cross the river (a) in a minimum time, (b) with a minimum distance traveled, (c) at a minimum speed relative to the river bank?

6-7 An airplane reaches an airport 100 miles distant to the northwest in 30 minutes. During the trip the airplane's air speed meter read (202) miles/hour and the plane traveled continuously in the northwest direction. What was the magnitude of the wind, blowing eastward and assumed constant, during the trip?

6-8 It is observed that when a lightweight ball strikes head on a massive ball at rest, the light ball bounces back with the same speed as that with which it approached the massive ball, the massive ball remaining essentially at rest. Prove that, if the massive ball approaches and strikes head on the light ball now at rest, the light ball after collision will move with twice the speed of the massive ball. (*Hint:* View the first collision from the reference frame of the massive ball.)

6-9 It is observed that when a light ball strikes head on a massive ball at rest, the light ball bounces back with the same speed as that with which it approached the massive ball, the massive ball remaining essentially at rest. Now suppose that the massive ball, moving initially with a speed of 16 feet/sec to the right, approaches the light ball, moving in the same direction at 12 feet/sec. What is the speed of the light ball after being struck by the massive ball? (*Hint:* Consider the collision from a reference frame in which the massive ball is at rest.)

6-10 ★ A satellite moves in a circular orbit near the Earth's surface, completing one revolution in 84 minutes relative to the distant stars. If the satellite moves above the Equator and to the east, what is (a) the speed of the satellite with respect to an observer on ground and (b) the period of the satellite with respect to the observer on ground?

6-11 An 8-foot-high elevator is descending at a constant speed of 10 feet/sec. A light bulb falls from the ceiling to the floor of the elevator. At an instant just before the light bulb hits the floor, what is the velocity and acceleration of the bulb (a) with respect to an observer in the elevator and (b) with respect to an observer at rest in the building?

6-12 A boy standing on the platform of a train traveling north at 30 feet/sec throws a ball at 40 feet/sec in the direction northeast with respect to the train. What are the magnitude and direction of the velocity of the ball relative to the Earth?

6-13 An observer on the ground sees a boy, in a train that is moving at 25 m/sec, throw a ball upward (relative to the reference frame of the train). The train has advanced a distance of 60 m during the time interval between the throwing and catching of the ball. With what velocity was the ball thrown (a) relative to the train and (b) relative to the Earth?

6-14 A train passes with a speed v_{0x}. Inside the train an object is thrown vertically upward with a speed v_{0y} with respect to the train. Show that the equation of the path traced out by the object, as viewed from the ground, is $y - (v_{0y}/v_{0x})x - (g/2v_{0x}{}^2)x^2 = 0$.

6-15 A ball is dropped from the mast of a ship moving at 20 feet/sec. The mast is 60 feet high. Neglect air effects: (a) where does the ball strike the ship relative to the base of the mast, (b) with what speed does it strike the deck relative to an observer on board ship, (c) with what speed does it strike the deck relative to an observer on land, and (d) through what horizontal distance does the ship move as the ball falls?

Galileo Galilei argued that an object dropped from the mast of a moving ship would strike the deck at the base of the mast, rather than fall behind. The dropped object has zero horizontal velocity relative to the ship or, equivalently, the object and the ship have the same horizontal velocity relative to an observer on land. This argument was used to make plausible the heliocentric cosmology proposed by Copernicus, in which the Earth and objects on its surface are imagined to hurtle through space at extraordinarily high speeds by virtue of the Earth's revolution about the Sun and its rotation about its own axis. An important objection to the Copernican cosmology was this: "If the Earth is not at rest, but rather travels at high speeds through space, how is it that objects on the Earth's surface are not left behind, that there is no strong wind, that birds can fly serenely through the atmosphere?"

6-16 Raindrops are falling vertically at 20 feet/sec with respect to the ground. A passenger in a train sees streaks on the window that make an angle of 30° below the horizontal. What is the speed of the train?

6-17 ★ A man walks in the rain at a speed of 6.0 feet/sec. The raindrops appear to him to move at a speed of 15 feet/sec and to fall toward him at an angle of 20° with respect to the vertical. What are the magnitude and direction of the raindrops' velocity relative to the ground?

6-18 At what angle would an astronomer on the planet Mercury have to tilt a telescope to observe a distant star directly overhead (and outward along the Sun-Mercury line)? Mercury's orbital radius about the Sun is 5.79×10^{10} m and its period about the Sun is 87.8 days.

6-19 ★ With respect to a reference frame whose origin is at the center of the Earth, find the distance, speed, and acceleration of the origin of a reference frame fixed on the Earth's surface (a) at the Earth's equator and (b) at the North Pole.

6-20 ★ Three reference frames, S_1, S_2, and S_3, have parallel X-axes and Y-axes. With respect to S_1, frame S_2 moves to the right with a constant speed of 20 feet/sec and frame S_3 accelerates to the right with a constant acceleration of 5 feet/sec^2. At the time $t = 0$, all three origins coincide, and S_3's velocity is zero with respect to S_1. An observer in S_1 sees a rabbit running to the right at a constant speed of 10 feet/sec, the rabbit being at the origin at $t = 0$. Describe the rabbit's motion from the viewpoint of observers in S_2 and S_3 and illustrate this on displacement-time, velocity-time, and acceleration-time diagrams.

6-21 An automobile, having wheels 15 inches in radius, travels at 50 miles/hour. (a) What is the speed of a point on the circumference of a wheel relative to the driver of the automobile? What is the velocity, relative to the ground, of a point on the circumference of the wheel when the point is (b) at the ground, (c) at the highest point, and (d) at the same elevation as the wheel axle?

6-22 A wheel 2.0 feet in radius rolls to the left along a level surface at a constant speed of 15 feet/sec. What is the *velocity* of a point on the rim of the wheel 2.0 feet above the surface and in front of the wheel's axis (a) with respect to the surface and (b) with respect to a point on the rim at the top of the wheel?

6-23 What is the speed relative to the ground of the tip of an airplane's propeller blade when the airplane is taxiing at 60 miles/hour and the propellers are turning at 600 revolutions/minute? The tip of the blade is 5.0 feet from the axis of rotation.

S E V E N

THE LAW OF INERTIA AND THE
CONSERVATION OF MASS

In this chapter we begin our study of mechanics, the oldest and most basic branch of physics. Mechanics is the foundation of all physics and engineering, and through the refinements of quantum mechanics and the theory of relativity during this century, mechanics is the basis of our present understanding of the atom, its nucleus, and the elementary constituents thereof.

Here we shall be concerned with *classical mechanics*, which treats of the motions and interactions of ordinary objects—objects which are large compared with the size of the atom (10^{-10} m) and which move at speeds appreciably less than the speed of light (3×10^8 m/sec). We go beyond kinematics, which merely describes the motion of bodies and does not relate the motion of one body to the motion of a second body nor give the causes of the motion: this is the function of mechanics, or dynamics. By ascribing physical attributes to particles—such as mass, momentum, and energy—and by introducing forces as the origin of the interactions between particles, we shall find that a very few fundamental relations, or laws, of physics underlie all physical phenomena.

Classical mechanics had its origins in the studies of Galileo Galilei (1564–1642) and, later, of Isaac Newton (1642–1727). Galileo was the first "physicist" in the modern sense of the word. His specific contributions to physics and astronomy were enormous. Some of Galileo's contributions in physics were: the recognition of the constant acceleration of all freely falling bodies (Section 2-7 of this book), the kinematics of projectile motion, including the resolution into independent components (Section 4-2), the Galilean coordinate and velocity transformations (Section 6-1), the independence of a pendulum's period to the mass and amplitude (Section 17-4), and the law of inertia (Section 7-1). Some of his contributions in astronomy were: the construction of the Galilean telescope, the observation of the phases of Venus, rings of Saturn, moons of Jupiter, sunspots, earthshine (on the Moon), height of the Moon's mountains, the observation of the Milky Way as a collection of discrete stars, and the confirmation of Copernicus' heliocentric model of the universe. But perhaps of even greater significance was Galileo's use of a strategy and program in attacking problems in physics that remains essentially unchanged and equally successful in present-day physics.

Galileo insisted that we first study simple things, by controlled observation (experiment), removing or minimizing nonessential disturbances, and that our results be expressed in the compact and precise language of mathematics. These elements in the strategy of physics are illustrated by our approach to the motion of falling bodies. If one is to learn about the physics of falling bodies, one must first study a falling body in an experiment in which the disturbing and complicating effect of air resistance and friction is minimized. Then the fact that a freely falling body has a constant acceleration is reflected in the experimental result, viz., the displacement of a body dropped from rest is proportional to the square of the time elapsed ($y = \frac{1}{2}gt^2$). The same procedure applies when one studies an even simpler situation, the motion of a body on a smooth horizontal plane. Friction, which otherwise obscures and interferes with the motion, must be eliminated or minimized. Considerations of this kind led Galileo to give simple and profound answers to questions that had troubled thinkers for centuries.

What is required to keep a body at rest? *Nothing.* What is required to keep a body in motion? Said Galileo: *nothing.* This is the essence of the *law of inertia.*

7-1   The law of inertia   Consider a hockey puck on a smooth horizontal surface of ice. Friction between the puck and the surface is small, but not entirely negligible. If the puck is initially at rest, it remains at rest, unless pushed; if the puck is set into motion, but then left undisturbed, it coasts in a straight line for considerable distances before coming finally to rest. The puck comes to rest because friction has not been entirely eliminated: one solid is in contact with, and rubs against, a second solid.

Suppose, now, that a puck is so constructed that it floats on air above a smooth horizontal surface and the effect of friction is thus reduced drastically. Such an air-suspended puck or disc is represented in Figure 7-1. When it is set in motion the disc can coast for amazingly large distances before coming to rest, its speed being reduced very slowly. We can well imagine that if external disturbances, or forces, were altogether absent, the disc would continue in its motion indefinitely, moving in a straight line at constant

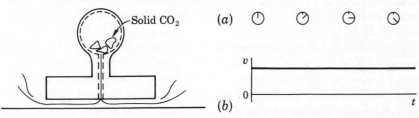

Figure 7-1. A simple type of air-suspended puck.

Figure 7-2. The observed motion for an air-suspended puck on a smooth horizontal surface is constant velocity. (a) Simulated multiflash photograph. (b) Velocity-time graph.

speed. In fact, *if a body is subject to no net external influence, it has a constant velocity, either zero or nonzero;* that is, *as long as there is no horizontal force acting on the disc to change its speed or direction of motion, it continues in uniform motion—along a straight line covering equal distances in equal time intervals* (see Figure 7-2). This is the *law of inertia*, sometimes referred to as the first of Newton's three laws of motion.

We have referred above to an external influence, or force, acting on an object. In Chapter 9 we shall give a precise definition of force. For our purposes in this chapter we shall take a force to be simply a push or pull, or an interaction of one body with a second body. For the moment, then, a force is an influence that can cause a body coasting on a smooth frictionless surface to depart from its motion of constant velocity. Therefore, if a body changes its speed or its direction of motion, it has been acted upon by an "unbalanced" external force.

The observations on the coasting disc implicitly were from the point of view of an observer in a particular reference frame—one fixed with respect to the surface of the Earth. As we know from Section 6-1, an observer in a reference frame moving at a constant velocity with respect to the Earth's surface would also agree that the undisturbed disc has a constant (but different) velocity. Indeed, if an observer moves in the same direction and with the same speed relative to the Earth's surface as the coasting disc, he would find the disc always at rest. Conversely, an undisturbed disc at rest on Earth has a constant velocity from the point of view of the moving observer. The states of uniform motion and of rest are *equivalent*. From the point of view of the law of inertia, motion is just as "natural" as rest.

The term *inertial frame* is used to designate a frame of reference in which the *law of inertia holds*—that is, a reference frame in which an undisturbed body maintains a constant velocity. If we find one inertial frame, then *any* other reference frame moving with constant velocity relative to the first frame—and there are an infinite number of such frames—is also an inertial frame.

On the other hand, not all reference frames are inertial frames. Suppose that we view a disc at rest on Earth from a reference frame accelerating, say, at 5 m/sec² to the east. The puck is then seen to accelerate to the west at 5 m/sec², even though there are *no forces* acting on the puck; therefore, this accelerating reference frame clearly is *not* an inertial frame.

Now suppose that our frictionless disc is placed upon, and set in motion on, a rotating platform, or merry-go-round. Viewed from the Earth, the undisturbed disc travels at constant velocity. However, viewed by an observer at rest on the merry-go-round, the disc's motion is not uniform: it moves in a complicated path with a varying speed. The rotating platform is not an inertial frame, and the law of inertia does not hold in this non-inertial frame of reference.

The Earth itself is, in effect, a slowly rotating platform by virtue of its rotation about its axis. Moreover, the Earth revolves about the Sun, and the Sun revolves about the center of our galaxy (the Milky Way) relative to the "fixed" stars. Therefore, a reference frame fixed on Earth accelerates relative to the fixed stars. Experiment shows that only the fixed stars, and any reference frame moving at constant velocity relative to them, are true inertial frames. Consequently, the Earth's surface does not constitute a true inertial system. The effects of rotation are so small (although detectable in subtle experiments) that the Earth serves as a good approximation to an inertial frame. Unless otherwise stated, we will always assume that this approximation can be made.

7-2 Inertial mass Experiments with air-suspended discs lead to the conclusion that any object acted upon by no net external influence will, when viewed from an inertial frame, maintain a state of constant velocity. This property of an object is called its inertia. Our task now is to develop a quantitative measure of inertia.

Consider two different frictionless discs set in motion in the same direction and with the same speed, on a smooth horizontal surface. As long as each of the discs is isolated from horizontal external forces, the two discs travel side by side, maintaining their same relative separation. See Figure 7-3. Suppose that we attach a thin rigid rod to the two discs. Nothing changes. If given the same velocity, they again move together, and the rod does not turn. This is the situation when the motion is viewed from any inertial frame. In particular, when the motion is viewed from an inertial frame traveling relative to the Earth with the same velocity as the discs, the discs are, and remain, at rest.

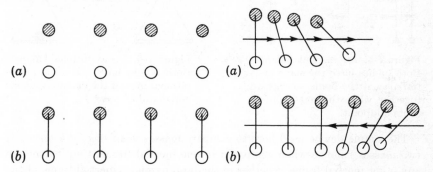

Figure 7-3. Multiflash photographs for two different pucks moving at the same constant velocity, (a) with no connection between them and (b) with a rigid rod connecting them.

Figure 7-4. The connecting rod is pulled suddenly at its center. (a) Both pucks are initially at rest. (b) Both pucks are initially in motion to the right at constant speed, and the pull on the connecting rod is to the left. The shaded puck shows a greater resistance to a change (inertia) in its state of rest or motion.

What happens if we change the state of motion of our system—that is, the velocity—by pulling or jerking on the rod at its center? The rod rotates, as shown in Figure 7-4. The shaded disc in the figure resists a change in its state of motion to a greater extent than does the unshaded disc. If the discs are originally at rest, the shaded disc lags behind the unshaded disc when the rod is pulled at its center. Furthermore, if the discs are originally in motion and the rod is then pulled at its center, to retard the motion, the shaded disc leads the unshaded disc. The shaded disc has a greater resistance to a change in velocity, whether the change is in magnitude, direction, or both. It is said to have a larger *inertia*, or *inertial mass*, than the unshaded disc. Hereinafter we shall call the inertial mass simply "the mass." Note that it is *not* necessary that the pull at the rod's center give this point a *constant* acceleration; all that is required is that the velocity of this point change.

When do two bodies have the same mass? When two bodies are connected to opposite ends of the rigid rod and the rod is pulled at its midpoint, and we find that the two bodies accelerate together, neither body lagging or leading the other. *By definition*, they are identical in mass. See Figure 7-5. The bodies have equal masses because they both exhibit the same inertial response to a change in their state of motion.

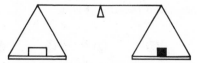

Figure 7-5. An inertial balance. Both bodies have the same inertial mass if the bodies accelerate together when the rod is pulled at its midpoint.

Figure 7-6. A gravitational balance. Both bodies have the same gravitational mass if the balance remains horizontal.

The simple device used here to compare masses is an *inertial balance*. If two masses balance when compared in one inertial frame, they balance in any other inertial frame, whether in the (approximate) inertial frame of the Earth's surface, or in a reference frame moving with constant velocity relative to the Earth, or even in an inertial frame in interstellar space (where the smooth horizontal surface is, of course, not required). Mass is an intrinsic property of a body. It is, unlike the *weight* of a body (about which much will be said later), the same at all points in space. The mass of a body is independent of the body's temperature, shape, and color and, for speeds appreciably less than the speed of light, independent of the body's speed. Mass is a quantitative measure of inertia alone.

An inertial balance is not a convenient instrument. When two bodies have equal inertial mass, as established by experiment with an inertial balance, we are not surprised to find that the two bodies are also in balance when placed on the pans of a sensitive beam balance of the familiar variety, shown in Figure 7-6. That is, if two bodies having identical inertial masses are simultaneously placed on the pans of a beam balance, initially at rest, the beam does not turn, or rotate. A beam balance is a *gravitational balance*. Actually, as we shall see later, the equivalence of the inertial balance, which compares the inertias of bodies, and the gravitational balance (Figure 7-6), which compares the gravitational force on bodies, is not obvious. The equivalence of the inertial mass as measured by an inertial balance and the gravitational mass as measured by the gravitational balance is a most remarkable and profound experimental result.

Masses add as scalar quantities; that is, the mass of a body is the sum of the masses of its parts. This assertion also is not obvious *a priori*; it must be, and is, confirmed by experiment. (Physical volumes do *not* always add as scalars: the volume of 1.0 m³ of water mixed with 1.0 m³ of alcohol is *not* 2.0 m³.) The scalar additivity of mass is established in considering two objects of identical mass: if one is subdivided into many parts, the mass of the parts, all taken together, is found to be equal to the mass of the whole. For example, the mass of a water molecule is, within experimental error, the same as the sum of the masses of two hydrogen and one oxygen atoms. Thus, scalar additivity of masses holds extremely well even in the atomic domain. It does *not*, however, hold in the nuclear domain.

7-3 The standard of mass As in the case of the fundamental units of length and of time, we must arbitrarily choose some object as a standard of mass. The standard of mass, to which ultimately all mass measurements are related, is a platinum-iridium cylinder carefully stored at the International Bureau of Weights and Measures in Paris. The mass of this cylinder is *by definition* exactly *one kilogram* (1 kg). Replicas of the standard kilogram have been made, and the one residing under double bell-jars in the U.S. Bureau of Standards is the standard of mass for the United States.

The kilogram is the unit of mass in the mks (*meter-kilogram-second*) system of units; the gram—one one-thousandth of the standard kilogram—is the unit of mass in the cgs (*centimeter-gram-second*) system of units; the *slug* is the unit of mass in the English gravitational system of units.

System of units	Mass unit
mks	kilogram
cgs	gram $= 10^{-3}$ kg
English	slug $= 14.593881$ kg

The familiar unit the pound appears as a unit of weight, *not* mass, in the English system. Therefore, we defer its definition and its relation to the slug to Section 9-6. As an indication of the size of a slug, a 160-pound man has a *mass* of about 5 slugs.

Because the masses of atoms are small, a special system of units is employed for measuring them. The basic unit is called the *atomic mass unit*, amu. By definition, the mass of an electrically neutral atom of carbon isotope 12 is exactly 12 amu.† Measurements show that 1 amu $= 1.660 \times 10^{-27}$ kg.

7-4 The law of conservation of mass Suppose that we build a completely leakproof container through which no material particles can pass,

† This definition of the amu in terms of the carbon-12 mass was adopted in 1961. It replaces the older oxygen standards. See *The Physics Teacher 1*, 11 (1963).

in or out. Whatever the nature of the contents of the container and despite any chemical or other changes that take place in its interior, the total mass of this isolated system is constant. This is the classical *law of conservation of mass*, the first of several fundamental conservation laws of physics.

Any object at a finite temperature radiates energy in the form of heat, light, or other types of electromagnetic radiation. Such radiation may also be absorbed by a body. Radiation has mass associated with it, as the special theory of relativity shows. In its modern, more general, form, the law of mass conservation can be stated as follows: the mass of an isolated system from which, or into which, no material particles *or radiation* can leak is constant.

The mass equivalent of radiation is ordinarily so very small that it can be neglected, and the classical conservation of mass law suffices. For example, a flashlight loses about 10^{-16} kg/sec in the form of radiation; the sun loses 4.2×10^9 kg/sec (out of 10^{30} kg total mass) as heat and light.

7-5 Density For a homogeneous material the mass m is proportional to the volume V of the material:

$$m = \rho V \qquad [7\text{-}1]$$

where ρ (Greek *rho*), called the *density*, is a constant which is characteristic of the particular material. The density is, therefore, the mass per unit volume of a material, and has the dimensions (M/L^3). Appropriate units for density are kilograms per cubic meter, grams per cubic centimeter, and slugs per cubic foot.

Strictly, the density of any material is always the *average* density over the chosen volume. For example, the density of a gas is meaningful only if the volume is large enough to contain a large number of molecules. On the other hand, if the chosen volume is very small, the density will fluctuate erratically. Similarly, a solid consists of atoms most of whose mass is located in the very small nucleus and, again, the density has meaning only for volumes larger than that of an atom.

Table 7-1

MATERIAL	DENSITY (kg/m³)
Interstellar space	10^{-18}
Air	1.2
Water	10^3
Lead	1.13×10^4
Any nucleus	10^{17}

The density of water at atmospheric pressure and at the temperature 3.98° Celsius, for which its density is a maximum, is close to 1.00 gm/cm³. More precisely, the density at this temperature is 0.999973 gm/cm³. At the time the metric system of units was introduced, in 1795, it was intended that the mass of one cubic centimeter of water be exactly one gram. We see that this is almost true.

Table 7-1 shows the (average) density of a few materials; the densities of some other substances are given in Table 18-2, Section 18-3.

PROBLEMS

7-1   In the heliocentric theory of our solar system, first proposed by Copernicus, the kinematics of planetary motion is simpler than, but equivalent to, the kinematics of the earlier geocentric description, in which the Earth is assumed to be at rest. In the heliocentric and geocentric systems the reference frames are, respectively, the Sun and the Earth. On what grounds is the heliocentric system preferable? (Support for the Copernican theory on physical grounds was first given by Galileo in 1632, in his *Dialogue Concerning the Two Chief World Systems.*)

7-2   A man is on a smoothly rotating platform. He observes that an air-suspended disc gently placed on the platform remains at one place over the platform when it is free of external influences. (a) Is he justified in concluding that the reference frame of the merry-go-round constitutes an inertial frame? (b) Where on the platform must the disc be? (c) Would the disc have remained at one place relative to the platform if it had been located at any other point over it?

7-3   A body consists of ten parts (by volume) of wood and one part of lead. The densities of wood and lead are, respectively, 0.50×10^3 kg/m³ and 11.3 kg/m³. What is the average density of the body?

7-4   In atomic mass units, nitrogen-14 has a mass of 14.0031. What is the mass in kilograms of an atom of nitrogen (isotope-14)?

7-5   The density of water is 1.0×10^3 kg/m³, and the molecular mass of the water molecule is 18 amu. Assuming that molecules in a liquid are in contact with one another, give the approximate size of the water molecule.

7-6   At standard temperature and pressure, the density of air is 1.2 kg/m³. Take the mass of a molecule of air to be 29 amu and assume that the diameter of a typical air molecule is 10^{-10} m. What is the average distance between air molecules?

7-7   A proton and a neutron, originally separated, collide and fuse into a nucleus called the deuteron. The masses, in atomic mass units, of the proton, neutron, and deuteron are, respectively, 1.00728, 1.00866, and 2.01355. How much mass must be released in the form of radiation when a deuteron is formed? (There is no measurable violation of the classical conservation of mass law in *chemical* reactions, but in *nuclear* reactions, such as this, the mass equivalent of radiation is measurable.)

E I G H T

LINEAR MOMENTUM AND ITS CONSERVATION

Historically and traditionally, classical mechanics begins with Newton's celebrated laws of motion. We have already discussed the first law, called the law of inertia. The concept of force plays a dominant role in the second and third laws. We shall not begin our study of mechanics with emphasis on force; instead, we shall begin with the concept of linear momentum and its conservation. There are a number of reasons for this choice: (a) linear momentum and the conservation of linear momentum emerge in a simple way from elementary experiment; (b) once the meaning and significance of momentum is clear, the concept of force and of Newton's second and third laws easily follows; (c) the conservation of momentum principle provides us with information about collisions without our knowing details of the collision, that is, without our knowing in detail the forces acting between colliding particles; and (d) momentum plays a dominant role in modern physics—in relativity physics and in quantum physics—while the concept of force is subordinate in the physics of the atom and nucleus.

8-1   Conservation of linear momentum in head-on collisions   There is only one way of finding out how bodies interact—by experiment. Here we consider a simple experiment in which one body collides head on with a second body. We suppose that we have found in advance that when set in motion on a frictionless horizontal surface, each body moves with unchanged velocity. (The bodies might be air-suspended pucks on a flat surface, or

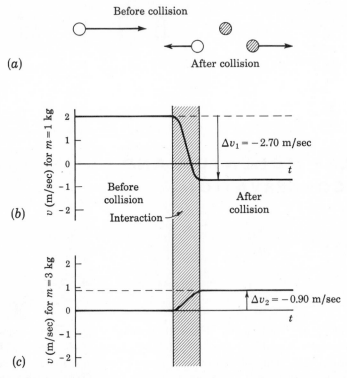

Figure 8-1. (a) Velocities of two bodies before and after a head-on collision. (b) Velocity-time graph for the 1.0 kg body. (c) Velocity-time graph for the 3.0 kg body.

small carts on a straight track.) Each of the two objects will depart from uniform velocity only to the extent that it interacts with—which is to say, collides with—the other body.

Consider the following experiment. A 1.00 kg body, initially moving at 2.00 m/sec to the right, collides with a 3.00 kg body originally at rest. The observed results are as shown in Figure 8-1a: the lighter body rebounds to the left at 0.70 m/sec and the more massive body is set in motion and moves to the right at 0.90 m/sec. The velocities of the bodies are plotted as a function of time in Figures 8-1b and c. Each body is observed to have a constant velocity before the collision and a constant (but different) velocity after the collision. The velocity changes only while the bodies interact, that is, during the time the two bodies are in contact. We see that the velocity of the 1.00 kg body changed by the amount $\Delta v_1 = -2.70$ m/sec and that the corresponding velocity change for the 3.00 kg body was $\Delta v_2 = 0.90$ m/sec (the subscripts 1 and 2 designate the 1 kg and 3 kg bodies, respectively). The velocity changes Δv_1 and Δv_2 and the masses m_1 and m_2 are found to be simply related:

$$\frac{\Delta v_1}{\Delta v_2} = \frac{-2.70\text{m/sec}}{0.90\text{ m/sec}} = -3.00$$

and

$$\frac{m_2}{m_1} = \frac{3.00\text{ kg}}{1.00\text{ kg}} = 3.00$$

or $$m_1 \Delta v_1 = -m_2 \Delta v_2$$

We can write this as

$$m_1\Delta v_1 + m_2\Delta v_2 = 0 \qquad\qquad [8\text{-}1]$$

We would, of course, wish to establish from further experiments whether the simple result expressed in Equation 8-1 holds for other head-on collisions. That is, we ask whether Equation 8-1 holds when we use bodies of different sizes, different materials, and different masses, and having various velocities. *It does.*

Equation 8-1 expresses a remarkable regularity in nature deserving the designation "Law of Physics," which operates in all two-body collisions. This law can be written more simply if we define a quantity p, known as the *linear momentum* of a body, as the *product of mass and velocity:*

$$\boxed{\text{Linear momentum} = \boldsymbol{p} = m\boldsymbol{v}} \qquad\qquad [8\text{-}2]$$

Linear momentum is a vector quantity (the product of a scalar m and a vector $\boldsymbol{v}$). Its direction is that of the body's velocity and its magnitude is the product of the body's mass and speed. See Figure 8-2. Linear momentum has the dimensions ML/T. Appropriate units for linear momentum are kilogram-meters per second (kg-m/sec), gram-centimeters per second (gm-cm/sec), and slug-feet per second (slug-ft/sec); it is to be noted that the hyphens in these indicate multiplication, as the slants indicate division. (We will later introduce the concept of *angular* momentum.)

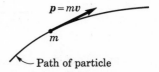

Figure 8-2. Linear momentum $\boldsymbol{p}$ of a particle of mass m and velocity $\boldsymbol{v}$.

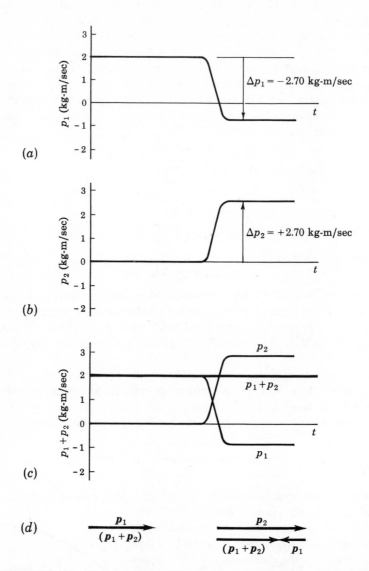

Figure 8-3. Linear-momentum–time graphs corresponding to the collision of Figure 8-1 for (a) the 1.0 kg body, (b) the 3.0 kg body, (c) the total linear momentum of the system of two bodies. (d) Linear momentum vectors before and after the collision.

We can write Equation 8-1 in terms of momentum. By definition,

$$p = mv$$
$$\Delta p = \Delta(mv) = m\Delta v$$

where it is assumed, in the last step, that the mass m remains constant. Equation 8-1 becomes

$$\Delta p_1 = -\Delta p_2$$

or $$\Delta p_1 + \Delta p_2 = 0 \qquad [8\text{-}2a]$$

Equation 8-2a says: when two bodies interact with one another in the absence of any net *external* influence, or force, the loss in the momentum of one body equals the gain in momentum of the second body. Or, stating this differently, the total change in momentum of the two bodies is zero. We can, therefore, think of a collision as a process in which momentum is transferred from one body to another, with no change in the total momentum of the system. Thus, if p_1 is the momentum of body 1 and p_2 is the momentum of body 2, the one body interacting with the other *in the absence of a net external force, the total momentum of the system,* comprised of the two interacting bodies 1 and 2, *is constant:*

$$\boxed{p_1 + p_2 = \text{constant (in direction and magnitude)}} \qquad [8\text{-}3]$$

This is the law of the *conservation of momentum.*

Let us return to our original example (Figure 8-1) and now plot graphs of momentum versus time. The momenta of the two bodies are, *before* collision,

$$p_1 = m_1v_1 = (1.00 \text{ kg})(2.00 \text{ m/sec}) = +2.00 \text{ kg-m/sec (to the right)}$$
$$p_2 = m_2v_2 = (3.00 \text{ kg})(0) = 0$$

and, *after* collision,

$$p_1 = m_1v_1 = (1.00 \text{ kg})(-0.70 \text{ m/sec}) = -0.70 \text{ kg-m/sec (to the left)}$$
$$p_2 = m_2v_2 = (3.00 \text{ kg})(0.90 \text{ m/sec}) = +2.70 \text{ kg-m/sec (to the right)}$$

Therefore,

$$\Delta p_1 = p_1 \text{ (after)} - p_1 \text{ (before)} = (-0.70 \text{ kg-m/sec}) - (2.00 \text{ kg-m/sec})$$
$$= -2.70 \text{ kg-m/sec}$$
$$\Delta p_2 = p_2 \text{ (after)} - p_2 \text{ (before)} = (2.70 \text{ kg-m/sec}) - (0)$$
$$= +2.70 \text{ kg-m/sec}$$

The momentum-time graphs for this collision are shown in Figure 8-3. We see that the 1.00 kg body loses a momentum of 2.70 kg-m/sec to the right, while the 3.00 kg body gains the same momentum to the right. Thus, a momentum of 2.70 kg-m/sec to the right was transferred from the 1.00 kg to the 3.00 kg mass, there being no change in the total momentum of the system:

$$p_1 + p_2 = 2.00 \text{ kg-m/sec to the right } before \text{ and } after \text{ collision}$$

Figure 8-3 shows, furthermore, that the total momentum is the same, not only before and after the collision, but also at each instant *during* the collision. (The recording of the rapidly changing motion throughout the

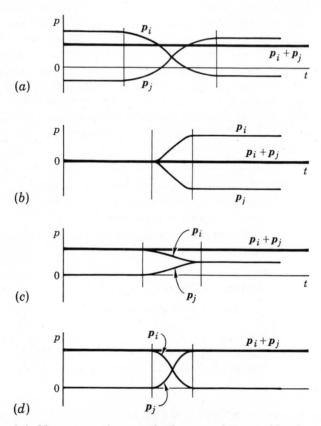

Figure 8-4. Momentum–time graphs for several types of head-on collisions. (a) Two bodies are initially in motion; their directions of motion are reversed after the collision. This collision is relatively "soft." (b) An explosive collision. (c) A body initially at rest is struck by a second body of the same mass, which sticks to the first. (d) Collision between two hard bodies of the same mass; note that the bodies interchange velocities.

very short time the bodies collide is made possible, theoretically, by the use of high-speed cameras.)

Other illustrations of the conservation of momentum law are given in Figures 8-4a, b, c, and d. We shall take these up one by one.

(a) In this collision both bodies are in motion initially, one to the right and one to the left. After the collision the directions of motion are reversed. The collision here is relatively "soft" in that the momentum transfer occurs slowly, in contrast to the relatively "hard" collision of Figure 8-3 in which the momentum changes abruptly. Whether a collision is soft or hard depends on the nature of the materials coming in contact. Colliding bodies, if composed of materials not readily deformed, typically have hard collisions; padded bodies, or bodies made of soft materials, have soft collisions.

(b) Here is an explosion, or an *explosive collision*. The two bodies are originally at rest and, by virtue of the explosion (produced, for example, by the release of an initially compressed spring between the two bodies), the bodies fly apart in opposite directions with the same magnitude of momentum. The total momentum of the system is zero—before, during, and after the explosion. Therefore, the speeds of the two bodies after the explosion are in the inverse ratio of their respective masses:

$$\boldsymbol{p_1} + \boldsymbol{p_2} = 0$$

$$m_1 \boldsymbol{v_1} + m_2 \boldsymbol{v_2} = 0$$

$$\frac{m_1}{m_2} = -\frac{v_2}{v_1} \qquad [8\text{-}4]$$

The minus sign implies that the two bodies move in opposite directions. The massive body moves with a low speed, and the light body with a high speed. For example, in the case of a fired rifle, free to recoil, the rifle's recoil speed is smaller than the bullet's speed by the ratio of bullet mass to rifle mass. If, on the other hand, a man holds the rifle firmly and fires it upward, the rifle, the man, and the Earth recoil together at an imperceptibly small speed.

We can compare, or measure, masses by an explosive collision. Equation 8-4 shows that, if the two bodies are at rest initially, the ratio of masses is simply the inverse ratio of speeds. Only when the speeds are equal do the two bodies have the same mass.

(c) In this collision a body initially at rest is struck by a moving body of the same mass. Both bodies leave the site of the collision with the *same* velocity. The two bodies are joined together as a single body. Because the amalgamated body has the same momentum, but twice the mass, as that of the originally moving body, it has one-half the speed.

(d) The collision here is exemplified by a head-on collision of two identical hard objects such as billiard balls. A moving body strikes a body at rest. After the collision the bodies have *interchanged velocities* and momenta, the originally moving body now being at rest and the body originally at rest moving forward with the initial speed of the first body.

Note that this collision and the one shown in Figure 8-4c are *identical* before the collision, but not after. Interacting bodies may leave the site of a collision in a variety of ways, conserving momentum in each instance. It is not possible, by using the conservation of momentum principle alone, to predict the individual velocities after the collision. We do know, however, that for an isolated system the total momentum out of *any* collision always equals the total momentum into the collision.†

We have used a very broad interpretation of the term "collision." It is any interaction that changes the momenta of the interacting particles. Although we commonly think of a collision as involving the contact of two bodies, this is not a requirement. We can, for example, have two strong magnets attached to two bodies in such a way that the bodies repel one another when brought together. Then, a "collision" occurs when the bodies approach one another even though the bodies never touch at all. Or, as another example, the deflection of an incoming comet by the Sun may properly be called a collision. In fact, even for the so-called contact forces, illustrated by two touching objects which resist interpenetration, there is no actual contact between the atomic particles comprising the objects.

Momentum conservation holds for two-body head-on collisions. Does it work with three or more bodies? Experiment shows that *it does*. In any two-body collision there is a momentum transfer without a change in the total momentum. So, too, when there are three or more mutually interacting bodies isolated from external influences, the total momentum P into the collision equals the total momentum out. Thus, for an isolated system,

$$P = \Sigma \, p_i = \text{constant (magnitude and direction)} \qquad [8\text{-}5]$$

There is a significant link between the law of inertia and the law of momentum conservation. When a body in an inertial frame is subject to no net external force, its velocity is constant. Because $p = mv$, the law of inertia may be stated as: *when a body is subject to no net external force, its momentum is constant.* The conservation of momentum law may be thought

---

† The collisions in (b), (c), and (d) are known as explosive, perfectly inelastic, and elastic collisions, respectively. We shall later (Section 12-4) identify an explosive collision with a gain of kinetic energy, an inelastic collision with a loss of kinetic energy, and an elastic collision with no net gain or loss of kinetic energy.

of as an extension of this law of inertia to two (or more) interacting bodies: *when a system of bodies is subject to no net external force, the total vector momentum of the system is constant.* The momenta of the individual inter-acting bodies may change, of course, but through the influence of strictly *internal* forces. For this isolated system we notice that it is not necessarily true that the total vector *velocity* of the system be constant.

Example 1   A bullet of 5.00 gm is shot horizontally into a 10.0 kg block resting on a smooth horizontal surface. The bullet comes to rest within the block, and the block slides at 25.0 cm/sec. What is the original speed of the bullet?

The conservation of momentum law requires that the momentum of the bullet before collision equal the momentum of the block (and bullet) after the collision. If m and v are the bullet's mass and initial speed, respectively, and M and V are the block's mass and final speed, respectively, then

$$mv = (M + m)V$$

$$v = (M + m)V/m = (10.0 \text{ kg} + 5.00 \times 10^{-3} \text{ kg})(0.25 \text{ m/sec})/(5.00 \times 10^{-3} \text{ kg})$$

$$v = 500 \text{ m/sec}$$

Example 2   A spring of negligible mass is compressed between two blocks A and B, which are at rest on a frictionless horizontal surface at a distance of 10.0 feet from a wall on the left and 30.0 feet from a wall on the right. The sizes of the blocks and spring are small. When the spring is released, body A moves toward the left wall and strikes it at the same instant that body B strikes the right wall. The mass of A is 0.60 slug. What is the mass of B?

The total momentum of the blocks is initially zero, and it remains zero during and after the explosion. Thus,

$$m_A v_A + m_B v_B = 0$$

$$m_B = m_A(-v_A/v_B)$$

Bodies A and B travel distances of 10.0 and 30.0 feet, respectively, in *opposite* directions in equal times. Thus, the ratio of velocities is $v_A/v_B = -10.0 \text{ m}/30.0 \text{ m} = -\frac{1}{3}$:

$$m_B = (0.60 \text{ slug})(\tfrac{1}{3}) = 0.20 \text{ slug}$$

Example 3   (a) A light ball of mass m moving at a speed v strikes a massive ball of mass M at rest. The light ball bounces back with nearly the same speed. What is the speed V of the massive ball after the collision?

Momentum conservation requires:

Momentum before collision = Momentum after collision

$$mv = MV - mv$$

$$V = 2mv/M$$

where the symbols represent the same quantities as in Example 1.

(b) Suppose, now, that the light ball sticks to the massive ball. What is the speed V' of the massive ball?

$$mv = (M + m)V' \simeq MV' \text{ since } m \ll M$$

$$V' = mv/M$$

Comparing the V' in part (b) with the V in part (a) we see that the massive ball moves only half as fast when the light ball sticks to it as it does when the light ball rebounds. If the light ball were to miss the massive ball, it would transfer zero momentum. When the light ball sticks to the massive ball it transfers momentum mv, and when it rebounds it transfers momentum $2mv$.

Example 4 The rocket is an important illustration of momentum conservation, and the basic physics of rocket behavior can be understood completely in terms of this principle.

In the rocket, particles of mass Δm (the exhaust-gas molecules) are ejected from the back end, each particle being ejected with a velocity v_e, the exhaust velocity. It is important to recognize that the particles are always ejected with the *same velocity, v_e, relative to the rocket.* The velocity of the ejected particles relative, for example, to the ground, is *not* the same for all particles because of the changing speed of the rocket with respect to the ground.

Let us suppose that the initial mass of the rocket (and its fuel) is m_0 and that the rocket is initially at rest. The rocket-fuel system is subject to no net external force (we assume that the rocket is out in space), and momentum conservation requires that the entire system's momentum remain zero. The mass Δm of each ejected particle is assumed to be very small compared with the remaining mass of the rocket. After the first particle has been ejected, the rocket has gained a speed Δv. Having lost a mass Δm, the rocket mass is now $m_0 - \Delta m$ and its momentum is $(m_0 - \Delta m)\Delta v$. The momentum of the ejected particle is $\Delta m v_e$ in the opposite direction.

By the conservation of momentum principle,

$$(m_0 - \Delta m)\Delta v = (\Delta m)v_e$$

Because Δm is very small compared with m_0, we may discard the Δm from the left side without any appreciable error, and we have

$$m_0 \Delta v = (\Delta m)v_e \qquad [8\text{-}6]$$

The rocket's mass is reduced by the factor $\Delta m/m_0$, and its speed increased by $\Delta v/v_e$.

The remaining mass of the rocket can be written

$$m_0 - \Delta m = m_0 \left(1 - \frac{\Delta m}{m_0}\right)$$

Thus, the rocket's final mass is related to its original mass by the factor $1 - \Delta m/m_0$. The rocket's speed is Δv relative to the reference frame with respect to which it was initially at rest.

Now suppose that we view the rocket from another reference frame, the one in which the rocket is at rest after ejecting the first particle. Then, when the second particle of mass Δm is ejected, its speed (relative to our new reference frame) is again v_e. Therefore, Equation 8-6 applies, as before, and the rocket again gains a speed in the forward direction of Δv. Relative to our initial reference frame, the speed of the rocket is now $2\Delta v$. This follows because the *change* in velocity, Δv, is the same, whether viewed from the second inertial frame or the first inertial frame. Furthermore, the mass of the rocket has been reduced once again by the factor $1 - \Delta m/m_0$ so that the remaining mass of the rocket is $m_0[1 - (\Delta m/m_0)][1 - (\Delta m/m_0)] = m_0[1 - (\Delta m/m_0)]^2$. See Figure 8-5.

We can continue this procedure, always choosing a reference frame in which the rocket is at rest and applying Equation 8-6. We find then that, after n particles have been ejected, the rocket has achieved a speed, relative to the reference frame in which it was initially at rest, of $n\Delta v$, and it has a residual mass m given by

$$m = m_0\left(1 - \frac{\Delta m}{m_0}\right)^n \qquad [8\text{-}7]$$

Designating the rocket's final speed $n\Delta v$ as v, Equation 8-6 can be written

$$\frac{\Delta m}{m_0} = \frac{\Delta v}{v_e} = \frac{1}{n}\left(\frac{v}{v_e}\right)$$

and Equation 8-7 becomes

$$m = m_0 \lim_{n \to \infty} \left(1 - \frac{(v/v_e)}{n}\right)^n \qquad [8\text{-}8]$$

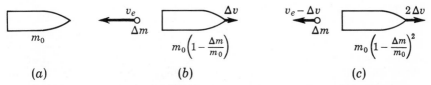

$$m_0 \qquad m_0\left(1 - \frac{\Delta m}{m_0}\right) \qquad m_0\left(1 - \frac{\Delta m}{m_0}\right)^2$$

(a) $\qquad\qquad\qquad (b)$ $\qquad\qquad\qquad (c)$

Figure 8-5. Emission of particles by a rocket. (a) The rocket initially at rest. (b) The rocket after a particle of mass Δm has been ejected to the left with the speed v_e, and the residual rocket moves to the right with the speed Δv, as viewed from the inertial frame of part (a). (c) The rocket after the second particle has been ejected, again as viewed from the initial inertial frame.

We have taken the limit as the number of particles n becomes infinite and the mass of each approaches zero. This corresponds to the continuous emission of molecules in an actual rocket.

By definition,

$$e^{-x} = \lim_{n \to \infty} \left[1 - \frac{x}{n}\right]^n \qquad [8\text{-}9]$$

Here e is the base of the natural logarithms: $e = 2.78 \ldots$.

Comparing Equations 8-8 and 8-9 we see that

$$m = m_0 e^{-v/v_e} \qquad [8\text{-}10]$$

We can arrive at this result differently, using integral calculus. Equation 8-6 is written

$$m\,dv = v_e\,dm$$

$$\int_0^v dv = v_e \int_{m_0}^m \frac{dm}{m} \qquad [8\text{-}11]$$

$$v = v_e \ln\,(m/m_0)$$

[8-10] $\qquad\qquad\qquad m = m_0 e^{-v/v_e}$

Note the assumptions implicit in this calculus derivation. Equation 8-6 applies at each instant of time because the residual rocket is regarded as being at rest instantaneously in an inertial frame, and the law of conservation of momentum holds for any inertial frame. Further, in Equation 8-11 the exhaust velocity v_e can be brought in front of the integral sign because all particles leave with the same speed relative to the instantaneous inertial frame of the rocket. Figure 8-6 is a graph of Equation 8-10.

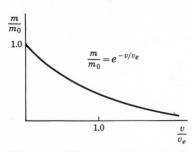

Figure 8-6. The ratio of the residual to the initial rocket mass (m/m_0) as a function of final residual rocket speed v divided by the exhaust velocity v_e. The mass decays exponentially with v.

In a typical rocket fuel the exhaust molecules have speeds of about 2 km/sec relative to the rocket. If the residual rocket is to achieve a speed $v = 8$ km/sec (the speed of a satellite in orbit close to the Earth), $v/v_e = 4$. Equation 8-10 shows that the corresponding mass ratio $m/m_0 = 0.0022$, or $m_0 = 45m$. The initial mass of the rocket is 45 times that of the payload. Moreover, the last particle ejected by such a rocket has a speed, relative to the reference frame in which the rocket was first at rest, of $4v_e - v_e = 3v_e = 6$ km/sec in the *same direction* as that of the rocket's motion. We leave it as an exercise for the reader to prove that if all the fuel is exhausted at a single instant, rather than continuously, then, to attain a payload velocity $v = 4v_e$ the payload must be much larger—*one fifth* of the initial mass of the rocket and fuel!

8-2 Conservation of linear momentum in two and three dimensions

Experiment emphatically shows that, in head-on collisions, for which the interacting bodies move along a single straight line, momentum is conserved. Is momentum conserved in two or three dimensions? Again, *the answer of experiment is "yes."*

Consider the non-head-on collision of two bodies shown in the simulated multiflash photograph of Figure 8-7. The bodies could be air-suspended discs coasting, before and after their interaction, on a smooth horizontal surface. When we compare the total vector linear momentum of the system before the collision with the total momentum after the collision, we find that they are identical. By the "total" momentum is meant, of course, the *vector* sum of the momenta of the parts of the system. Therefore, linear momentum is indeed a vector quantity, not only because it has magnitude and direction but also because it obeys the laws of vectors. Therefore, the relation (Equation 8-5) $P = \Sigma p_i =$ constant, in the absence of a net external force, applies also to collisions in two and three dimensions.

Since linear momentum is a vector, the algebraic sum of the components of the momenta of all particles along *any direction* in space is constant before, during, and after interaction, provided only that the system is free of external influence.

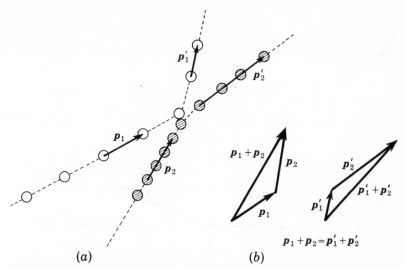

Figure 8-7. (a) Simulated multiflash photograph of a collision in two dimensions. The vectors show the linear momenta of the particles before and after the collision. (b) The total vector linear momentum before the collision equals the total vector linear momentum after the collision.

Example 5   A package originally at rest explodes into three parts A, B, and C. Parts A and B have equal masses; C's mass is twice that of A or B. Part A flies west at 80 m/sec and part B flies south at 60 m/sec. What are (a) the speed v_C and (b) the direction θ, with respect to east, of part C after the explosion?

The total momentum of the system is initially zero, and it remains zero during and after the explosion. Therefore,

$$0 = \boldsymbol{p}_A + \boldsymbol{p}_B + \boldsymbol{p}_C$$

and the momentum vectors are arranged as shown in Figure 8-8.

After the collision the components of momentum must add up to zero algebraically along the east-west direction, along the north-south direction, and along the direction perpendicular to the plane of the paper. Therefore, the component of C's momentum to the east must equal (in magnitude) A's momentum west, and the component of C's momentum north must equal B's momentum south. Moreover, C's component of momentum perpendicular to the paper must be zero; thus C travels in the plane of A and B:

$$p_C \cos \theta = p_A$$

$$p_C \sin \theta = p_B$$

Dividing the second equation by the first yields

$$\tan \theta = \frac{p_B}{p_A} = \frac{M(60 \text{ m/sec})}{M(80 \text{ m/sec})} = 0.75$$

$$\theta = 37° \text{ north of east}$$

The first equation yields

$$p_C \cos \theta = p_A$$

$$2Mv_C \cos 37° = M(80 \text{ m/sec})$$

$$v_C = 50 \text{ m/sec}$$

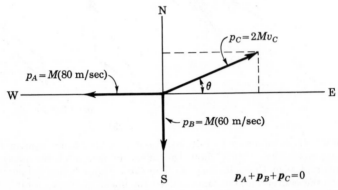

Figure 8-8. A package explodes into three parts with momenta $\boldsymbol{p}_A$, $\boldsymbol{p}_B$, and $\boldsymbol{p}_C$, respectively.

Example 6 A 1.0 kg body A with a velocity of 4.0 m/sec to the right strikes a second body B of 3.0 kg originally at rest. Body A is deflected in the collision from its original direction through an angle of 50°; its speed after the collision is 2.0 m/sec. What is (a) the angle θ of B's velocity after the collision with respect to the original direction of A, and (b) the speed v_B' of B after the collision?

The system is subject to no net external force and the conservation of momentum requires that

$$\boldsymbol{p}_A = \boldsymbol{p}_A' + \boldsymbol{p}_B' \tag{8-12}$$

as shown in Figure 8-9, where $\boldsymbol{p}_A$ and $\boldsymbol{p}_A'$ are the momenta of A before and after the collision, respectively, and $\boldsymbol{p}_B'$ is the momentum of B after the collision. The total vector momentum is constant throughout the collision. Therefore, the algebraic sum of the components of A's and B's momenta along any given direction is also constant. We first choose the original direction of A as the direction for computing momentum components:

$$p_A = p_A' \cos 50° + p_B' \cos \theta \tag{8-13}$$

$$(1.0 \text{ kg})(4.0 \text{ m/sec}) = (1.0 \text{ kg})(2.0 \text{ m/sec}) \cos 50° + (3.0 \text{ kg})(v_B') \cos \theta$$

Equation 8-13 implies that the total linear momentum is unchanged along the forward direction, body B acquiring a momentum component along this direction which is just equal to the component of momentum lost by A.

Now consider the components of momentum along a direction perpendicular to that of A's original motion:

$$0 = p_A' \sin 50° - p_B' \sin \theta \qquad [8\text{-}14]$$

$$0 = (1.0 \text{ kg})(2.0 \text{ m/sec}) \sin 50° - (3.0 \text{ kg})(v_B') \sin \theta$$

Before the collision there is no component of momentum along this direction; after the collision the transverse momentum component of A is just balanced by that of B. The scalar Equations 8-13 and 8-14 are equivalent to the single vector Equation 8-12. (There is no component of momentum, before or after the collision, in a direction perpendicular to the plane of vectors p_A' and p_B'.)

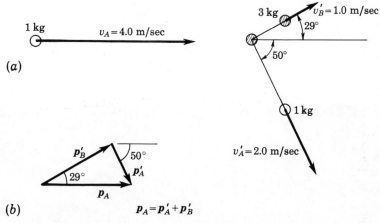

Figure 8-9. (a) The velocity vectors for a non-head-on collision. (b) The momentum vectors for this collision.

We have two equations, 8-13 and 8-14, and two unknowns, v_B' and θ. We can eliminate v_B' from the two equations by solving for v_B' in 8-14 and substituting in 8-13. The result, after a little algebra, is

$$\theta = 29°$$

Using $\theta = 29°$ in Equation 8-13 or 8-14 gives

$$v_B' = 1.0 \text{ m/sec}$$

8-3 The conservation of momentum in atomic collisions Momentum conservation applies to collisions of molecules, atoms, and their constituent particles. By applying the conservation of momentum principle to such collisions much information concerning atomic or subatomic particles can be extracted.

An atomic collision is shown in Figure 8-10a. The actual tracks of electrically charged particles are rendered visible and can be photographed when these charged particles pass through the supersaturated vapor of a cloud chamber or the superheated liquid of a bubble chamber. In the first instance, liquid droplets are formed along the wake of the charged particle's path; in the latter case, bubbles form along the wake. Inasmuch as the colliding

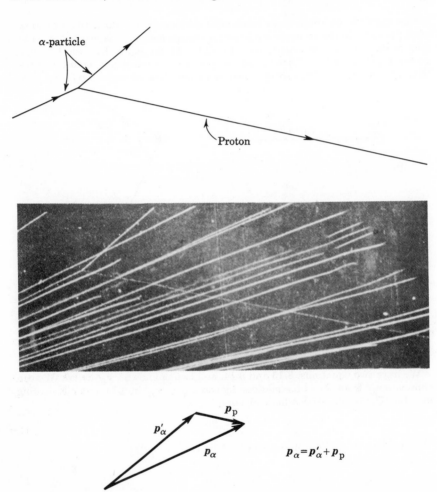

Figure 8-10. Cloud-chamber photograph showing an α-particle (helium nucleus) colliding with a proton initially at rest. Linear momentum is conserved in the collision. (From *An Atlas of Typical Expansion Chamber Photographs*, W. Gentner, H. Maier–Leibnitz, and W. Bothe, Pergamon Press, Ltd., 1954. Courtesy of Pergamon Press, Ltd.)

particles are free of external forces, the momentum going into the atomic collision is exactly equal to the momentum coming out of the collision.

Atomic collisions differ from the collisions of ordinary-sized objects in one important respect: some of the particles involved in atomic collisions may be moving with speeds comparable (or equal) to that of light, $c = 3 \times 10^8$ m/sec. The conservation of momentum law holds for collisions in which such very-high-speed particles participate; however, the relation between linear momentum, mass, and velocity is not that given by classical mechanics (Equation 8-2). The correct formula for the linear momentum of a particle moving at, or nearly at, the speed of light is obtained from the special theory of relativity (see Section 9-7 and Equation 9-19).

Material particles, such as electrons, protons, and neutrons, all have linear momentum. Furthermore, electromagnetic radiation, illustrated by radio waves, visible light, and x-rays, carries linear momentum. (Light exerts a pressure on objects it strikes.) The quantum theory of modern physics shows such radiation has particle-like aspects, the particles of electromagnetic radiation being called "photons." Each photon carries momentum, and the collision between a photon and a material particle is also governed by the conservation of momentum principle.

A number of atomic collisions are shown in Figure 8-11 on pages 142, 143, and 144.

Figure 8-11. Bubble-chamber photographs illustrating linear-momentum conservation. In each photograph a π^--meson, an elementary particle nearly 300 times more massive than an electron, enters from the left and collides with a proton initially at rest. (a) The proton is set in motion obliquely upward as the π^--meson is deflected downward. (b) The π^--meson is now scattered backward, while the proton acquires momentum in the forward direction whose magnitude *exceeds* the momentum magnitude of the incident π^--meson. The resultant linear momentum is unchanged in the collision. (c) Here is a series of events initiated by the π^--meson entering from the left. ① The meson combines with the proton it strikes to produce a K^0-meson and lambda particle. These particles, being electrically neutral, produce no tracks. ② The K^0-meson decays in flight (explodes) into a positive and negative π-meson. ③ The Λ^0 particle decays in flight into a π^--meson and proton. The tracks of the electrically charged particles are curved because the particles pass through a magnetic field, the radius of curvature of each particle track being directly proportional to the magnitude of the particle's linear momentum. As the vector diagrams show, the total linear momentum of the four emerging particles is equal to that of the single incident particle. (Photographs (a) and (b) courtesy of Professor R. J. Plano, Rutgers University; photograph (c) courtesy of Professor L. W. Alvarez, University of California, Lawrence Radiation Laboratory.)

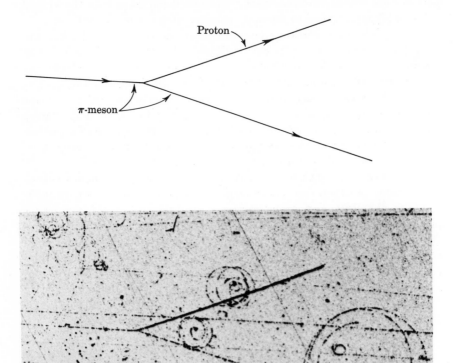

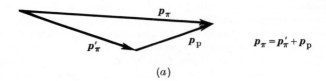

$$p_\pi = p'_\pi + p_p$$

(a)

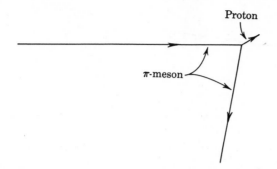

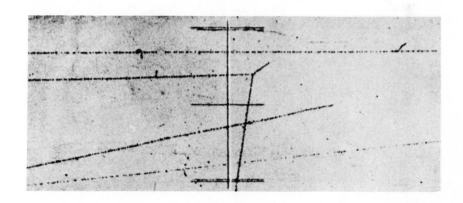

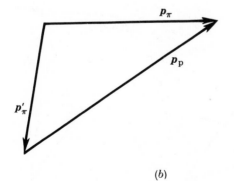

$$p_\pi = p_\pi' + p_p$$

(b)

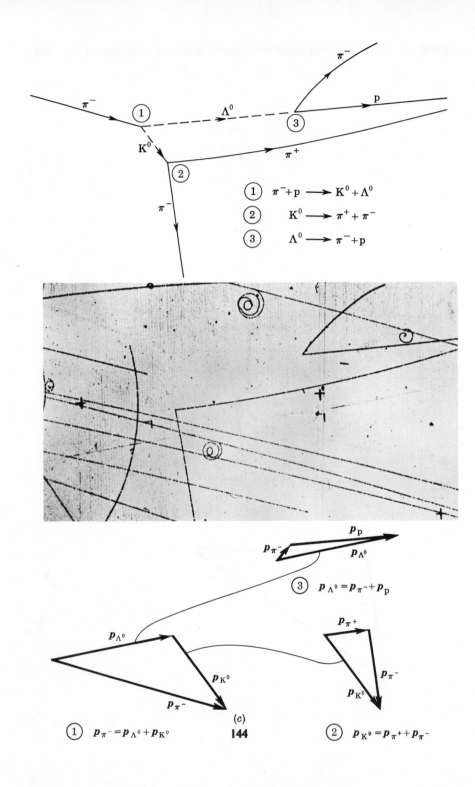

8-4 Center of mass The concept of center of mass is of fundamental importance in mechanics because it permits us to treat otherwise complicated problems with remarkable simplicity.

Suppose that we have two air-suspended discs on a smooth horizontal surface joined by a massless rod, as described in our discussion of inertial mass in Section 7-2. We know that if the discs have different masses and the rod is accelerated at a point midway between the ends, the disc with the larger mass will show the larger inertia, lagging behind the lighter mass if the rod is set into motion or leading the lighter mass if the rod is decelerated and brought to rest. Only if the two masses are exactly equal will the rod show no rotation upon being accelerated.

We now inquire into a closely related situation. Here we imagine that two discs of different masses are attached to the ends of the rod but that the rod is *not* accelerated at the *midpoint*. Instead, we suppose that we are to find that point—between the two discs—called the *center of mass*, at which the rod may be accelerated without producing a turning of the rod. Our intuition tells us that the center of mass, so defined, should be closer to the more massive body than to the lighter body. Experiment confirms this.

More specifically, if a body of mass m_1 has a displacement X_1 and a second body of mass m_2 has a displacement X_2, both displacements being

Figure 8-12. The center of mass is a distance X_1 from m_1, and X_2 from m_2.

measured from the center of mass, as shown in Figure 8-12, the ratio of distances is found to be inversely proportional to the ratio of masses:

$$-X_1/X_2 = m_1/m_2 \qquad [8\text{-}15]$$

The minus sign appears in Equation 8-15 because the displacements X_1 and X_2 have different signs; one is to the right, the other to the left. Thus, if masses of 1 kg and 3 kg are placed at the ends of a rod 80 cm long, $m_1/m_2 = \frac{1}{3}$ and $X_1/X_2 = -3$. The center of mass of this two-body system is 20 cm from the 3 kg mass and 60 cm from the 1 kg mass. Our intuition also suggests that if such a rod were held up and supported under the location of the center of mass, the rod would balance. This is true (Section 16-7).

Equation 8-15 can be written in the form

$$m_1X_1 + m_2X_2 = 0 \qquad [8\text{-}16]$$

This equation applies only if the origin of the coordinates X_1 and X_2 is at the center of mass. Let us now choose a more general coordinate origin, not necessarily coincident with the center of mass. Relative to the new origin, the displacements of m_1 and m_2 are labeled x_1 and x_2, respectively, and the coordinate of the center of mass $\bar{x}$, as shown in Figure 8-13. Consequently,

$$X_1 = x_1 - \bar{x}$$
$$X_2 = x_2 - \bar{x} \qquad \text{[8-17]}$$

Substituting Equations 8-17 into 8-16, we have

$$m_1(x_1 - \bar{x}) + m_2(x_2 - \bar{x}) = 0$$

$$m_1 x_1 + m_2 x_2 = (m_1 + m_2)\bar{x}$$

$$\bar{x} = \frac{m_1 x_1 + m_2 x_2}{m_1 + m_2} \qquad \text{[8-18]}$$

Equation 8-18 gives the coordinate $\bar{x}$ of the center of mass in terms of the coordinates x_1 and x_2 of m_1 and m_2.

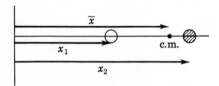

For example, if $m_1 = 1\,\text{kg}$, $x_1 = 100\,\text{cm}$, $m_2 = 3\,\text{kg}$, and $x_2 = 180\,\text{cm}$ (our earlier example with a different coordinate origin), Equation 8-18 gives $\bar{x} = 160\,\text{cm}$, and the center of mass has the same location, *relative to the bodies*, as before (20 cm from the 3 kg mass, 60 cm from the 1 kg). If the origin is chosen to be

Figure 8-13. The center of mass of the particles shown in Figure 8-12, now referred to a different origin.

at the center of mass, $\bar{x} = 0$, then Equation 8-18 reduces, as it must, into Equation 8-16.

We have defined the center of mass for a system composed of only two mass points located on the X-axis. It is easy to extend this definition to a collection of mass points distributed throughout space. The X-, Y-, and Z-components of the center of mass are given by the general relations:

$$\bar{x} = \frac{m_1 x_1 + m_2 x_2 + m_3 x_3 + \cdots}{m_1 + m_2 + m_3 + \cdots} = \frac{\Sigma\, m_i x_i}{\Sigma\, m_i}$$

$$\bar{y} = \frac{m_1 y_1 + m_2 y_2 + m_3 y_3 + \cdots}{m_1 + m_2 + m_3 + \cdots} = \frac{\Sigma\, m_i y_i}{\Sigma\, m_i} \qquad \text{[8-19]}$$

$$\bar{z} = \frac{m_1 z_1 + m_2 z_2 + m_3 z_3 + \cdots}{m_1 + m_2 + m_3 + \cdots} = \frac{\Sigma\, m_i z_i}{\Sigma\, m_i}$$

To find, for example, the X-coordinate $\bar{x}$, of the center of mass, we take the sum, indicated by the Greek capital sigma, Σ, of each mass m_i multiplied by its coordinate x_i and we divide this sum by the sum of the masses of all particles, $\Sigma\, m_i$, which is just the entire mass of the system.

The three scalar equations of Equation 8-19 may be expressed by a single vector equation,

$$\bar{r} = \frac{\Sigma\, m_i r_i}{\Sigma\, m_i} \qquad [8\text{-}20]$$

where the vector displacement of the center of mass $\bar{r}$ has the components $\bar{x}$, $\bar{y}$, and $\bar{z}$, and the position of any mass m_i is given by the displacement r_i with the rectangular components x_i, y_i, and z_i.

The location of the center of mass, as given by Equations 8-19 or Equation 8-20, is confirmed by experiment. For, if the point masses are connected by massless rods and the resultant rigid system is accelerated from rest in any direction from the center of mass, the whole system accelerates without rotating. On the other hand, accelerating the system along a line *not* passing through the center of mass produces a rotation.

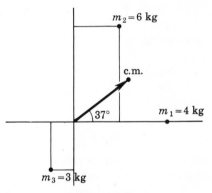

Example 7 Find the location of the center of mass of three particles with the following masses and coordinates (Figure 8-14):

Figure 8-14.

$$m_1 = 4.0 \text{ kg} \qquad x_1 = 4.0 \text{ m} \qquad y_1 = 0$$
$$m_2 = 6.0 \text{ kg} \qquad x_2 = 2.0 \text{ m} \qquad y_2 = 4.0 \text{ m}$$
$$m_3 = 3.0 \text{ kg} \qquad x_3 = -1.0 \text{ m} \qquad y_3 = -2.0 \text{ m}$$

Equation 8-19 gives

$$\bar{x} = \frac{m_1 x_1 + m_2 x_2 + m_3 x_3}{m_1 + m_2 + m_3} = \frac{(4.0)(4.0) + (6.0)(2.0) + (3.0)(-1.0)}{4.0 + 6.0 + 3.0} \text{ m} = +1.9 \text{ m}$$

$$\bar{y} = \frac{m_1 y_1 + m_2 y_2 + m_3 y_3}{m_1 + m_2 + m_3} = \frac{(4.0)(0) + (6.0)(4.0) + (3.0)(-2.0)}{4.0 + 6.0 + 3.0} \text{ m} = +1.4 \text{ m}$$

The vector displacement of the center of mass relative to the origin has the magnitude and direction

$$\bar{r} = \sqrt{\bar{x}^2 + \bar{y}^2} = \sqrt{(1.9)^2 + (1.4)^2} \text{ m} = 3.4 \text{ m}$$
$$\tan \theta = \bar{y}/\bar{x} = 1.4 \text{ m}/1.9 \text{ m}$$
$$\theta = 37°$$

It can *not* be assumed that the three masses are necessarily at rest, or connected by rods to form a rigid system. The particles may be moving relative to one another, and the center of mass itself may be in motion relative to the particles.

A perfectly rigid body is defined as a collection of particles whose relative positions remain fixed with respect to one another. The center of mass of a rigid body is then fixed relative to the system and moves with the rigid body. To compute the position of the center of mass of a solid body, such as a rectangular plate of uniform density, one could theoretically add up the contributions, $\Sigma\, m_i x_i$ and $\Sigma\, m_i$, of all of the atomic particles comprising the system. This would be extraordinarily difficult, if not impossible.

Such a computation is also unnecessary, for we can properly assume that, if the body's size is large compared with the distance between atoms (typically 10^{-10} m), then the actual structure of discrete particles is equivalent to a continuous medium having a constant density. The summation $\Sigma\, m_i x_i$ over the many discrete particles may be replaced by the readily calculable integral $\int x\, dm$, where dm is the mass of a small element at the coordinate x. The X-coordinate for the center of mass is then given by

$$\bar{x} = \frac{\int x\, dm}{\int dm} \qquad [8\text{-}21]$$

where the integration is taken over the entire mass of the body. Analogous expressions give $\bar{y}$ and $\bar{z}$.

The mass element dm has a volume dV, and $dm = \rho\, dV$, where the density ρ is the mass per unit volume. If the density is constant throughout the body, Equation 8-21 can be written

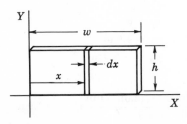

$$\bar{x} = \frac{\int x\, dV}{\int dV} \qquad [8\text{-}22]$$

and again there are analogous expressions for $\bar{y}$ and $\bar{z}$.

Figure 8-15. Center of mass of a rectangular plate. An element of mass is contained in the vertical strip of displacement x and thickness dx.

Example 8 Find the center of mass of a uniform rectangular plate.

We make the width w, the height h, and the thickness t. The origin of coordinates is chosen to be at a corner of a rectangle, as shown in Figure 8-15. To determine the X-component of the center of mass, we imagine the rectangle to be divided into thin vertical sections, each of width dx. All mass points within any one section have the same X-coordinate

x. We then add up the contributions from the vertical sections from $x = 0$ to $x = w$. The volume element is $dV = ht\,dx$, and Equation 8-22 gives

$$\bar{x} = \frac{\int x\,dV}{\int dV} = \frac{\int_0^w x(ht\,dx)}{htw} = \frac{\int_0^w x\,dx}{w} = \frac{w^2/2}{w}$$

$$\bar{x} = \frac{w}{2}$$

The center of mass is halfway between the ends. In similar fashion, we find that the center of mass is halfway up. In short, the center of mass is the center of symmetry of the rectangle.

The center of mass of any uniform symmetrical solid is at the center, or on the line, of symmetry—that is, at the center of a sphere, or spherical shell, or ring, or along the axis of symmetry of a cylinder or a cone. In every instance, if the origin of coordinates is at the center, or line, of symmetry, for each contribution $m_i x_i$ from one side there is a contribution $-m_i x_i$ from the opposite side, yielding, therefore, the center of mass at the center of symmetry, $\bar{x} = 0$.

8-5 The center of mass and collisions The center of mass of any system of particles takes on important significance when the system as a whole is subject to no net external influence, for then the total momentum of the system is constant.

Consider the collision in Figure 8-16 (the same as that shown in Figure 8-9). Here a 3 kg mass initially at rest is struck by a 1 kg mass moving to the right. The center of mass of the two bodies lies on a line connecting them. Before the collision, the center of mass is 3 times farther from the 1 kg mass than from the 3 kg mass. The center of mass moves to the right at constant speed to maintain this 3-to-1 separation ratio. After the collision, the two bodies leave in oblique directions. But the center of mass must still be so located as to maintain the 3-to-1 dis-

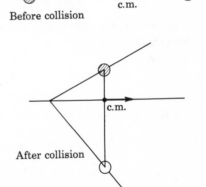

Figure 8-16. Motion of the center of mass at constant velocity in a collision. This is the collision shown also in Figure 8-9.

tance ratio to the two masses, and it continues moving to the right with the same speed and direction it had before the collision! The motion of the center of mass of a system isolated from external influences is remarkably simple: it is motion at constant velocity. Let us prove this.

The displacement $\bar{r}$ gives the location of the center of mass relative to some coordinate system fixed in the laboratory; it is related to the co-ordinates $r_1, r_2, r_3, \ldots$ of the particles in the system by Equation 8-20, which we may write

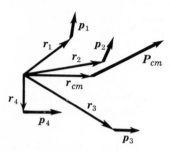

$$(m_1 + m_2 + m_3 + \cdots)\bar{r} = m_1 r_1 \\ + m_2 r_2 + m_3 r_3 + \cdots \quad [8\text{-}23]$$

If the particles of the system are in motion, $r_1, r_2, r_3, \ldots$, and $\bar{r}$ will, in general, change with time. We take the time rate, or derivative with respect to time, of both sides of Equation 8-23, using $\boldsymbol{v}_{cm} = d\bar{r}/dt$ to represent the velocity of the center of mass, and $\boldsymbol{v}_1 = dr_1/dt$, etc., to represent the velocities,

Figure 8-17. Momenta of the particles of a system, together with the momentum of the system's center of mass.

relative to the laboratory, of the several particles of the system. See Figure 8-17. The total mass of the system is M,

where $$M = m_1 + m_2 + m_3 + \cdots = \Sigma\, m_i$$

Then Equation 8-23 becomes

$$M\boldsymbol{v}_{cm} = m_1 \boldsymbol{v}_1 + m_2 \boldsymbol{v}_2 + m_3 \boldsymbol{v}_3 + \cdots \qquad [8\text{-}24]$$

This equation is still simpler when we write it in terms of linear momentum, defining $M\boldsymbol{v}_{cm}$ as $\boldsymbol{P}_{cm}$:

$$\boxed{\boldsymbol{P}_{cm} = \boldsymbol{p}_1 + \boldsymbol{p}_2 + \boldsymbol{p}_3 + \cdots} \qquad [8\text{-}25]$$

But the total momentum of the system $\boldsymbol{P}$ is the sum of the momenta of the parts:

$$\boldsymbol{P} = \boldsymbol{p}_1 + \boldsymbol{p}_2 + \boldsymbol{p}_3 + \cdots \qquad [8\text{-}26]$$

Combining Equations 8-25 and 8-26 yields

$$\boldsymbol{P}_{cm} = \boldsymbol{P} \qquad [8\text{-}27]$$

The momentum of a hypothetical particle, having a mass equal to that of the whole system and traveling so as to remain at the center of mass, is equal to the total vector linear momentum of a system of interacting particles subject to no net external influence. The total momentum of an isolated system may be replaced by the momentum of a single particle.

Note the power of this proof. We may be completely ignorant of the forces between the particles of a system—of whether they are due to springs, magnets, electric charges, gravity, or any other cause—and the motion of individual particles may be very complicated. Yet, if the system as a whole is isolated, we know that the center of mass remains at rest if initially at rest or, if initially in motion, that it travels in a straight line at constant speed. For example, we know that a block of material is composed of an enormous number of electrons and nuclei, all moving in various directions with various speeds. These particles continuously interact with one another, transferring momenta; yet, even though the momentum of any one particle is rapidly changing, the total momentum of the entire block remains constant if it is free of external influence. It is for this reason that we can treat a very complicated collection of particles as if it were a single particle at the center of a mass.

Now consider a situation in which the total momentum of a system is zero. Then $P_{cm} = Mv_{cm} = 0$, and the center of mass is always at rest, with $v_{cm} = 0$. This is illustrated in Figure 8-18. Before the collision the two particles approach the center of mass in opposite directions; the vector sum of their momenta is zero. After the collision the two particles leave the center of mass, which is the site of the collision, in opposite directions; again the total momentum is zero.

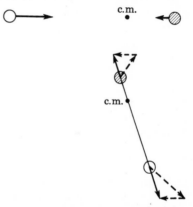

In the collision given in Figure 8-16 the center of mass is in motion; in Figure 8-18 the center of mass is at rest. These motions are, in fact, the *same* motion, but viewed from two different frames of reference: the first from a reference frame at rest in the laboratory, and the second from a *center of mass reference frame* which is

Figure 8-18. A collision as viewed from a reference frame in which the center of mass is at rest. The total momentum of the system is zero.

moving to the right relative to the laboratory. The center of mass reference frame is, by definition, that frame in which the center of mass is at rest. Figure 8-18 shows that each velocity in the center of mass frame is the vector sum of two contributions: (a) the velocity of the particle relative to the laboratory and (b) the velocity of the laboratory frame relative to the center of mass frame (which is, of course, merely the negative of the velocity of the center of mass relative to the laboratory frame).

It is interesting to examine momentum-time graphs for the laboratory and center of mass reference frames, as shown in Figure 8-19. The X- and Y-components of the momenta are shown separately. The X-components of the momenta of the two particles are different in the two reference frames. In fact, one can say that the way in which the two reference frames differ is simply in the choice of the zero of momentum. Only in the center of mass reference frame is the total momentum of the system zero. Because the center of mass moves along the X-axis, the Y-components of the momentum of the two particles are the same for the laboratory and the center of mass reference frames.

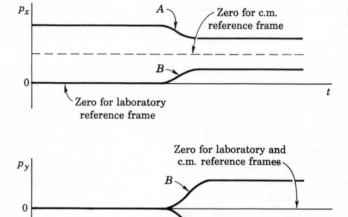

Figure 8-19. Momentum-time graph for the X- and Y-components of the collision shown in Figure 8-18. Note that the momenta for the laboratory and center of mass reference frames differ only in the zero for momentum.

8-6 Summary According to the law of inertia, the linear momentum $p = mv$ of a single particle free of external influence is constant. According to the law of linear-momentum conservation, the total momentum $\Sigma\, p_i$ of a system of interacting particles free of external influence is constant.

The total linear momentum $\Sigma\, p_i$ of a system is equal to P_{cm}, the linear momentum of the system's center of mass, where

[8-25] $$\Sigma\, p_i = P_{cm} = Mv_{cm}$$

M is the total mass of the system, and v_{cm} is the velocity of the system's center of mass. The location of the center of mass is given by

[8-20]
$$\bar{r} = \frac{\Sigma \, m_i r_i}{\Sigma \, m_i}$$

For any isolated system of particles, having masses that range from those of subatomic particles to those of astronomical bodies, moving at speeds of from zero to the speed of light, interacting with one another by any type of interaction (electric, gravitational, nuclear), observed from the point of view of an observer in the laboratory or of one moving with the center of mass, or from any other inertial frame—*momentum is conserved.*

PROBLEMS

8-1 A body of mass m is dropped from rest near the Earth's surface. Write an expression giving the body's linear momentum as a function of the time t.

8-2 A body of 2.0 kg undergoes simple harmonic motion with an amplitude of 0.040 m and a frequency of 10 cycles/sec. The body is at the amplitude position at time $t = 0$. Write an expression giving the linear momentum of the body as a function of time.

8-3 A 1.0 kg rifle, at rest on a smooth surface, fires a 3.5 gm bullet at a muzzle speed of 500 m/sec. What is the recoil speed of the rifle?

8-4 A 1.2 kg mass sliding on a horizontal frictionless surface to the right at 2.0 m/sec collides head on with a 3.6 kg mass moving to the right at 1.0 m/sec. After the collision the 3.6 kg mass moves to the right at 1.5 m/sec. What is the final velocity of the 1.2 kg mass?

8-5 To measure the mass of a certain object, the object and a 1.00 kg mass are held at rest on a frictionless surface with a light spring under compression between the two objects. The system is then released and it is found that the 1.00 kg mass moves away from the "explosion" with a speed of 3.20 m/sec and the unknown mass moves away with a speed of 1.70 m/sec. What is the mass of the object?

8-6 A 5.0 gm bullet moving horizontally at 300 m/sec strikes a 500 gm steel block initially at rest. Following the collision the bullet moves in the opposite direction at speed 290 m/sec. Sketch momentum-time graphs for the bullet and the block and give the final speed of the block.

8-7 A 5.0 gm bullet moving horizontally at 300 m/sec passes through a 500 gm block of wood initially at rest on a frictionless surface. The bullet emerges with a speed of 100 m/sec. Sketch momentum-time graphs for the bullet and the block, and calculate the final speed of the block.

8-8 Show on a momentum-time graph that if two impenetrable bodies collide head on and leave the collision with different velocities, then their momentum-time curves must cross.

8-9 A 5.0-slug man is standing on the bow of a 25-slug iceboat. The boat is moving at 4.0 feet/sec with respect to the shore. Assume that the ice surface is frictionless. The man now walks aft at 2.0 feet/sec with respect to the 20-foot boat. With respect to the shore, (a) how far does the center of mass of the man-boat system move while the man goes forward to aft and (b) how far does the boat's bow move during this time?

8-10 A 10.0 kg block is initially sliding on a frictionless surface at 50 m/sec. It explodes into two parts, one of 1.0 kg and the other of 9.0 kg. The 1.0 kg part is at rest on the surface after the explosion. What is the speed of the 9.0 kg part?

8-11 A 70 kg man standing at rest on frictionless ice sees a 20 kg ball approaching from the north at a speed of 5.0 m/sec. The man catches the ball, then throws it southward at the speed of 5.0 m/sec relative to himself. What is the final velocity of the man?

8-12 A 460 gm ball 2.0 m above the floor is released, falls, strikes the floor, and rises to a maximum height of 1.5 m. Find the momentum transferred from the ball to the floor in the collision.

8-13 A rocket exhausts gas atoms at the speed $v_e = 2000$ m/sec. When at rest relative to an inertial observer, the total mass of the rocket and fuel is 1.00×10^4 kg. Ignore external influences: (a) what would be the payload mass when the rocket has reached a speed of 8000 m/sec? (b) What is the speed and direction of the exhaust gases at this time (relative to the original observer)?

8-14 ★ Two rockets, A and B, have the same initial mass m when at rest in an inertial system. Rocket A uses a fuel which enables it to exhaust gases at speed $2v_0$, whereas rocket B can exhaust only at speed v_0. What is the ratio of the payload masses of rocket A to rocket B when they both move at $3v_0$?

8-15 Find (a) the speed of a rocket and (b) the ratio of payload to original mass of a rocket when the exhaust particles have zero speed relative to a ground observer. (Ignore the effects of gravity.)

8-16 A rocket-fuel system of total mass M is at rest on a horizontal frictionless surface. What is the final velocity of the remaining rocket with respect to the surface if (a) one shot of mass $(\frac{3}{5})M$ is fired to the left at speed v_e relative to the rocket and (b) three separate shots, each of mass $M/5$, are fired successively, each shot moving leftward at a speed v_e relative to the rocket.

8-17 A block of mass $(\frac{2}{5})M$ is initially at rest on a smooth horizontal surface. What is the final velocity of the system if three separate shots, each moving to the right with velocity v with respect to the surface and each of mass $M/5$, strike and stick to the original mass. Compare the result here with that of Problem 8-16.

8-18 At an icy intersection a 100-slug car traveling north collides with a 300-slug truck traveling west. Immediately after the collision, the car and truck are observed to be moving together at a speed of 30 miles/hour along the direction 30° north of west. What were the original speeds of the car and truck?

8-19 A 50.0 kg bomb, originally moving northward at 200 m/sec, explodes into three fragments. After the explosion, a 25.0 kg fragment is observed moving northward at 100 m/sec and a 150 kg fragment is moving southward at 200 m/sec. Find the direction and speed of the third fragment.

8-20 A 100 gm steel ball, moving with a speed of 50 m/sec, strikes a flat horizontal surface, its velocity making an angle of 30° with the horizontal before and after the collision. The ball has the same speed after the collision as before. Calculate the magnitude and direction of the momentum transferred to the plate.

8-21 A mass m moving initially at a velocity v strikes a second mass M which was initially at rest. After the collision the mass m moves with speed v' at a 90° angle with respect to its original velocity v. Find the angle θ (with respect to v) with which the mass M moves away from the collision.

8-22 ★ A body A with a momentum of $\boldsymbol{p}_A$ collides with body B originally at rest. After the collision A is deflected through an angle θ and has a momentum magnitude of p_A'. Show that after the collision body B moves in the direction φ (relative to the original direction of A) with a momentum magnitude p_B' where $\tan \varphi = (p_A' \sin \theta)/(p_A - p_A' \cos \theta)$ and $p_B' = [1 + (p_A/p_A')^2 - (2p_A/p_A') \cos \theta]^{1/2}$.

8-23 A train is moving north at 60 miles/hour. A passenger at rest in the train observes a package on the train floor to explode into two equal parts. He sees one part moving to the east at 40 miles/hour. What are the directions and speeds of the two parts relative to an observer on the ground?

8-24 ★ A 10 kg projectile is fired from a gun at an angle of 30° above the horizontal. The initial velocity of the projectile is 800 feet/sec. At its maximum height, the projectile explodes into two parts. One part, having a mass of 4.0 kg, strikes the ground directly below the point of explosion at 800 feet/sec. The other part strikes the ground later. (a) Where does the second part strike the ground? (b) Sketch the trajectories of the projectile and the two fragments.

8-25 ★ A frictionless sled resting on ice has four fixed guns located as shown in Figure 8-20. Each gun is capable of firing a 1.0 kg shot at a speed of 10 m/sec relative to the sled. The total mass of the system before the

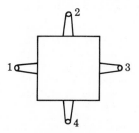

Figure 8-20.

guns are fired is 10 kg. Which order of firing of the four guns, 1-2-3-4 or 1-3-2-4, will result in the largest final speed to the sled? Explain.

8-26   A proton strikes an atom of gold and is thereby scattered from its original direction by an angle of 60°. Its speed after the collision is essentially the same as its speed before the collision. In what direction relative to the original direction of the proton does the gold atom recoil? A gold atom is much more massive than a proton.

8-27   An α-particle (helium nucleus), originally moving at 1.5×10^7 m/sec, collides with the nucleus of a gold atom at rest. Find the recoil speed of the gold nucleus if (a) the α-particle comes out of the collision in the opposite direction, with (essentially) its original speed, and (b) the α-particle leaves the collision along a direction 30° to its original motion and with its original speed. A gold nucleus has a mass of 197 amu; the α-particle's mass is 4 amu.

8-28   The uranium-238 nucleus is unstable and decays into a thorium-234 nucleus and an α-particle. The alpha particle is emitted with a speed of 1.4×10^6 m/sec. What is the recoil velocity of the thorium-234 nucleus, assuming the uranium-238 atom to be at rest at the time of decay? The thorium-234 and α-particle masses are in the ratio 234 to 4.

8-29   The diatomic molecule $I^{127}Cl^{35}$ has an interatomic distance of 2.32×10^{-10} m. (a) What is the distance of each atomic nucleus from the center of mass of the molecule? (The post-superscripts give the approximate masses in amu.) (b) Both atoms rotate at the same angular speed about the center of mass. What is the ratio of the speeds of Cl^{35} to I^{127}?

8-30   The nucleus of a nickel-60 atom is unstable and undergoes radioactive decay by emitting a gamma-ray (a photon, or particle of electromagnetic energy). If the nucleus is originally at rest, it recoils with a speed of 6.6×10^3 m/sec when the gamma-ray is emitted. What is the momentum of the gamma-ray? (The mass of nickel-60 is 9.9×10^{-26} kg.)

8-31   When an electron meets a positron (a particle having the same mass as the electron but carrying a positive, rather than a negative, electric charge), the two particles may annihilate one another, the particles disappearing and electromagnetic radiation appearing in the form of photons. (a) Show that electron-positron annihilation must produce at least two photons. (b) In what relative directions must the two photons travel if the electron and positron are initially at rest?

8-32   In the β radioactive decay process known as electron capture, one of the inner electrons of an atom is captured by the nucleus. Experiment shows that the nucleus recoils when the electron is captured. If the conservation of momentum principle holds for such an isolated system, what must one conclude? A neutrino, an elusive particle, without electric charge and moving at the speed of light, is emitted in the electron-capture process.

8-33   Find the center of mass of the three point masses: 2.00 kg at $x = 0$ and $y = +3.00$ m, 3.00 kg at $x = 0$ and $y = -3.00$ m, and 5.00 kg

located 5.00 m from the origin at an angle of 45° below the negative
X-axis.

8-34   Assume that the three point masses in Problem 8-33 move with the
following constant velocities: 2.00 kg at 1.77 m/sec along the negative
Y-axis, 3.00 kg at 1.18 m/sec in the negative X-direction, and 5 kg at
1.0 m/sec toward the origin. Where will the center of mass of the
system be when the 5.0 kg mass reaches the origin?

8-35   The Sun's mass is 3.0×10^5 times that of the Earth, and the Earth is
9.3×10^7 miles from the Sun. Find the speed of the Sun around the
center of mass of the Earth-Sun system.

8-36   Find the center of mass of the homogeneous L-shaped plate shown in
Figure 8-21. (*Hint:* Subdivide the plate into two rectangles; find the
center of mass of each rectangle; use the fact that the mass of each
rectangle is proportional to its area.)

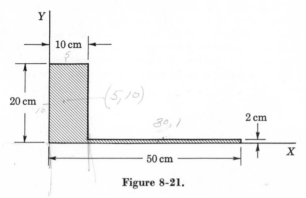

Figure 8-21.

8-37 ⋆ Where is the center of mass of a uniform right circular cone of height
h and base radius r?

8-38   Show that the center of mass of a uniform triangular plate lies at the
intersection of the three lines joining the center of each side with the
opposite vertex.

8-39 ⋆ Find the center of mass of the circular disc (radius R) with the square
hole, shown in Figure 8-22.

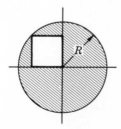

Figure 8-22.

8-40   Find the velocities relative to a reference frame attached to the center of mass of the particles before, and also after, the collision for the conditions given in Example 6. Confirm your results by reference to Figure 8-18.

8-41   A 20 kg mass travels to the right at 15 m/sec and a 10 kg mass travels to the left at 25 m/sec. (a) What is the total linear momentum of the system of two bodies as viewed from the laboratory? (b) What is the velocity of the center of mass of the system? (c) What is the velocity of each body relative to the center of mass? (d) What is the linear momentum of each of the bodies relative to a reference frame moving with the center of mass?

8-42   A 1.0 kg body strikes a 4.0 kg body originally at rest on a smooth horizontal surface. Before the collision the 1.0 kg body moves at 3.0 m/sec; after the collision its velocity is 2.0 m/sec at an angle of 30° with respect to its original velocity. (a) What is the velocity of the 4.0 kg body after the collision? (b) Draw momentum vectors for the situation before and after the collision as viewed in the laboratory. (c) Find the velocities of the two bodies before and after the collision relative to a reference frame attached to the center of mass of the system. (d) Draw vectors showing the momentum of the bodies before and after the collision in the center of mass reference frame.

N I N E

FORCE

This chapter is concerned with force—its fundamental origins, its relation to linear momentum, and its appearance in the fundamental laws of mechanics. We first consider qualitatively the sources, or origins, of force in the fundamental interactions between bodies. Then we define force as the time rate of linear momentum and explore the consequences of this definition. The superposition principle for forces, which shows that simultaneous forces add as vectors, leads us to Newton's second law of motion. The impulse of a force is defined, and the impulse-momentum theorem is developed. Next, the appearance of equal and opposite action-reaction pairs of forces, known as Newton's third law of motion, is derived from the conservation of momentum law. Weight is defined, and its relation to mass is given. Finally, Newton's laws are applied to situations involving nonconstant mass.

In this chapter we lay the foundations of the meaning of force and of Newton's laws. In the next chapter we apply these laws to a wide variety of physical situations. Newton's laws of motion—which are equivalent to the law of linear momentum conservation and the superposition principle for forces—are the foundations of all classical mechanics.

9-1   The fundamental origins of force   In this section we give some qualitative aspects of force; we shall give its precise definition in Section 9-2.

A single body is said to be acted upon by a force when its momentum changes, and to test whether a body is subject to an unbalanced, or net,

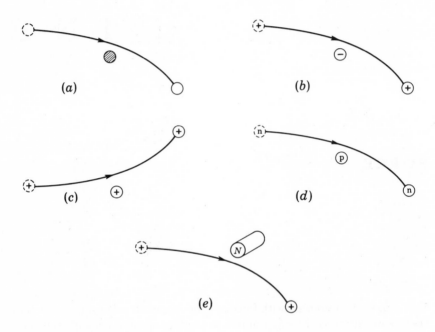

Figure 9-1. Some fundamental forces of physics: (a) the gravitational force, (b) the attractive electric force between two unlike charged particles, (c) the repulsive electric force between two like charged particles, (d) the nuclear force between a proton and a neutron, and (e) the magnetic force between a magnet and a moving, charged particle.

force one simply notes whether the body departs from motion at constant velocity. A force is most easily illustrated when one has only two bodies interacting with one another; each body influences the motion of the other, and we can describe this influence in terms of a force acting on each body by virtue of the presence of the other.

There is a variety of forces with which we are familiar: a muscular exertion producing a push or pull, the force of one object on another when they come in contact, the gravitational force between the Earth and a satellite, the force of a magnet on a piece of iron, the electrostatic force of a rubbed insulator, such as a plastic rod, on bits of paper, the force of one current-carrying conductor on another conductor, the force of the atomic nucleus on the electrons surrounding it, the force of one nucleus on another nucleus. Despite the diversity of these forces it is a remarkable fact that all of them—indeed all forces in physics now known—can be traced to four basic types of force. They are (a) the universal gravitational force of attraction between any two bodies, (b) the so-called "weak-interaction" force appearing in the β-decay of certain radioactive particles; (c) the force between electric charges, at rest or in motion, which gives rise to the electric and magnetic forces, and (d) the very strong nuclear force between the constituents of the atomic nucleus. The weak-interaction and nuclear forces, although important in nuclear structure, have virtually no effect in atomic structure. Therefore, the only forces that play a role in classical physics are the gravitational, electric, and magnetic forces. *All* other forces in classical physics can be traced ultimately to these.

Fundamental forces occurring in physics are illustrated in Figure 9-1. In each instance a relatively massive body, called the scattering center, interacts with an incoming body of small mass. That a force acts between the pair of bodies is demonstrated by the departure of the incident body from straight-line motion at constant speed. As the incoming body approaches, interacts with, and recedes from, the scattering center, its momentum is changed in magnitude and direction. Note that no material substance occupies the region between the interacting bodies—forces act at a distance through a vacuum. One of the principal tasks of physics is to describe forces in terms of the distance separating the bodies and certain properties of the interacting bodies, such as their masses, electric charges, and velocities.

9-2 The definition of force The concept of force is easily understood when we enquire again into the head-on collision between two bodies illustrated in Figure 8-1. This time, we focus our attention on one of the bodies, whose momentum-time graph is shown in Figure 9-2a. For simplicity, the graph is shown with three straight-line segments: a horizontal segment corresponding to the initial motion at constant velocity, a sloping portion during which the body changes momentum because of the external influence, or force, of the second body and, finally, a horizontal segment corresponding to motion with a higher constant velocity as the body again coasts free of external influence.

Over the time interval Δt, the momentum of the body has changed by an amount $\Delta \boldsymbol{p}$. *By definition, the average force $\overline{F}$ acting on the body is the change in its momentum divided by the elapsed time:*

$$\overline{F} = \frac{\Delta \boldsymbol{p}}{\Delta t}$$

[9-1]

The force $\vec{F}$ is a vector, having the same direction as the momentum change Δp. For the head-on collision in Figure 9-2, the momentum change Δp and, hence, $\vec{F}$ are *along* the direction of the initial momentum. In the more general case, in which Δp is not along the direction of the initial momentum, Equation 9-1 still defines the average force. The average force for the

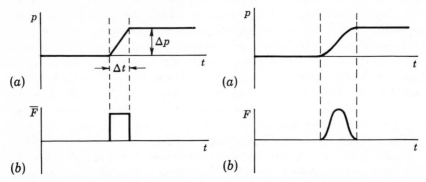

Figure 9-2. (a) Momentum-time graph. (b) The corresponding force-time graph; for simplicity, the force is shown constant.

Figure 9-3. A variable force: (a) momentum-time and (b) force-time graph.

head-on collision of Figure 9-2a is plotted as a function of time in Figure 9-2b. A force acts only while the momentum changes. Here the momentum changes at a constant rate during the interaction time Δt, and the force acting during this time is constant.

The formal definition of force agrees with our intuitive ideas about force. Over a given time interval Δt, the bigger the push on an object the bigger the change in its momentum and therefore the bigger the change in velocity. A larger force is required to accelerate a massive body from rest up to a certain speed than is required to set a less massive body in motion to this same speed over the same time interval, because the rate of momentum change must be greater for the more massive body.

A more realistic collision between two bodies is shown in the momentum-time graph of Figure 9-3a. Here, during the interaction, the momentum of a body changes smoothly with time. The *instantaneous force* (which we shall call simply the force) is defined as the time rate of the linear momentum, or the derivative with respect to time of the linear momentum:

$$F = \frac{dp}{dt}$$

[9-2]

The component of the force acting on the body along any direction is the slope of the corresponding momentum-time graph. The force is given as a function of time in Figure 9-3b. The force is not constant: it starts at zero (before the collision), rises to a maximum and falls (as the bodies interact), and then goes to zero (as the bodies separate).

Table 9-1

SYSTEM OF UNITS	FORCE UNIT	EQUIVALENT FUNDAMENTAL UNITS
mks	newton (nt)	kg-m/sec²
cgs	dyne	gm-cm/sec²
English	pound (lb)	slug-ft/sec²

The linear momentum of a body is the product of its mass and velocity. Therefore, the momentum of a body may change under the influence of a force by virtue of a change in the velocity, or in mass, or both:

$$F = \frac{d\boldsymbol{p}}{dt} = \left(\frac{d}{dt}\right)(m\boldsymbol{v}) = m\left(\frac{d\boldsymbol{v}}{dt}\right) + \boldsymbol{v}\left(\frac{dm}{dt}\right)$$

$$\boxed{F = m\boldsymbol{a} + \boldsymbol{v}\left(\frac{dm}{dt}\right)} \qquad [9\text{-}3]$$

The force is, in general, the sum of two terms: the product of mass and acceleration, $m\boldsymbol{a}$, and the product of the instantaneous velocity and the rate of change of the mass, $\boldsymbol{v}(dm/dt)$.

In most problems in classical physics, the mass of the body is constant and $dm/dt = 0$. Then Equation 9-3 reduces to:

$$F = m\boldsymbol{a} \qquad \text{(constant } m\text{)} \qquad [9\text{-}4]$$

That is, the force acting on the body is simply the product of the mass and the acceleration. The direction of the acceleration is parallel to the acting force.

Situations in which the body's mass does *not* remain constant will be illustrated in Section 9-7.

From its definition force must have dimensions of ML/T^2 and the units of momentum divided by time: kilogram-meters per square second, gram-centimeters per square second, slug-feet per square second. Special names are assigned to these force units, namely, the *newton, dyne,* and *pound,* respectively, as shown in Table 9-1.

The force units in the three systems are related as shown below:

$$1 \text{ nt} = (1 \text{ kg-m/sec}^2) = (10^3 \text{ gm})(10^2 \text{ cm/sec}^2) = 10^5 \text{ gm-cm/sec}^2$$

Therefore, $1 \text{ nt} = 10^5 \text{ dyne}$

$$1 \text{ lb} = (1 \text{ slug-ft/sec}^2) = (14.59 \text{ kg})(0.3048 \text{ m/sec}^2) = 4.448 \text{ kg-m/sec}^2$$

Therefore, $1 \text{ lb} = 4.448 \text{ nt}$

A force of one newton causes the momentum of a body to change by 1 kg-m/sec in 1 sec; equivalently, one newton of force imparts an acceleration of 1 m/sec² to a 1 kg body. In similar fashion, the dyne is the force required to give a 1 gm mass an acceleration of 1 cm/sec², and a pound of force imparts an acceleration of 1 foot/sec² to a 1-slug mass.

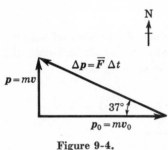

Figure 9-4.

Example 1 A 10 kg body interacts with a second body. The 10 kg body is observed to be initially moving east at 20 m/sec. One-half second later it is traveling north at 15 m/sec. What is the average force acting on the 10 kg body during the half-second time interval?

To compute the force we first find the change in momentum, Δp. See Figure 9-4. The momentum vector diagram shows that $\Delta p = p - p_0$ is 250 kg-m/sec in the direction 37° north of west. Therefore, from Equation 9-1, the average force is

$$\bar{F} = \frac{\Delta p}{\Delta t} = \frac{250 \text{ kg-m/sec}}{0.50 \text{ sec}}$$

$$\bar{F} = 500 \text{ kg-m/sec}^2 = 500 \text{ nt at } 37° \text{ north of west}$$

Example 2 A 0.25-slug body is initially moving east at 16 feet/sec. What is the acceleration of the body, both its magnitude and direction, if a single constant force of 2.0 pounds acts on the body, the direction of the constant force being (a) east, (b) west, and (c) south?

From equation 9-3 we have

$$a = F/m = 2.0 \text{ lb}/0.25 \text{ slug} = 8.0 \text{ ft/sec}^2 \text{ along the direction of } F$$

(a) When the force is in the same direction as the initial velocity, the body has an acceleration of 8.0 feet/sec² *to the east*. Here the body is speeded up at a constant rate along the direction of motion. See Figure 9-5a.

(b) When the force is opposite in direction to the initial velocity, the body has an acceleration of 8.0 feet/sec² *to the west*. In this situation the body is slowed down, brought to rest and, if the constant force continues to act, the body will then move to the west and be speeded up at a constant rate. See Figure 9-5b.

(c) Here the force is initially at right angles to the velocity, and the body has a constant acceleration of 8.0 feet/sec² *south*. The *component* to the south of the body's velocity increases at a constant rate, whereas the velocity component to the east is unchanged. Therefore, as was shown in Section 4-3, the body traces out a parabolic path as long as the constant force acts on it. See Figure 9-5c.

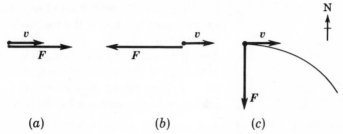

(*a*) (*b*) (*c*)

Figure 9-5. A body moves east initially and is acted on by (a) a force to the east, (b) a force to the west, and (c) a force to the south.

Example 3 An electron (mass, 9.1×10^{-28} gm) starts from rest at a negatively charged, vertical, metal plate and arrives at a positively charged, vertical, metal plate, 2.0 cm to the right in a time of $1.4 + 10^{-7}$ sec. If the electron's acceleration is constant throughout its motion, what is the constant force on the electron?

The constant acceleration can be computed from the kinematic relation:

[2-8]
$$x = v_0 t + \tfrac{1}{2} a t^2$$

For $v_0 = 0$, we have

$$a = 2x/t^2 = 2(2.0 \text{ cm})/(1.4 \times 10^{-7} \text{ sec})^2$$

$$= 2.0 \times 10^{14} \text{ cm/sec}^2, \text{ to the right}$$

Therefore, the constant force on the electron is

$$F = ma = (9.1 \times 10^{-28} \text{ gm})(2.0 \times 10^{14} \text{ cm/sec}^2)$$

$$= 1.8 \times 10^{-13} \text{ dyne, to the right}$$

9-3 The superposition principle for forces When a body interacts with a second body, it is subject to a force which is, by definition, equal to the body's time rate of momentum. In this section we establish that if a body interacts with *two or more* other bodies and is, therefore, subject to several forces simultaneously, the time rate of the body's momentum is equal to the *vector sum* of all the external forces acting on it.

First suppose that we have a frictionless air-suspended disc at rest on a smooth surface. We attach an ordinary helical spring to the disc and pull horizontally on the spring in such a way as to give the disc a constant acceleration. By Equation 9-3, the applied force must also be constant and parallel to the acceleration. Experiment shows that the direction of the acceleration is along the direction of the spring's symmetry axis. Further-more, a constant acceleration is achieved only if the amount by which the spring is stretched or compressed is kept constant.

An ordinary spring is, then, a simple device for producing and measuring a constant force, and the spring may be calibrated to read forces in terms of its elongation. In fact, if the elongation of the spring is not too great, the magnitude of the force exerted by the spring is found to be directly proportional to its elongation, as shown in Figure 9-6. Therefore, the *magnitude* of the force F_s exerted by the stretched spring is related to its elongation x by the relation

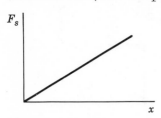

Figure 9-6. Magnitude of the force exerted by a simple spring as a function of its elongation.

$$F_s = kx \qquad [9\text{-}5]$$

where k is the *force constant*, characteristic of the spring, which determines its calibration and has the dimensions of force per unit length.

Similarly, when the spring is compressed an amount x from its unstretched length, the magnitude of the force F_s applied by the spring is again given by Equation 9-5.

If a spring produces a constant acceleration a_1 on a mass m, the force applied by the spring is $F_1 = ma_1$. If a second spring produces a different constant acceleration, a_2, on the *same* mass m, the force produced by this spring is $F_2 = ma_2$. These two situations are shown in Figure 9-7a and b.

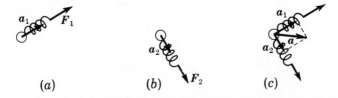

$$(a) \qquad\qquad (b) \qquad\qquad (c)$$

Figure 9-7. A body acted on by (a) force F_1 alone, (b) force F_2 alone, (c) forces F_1 and F_2 simultaneously.

Now suppose that both springs are attached to the body, each spring being stretched by the same amount and in the same direction as before. The disc is now subjected to two forces simultaneously. Experimentally, we find that the disc's acceleration a is again *constant*; therefore the acceleration a can be related to a single equivalent force, say F', where

$$a = \frac{F'}{m}$$

We now ask how the single equivalent force F' is related to the simultaneous forces F_1 and F_2. Experiment shows that

$$a = a_1 + a_2$$

But

$$a_1 + a_2 = \frac{F_1}{m} + \frac{F_2}{m}$$

Therefore,

$$a = \frac{F_1{}'}{m} = a_1 + a_2 = \frac{F_1 + F_2}{m}$$

or

$$F' = F_1 + F_2$$

The direction of the acceleration is the same as that of the *vector sum* of the applied forces, and the mass times the magnitude of the acceleration is equal to the magnitude of the vector sum of the applied forces. In short, two forces acting simultaneously on a body are altogether equivalent to a single force equal to their vector sum. Further experiments show that the same relation holds for three or more forces. That is,

$$\boxed{F' = F_1 + F_2 + F_3 + \cdots = \Sigma\, F} \qquad [9\text{-}6]$$

Thus, when several forces act simultaneously on a body, we may add, or superpose, them by the rule of vector addition to find the single equivalent force. This is the *superposition principle* for forces.

Using Equation 9-4 we can find the acceleration on the body due to the net force $\Sigma\, F$:

$$\boxed{\Sigma\, F = ma} \qquad [9\text{-}7]$$

Written in its more general form, this equation is

$$\boxed{\Sigma\, F = \frac{dp}{dt}} \qquad [9\text{-}8]$$

The time rate of momentum of a body is equal, in magnitude and direction, to the *vector sum* of the forces acting on it. This result, which arises from the definition of force and the superposition principle, is known as *Newton's second law of motion*. This is the fundamental law governing the motion of interacting bodies. The next chapter will be devoted to illustrating its wide applicability.

Example 4 A 1.0 kg body is subjected to two simultaneous forces, 4.0 nt east and 3.0 nt north. What is the acceleration of the body?

By the principle of superposition, Equation 9-6 yields

$$\Sigma \boldsymbol{F} = \boldsymbol{F}_1 + \boldsymbol{F}_2 = 5.0 \text{ nt } 37° \text{ north of east}$$

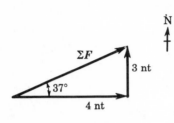

as shown in Figure 9-8. From Equation 9-7 the acceleration of the body is

$$a = \Sigma \boldsymbol{F}/m = (5.0 \text{ nt})/(1.0 \text{ kg})$$

Figure 9-8.

$$= 5.0 \text{ m/sec}^2 \text{ at } 37° \text{ north of east}$$

9-4 Impulse and momentum   Let us look further into the relationship between a momentum-time graph and the force-time graph derived from it. Figures 9-9a and b show an idealized situation in which the momentum of the body is first constant, then increases at a constant rate, and finally is again constant. The force is constant while it acts on the body and zero at all other times. From Equation 9-1 we may write

$$\Delta \boldsymbol{p} = \overline{\boldsymbol{F}} \, \Delta t$$

That is, the change in momentum is the average force multiplied by the time interval during which the force acts. The name *impulse* is given to the

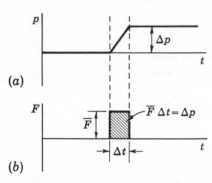

(a)

(b)

Figure 9-9. Graphs for a constant force: (a) momentum-time and (b) force-time. The impulse is the area under the force-time graph.

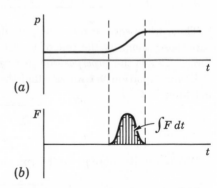

(a)

(b)

Figure 9-10. Graphs for a variable force: (a) momentum-time and (b) force-time.

product $\overline{\boldsymbol{F}} \, \Delta t$. Impulse is a *vector* having the same direction as the applied force; its magnitude is represented by the area under the force-time curve in Figure 9-9b.

Now consider a more realistic situation in which the force varies continuously. See Figure 9-10. From Equation 9-2, the change in momentum $d\boldsymbol{p}$

over the small time interval dt is given by

$$d\boldsymbol{p} = \boldsymbol{F}\,dt \qquad [9\text{-}9]$$

where $\boldsymbol{F}$ is the instantaneous force acting at the time t. The magnitude of $\boldsymbol{F}\,dt$ is shown in Figure 9-10b as the area of a thin rectangle of width dt and height F. If we sum up the areas of all the small rectangles fitted under the force-time graph, we obtain the total area under the curve. This vector quantity, again known as the impulse, is given by

$$\boxed{\text{impulse} = \int \boldsymbol{F}\,dt = \bar{\boldsymbol{F}}\,\Delta t} \qquad [9\text{-}10]$$

where the integration is over the entire time interval during which a nonzero force acts. Integrating both sides of Equation 9-9 over the total time of interaction, from the *i*nitial time t_i to the *f*inal time t_f, and the corresponding momentum change, from $\boldsymbol{p}_i$ to $\boldsymbol{p}_f$, yields

$$\int_{\boldsymbol{p}_i}^{\boldsymbol{p}_f} d\boldsymbol{p} = \int_{t_i}^{t_f} \boldsymbol{F}\,dt$$

or

$$\boxed{\boldsymbol{p}_f - \boldsymbol{p}_i = \Delta \boldsymbol{p} = \int_{t_i}^{t_f} \boldsymbol{F}\,dt} \qquad [9\text{-}11]$$

where $\Delta \boldsymbol{p}$ represents the change in momentum resulting from the application of the variable force $\boldsymbol{F}$ over the time interval $t_f - t_i$. Thus, the impulse of a force equals the change in momentum of the body on which the force acts. This is known as the *impulse-momentum theorem:*

$$\text{impulse vector} = \text{vector change in momentum} \qquad [9\text{-}12]$$

When an agent exerts a force on a body, the body's momentum changes. One can say that momentum has been transferred from the agent to the body. The agent can be identified with a second body, with which the first body interacts. The momentum is a property of the body only, the product of its mass and velocity. On the other hand, the impulse is *not* a property of the body itself, but is a measure of the influence of the external agent on the body. The transfer of momentum to a body by an agent is shown symbolically in Figure 9-11.

By definition, Equation 9-10, the dimensions of impulse are ML/T, and the appropriate units for impulse are those of force multiplied by time: newton-seconds, dyne-seconds, or pound-seconds (nt-sec, dyne-sec, or lb-sec). From Equation 9-11 we see that these units are equivalent to the units for momentum (kg-m/sec, gm-cm/sec, and slug-ft/sec, respectively).

Colloquially, the term "impulse" usually implies a force which acts for only a very short time. The formal definition of impulse includes any force, however long the time during which it acts. On the other hand, one can speak of an "impulsive force" as a force which acts for a very short time. Impulsive forces typically act when one hard body is struck by a second hard body, as in the case of a baseball struck by a bat or a nail by a hammer.

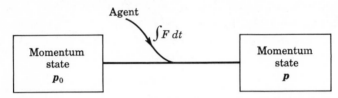

Figure 9-11. Schematic representation of the transfer of momentum from an agent to a body.

In these cases a very large force acts for a very short time. It must be emphasized, however, that Equation 9-11 always holds, whether the inter-action time is short or long.

Example 5 A block of mass 3.0 kg slides on a frictionless horizontal surface. The block is initially moving to the left with a speed of 50 m/sec, as shown in Figure 9-12a. It collides with the spring, compresses it, and is brought to rest.

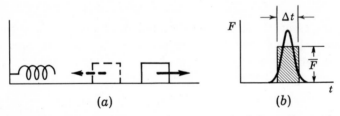

(a)   (b)

Figure 9-12. (a) A body initially moving to the left, strikes and com-presses a spring, and then moves to the right. (b) Force-time graph for the collision in (a).

The body continues to be accelerated to the right by the force of the compressed spring. Finally, the body moves to the right at a constant speed of 40 m/sec. By the use of slow-motion pictures it is found that the block remained in contact with the spring for 0.020 sec. (a) What was the direction and magnitude of the impulse of the spring on the block? (b) What was the average force of the spring on the block?

(a) In this problem we do not have a record of the force on the block as a function of time; therefore, it is not possible to compute the impulse by finding the area under the force-time graph. However, we do know the change in momentum Δp of the block, arising from the impulse. It is

$$\Delta p = p_f - p_i$$

Choosing the right as the positive direction, we have

$$\Delta p = (3.0 \text{ kg})(+40 \text{ m/sec}) - (3.0 \text{ kg})(-50 \text{ m/sec}) = +270 \text{ kg-m/sec}$$

Note that initial momentum p_i is *negative*, signifying a momentum to the left. We now know the impulse from Equation 9-11:

$$\text{impulse} = \Delta p = 270 \text{ kg-m/sec} = 270 \text{ nt-sec, to the right}$$

(b) To find the average force acting on the block during the collision let us recall the relations between the impulse, average force $\bar{F}$, and instantaneous force F. By Equations 9-10,

$$\text{impulse} = \bar{F} \, \Delta t = \int_{t_i}^{t_f} F \, dt$$

where $\Delta t = t_f - t_i$ is the interaction time. We know that the block and spring were in contact for $\Delta t = 0.020$ sec. Therefore, we can compute the average force:

$$\bar{F} = \text{impulse}/\Delta t = (270 \text{ nt-sec})/(0.020 \text{ sec})$$

$$\bar{F} = 13,000 \text{ nt} \simeq 1.5 \text{ ton!} \quad \text{(to the right)}$$

Thus, a *constant* force of 13,000 nt acting over a time of 0.020 sec would produce the same impulse as that produced by the spring on the block. Inasmuch as the force of the spring on the block must first increase from zero to a maximum, then decrease to zero again, the maximum instantaneous force of the spring on the block will *exceed* the equivalent constant force of 13,000 nt, as shown in Figure 9-12. By definition, the average force $\bar{F}$ is so chosen that its impulse, $\bar{F} \, \Delta t$, over the interaction time Δt, is equal to the actual impulse, $\int F \, dt$; that is, the area of the rectangle in Figure 9-12b equals the area under the actual force-time graph (both areas representing, of course, the magnitude of the impulse).

9-5 Force pairs When two bodies interact, body 1 exerts a force on body 2, and body 2 exerts a force on body 1. In this section we will find the relation between this pair of forces.

Again consider two bodies in a head-on collision, the situation being described by the momentum-time and the related force-time graphs of Figure 9-13. The conservation of momentum law requires that the total momentum of this isolated system be constant at all times. Thus, the momentum gained by body 1 is balanced at all times by an equal momentum loss by body 2, the momentum-time graph for body 1 being of exactly the same shape as that for body 2, but inverted. The force-time graphs are also of the same shape, but the force on body 1 is always positive (to the right) while the force on body 2 is always negative (to the left). *The instantaneous force on body 1*, representing the influence of body 2, *is exactly equal in magnitude but opposite in direction to the instantaneous force on body 2*, representing the influence of body 1. This important result, which is known as *Newton's third law of motion*, is a direct consequence of the conservation of momentum law and the definition of force.

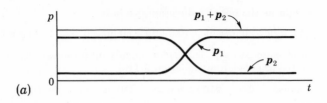

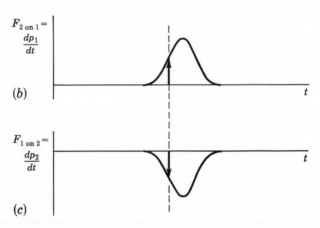

Figure 9-13. (a) Momentum-time curves for two colliding bodies. (b) Force-time graph for body 1. (c) Force-time curve for body 2.

Let us prove this formally:

$$\boldsymbol{p}_1 + \boldsymbol{p}_2 = \text{constant}$$

$$\frac{d\boldsymbol{p}_1}{dt} + \frac{d\boldsymbol{p}_2}{dt} = 0$$

$$\frac{d\boldsymbol{p}_1}{dt} = -\frac{d\boldsymbol{p}_2}{dt}$$

$$\boxed{\boldsymbol{F}_{2\,\text{on}\,1} = -\boldsymbol{F}_{1\,\text{on}\,2}} \qquad [9\text{-}13]$$

The two forces—often referred to as the *action* and *reaction* forces—are equal and opposite, act along the line connecting the two bodies, and act on *different* bodies. It cannot be emphasized too strongly that the two forces do *not* act on the same body; they cannot cancel out one another and thus place one of the bodies in equilibrium.

Forces occur in pairs only. When a hammer strikes a nail, the force of the hammer on the nail is precisely equal in magnitude to the force of the nail on the hammer. When a ball crashes through a window, the force of the ball on the window is exactly equal to the force of the window on the ball. The force of a rocket on its exhaust particles is exactly equal to the force of the exhaust particles on the rocket. The force of the Earth on a falling apple is precisely equal in magnitude to the force of the falling apple on the Earth.

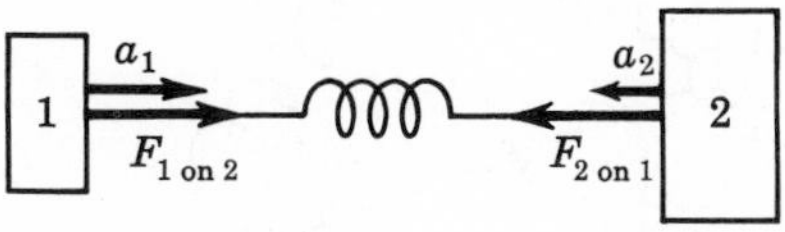

Figure 9-14. The ratio of the acceleration magnitudes for two interacting bodies is equal to the inverse ratio of their respective masses.

We can use Newton's third law to compare masses. Consider the accelerations of two interacting, but otherwise isolated, particles. From Equation 9-13,

$$F_{2 \text{ on } 1} = - F_{1 \text{ on } 2}$$

Each particle has only one force acting on it and, by Newton's second law,

$$m_1 a_1 = - m_2 a_2$$

or

$$\frac{m_1}{m_2} = - \frac{a_2}{a_1} \tag{9-14}$$

The ratio of the masses is equal to the inverse ratio of the magnitudes of the measured accelerations. See Figure 9-14. If the accelerations of two interacting particles are found to be equal, the two particles have the same mass.

Example 6 Three bodies, 1, 2, and 3, interact with one another as shown in Figure 9-15. Bodies 1 and 2 repel each other through a compressed spring; bodies 2 and 3 attract each other through a stretched spring; and bodies 3 and 1 attract each other through an electric force arising from their opposite net electric charges. See Figure 9-15a. (a) Find the forces that act on each of the three particles. (b) Identify the action-reaction force pairs.

Each of the forces acts along the line connecting the two interacting particles. The forces on body 1 arise from the external influences of bodies 2 and 3. The compressed spring exerts a force on 1. The size of this force depends on the separation distance between bodies 1 and 2; therefore, we call it $F_{2 \text{ on } 1}$. Body 1 is also acted on by body 3 by the attractive electric force, called $F_{3 \text{ on } 1}$. See Figure 9-15b. In similar fashion, the forces on body 2 are $F_{1 \text{ on } 2}$ and $F_{3 \text{ on } 2}$, and the forces on body 3 are $F_{1 \text{ on } 3}$ and $F_{2 \text{ on } 3}$, as shown in Figures 9-15b and c. A resultant force acts on each body; therefore, each body at this instant is accelerated in the direction of the resultant force acting on it.

The action-reaction force pairs are:

$$F_{2 \text{ on } 1} \text{ and } F_{1 \text{ on } 2}$$

$$F_{3 \text{ on } 2} \text{ and } F_{2 \text{ on } 3}$$

$$F_{1 \text{ on } 3} \text{ and } F_{3 \text{ on } 1}$$

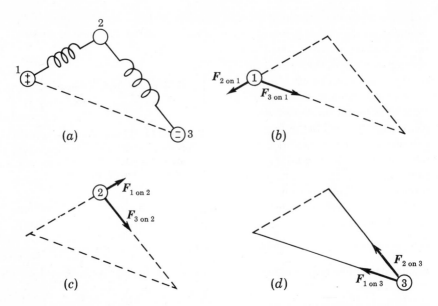

Figure 9-15. (a) Three interacting particles. The forces on (b) particle 1, (c) particle 2, and (d) particle 3.

We notice that the forces composing an action-reaction pair never act on the same particle.

Example 7 A machine gun shoots 20 gm bullets horizontally with a muzzle velocity of 1000 m/sec at the rate of 240 bullets/minute. The bullets strike, and are stopped in, a target. What is the average force of the bullets on the target?

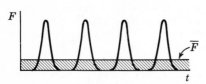

The force of the bullets on the target is equal and opposite to the force of the target on the bullets. We can compute the average force of the target on the bullets from a knowledge of the bullets' rate of change of momentum.

The instantaneous force on the target is not constant. It rises abruptly whenever a bullet hits, and is zero at all other times, as shown in the force-time graph of Figure 9-16. We wish to find the constant force $\bar{F}$ whose impulse is equal to the momentum change of the bullets. The impulse-momentum relation may be written

Figure 9-16. Force-time graph for bullets striking a target. The area under the several peaks is equal to the area shown shaded and corresponding to a constant average force $\bar{F}$.

$$\bar{F}\,\Delta t = \Delta n(mv)$$

where Δn is the number of bullets striking the target in the time Δt, mv is the change in momentum of each bullet on being brought to rest from the initial speed v, $\Delta n(mv)$ is the total change in momentum in the time Δt, and $\bar{F} \Delta t$ is the corresponding impulse applied to the bullets. Solving for $\bar{F}$, we have

$$\bar{F} = (\Delta n/\Delta t)(mv)$$

$$\bar{F} = (4.0 \text{ bullets/sec})(0.020 \text{ kg})(1000 \text{ m/sec})$$

$$\bar{F} = 80 \text{ nt}$$

The magnitude of the average force of the target on the bullets, and therefore also of the force of the bullets on the target, is 80 nt, but the momentum change for each bullet as it is accelerated and expelled from the machine gun is exactly the same in magnitude as the momentum change when it is brought to rest. Thus, 80 nt is also the magnitude of the average force exerted by the gun barrel on the bullets and, by the third law, the average force of the bullets on the gun.

Imagine that the gun and target are both mounted on the same frictionless platform and that a short burst of bullets was fired to the right at the target. Then the platform would first recoil to the left as the burst of bullets emerges from the barrel, because the bullets exert a force to the left on the gun and platform. The gun, target, and platform would coast to the left until the bullets were brought to rest at the target. The force of the bullets to the right on the target and platform would bring the platform exactly to rest, but not quite at the same place as before the gun was fired. Because the bullets have been transferred to the right from the gun to the target, the center of mass *of the platform* has been shifted slightly to the right. The location of the center of mass of the *whole system* relative to the ground is unchanged, however. The system as a whole has been subjected to no net external force.

9-6 Weight   Experiment shows that any body in free flight over short distances near the Earth has a constant acceleration g toward the Earth's center. This implies that any body is acted upon by a constant force arising from its inter-action with the entire Earth. The phenomenon of a body's being attracted by the Earth is called *gravitation*, and the force on a body due to the gravitational attraction of the Earth is called the *weight* of the body.

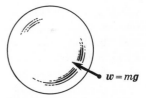

Figure 9-17. Newton's second law applied to a freely falling body.

When we apply Newton's second law to a freely falling body of mass m, weight w, and acceleration g, we have (Figure 9-17)

$$\Sigma \, F = m a$$

$$\boxed{w = m g} \qquad\qquad [9\text{-}15]$$

The magnitude of the weight is simply the mass multiplied by g, the acceleration due to gravity. The direction of the weight is "down," which is to say, toward the Earth's center. The weight is truly a vector; but, because it always points toward the Earth's center, it is not necessary to specify its direction in each instance. Equation 9-15 shows that the acceleration of a freely falling body is that vector, $g = w/m$ which gives the gravitational force, or weight, per unit mass.

Consider the weights of the standard masses: 1 kg, 1 gm, and 1 slug. We use for g the so-called *standard* acceleration due to gravity, which is close to the measured value of g at latitudes of 45° near sea level:

$$\text{Standard } g = 9.80665 \text{ m/sec}^2 = 32.17398 \text{ ft/sec}^2$$

Weight of a 1 kg mass $= (1 \text{ kg})(9.80665 \text{ m/sec}^2) = 9.80665 \text{ nt}$

Weight of a 1 gm mass $= (1 \text{ gm})(980.665 \text{ cm/sec}^2) = 980.665 \text{ dyne}$

Weight of a 1-slug mass $= (1 \text{ slug})(32.17398 \text{ ft/sec}^2) = 32.17398 \text{ lb}$

The weight of a 1 kg mass is about 9.8 nt; the weight of a 1 gm mass is about 980 dynes; and the weight of a 1-slug mass is about 32 pounds.* A dyne, a newton, and a pound are, respectively, the approximate weights of a mosquito, a small apple, and a pint of milk.

In nonscientific usage, the terms mass and weight are often taken as interchangeable. Mass and weight are, however, quite different quantities.

Weight is a vector; it is a measure of the Earth's pull on an object (or of the object's pull on the Earth). The magnitude of the weight is not a constant but depends on the magnitude of g, which, although constant at one location near the Earth, shows variations with altitude and latitude and which is, in fact, zero for bodies far from the Earth in interstellar space. Thus, the weight of a 1 kg mass is 9.80 nt at a location where g is 9.80 m/sec²; at another location on Earth, where g is 9.79 m/sec², the weight is 9.79 nt. A 1 kg object, or an object of any mass, is truly weightless† when far from objects in interstellar space.

On the other hand, mass is a scalar; it is an intrinsic property of the body, not dependent on its interaction with other bodies. A force of 1 nt must act on a mass of 1 kg to produce an acceleration of 1 m/sec², whether the body is at the Earth's surface or center, or at any other location. When it is said (improperly) that a body has a "mass" of, say, 5 pounds, what is meant is that the mass is that of a body having a weight of 5 pounds. Similarly, a 10 gm "weight" means the Earth's pull on a 10 gm mass. To say "1 kg = 2.2 pounds" is to say that the Earth pulls on a 1 kg mass with a force of 2.2 pounds.

---

* Strictly, the pound as a unit of force in the English system of units is defined, legally, as the weight of a 0.45359237 kg mass at a location where $g = 32.17398$ feet/sec².
† See Section 10-6 for a discussion of *apparent* weightlessness.

If we compare the weights of two bodies of masses m_1 and m_2 at the same location, both bodies have the same acceleration g when falling; therefore,

$$w_1 = m_1 g, \qquad w_2 = m_2 g$$

and
$$\frac{w_1}{w_2} = \frac{m_1}{m_2} \qquad\qquad [9\text{-}16]$$

The ratio of the masses of the two bodies at the same location is the same as the ratio of their respective weights. Thus, an ordinary gravitational beam balance, which compares the *weights* of two bodies, also indicates, when it is in balance, that the *masses* are equal (see Section 7-2).

The weight of a body is independent of the body's state of motion. We see this by considering a body tossed upward into the air: the body's acceleration is *always* g, whether it is going up or down or is momentarily at rest at the zenith. Therefore, the gravitational force $w = mg$ of the Earth on a body is likewise independent of the body's motion.

For example, when a 1 kg body is at rest on a horizontal surface, the body is said to be in equilibrium, and there is no net force on it. The Earth exerts the force w downward on the body; therefore an upward force N, equal in magnitude to the weight, acts as shown in Figure 9-18a. The

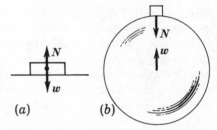

Figure 9-18. (a) Forces on a body at rest on a horizontal surface. (b) The reaction forces to the forces shown in (a).

upward force on the body arising from its interaction with the surface is perpendicular (normal) to the surface; it is termed the *normal force*. In magnitude, $N = w$ for this situation. The normal force and weight, although equal and opposite forces, do *not* comprise an action-reaction pair.

Consider the reaction forces in Figure 9-18b. The weight is the force of the Earth on the block; the reaction force is the pull of the block on the Earth. The normal force is the force of the surface on the block; the reaction force is the force of the block on the surface. The only forces that are relevant in describing the state of motion, or rest, *of the block* are the forces acting *on it*—the weight and the normal force. The reactions to these forces do *not* act on the block and are irrelevant to its motion.

The normal force has its origin in the electric forces that act between the particles at the two surfaces coming in contact. This force is zero until the atoms of the respective surfaces are within about 10^{-7} m of each other. As the separation decreases, the repulsive force increases drastically, the surfaces resist interpenetration, and the body is deformed slightly.

9-7   Non-constant mass and Newton's second law   In its most general form, Newton's second law is written

[9-3] $$\Sigma \boldsymbol{F} = \frac{d\boldsymbol{p}}{dt} = m\frac{d\boldsymbol{v}}{dt} + \boldsymbol{v}\frac{dm}{dt}$$

The resultant force acting on a body equals the mass times the rate of change of velocity *plus* the velocity times the rate of change of the mass. When a body's mass is constant, $dm/dt = 0$ and $\Sigma \boldsymbol{F} = m\boldsymbol{a}$. On the other hand, when a body of non-constant mass moves at constant velocity, $d\boldsymbol{v}/dt = 0$, and

$$\Sigma \boldsymbol{F} = \boldsymbol{v}\frac{dm}{dt} \quad \text{for constant } \boldsymbol{v} \qquad [9\text{-}17]$$

The instantaneous velocity $\boldsymbol{v}$ is the body's velocity with respect to the observer, and the quantity dm/dt is the rate at which the body accumulates mass. Equation 9-17 implies that a force is required to maintain a body at constant velocity, if its mass changes. This statement requires precise elaboration: if, in a time dt, an element of mass dm is brought *from rest* to the same velocity $\boldsymbol{v}$ as that of the moving body, a force equal to $\boldsymbol{v}\,dm/dt$ must be applied to the body to maintain it at the constant velocity $\boldsymbol{v}$. This is nothing more than an application of Newton's second law, $\boldsymbol{F} = m\boldsymbol{a}$, to the mass element dm which has undergone a velocity change of

$$d\boldsymbol{v} = \boldsymbol{v} - \boldsymbol{v}_0 = \boldsymbol{v} - 0 = \boldsymbol{v}$$

in the time dt; therefore, the required force on dm is

$$\boldsymbol{F} = (dm)\boldsymbol{a} = dm(\boldsymbol{v}/dt) = \boldsymbol{v}(dm/dt)$$

Example 8   Sand falls *vertically* and accumulates on a coasting 100 kg box at the rate of 5.0 gm/sec. The body's original velocity is 0.40 m/sec to the right. See Figure 9-19a. (a) What horizontal force is required to maintain the box in motion at a constant velocity? (b) What force is required if the sand falls obliquely with a horizontal velocity component of 0.40 m/sec to the right?

(a) The velocity of the box is to be kept constant, and Equation 9-17 applies. Since the sand falls *vertically*, it has no component of velocity along the direction of motion of the box, and if the sand is to become a part of the box, thereby increasing the total mass, the sand granules must acquire a horizontal velocity of 0.40 m/sec. (We are not concerned with *vertical* force components here.) A horizontal force must act on each sand granule to accelerate it from rest to the velocity of the box and, therefore, a horizontal force to the right must be applied to the box. The magnitude of the horizontal force is

$$F = v\,dm/dt = (0.40\ \text{m/sec})(5.0 \times 10^{-3}\ \text{kg/sec}) = 2.0 \times 10^{-3}\ \text{nt}$$

Let us consider this same situation from the point of view of an observer at rest on the box. See Figure 9-19b. From this reference frame, the sand is *not* falling vertically downward; it falls obliquely toward the observer with a horizontal velocity component of 0.40 m/sec to the left. To unite the sand with the box the sand must be brought to rest; therefore, the box must exert a force to the right on the sand granules. But if the box exerts a force to the right on the sand, then, by Newton's third law, the sand granules must exert a force of equal magnitude to the left on the box. If no *external* force were applied to the box it would be decelerated. Thus, to maintain the box at constant velocity, an outside force must be applied to the right whose magnitude is equal to that of the force of the sand on the box, i.e., equal to $v\, dm/dt$.

(b) If the sand were to fall obliquely in the direction of the box's motion with a horizontal velocity component equal to that of the box, *no horizontal force* would be required to have the sand travel with the box. See Figure 9-19c.

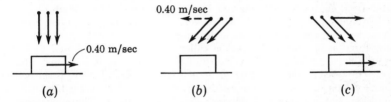

Figure 9-19. (a) Sand falls vertically on a box coasting to the right. (b) The situation of part (a) as viewed by an observer at rest on the box. (c) Sand falling obliquely on a box coasting to the right.

In this instance the box's mass would truly increase, and its velocity would remain constant *without* the application of an external force. In effect, the sand granules are—in so far as their horizontal motion is concerned—at all times *at rest* relative to the coasting box.

Parts (a) and (b) make clear that Equation 9-17 applies only if the added mass is initially *at rest* in the inertial frame of the observer. If the mass to be added has an initial velocity $\boldsymbol{v_0}$ with respect to the observer, Equation 9-17 becomes

$$\boldsymbol{F} = (\boldsymbol{v} - \boldsymbol{v_0})\,\frac{dm}{dt}$$

and Newton's second law is

$$\boxed{\boldsymbol{F} = m\,\frac{d\boldsymbol{v}}{dt} + (\boldsymbol{v} - \boldsymbol{v_0})\,\frac{dm}{dt}} \qquad \text{[9-18]}$$

Example 9 A man in a space suit is floating in empty space. He is equipped with a gas pistol which he uses to propel himself back to a near-by space ship from which he has drifted. The pistol expels gas at a speed of 2000 m/sec and at the rate of 0.010 kg/sec. The total mass of man, gun, and suit is 100 kg. What is the man's acceleration when the pistol is turned on?

We first find the force acting on the gas molecules while they are being accelerated and expelled from the pistol. By Newton's third law, the force of the molecules on the pistol is of equal magnitude to the force of the pistol on the molecules. From Equation 9-17 the force is given by

$$F = v \frac{dm}{dt} = (2000 \text{ m/sec})(0.010 \text{ kg/sec})$$

$$F = 20 \text{ nt}$$

The acceleration a of the man is then

$$a = \frac{F}{m} = \frac{(20 \text{ nt})}{(100 \text{ kg})}$$

$$a = 0.20 \text{ m/sec}^2$$

An important assumption was made here. It was that the mass of the man and pistol remained constant. This is not quite true because mass is being ejected from the pistol, although at a very slow rate. The system of the man and pistol comprise, in effect, a "rocket" and, strictly, one must take into account the fact that the mass m is decreasing.

The force *on the residual rocket* is called the *thrust* and is equal to $m \, dv/dt$, where dv is the change in the velocity of the rocket and m is its instantaneous mass. The force *on the ejected gas molecules* is $v_e \, dm/dt$, where v_e is the constant exhaust velocity relative to the residual rocket. The two forces have the same magnitude, but v is positive whereas dm/dt is negative. Therefore, since the total force on the rocket-fuel system is zero, we have

$$m \, dv/dt = -v_e \, dm/dt$$

or
$$m \, dv = -v_e \, dm$$

This differential equation is precisely the equation that was used in discussing rocket motion in Example 8-4, the solution of which was

[8-10] $$m = m_0 \, e^{-v/v_e}$$

where m_0 is the initial mass of the rocket-fuel system. In Chapter 8 we solved the rocket problem by using the law of conservation of momentum alone. In this chapter we solved the rocket problem by using forces and Newton's laws.

For bodies moving at speeds close to the speed of light ($c = 3 \times 10^8$ m/sec) relativistic mechanics is required. The resultant force still gives the time rate of linear momentum, $\Sigma \, F = dp/dt$. The linear momentum p is, however, defined as

$$p = \frac{mv}{\sqrt{1 - (v/c)^2}}$$ [9-19]

inasmuch as it is this quantity which is conserved in the collision of very-high-speed particles. The quantity p in Equation 9-19 is called the *relativistic momentum*. For ordinary speeds the relativistic momentum reduces to the classical momentum, $p = mv$, because the denominator in Equation 9-19, $\sqrt{1 - (v/c)^2}$, is essentially equal to 1. For example, with v as large as 20,000 miles/sec $= 3 \times 10^7$ m/sec, v/c is only $\frac{1}{10}$, and the denominator differs from 1 by only 0.5 per cent.

9-8 Summary When two bodies interact, the instantaneous force, $F_{1 \, on \, 2}$, of body 1 on body 2 is defined as the derivative with respect to time of the linear momentum of body 2:

[9-2] $$F_{1 \, on \, 2} = \frac{dp_2}{dt}$$

In its general form Newton's second law of motion for a particle is

[9-3] $$\Sigma F = \frac{dp}{dt} = ma + v \frac{dm}{dt}$$

where $\Sigma F = F_1 + F_2 + \cdots$ is the vector sum of all the external forces acting on the body and p is the body's linear momentum.

The impulse-momentum theorem is

[9-11] $$\int_{t_i}^{t_f} F \, dt = p_f - p_i$$

where the left-hand side is called the impulse of the force F, and the right-hand side is the resultant change in linear momentum.

Newton's third law of motion, a direct consequence of momentum conservation, states that, when two bodies interact through a mutual force,

[9-13] $$F_{2 \, on \, 1} = -F_{1 \, on \, 2}$$

Forces occur in pairs: an action force and a reaction force. These forces act on different bodies.

The weight of a body is the gravitational force w of the Earth on the body:

[9-15] $$w = mg$$

This force acts toward the Earth's center and has the magnitude mg.

PROBLEMS

9-1 A 3.0-ton truck is traveling south at 40 miles/hour. Eight seconds later, after making a turn, it is traveling west at 30 miles/hour. What is the direction and magnitude of the average force on the truck over the 8.0 sec interval?

9-2 A particle of 50 gm mass, traveling at a constant speed of 25 cm/sec, completes one circular loop. What is the average force acting on it over this time?

9-3 A 0.50-pound ball is dropped from 4.0 feet. It rebounds to 3.0 feet. The time the ball is in contact with the floor is 0.015 sec. (a) What is the average force acting on the ball during its collision? (b) Plot an approximate graph that gives the vertical force on the ball as a function of time. (c) What is the average force on the ball over the entire motion?

9-4   Show that a body that is struck by a rapid succession of identical impulsive forces, always at right angles to the body's motion, will travel in a circular path.

9-5   A parachute and its load have a total weight of 180 pounds. The parachute descends at a constant speed of 30 feet/sec. What is the upward force of the air on the parachute?

9-6   A body subject to forces of 26 nt north and 10 nt east travels with constant velocity. What third force must act on the body?

9-7   A spring is 10.0 cm long when unstretched and 12.0 cm long when a force of 2.00×10^3 dynes is applied to it. Fifteen such springs are connected together, head-to-tail fashion, and one end of the series is attached to a body. A force stretches the springs so that their over-all length is 165 cm. (a) What is the force of the springs on the body? (b) What force do the fifteen springs apply to the body when they are attached in parallel fashion to the body and stretched to a length of 11.0 cm (which is 165 cm divided by 15)?

9-8   A spring which is 4.00 inches long when unstretched has a length of 4.50 inches when a force of 10 pounds is applied to it. Two such springs are attached to a 0.40-slug body initially at rest on a smooth horizontal surface. One spring has a constant length of 4.25 inches and has its axis of symmetry along the positive X-axis; the second spring has a constant length of 4.40 inches and has its axis of symmetry along a direction $53°$ above the X-axis. (a) What is the resultant force on the body? (b) What is the body's acceleration? What are the body's (c) displacement and (d) velocity after 3.00 sec?

9-9   A billiard ball of mass m and speed v strikes a cushion at an angle θ with respect to the cushion. The ball leaves at the same speed and angle with respect to the cushion as those with which it struck. What are the magnitude and direction of the impulse on the cushion?

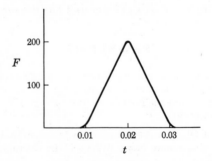

Figure 9-20

9-10   Figure 9-20 is a graph of the horizontal instantaneous force as a function of time acting on a 3.0 kg body whose initial velocity is 15 m/sec to the right. (a) What is the impulse of the force over the entire interaction time? (b) What is the average force over this time interval? (c) What is the final velocity of the body?

9-11   A pitched baseball of 0.35 pound traveling at 80 feet/sec toward the
batter is struck by the bat and leaves in the opposite direction with a
speed of 100 feet/sec. The ball is in contact with the bat for $\frac{1}{1000}$ sec.
(a) What is the average force of the ball on the bat? (b) What is the
average force of the bat on the ball? (c) Is it proper to neglect the fact
that the weight of the ball is a force acting on it continuously? (d) Plot
an approximate graph showing the horizontal and vertical components
of the ball's momentum and the force on the ball as a function of time.

9-12   A 0.80 kg ball is thrown into the air at a speed of 10 m/sec at an angle
of 30° with respect to the horizontal. (a) What is the impulse on the
ball over the first 2.0 sec? (b) What is the ball's momentum after 2.0
sec? (c) Plot graphs showing the vertical momentum component and
force as functions of time.

9-13   A ball of 200 gm is dropped from a height of 4.0 m. It makes a number
of bounces before coming essentially to rest in 4.0 sec. What is the
average force exerted by the ball on the floor over the 4.0 sec?

9-14   The weight of a vessel containing a gas exceeds the weight of the vessel
when empty by exactly the weight of the molecules within the vessel.
The molecules of the gas are in constant motion, moving in random
directions, striking the walls of the vessel, rebounding with equal speed,
and being "in contact" with the walls for only a small fraction of the
time. Explain, in terms of the impulse and momenta of the molecules,
why it is that a weight-measuring device will register exactly the weight
of the vessel plus that of its contained molecules.

9-15 ★ A beam of molecules, each molecule of mass 5.4×10^{-26} kg and speed
460 m/sec, strikes a wall perpendicular to the surface. The molecules
bounce back at the same speed. What is the average force per unit
area on the wall if the beam contains 1.5×10^{20} molecules/m³?

9-16   (a) Show that the *specific impulse* of a rocket, the impulse on the rocket
per unit ejected mass, is equal to the exhaust velocity. (b) At what
rate must mass be ejected from a rocket that uses fuel having an exhaust velocity of 2 km/sec to achieve a thrust of 10 tons?

9-17   A system consists of n interacting particles, each particle producing a
force on every other particle. (a) Show that the total number of forces
in the system is $n(n-1)$. (b) What is the vector resultant of all of these
internal forces of the system?

9-18   A ball of 0.25 slug is thrown into the air at a speed of 30 feet/sec at an
angle of 60° with respect to the horizontal. Ignoring air resistance,
give the (a) vertical, (b) horizontal, (c) tangential, and (d) radial
components of the force on it 1.0 sec later.

9-19   On the Moon the acceleration due to gravity will be found to be 1.6
m/sec². What is the (a) mass and (b) weight of a 160-pound man on
the Moon?

9-20   Show that for particles traveling at speeds close to that of light the
resultant force on the body is *not* given by the body's mass multiplied
by its acceleration.

9-21   Sand falls vertically downward at the constant rate of 0.20 kg/sec and with the constant speed of 5.0 m/sec. The sand is caught in an empty bucket 4.0 kg in mass, which rises at the constant speed of 2.0 m/sec. Find the expression giving the vertical force which must be applied to the bucket as a function of time.

TEN

NEWTONIAN MECHANICS AND ITS APPLICATIONS

Classical mechanics is sometimes referred to as Newtonian mechanics because of the profound contributions of Sir Isaac Newton. This formulation of classical mechanics was, however, but a part of Newton's scientific work. He discovered the binomial theorem and invented the differential and integral calculus. He made important contributions to the study of light, showing that color was an intrinsic property of light and not of the refracting medium, he devised the reflecting telescope, and he observed the phenomenon known as Newton's rings. He formulated the law of universal gravitation (Section 16-1) and thereby established the basic laws of celestial mechanics.

Newton's greatest contribution was his three laws of motion, already encountered in Chapter 9. We shall now restate and discuss these laws, and then apply them to various physical problems.

10-1 Newton's laws of motion Newton's three laws of motion are:

(1) *When a body is subject to no resultant external force it moves with a constant velocity.* (When $\Sigma \boldsymbol{F} = 0$, $\boldsymbol{v} = \boldsymbol{p}/m = $ constant.)

(2) *When a body is subject to one or more external forces, the time rate of the body's momentum is equal (in magnitude and direction) to the vector sum of the external forces acting on it.* (Σ $F = dp/dt$.)

(3) *When one body interacts with a second body, the force of the first body on the second is equal in magnitude but opposite in direction to the force of the second body on the first.* ($F_{2 \text{ on } 1} = -F_{1 \text{ on } 2}$.)

Consider some implications of these laws.

(1) The first law is Galileo's law of inertia. It gives the definition of an inertial frame, a reference system in which an undisturbed body moves with constant velocity.

(2) The second law applies only for observers in inertial frames of reference. (Noninertial reference frames are treated in Section 10-6.) The second law provides us with a procedure for finding an unknown force; for, if a body's motion is recorded in experiment and its acceleration at each instant is computed, then the resultant force on the body at any instant is simply the acceleration multiplied by the mass. Conversely, the second law permits us to predict in complete detail the future history of a body, provided that the forces acting on it are known; for, if one knows the forces and computes the acceleration, one can derive the future displacement and velocity from the present displacement and velocity. Kinematics and dynamics are thus united.

The resultant instantaneous force on a body can influence the body's motion in two ways. (a) The component of the force *along* the line of the instantaneous velocity changes the *magnitude* of the velocity but *not* the *direction;* which is to say, a tangential force component changes the body's speed. (2) The component of the force at *right angles* to the velocity changes the *direction* of the instantaneous velocity but *not* the *magnitude;* which is to say, a radial force component deflects the body. See Figure 10-1.

The second law embodies the principle of superposition for forces. This allows us to replace a number of forces acting simultaneously on the body by a single resultant force equal to their vector sum. For the typical situation, in which the mass of the body remains constant, the second law may be written

[9-4] $$\Sigma \, F = m\boldsymbol{a}$$

This vector equation is, of course, equivalent to three component scalar equations:

$$\boxed{\begin{aligned} F_{1x} + F_{2x} + F_{3x} + \cdots = \Sigma \, F_x = ma_x \\ F_{1y} + F_{2y} + F_{3y} + \cdots = \Sigma \, F_y = ma_y \\ F_{1z} + F_{2z} + F_{3z} + \cdots = \Sigma \, F_z = ma_z \end{aligned}}$$ [10-1]

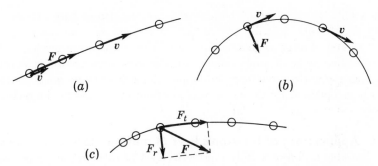

Figure 10-1.(a) A force along the instantaneous velocity changes the body's speed but not its direction. (b) A force at right angles to the instantaneous velocity changes the body's direction but not its speed. (c) Radial (F_r) and tangential (F_t) force components.

where F_{1x}, F_{2x}, F_{3x}, ..., are the X-components of the forces F_1, F_2, F_3, ..., respectively, and a_x is the X-component of the acceleration a; similarly, for the Y- and Z-components. In solving problems involving Newton's second law, it is often most convenient to employ the component scalar equations, Equations 10-1.

If a body has zero acceleration, then $a = 0$, and hence $a_x = a_y = a_z = 0$. The body then has a constant velocity (including, of course, the special case of zero velocity, or rest). Such a body is said to be in *translational equilibrium*.* By Equations 10-1 we see that a body can be in translational equilibrium only if the resultant force acting on the body is zero or, equivalently, if the sum of the force components along any direction is zero. Thus, equilibrium (in which a body has constant velocity) is a special case of dynamics, and statics (in which a body is at rest) is a special case of equilibrium.

The second law is, of course, consistent with the first law, for when no net external force acts on the body, the second law gives $\Sigma F = ma = 0$ and the body moves with a constant velocity.

(3) Newton's third law of motion is a consequence of the conservation of momentum law and the definition of force as the time rate of the linear momentum. Since the action-reaction pair consists of equal and opposite forces on different bodies, during a given time interval the impulse of one body on the second is equal but opposite to the impulse of the second on the first. Thus, the momentum lost by one body is equal to the momentum gained by the other, the total momentum of the system remaining constant. In Section 9-5 we showed this in reverse: starting with the conservation of momentum law, a direct result of experiment, we found that the action and reaction forces were equal in magnitude but opposite in direction.

---

* The condition for translational equilibrium of a body insures that the *center of mass* have a constant velocity. Complete equilibrium of a rigid body requires a second condition, to be treated in Section 14-7, relating to the *rotation* of the body.

Newton's laws are "true" because they are consistent with experiment. They successfully describe the motion of objects as small as molecules (10^{-9} m) and as large as galaxies (10^{21} m). Thus, Newtonian mechanics has an enormous range of applicability. Only for the submicroscopic world of the atom and nucleus and for speeds approaching that of light must Newton's laws be supplanted by the more nearly correct mechanics of the quantum theory and the theory of relativity.

10-2 Applications of Newton's laws of motion It is neither possible nor desirable to follow blindly a prescribed set of rules in solving problems involving Newton's laws. Nevertheless, there is a general procedure which is useful.

(1) Draw a simple, clear diagram. '

(2) Choose the body whose motion is to be analyzed. It is often helpful to draw this body, isolated from its surroundings, on a separate diagram. This is called a force diagram, or a free-body diagram.

(3) Draw *all* the forces acting *on* the chosen body. Typical forces which might act on the body are: the body's weight, forces applied by other bodies with which the chosen body is in contact, and noncontact forces (in addition to the weight), such as electric and magnetic forces which may act on the body. (Remember that when we apply Newton's second law we are concerned only with the external forces acting on the chosen body. It is true, of course, that the chosen body exerts forces on its surroundings, but such forces are irrelevant because they do not act *on* the chosen body.) Indicate on the force diagram the magnitude and direction of each force, if known; otherwise, choose symbols to represent the unknown forces.

(4) Choose appropriate axes for finding the components of the forces acting on the body. By a judicious choice of axes one can often simplify the computation of the components of forces. Find the components along the chosen axes of the acting forces by resolving each force vector into its components.

(5) Use the component form of Newton's second law, Equations 10-1, to solve algebraically for the unknowns. Some worked-out examples will illustrate these steps.

Example 1 What is the nature of the forces exerted by an ideal rope, one which is perfectly flexible, inextensible (unstretchable), and massless?

No such rope (or cord, string, or wire) exists. But in many situations a real rope closely approximates the ideal.

We now prove that the tension in the rope is the same at all points along the length of the rope, whether the rope is accelerated or in equilibrium.

Consider the situation shown in Figure 10-2a. A body of mass M, to which a rope of mass m is attached, is accelerated upward by a force P applied to the upper end of the rope. Choosing the system to be the body and rope, we draw

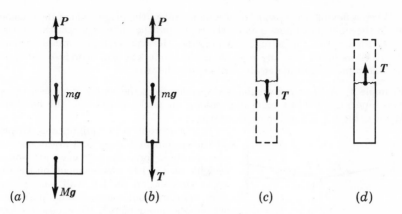

Figure 10-2. (a) A body of mass M attached to a rope of mass m. (b) The forces acting on the rope alone. (c) Forces acting on a small rope segment. (d) Forces acting on the adjoining segment.

the three forces acting on this system: the weight of the body $M\boldsymbol{g}$, the weight of the rope $m\boldsymbol{g}$, and the upward pull $\boldsymbol{P}$. By Newton's second law,

$$\Sigma F_y = (M + m)a_y$$
$$P - Mg - mg = (M + m)a_y$$

where $(M + m)$ is the total mass of the accelerated system and a_y is its acceleration. If the rope's mass is much less than that of the body, $m \ll M$, and the equation above reduces to

$$P - Mg = Ma_y$$

The acceleration of the rope and the body is given by

$$a_y = (P - Mg)/M$$

Now we focus our attention on the rope alone. The forces on it, as shown in Figure 10-2b, are the same upward force $\boldsymbol{P}$, the force $\boldsymbol{T}$ of the block on the rope at the lower end, and the rope's weight $m\boldsymbol{g}$. We wish to prove that $T \simeq P$ when m is very small. Applying Newton's second law to this system we have

$$P - T - mg = ma_y$$

Again we discard the small term mg and, using the relation for a_y above, obtain

$$P - T = \frac{m}{M}(P - Mg)$$

Because $m/M \ll 1$, the right-hand side is essentially zero. Therefore,

$$P = T$$

The force T is the *tension* of the rope. The tension is the force exerted by *any* segment of rope on an adjoining segment, as seen in Figure 10-2c, again provided that the weight of the rope segment is negligible. Thus, the tension force $\boldsymbol{T}$ in Figure 10-2c is the downward force on the molecules just above the imaginary cut, arising from the molecules just below the cut. By Newton's third law, the upward force on the molecules just below the cut is of equal magnitude (Figure 10-2d) to the tension $\boldsymbol{T}$ in Figure 10-2c.

When a flexible rope passes over a light pulley, the magnitude of the tension is again the same at all points along the rope, and the pulley changes the direction of the force without affecting its magnitude. Hereinafter, unless stated otherwise, it will be assumed that any rope is an ideal rope and that therefore the tension has the same magnitude at all points along the rope.

Example 2 A 10-pound weight is suspended from the center of a massless rope. The rope sags, its two segments making an angle of 10° with the horizontal. What is the tension in the rope segments?

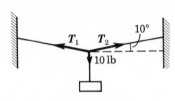

Figure 10-3

This is a problem in equilibrium. All parts of the system in Figure 10-3 are at rest, and the resultant force on any one part—on the weight, on the left rope segment, on the right rope segment, on the left wall, on the right wall, or on the knot—is zero. What part should we choose as our body? We choose the knot, because the forces on it—the tension T_1 by the left rope segment, the tension T_2 by the right rope segment, and the suspended weight W—are the forces we either know or wish to find.

Choosing the X- and Y-axes as horizontal and vertical, respectively, and resolving each of the tensions into X- and Y-components, we have, using Equations 10-1,

$$\Sigma\, F_x = ma_x$$

$$-T_1 \cos 10° + T_2 \cos 10° = 0$$

$$\Sigma\, F_y = ma_y$$

$$T_1 \sin 10° + T_2 \sin 10° - W = 0$$

Both a_x and a_y have been set equal to zero because the knot is at rest. The first equation yields

$$T_1 = T_2$$

The magnitude of the tension is the same in the left- and right-hand segments, as we would have imagined on the basis of symmetry. The second equation then gives, for the magnitude of the tension,

$$T_1 = T_2 = \frac{W}{2 \sin 10°} = \frac{10\ \text{lb}}{2 \times 0.174} = 39\ \text{lb}$$

The tension *exceeds* the weight. If the angle were smaller, the tension would be larger.

Example 3 A 160-pound man stands on a scale in an elevator (Figure 10-4). The elevator originally moves downward at constant speed, then it decelerates at 4.0 feet/sec², and finally comes to rest. What does the scale read before, during, and after its acceleration?

When the man moves with constant velocity, as is the case both before and after the deceleration, the resultant force on him is zero and the scale registers his true weight, 160 pounds.

Now we are to find the force of the man on the scale while he is decelerating. We do this by finding the magnitude of the equal and opposite force F of the scale on the man, whose mass is m and weight is mg. Since the velocity *decreases* in the *downward* direction, the acceleration is *upward*. We make the positive direction that of the acceleration, which is upward. Therefore,

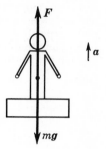

$$\Sigma F_y = F - mg = ma_y$$

or

$$F = m(g + a_y) \qquad [10\text{-}2]$$

$$F = \left(\frac{160 \text{ lb}}{32 \text{ ft/sec}^2} \right)(32 + 4) \text{ ft/sec}^2$$

$$F = 180 \text{ lb}$$

The scale registers 180 pounds. The force of the scale on the man (180 pounds) must exceed the weight (160 pounds) if it is to produce a resultant force upward. If the elevator were accelerated downward, the acceleration a above would be negative and the corresponding force F would be less than the weight.

Figure 10-4. The forces acting on a man on an elevator accelerating upward.

Example 4   A 2.0 kg block on a perfectly smooth inclined plane of 30° is acted on by a constant force of 15 nt upward along the direction of the plane. (a) What is the acceleration of the body along the incline? (b) What must be the force along the incline if the body is to move with constant velocity?

(a) In this problem, as in all problems, it is simplest first to use symbols for all quantities, and only after the problem has been solved in symbols to substitute the specific numerical quantities. In so doing, one solves, in effect, all problems of

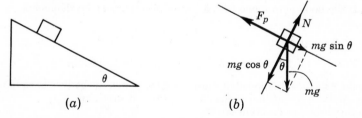

(a)   (b)

Figure 10-5. (a) A block sliding on an inclined plane of angle θ. (b) The forces acting on the block, resolved into components parallel and perpendicular to the incline.

that particular type. Moreover, certain quantities may cancel out! Here we take the mass of the block to be m, the angle of the incline to be θ, and the upward force *parallel* to the incline to be F_p.

The forces acting on the block are shown in Figure 10-5. They are the weight mg, the force F_p, and the normal force N of the incline on the body. The force of the incline is normal, or perpendicular, to the surface inasmuch as the surface is assumed perfectly smooth so that no frictional force can act along the surface.

A convenient choice of coordinate axes is that in which the X-axis is along the incline and the Y-axis is perpendicular to it. Then N is completely along Y, and F_p is along X. We may replace the weight mg, acting vertically downward, by two force components: one of magnitude $mg \cos \theta$ and along the negative Y-axis, and the other of magnitude $mg \sin \theta$ and along the positive X-axis. (The Earth pulls vertically downward on the block; its pull, however, is altogether equivalent to the simultaneous action of the two force components of the weight.)

Applying Newton's second law in the form given in Equations 10-1, we have

[10-1]
$$\Sigma F_x = ma_x$$

$$mg \sin \theta - F_p = ma_x \qquad \text{[10-3]}$$

$$\Sigma F_y = ma_y$$

$$N - mg \cos \theta = 0 \qquad \text{[10-4]}$$

We have set a_y equal to zero because the block has no motion along Y. Equation 10-4 gives the magnitude of the normal force as $N = mg \cos \theta$. The normal force is *not* equal to the weight.

We can solve for a_x from Equation 10-3:

$$a_x = \frac{mg \sin \theta - F_p}{m}$$

Substituting the given numerical values, $m = 2.0$ kg, $mg = (2.0 \text{ kg})(9.8 \text{ m/sec}^2) = 19.6$ nt, and $F_p = 15$ nt, yields

$$a_x = \frac{(19.6 \text{ nt})(\sin 30°) - (15 \text{ nt})}{(2.0 \text{ kg})} = -2.6 \text{ m/sec}^2$$

The minus sign indicates that the body accelerates along the *negative* X-axis, that is, *up* the plane.

(b) If the body is to move with a constant velocity along the incline,

$$a_x = 0$$

and Equation 10-3 reduces to

$$F_p = mg \sin \theta = (19.6 \text{ nt})(\sin 30°) = 9.8 \text{ nt}$$

When a 9.8 nt force is applied upward along the plane, the body is in equilibrium; it may go down the incline at constant speed, or it may remain at rest, or it may go up the incline at constant speed.

Example 5 A block coasts down a perfectly smooth inclined plane of angle θ. What is the magnitude of its acceleration?

We solve this problem simply by setting $F_p = 0$ in Example 4. Then Equation 10-3 becomes

$$mg \sin \theta \doteq ma_x$$

or
$$a_x = g \sin \theta$$

The acceleration is constant and *independent* of the block's mass. If the "incline" is made vertical ($\theta = 90°$), the body falls freely with acceleration g. If the "incline" is made horizontal ($\theta = 0$), the body is unaccelerated. For intermediate angles, the acceleration is less than g because the factor $\sin \theta$ is less than 1.

Motion down a smooth incline is, in effect, slow motion of a freely falling body. Galileo recognized this as a way of "diluting" gravity. He proved that a freely falling body has a constant acceleration by showing that a block sliding freely down an incline had a constant acceleration.

Example 6   A mass m_1 on a frictionless incline of angle θ is attached to an inextensible massless cord which passes over a small frictionless pulley to a second mass m_2, as shown in Figure 10-6a. (a) What is the acceleration of the two masses and the tension in the cord connecting them? (b) What are the acceleration and tension when $\theta = 90°$?

(a) Here we have a system comprised of two coupled bodies. Both bodies have the same acceleration magnitude because they are connected by a stretchless cord. To solve this problem we will first consider how Newton's laws apply

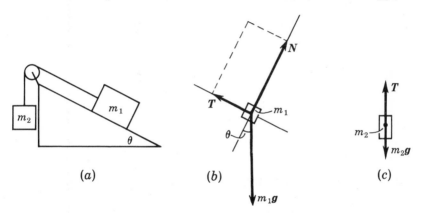

(a) (b) (c)

Figure 10-6. (a) Two blocks attached to a pulley. (b) The forces on m_1. (c) The forces on m_2.

to the mass m_1 alone and the forces that act on *it*. See Figure 10-6b. This problem is just that of Example 4 (Figure 10-5), where the tension in the cord T replaces the force $\boldsymbol{F}_p$. Therefore, Equation 10-3 becomes

$$m_1 g \sin \theta - T = m_1 a \qquad [10\text{-}5]$$

where the acceleration a is positive when m_1 accelerates down the incline.

Figure 10-6c shows the forces acting on m_2: the upward tension and the downward weight. The tension T of the cord on m_2 is equal in magnitude to the tension T on the mass m_1 in Figure 10-6b. The tension is *not*, however, equal to the weight $m_2 g$; if it were, the body would not accelerate, but would move with constant velocity. The positive direction (for forces, accelerations, velocities) was chosen as *down* the incline for body m_1. To be consistent and to take into account the fact that the bodies are coupled, we must designate the *positive* direction for body m_2 as upward. Applying Newton's second law to m_2 yields

$$\Sigma \, F_y = T - m_2 g = m_2 a \qquad [10\text{-}6]$$

Solving Equations 10-5 and 10-6 simultaneously for the unknowns a and T yields

$$a = \frac{(m_1 \sin \theta - m_2)g}{m_1 + m_2} \qquad [10\text{-}7]$$

$$T = \frac{m_1 m_2 g(1 + \sin \theta)}{m_1 + m_2} \qquad [10\text{-}8]$$

The equation for a shows that the acceleration is positive, m_2 accelerating upward and m_1 accelerating down the incline only if $m_1 \sin \theta$ exceeds m_2; otherwise, the acceleration is reversed.

(b) It is very simple to solve for the acceleration and tension when $\theta = 90°$. See Figure 10-7. The masses m_1 and m_2 are attached to a cord hung over a frictionless massless pulley. For $\theta = 90°$, $\sin \theta = 1$, and Equations 10-7 and 10-8 become

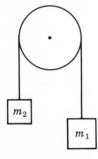

$$a = \left(\frac{m_1 - m_2}{m_1 + m_2}\right)g \qquad [10\text{-}9]$$

$$T = \left(\frac{2m_1 m_2}{m_1 + m_2}\right)g \qquad [10\text{-}10]$$

The device shown in Figure 10-7 can be used to calculate the acceleration due to gravity g by measuring m_1, m_2, and a, and applying Equation 10-9. If m_1 and m_2 are approximately equal, the quantity $m_1 - m_2$ is much less than $m_1 + m_2$, and then a is much less than g and therefore easily measured, Note also, from Equation 10-10, that when $m_1 = m_2$, the tension $T = m_1 g = m_2 g$.

Figure 10-7

10-3 Friction Once set in motion on a smooth horizontal surface, an air-suspended disc maintains an (almost) constant velocity, and even a very small horizontal force will accelerate such a disc. Most objects do not exhibit this simple behavior. Whenever two surfaces are in contact and one surface is moved relative to the other, the friction forces are quite noticeable. An exact analysis of them is very complicated because it involves interactions between protuberances on the two surfaces and, ultimately, the forces between the atoms or molecules on the surface. Our discussion of friction will be limited to the approximate empirical relations that are found to hold for some surfaces in contact with one another.

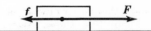

Figure 10-8. A block subject to two horizontal forces: the applied force F and the friction force f.

Consider a block at rest on a horizontal surface. What happens when we apply a horizontal force to the block (Figure 10-8)? We find that if the external force is not too large, the block remains at rest. By Newton's second law this implies that there is an equal and opposite force acting on the block to maintain its state of equilibrium. This force, called the *static-*

friction force, f_s, is produced by the surface on which the block rests. As we increase the magnitude of the external force F, the block remains at rest; therefore, the magnitude of f_s increases so that $f_s = F$. This situation persists until F reaches a critical value called $f_s(\text{max})$. For F larger than this maximum static-friction force, the block is set in motion and accelerates to the right. We find, however, that once the block moves, the retarding force of friction is *less* than $f_s(\text{max})$. The friction force now acting is called the *kinetic-friction force*, f_k. We will take f_k to be a constant, independent of the speed. (Strictly, f_k decreases with increasing speed.) Thus, once set in motion, the block is subject to a resultant force $F - f_k$ to the right, as shown in Figure 10-9. If the applied force were removed, the block would then be subject to an unbalanced force (f_k) alone, and it would eventually come to rest.

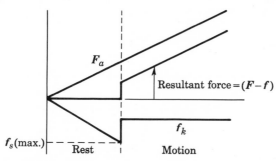

Figure 10-9. Applied force F as a function of the friction force f.

It is found by experiment that, for a given pair of surfaces, the magnitudes of f_s and f_k are directly proportional to the normal force N pressing the two surfaces together, and independent of the area in contact or the surfaces' relative velocity. Therefore, by introducing proportionality constants, we may write for the static and kinetic friction forces,

$$f_s \leq \mu_s N \qquad [10\text{-}11]$$
$$f_k = \mu_k N \qquad [10\text{-}12]$$

the constants μ_s and μ_k being called the coefficients of static and kinetic friction, respectively. They are dimensionless numbers and depend only on the pair of surfaces in contact.

Typically, $\mu_s > \mu_k$; this implies that it takes a larger force to set a body in motion than to maintain it in motion at constant speed. Values of μ are usually, but not necessarily, less than 1.00. The rougher the surfaces, the larger the μ. The inequality sign in Equation 10-11 indicates that the force of static friction can assume any value from zero to $\mu_s N$; its value is governed by the applied force.

In summary: (a) the frictional force is parallel to the surfaces in contact; (b) the static frictional force is always opposite to the applied force when the surfaces are at rest relative to one another; (c) the kinetic frictional force on one surface is always opposite to the direction of the velocity of that surface relative to the other surface; (d) both frictional forces are proportional to the normal force.

Example 7   A block is projected with an initial speed of 2.0 m/sec up an inclined plane whose angle is 30°, as shown in Figure 10-10. The coefficients of static and

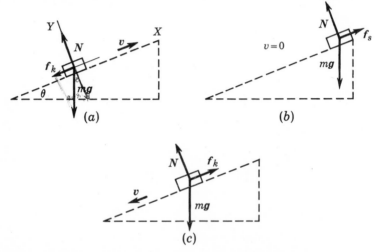

Figure 10-10. Forces on a block (a) sliding *up* a rough plane, (b) at rest at the highest point, and (c) sliding *down* the rough plane.

kinetic friction between the block and the surface of the incline are $\mu_s = 0.40$ and $\mu_k = 0.30$. (a) How far up the plane will the block slide before stopping? (b) After coming to rest at this point, will the block remain at rest? (c) If the block slides down, what is its speed at the bottom?

(a) The external forces acting on the block during its motion *up* the plane are shown in Figure 10-10a. We choose positive X- and Y-directions as indicated in the figure. Then, by Newton's second law,

$$\Sigma F_y = ma_y = 0$$

$$N - mg \cos \theta = 0$$

$$N = mg \cos \theta \qquad [10\text{-}13]$$

and

$$\Sigma F_x = ma_x$$

$$-f_k - mg \sin \theta = ma_x \qquad [10\text{-}14]$$

By definition (Equation 10-12),
$$f_k = \mu_k N$$

From Equation 10-13, this may be written
$$f_k = \mu_k mg \cos \theta \qquad [10\text{-}15]$$

Therefore, Equation 10-14 becomes
$$-\mu_k mg \cos \theta - mg \sin \theta = ma_x$$

Notice that the mass cancels out, and the acceleration is
$$a_x = -g(\sin \theta + \mu_k \cos \theta) \qquad [10\text{-}16]$$

Because a_x is negative, the block decelerates up the incline, and because a_x is constant in magnitude, we may use the kinematic relation,

[2-11]
$$v_x^2 = v_{0x}^2 + 2a_x x \qquad [10\text{-}17]$$

When the block reaches its highest point, $v_x = 0$; Equations 10-16 and 10-17 then yield
$$x = -\frac{v_{0x}^2}{2a_x} = \frac{v_{0x}^2}{2g(\sin \theta + \mu_k \cos \theta)} \qquad [10\text{-}18]$$

Substituting the numerical quantities for v_{0x}, θ, and μ_k, and using $g = 9.8$ m/sec^2, we obtain
$$x = 0.27 \text{ m} = 27 \text{ cm}$$

(b) The block is now at rest on the incline. Whether it remains at rest depends upon the relative magnitudes of the *maximum static* force of friction, f_s(max), *up* the incline, and the component of the weight down the incline, $mg \sin \theta$ (see Figure 10-10b):
$$f_s(\text{max}) = \mu_s N = \mu_s mg \cos \theta = (0.35)mg$$
and
$$mg \sin \theta = (0.50)mg$$

Inasmuch as f_s(max) $< mg \sin \theta$, the block is subject to a resultant force *down* the incline, even at the instant when it is at rest. Therefore, the block does not remain at rest at its highest point.

(c) The forces acting on the body while it slides down the incline are shown in Figure 10-10c. The friction force, now acting *up* the incline, again opposes the motion. The forces in Figure 10-10c differ from those in Figure 10-10a only in the direction of f_k. Thus, to obtain the acceleration for motion down the incline, we merely change the sign of f_k in Equation 10-15, and Equation 10-16 becomes
$$a_x = -g(\sin \theta - \mu_k \cos \theta) \qquad [10\text{-}19]$$

Again using the kinematic relation (Equation 10-17), we obtain
$$v_x = \pm \sqrt{2a_x x} \qquad [10\text{-}20]$$

where v_{0x} is zero. Using Equation 10-19 in Equation 10-20, we have
$$v_x = \pm \sqrt{-2gx(\sin \theta - \mu_k \cos \theta)}$$

When we substitute the numerical values, we must write
$$x = -0.27 \text{ m}$$

where the minus sign indicates that the displacement is down the plane, along the *negative* X-axis. We have, finally, for the *speed* down the plane,

$$v_x = 1.1 \text{ m/sec}$$

Because the kinetic friction always opposes the motion—the friction force is *velocity*-dependent, but *not* speed-dependent—the block's speed upon return (1.1 m/sec) is less than its initial speed (2.0 m/sec).

10-4 Systems of interacting particles The acceleration of a single body is determined by the resultant of all forces acting on it. In this section it will be proved that for a *system* of particles, interacting with one another

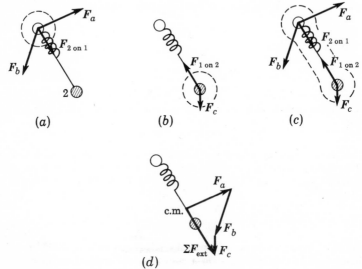

Figure 10-11. Two bodies interacting by a spring and being subject, in addition, to the forces F_a, F_b, and F_c. (a) Body 1 chosen as the system (dotted lines) and the forces on it. (b) Body 2 chosen as the system and the forces on it. (c) *External* forces on the system comprised of bodies 1 and 2. (d) The motion of the center of mass is determined by the resultant of the *external* forces on the system only.

through *internal* forces and also subject to *external* forces, the acceleration of the *center of mass of the system* is determined by the resultant of the *external* forces on the system.

First, the meaning of "the system" and its boundaries, and the distinction between an internal and an external force, must be clearly understood. We can illustrate this by considering the simple case of two particles connected by a (massless) spring and subject to external forces, as shown in Figure 10-11.

We first choose as our system body 1. To emphasize this choice, the boundaries of the system are shown by dotted lines in Figure 10-11a. Any force penetrating this boundary is an external force *on body 1*. Newton's second law for body 1 is

$$\Sigma\, F = ma$$

$$F_a + F_b + F_{2\,\text{on}\,1} = m_1 a_1 \qquad [10\text{-}21]$$

where m_1 and a_1 are the mass and acceleration of body 1.

Next let us choose as our system body 2. The boundary of this system is shown in Figure 10-11b, and the forces penetrating this boundary are external forces on body 2. Thus, for body 2 we have

$$\Sigma\, F = ma$$

$$F_c + F_{1\,\text{on}\,2} = m_2 a_2 \qquad [10\text{-}22]$$

where m_2 and a_2 are the mass and acceleration of body 2.

Finally, we choose as our system bodies 1 and 2 and the spring connecting them, as shown in Figure 10-11c. The only forces penetrating the boundary of the system, and therefore the only *external* forces, are F_a, F_b, and F_c; the forces $F_{2\,\text{on}\,1}$ and $F_{1\,\text{on}\,2}$ do not penetrate the boundary and are internal forces. For the combined system of bodies 1 and 2,

$$\Sigma\, F = ma$$

$$F_a + F_b + F_c = (m_1 + m_2)A = MA \qquad [10\text{-}23]$$

where $m_1 + m_2 = M$ is the total mass of the system and A is the acceleration whose significance we wish to find. Adding Equations 10-21 and 10-22 gives

$$(F_a + F_b + F_{2\,\text{on}\,1}) + (F_c + F_{1\,\text{on}\,2}) = m_1 a_1 + m_2 a_2$$

or, regrouping,

$$(F_a + F_b + F_c) + (F_{2\,\text{on}\,1} + F_{1\,\text{on}\,2}) = m_1 a_1 + m_2 a_2 \qquad [10\text{-}24]$$

By Newton's third law we have $F_{2\,\text{on}\,1} = -F_{1\,\text{on}\,2}$ and thus Equation 10-24 reduces to

$$F_a + F_b + F_c = m_1 a_1 + m_2 a_2 \qquad [10\text{-}25]$$

Comparing Equations 10-25 and 10-23 shows that

$$(m_1 + m_2)A = m_1 a_1 + m_2 a_2 \qquad [10\text{-}26]$$

By definition, the velocity of the center of mass v_{cm} is given by

[8-24] $$(m_1 + m_2)v_{\text{cm}} = m_1 v_1 + m_2 v_2$$

and, taking the derivative with respect to time of the above equation, yields

$$(m_1 + m_2)a_{\text{cm}} = m_1 a_1 + m_2 a_2 \qquad [10\text{-}27]$$

where a_{cm} is the acceleration of the center of mass of the system comprised of m_1 and m_2.

When we compare Equations 10-26 and 10-27, it is clear that $A = a_{cm}$ and so Equation 10-23 becomes

$$F_a + F_b + F_c = Ma_{cm}$$

Thus, we arrive at the result: for any system of interacting particles the *resultant* of the *external forces* acting on the system is equal to the mass of the entire system multiplied by the acceleration of the center of mass, or

$$\boxed{\Sigma\, F_{\text{ext}} = Ma_{cm}} \qquad\qquad [10\text{-}28]$$

where M is the system's total mass and $\Sigma\, F_{\text{ext}}$ is the sum of the *external forces only*. This remarkable result, derived by considering a simple system of only two bodies, holds for a system comprised of any number of interacting particles. The resultant of the internal forces is zero because they occur in pairs of equal but opposite forces.

Whether a particular force is an internal or external force is determined solely by our choice of the boundaries of the system. Equation 10-28 implies that a system of interacting particles may be replaced, in effect, by a *single* particle having the mass of the whole system. This equivalent particle at the center of mass of the system has an acceleration that is determined solely by the external forces. Thus, the motion of any one particle of a system can be thought of as a combination of two motions: first, it has the motion of the center of mass and, second, it has motion relative to the center of mass. It is because of Equation 10-28 that we may treat a complicated system, such as an air-suspended disc, with its myriad of interacting nuclei and electrons, as a mere mass point!

The more general form for Equation 10-28 is

$$\Sigma\, F_{\text{ext}} = \frac{d}{dt}\, P_{cm} \qquad\qquad [10\text{-}29]$$

where P_{cm} is the momentum of the center of mass of the system and is equal to $\Sigma\, p_i$ (Equation 8-25), the total momentum of the system. When $\Sigma\, F_{\text{ext}} = 0$, $d/dt(P_{cm}) = 0$ and, therefore, $P_{cm} = \Sigma\, p_i = $ constant. For an isolated system (one subject to no net external force), the total momentum of the system remains constant—the conservation of momentum law.

Example 8 A shell shot into the air explodes into two parts of equal mass. Describe the motion of the center of mass and that of the two fragments.

The shell, which becomes the two fragments after the explosion, is chosen as our system. The total external force on the system, which is the weight of the shell, is constant. Any particle subject to a constant force moves in a parabolic trajectory. Therefore, by Equation 10-28, the center of mass of the shell, before and after the explosion, traces out a parabolic path, as shown in Figure 10-12.

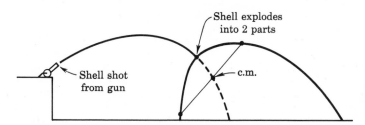

Figure 10-12. A shell exploding into two parts of equal mass. The center of mass traces out a parabolic path.

Because the two fragments are assumed to be of equal mass, the center of mass always lies midway between the two fragments, each of which also traces out a parabolic path.

When the first fragment strikes the ground, the system is subject to another external force, the force of the ground on the fragment. Thereafter, the center of mass no longer follows the same parabolic path.

Example 9 Two air-suspended discs, of masses 1.0 kg and 2.0 kg, are initially at rest on a smooth horizontal surface. Discuss the motion of the center of mass when (a) a constant force is applied to the 2.0 kg mass alone, (b) a constant force is applied to the 2.0 kg mass when it is connected by a thin rigid rod to the 1.0 kg mass and, (c) the constant force is applied at the location of the center of mass.

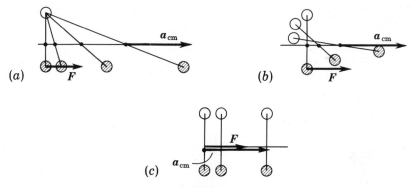

Figure 10-13. Two bodies of unequal mass acted on by a constant force. The center of mass of the system has a constant acceleration. (a) A force acts on one body only. (b) The two bodies are connected by a rigid rod and the force is applied at the 2.0 kg mass. (c) The force is applied at the center of mass.

If in all three situations the system is chosen as the two discs (and the massless rod that may join them), and if the same constant force is applied to this system in all three cases, then the acceleration of the center of mass, given by Equation 10-28, must be the same for all three, as shown in the multiflash photographs of Figure 10-13. Although the motion of the center of mass is the same for all three situations, the motion of the two discs relative to the center of mass depends on the internal forces between the discs.

In Figure 10-13a, the 1.0 kg body remains at rest, and the center of mass moves so as to maintain a 2-to-1 separation ratio between the center of mass and the respective discs. In Figure 10-13b the rod turns with respect to the center of mass. In Figure 10-13c the two discs have the same acceleration as that of the center of mass, and the rod does not turn. This was, of course, the basis of the definition of the center of mass given in Section 8-4. If the two masses in Figure 10-13c are equal, the center of mass is midway between them, and a force applied at this point does not cause a turning of the rod if initially at rest. This is nothing more than the inertial balance, discussed in Section 7-2.

10-5 Uniform circular motion A body is accelerated whenever an unbalanced force acts on it. If the resultant force is along the direction of the velocity, the speed changes, but not the direction of the velocity. If the resultant force is always at right angles to the velocity, the direction changes, but not the speed. The body is again accelerated. A body moves in a circle with constant speed when the resultant force is perpendicular to the velocity and is of constant magnitude.

The kinematics of uniform circular motion was treated in Section 5-1. The results were these: a body in motion at speed v in a circular arc of radius r has a radial, or centripetal, acceleration a_r whose direction is toward the center of the circular arc and whose magnitude is v^2/r; equivalently, $a_r = \omega^2 r$, where ω is the angular speed (in *radians* per unit time).

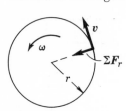

Therefore, if a body is to move in uniform circular motion, the resultant force along the radial direction is *not* zero. Indeed, by Newton's second law it must be

$$\Sigma F_r = ma_r$$

$$\Sigma F_r = \frac{mv^2}{r} = m\omega^2 r \qquad [10\text{-}30]$$

Figure 10-14. A particle in uniform circular motion under the influence of a resultant radial force F_r.

By the same token, for *uniform* circular motion (constant speed), the resultant *tangential* force is zero: $\Sigma F_t = ma_t = 0$. See Figure 10-14.

As always, it is essential that we apply Newton's second law from the point of view of an observer in an *inertial frame*. This deserves special emphasis when one deals with bodies moving in circles. For example, if one considers the motion of a man in an automobile traveling in a circle, one must view the motion as an observer fixed in the inertial frame of the Earth (or in a reference frame moving with constant velocity relative to it). One cannot properly apply Newton's second law from the point of view of the occupant, as is perhaps psychologically more appealing. Such an observer is in an accelerated, and therefore noninertial, frame; the law of inertia does not hold in such a reference frame.

Example 10   An astronaut is riding in a space capsule in a circular orbit at constant speed about the Earth. What is the resultant force on the astronaut?

The forces on the astronaut, his weight $m\mathbf{g}$ and the force $\mathbf{N}$ of the seat on the astronaut, are shown in Figure 10-15. These are the only possible forces acting on the astronaut if we observe the motion from an inertial frame of reference. We know that the force $\mathbf{N}$, if it exists, must be along the radial direction, inasmuch as there can be no resultant force along the tangential direction. Applying Newton's second law along the radial direction (taking inward as positive), gives

$$\Sigma\, \mathbf{F}_r = ma_r$$

$$mg - N = mv^2/r \qquad [10\text{-}31]$$

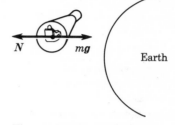

Figure 10-15. Forces on an astronaut in a satellite orbiting the Earth in uniform circular motion.

where v is the speed of the capsule and r is the radius of the orbit.

From the kinematical analysis of satellite motion in Example 2, Section 5-1, we found that the centripetal acceleration g is related to the orbital speed and radius by

$$g = v^2/r$$

Using this result in Equation 10-31 yields

$$\mathbf{N} = 0$$

While in orbit at constant speed, the space ship applies *no* force on the astronaut or, for that matter, on any object within the capsule. The only force acting on the astronaut is the weight arising from the gravitational pull of the Earth. This is the resultant force that permits the astronaut to go in circular orbit.

The astronaut, or any other object in the capsule, is, of course, *not* weightless, the quantities g and mg being nonzero. Because N is zero, all objects in the capsule float about when unattached. For this reason the astronaut experiences *apparent weightlessness*. Paradoxically, the only time a body experiences apparent weightlessness is when the only force acting on it is its weight!

Example 11   Show all forces acting on (a) a conical pendulum and (b) a simple pendulum, and discuss how these forces are related to the centripetal acceleration.

(a) A conical pendulum consists of a small body of mass m attached to a string of length l moving in a *horizontal* circle at *constant* speed v. The string thereby sweeps out a cone of fixed angle θ with respect to the vertical, as shown in Figure 10-16a.

The forces acting on the small mass m are the tension $\mathbf{T}$ and the weight $m\mathbf{g}$. Because the body moves in a *horizontal* plane, there is no vertical acceleration. Therefore, it is convenient to resolve the two forces into horizontal and vertical

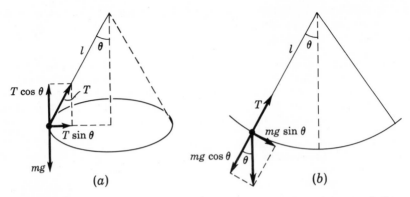

Figure 10-16. Forces on the particle of (a) a conical pendulum and (b) a simple pendulum.

components, the horizontal component being chosen as radially inward, to correspond with the direction of the radial acceleration.

Applying Newton's second law gives

$$\Sigma \, \boldsymbol{F} = m\boldsymbol{a}$$

Vertical components: $T \cos \theta - mg = 0$

Horizontal components: $T \sin \theta = ma_r = mv^2/r$

where the radius of the circle is $r = l \sin \theta$. The resultant force giving rise to the centripetal acceleration is the horizontal component of the tension.

(b) A simple pendulum consists of a small body of mass m attached to a string of length l moving in a *vertical* circular arc at a *nonconstant* speed v. The swinging motion can be initiated by pulling the body to the side and releasing it (see Figure 10-16b).

The forces acting on the body, the tension $\boldsymbol{T}$ and the weight $m\boldsymbol{g}$, are shown at the moment when the string makes an angle θ with respect to the vertical and the body is descending with instantaneous speed v along the circular path. It is most convenient in this problem to resolve the forces into radial and tangential components, that is, into components along the direction of the string and along the path. Newton's second law yields

$$\Sigma \, \boldsymbol{F} = m\boldsymbol{a}$$

Radial components: $T - mg \cos \theta = ma_r = m(v^2/l)$

Tangential components: $mg \sin \theta = ma_t$

Inasmuch as there exists a tangential component of the resultant force, the speed of the body changes. The magnitude of the radial acceleration, $a_r = v^2/l$ (the length l is the constant radius of the vertical circle), is *not* constant, because the speed is changing. The tension is *not* the same for all points along the path. For example, at the highest point, where the body is momentarily at rest, $a_r = 0$ and $T = mg \cos \theta_{max}$. At the lowest point the tension and the weight have radial components only, and $T = mg + mv_{max}^2/l$. We see that, at the lowest point, the tension *exceeds* the weight, as it must if the body is to move in a circle.

If the string were cut while the body was in motion, the only force acting thereafter would be its weight; therefore, the body would fly off initially along a tangent to the circular arc. Thereafter it would move in a parabolic path because a constant force acts on it.

The resultant force acting on a body in uniform circular motion is often referred to as the *centripetal force*. This designation is mischievous because the centripetal force is not a distinctive type of force. A body may move in a circle under the influence of its weight, or the tension of a cord, or a friction force, or a normal force, or a combination of forces. If the resultant of all forces acting on the body produces circular motion, this resultant is *the* centripetal force.

The term *centrifugal force* is also used in discussions of circular motion, often misleadingly. A centrifugal force does not exist when one applies Newton's laws in an inertial frame. As we shall see in the next section, the centrifugal force is a fictitious force introduced to describe motion in a rotating, and therefore noninertial, reference frame.

10-6   Noninertial reference frames and inertial forces   If an observer is to apply Newton's second law to the motion of a body, it is

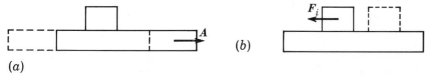

(a) (b)

Figure 10-17. (a) A frictionless puck on a platform moving to the right with acceleration A. (b) The puck's motion from the point of view of an observer at rest on the accelerating platform. The puck has an acceleration $-A$ under the influence of an inertial force F_i.

required that he make his observations from an inertial frame, a reference frame in which the law of inertia, or Newton's first law of motion, holds. He can make a preliminary test of whether he is indeed in an inertial frame by seeing whether a body free of external influence moves in a straight line at constant speed. If it does, he can proceed to use Newton's second law with impunity. In this section we analyze what happens if an observer in an accelerated, and therefore noninertial, frame attempts to apply Newton's second law.

Consider the situation illustrated in Figure 10-17, where an air-suspended disc of mass m sits on a frictionless horizontal platform initially at rest relative to the ground. The platform is then accelerated to the right with an acceleration A relative to the *inertial observer* on the ground. A *noninertial observer* is at rest on the accelerating platform.

Each observer applies Newton's second law to the motion of the disc relative to his reference frame. With respect to the inertial observer, the disc is, and remains, at rest; he concludes that no resultant force acts on the disc. With respect to the noninertial observer, the disc has a constant acceleration of magnitude A to the left; therefore, as a confirmed Newtonian, he concludes that a force F_i acts on the disc to accelerate it. Each observer applies Newton's second law to the motion of the same disc as follows:

$$\Sigma \, \boldsymbol{F} = m\boldsymbol{a}$$

Inertial observer: $0 = 0$

Noninertial observer: $\boldsymbol{F}_i = -m\boldsymbol{A}$

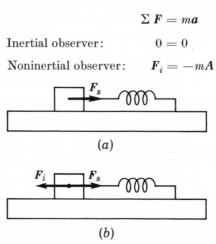

(a)

(b)

Figure 10-18. (a) Disc fastened to an accelerating platform by a spring. The spring force $\boldsymbol{F}_s$ acts on the disc to give it an acceleration $\boldsymbol{A}$. (b) The same situation as viewed by an observer at rest on the accelerating platform. The disc is at rest under the influence of the spring force $\boldsymbol{F}_s$ and an inertial force $\boldsymbol{F}_i$.

The inertial observer sees the disc in equilibrium, with no resultant force on it; the noninertial observer sees the disc accelerated by an *inertial force*, $\boldsymbol{F}_i = -m\boldsymbol{A}$. This inertial force is fictitious in the sense that it does not have its origin in the interaction of the disc with other objects. *The noninertial observer invents the inertial force to preserve Newton's second law in his reference frame.* The inertial force is equal in magnitude to the mass m of the "accelerated" object multiplied by the magnitude of the acceleration A of the noninertial frame relative to an inertial frame; its direction is opposite to that of the accelerated frame relative to the inertial frame.

Now suppose that the disc is attached to a spring which is, in turn, fastened to the accelerating platform. See Figure 10-18. When the platform is accelerated to the right, again with acceleration A, the spring stretches. The spring applies a force $\boldsymbol{F}_s$ to the disc so that the disc's acceleration is also $\boldsymbol{A}$ relative to the inertial observer.

How does the situation appear to the noninertial observer? He also sees that the spring is stretched by the same amount; therefore, the spring applies the same force F_s on the disc to the right. But from his point of view, the disc is at rest. Therefore, it must be subject, in addition, to an inertial force to the left. The observers now write, for Newton's second law,

$$\Sigma \boldsymbol{F} = m\boldsymbol{a}$$

Inertial observer: $\boldsymbol{F}_s = m\boldsymbol{A}$ [10-32]

Noninertial observer: $\boldsymbol{F}_s + \boldsymbol{F}_i = 0$ [10-33]

From Equations 10-32 and 10-33 we obtain

$$\boldsymbol{F}_i = -m\boldsymbol{A} \qquad [10\text{-}34]$$

Whereas the inertial observer deals only with "real" forces having their origins in other bodies, the noninertial observer must invoke a fictitious, an

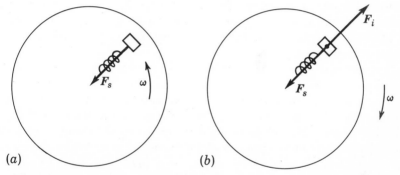

Figure 10-19. (a) Disc connected by a spring to a uniformly rotating platform, as viewed by an inertial observer; the disc is subject to an inward radial spring force $\boldsymbol{F}_s$. (b) The same situation as viewed by a noninertial observer at rest on the rotating platform; the disc is in equilibrium under the influence of the spring force $\boldsymbol{F}_s$ and an inertial force $\boldsymbol{F}_i$, the *centrifugal force*.

inertial, force, $\boldsymbol{F}_i = -m\boldsymbol{A}$, in addition to the real forces, to maintain Newton's second law.*

Let us look at another example of observations from a noninertial system. Our noninertial frame is now a uniformly rotating platform, a merry-go-round. We consider the motion of a disc attached by a spring to a point on the rotating platform. See Figure 10-19. From the point of view of an

---

* A disquieting note: If an observer is inside a closed room and cannot see whether there are objects outside of the room which may exert forces on the disc, how can he decide whether the forces that act are real or fictitious? More about this question, and Einstein's answer, in Section 16-7.

inertial observer, standing outside of the rotating platform, the disc executes uniform circular motion under the action of the spring force F_s toward the center of the circle.

How do things look to the noninertial observer? He sees the spring stretched the same amount and the disc at rest. He must conclude, therefore, that the disc is subject to two forces: the spring force F_s acting toward the center of the rotating platform, and an inertial force F_i acting away from the center. The two observers write Newton's second law as

$$\Sigma\, F = m a$$

Inertial observer: $\qquad F_s = m \omega^2 r$

Noninertial observer: $\qquad F_s + F_i = 0$

Eliminating F_s in these two equations yields $F_i = -m\omega^2 r = -mA$, where $A = v^2/r = \omega^2 r$ is the acceleration of a point on the rotating platform relative to the inertial observer. The inertial force F_i arising in the rotating reference frame acts in the direction away from the center of the circle (and is equal in magnitude to the centripetal force). This inertial force is called the *centrifugal force*.

A centrifugal force arises only in a rotating reference frame. It is the fictitious force that exists, for example, for an occupant in an automobile rounding a curve; the centrifugal force pushes him outward from the center of the circle. The centrifugal force also exists for an astronaut circling the Earth in a space ship. From *his* point of view, every object in the space ship is subject to two forces: the pull of the Earth and a centrifugal force away from the Earth. The net force on any object is, in *his* view, zero. Unattached objects float *relative to the astronaut*, and he may conclude that all objects in the space ship *are weightless*. On the other hand, an inertial observer says that the objects in the space ship *appear* to be weightless because all such objects have the *same* acceleration.

If a noninertial observer is to apply Newton's second law, he must include, in addition to any real forces which act on the body, the inertial force $F_i = -mA$, where m is the body's mass and A is the acceleration of the noninertial reference system relative to an inertial frame. This allows us to write Newton's second law in its most general form, applicable to any observer whether inertial or noninertial:

$$\boxed{\Sigma F + F_i = m a, \qquad \text{where } F_i = -mA} \qquad [10\text{-}35]$$

Example 12   How do we know that the Earth rotates?

We find that Galileo's law of inertia does not quite hold for free objects on Earth. Consider an air-suspended disc set in motion on a flat surface so as to pass over the Earth's axis of rotation at the North Pole. If the Earth were indeed an inertial frame, the disc would not deviate from a straight line drawn on it. But if the disc did deviate, it would appear to be deflected by a force, albeit an inertial force.

The same test may be made indirectly by imagining a pendulum to swing so as to pass over the North Pole. If the Earth were an inertial frame and did not rotate, the plane of the pendulum would appear, from Earth, to remain fixed. Now, the plane of the pendulum's motion does *not* remain fixed; it rotates very slowly (once a day). We can interpret this behavior in either of two equivalent ways: (a) we can say that the plane of the pendulum's motion is indeed unchanged when viewed from the fixed stars and that the pendulum merely appears to rotate to an observer on Earth because it is the Earth itself which is truly rotating, or (2) we may say that the pendulum is subject to a fictitious or inertial force which deflects it and causes the plane in which it oscillates to rotate. This analysis was first made by L. Foucault, and a pendulum that demonstrates this phenomenon is known as a *Foucault pendulum*.

10-7 Summary Newton's laws of motion may be written symbolically as:

(1) When $\Sigma \, \boldsymbol{F} = 0$, then $\boldsymbol{v} = \dfrac{\boldsymbol{p}}{m} = \text{constant.}$

(2) $\Sigma \, \boldsymbol{F} = \dfrac{d\boldsymbol{p}}{dt} = m\boldsymbol{a}.$

(3) $\boldsymbol{F}_{2 \text{ on } 1} = -\boldsymbol{F}_{1 \text{ on } 2}.$

The vector form of Newton's second law implies that the algebraic sum of the components of the external forces along any direction is equal to the body's mass multiplied by the component of the body's acceleration along that same direction.

The friction forces between surfaces are closely approximated by the following relations:

[10-11]   Static friction: $f_s \leq \mu_s N$

[10-12]   Kinetic friction: $f_k = \mu_k N$

When a system of interacting particles is subject to external forces,

[10-28] $$\Sigma \, \boldsymbol{F}_{\text{ext}} = \frac{d\boldsymbol{P}_{\text{cm}}}{dt} = M\boldsymbol{a}_{\text{cm}}$$

where $\Sigma \, \boldsymbol{F}_{\text{ext}}$ is the vector sum of external forces only, M is the total mass of the system, and $\boldsymbol{a}_{\text{cm}}$ is the acceleration of the system's center of mass.

When applied to a body undergoing uniform circular motion, Newton's second law becomes

[10-30] $$\Sigma \, F_r = \frac{mv^2}{r} = m\omega^2 r$$

where $\Sigma \, F_r$ is the resultant radial force.

Newton's second law of motion can be applied in a noninertial frame of reference having an acceleration A relative to an inertial frame if, in addition to the real forces $\Sigma\,F$, the noninertial observer introduces an inertial force F_i:

[10-35] $\Sigma\,F + F_i = ma,$ where $F_i = -mA$

PROBLEMS

10-1   A 1.0-slug body falls from rest with a constant horizontal force of 24 pounds acting on it. What are (a) the acceleration, (b) the displacement, and (c) the velocity of the body after 2.0 sec?

10-2   A body of 4.0 kg is subject to simultaneous constant forces of 6.0 nt south, 5.0 nt northeast, and 8.0 nt 30° west of north. If the body is initially at rest, what are (a) the displacement and (b) the velocity of the body after 2.0 sec?

10-3   When thrown in the air, a ball is subject to a single constant force of 0.40 pound in the downward direction. The ball is thrown horizontally with an initial speed of 30 feet/sec from a high cliff. Compute from Newton's laws (a) the horizontal and (b) the vertical components of its momentum 4.0 sec later.

10-4   An electron in the region between two parallel, oppositely charged, metal plates to which a 10-volt battery has been attached has a constant acceleration arising from the electric charges on the plates of 1.7×10^{14} m/sec². The electron's mass is 9.1×10^{-31} kg. What is the ratio of the electric force to the gravitational force on the electron? (In atomic physics, in which the principal forces are of electric origin, the gravitational force between particles is entirely negligible.)

10-5   What is the weight of a 2.00 kg mass at a point on the Earth's surface where $g = 32.2$ feet/sec² $= 9.80$ m/sec²? Express the weight in all three systems of units.

10-6   A 1.0 kg body initially at rest on a smooth horizontal surface is subject to a constant force of 5.0 nt east for 2.0 sec. After this, the body coasts freely for 2.0 sec. Then a constant force of 4.0 nt is applied to the body for 2.0 sec to the north. What are (a) the final displacement and (b) the final velocity of the body relative to the starting point?

10-7   An accelerometer is a device for measuring accelerations. In its simplest form an accelerometer consists of a spring with a mass attached to a free end. The acceleration is determined by the position of the mass. An accelerometer having a spring with a force constant of 1.4×10^3 nt/cm has a 0.30 kg mass attached to it. The mass is found to undergo a maximum displacement of 0.40 cm from its equilibrium position. What is the maximum acceleration experienced by the accelerometer?

10-8   An electron (mass, 9.1×10^{-31} kg) is subject to a force of 4.0×10^{-17} nt. If the electron starts from rest, (a) how long does it take the electron to travel 4.0 cm, (b) what is its speed at this time, and (c) is the weight of the electron a force of any consequence?

10-9   A proton (mass, 1.67×10^{-27} kg) is traveling at a speed of 2.5×10^8 m/sec. (a) What is the magnitude of the proton's momentum according to the relativistic relation for momentum? (b) What would be (improperly) the magnitude of the proton's momentum according to the classical relation for momentum? (c) What force is required to bring the proton to rest in 2.0×10^{-5} sec?

10-10   A body of mass m is subject to a force that varies with time according to $F_y = 0$ and $F_x = A + Bt$, where A and B are constants. Find the equation of motion of the body, giving the displacements x and y of the body as a function of time.

10-11   A 10-pound weight is suspended from a cord attached to the ceiling of an elevator. The elevator, traveling initially upward at 3.0 feet/sec, comes to rest at constant acceleration in 1.5 sec. What is the tension in the cord during this time?

10-12   One end of a rope is attached to a ceiling, and a 100 kg block is suspended from the other end. The rope has a constant density and diameter; the total mass of the rope is 10 gm. Find the tension in the rope at (a) its lower end, (b) its midpoint, and (c) its upper end.

10-13   A weight w is suspended from the center of a light, taut, and originally horizontal rope. After suspending the weight w, what angle must the rope make with the horizontal if the tension in the rope is to equal the weight w?

10-14   A 0.50-pound bird lands on a taut telephone wire whose mass is negligible. The weight of the bird depresses the wire into two straight segments, one making an angle of 2.0° with respect to the horizontal, the other making an angle of 4.0° to the horizontal. Calculate the tensions in the two segments of wire.

10-15   A 1.5-pound sphere is attached to the lower end of a 2.0-foot string of negligible mass. The upper end of the string is held fixed. (a) What horizontal force must be applied to the sphere to have it be in equilibrium with an angle of 37° between the string and the vertical? (b) Find the tension in the string for the conditions of part (a). (c) If the sphere in part (a) were to be held in equilibrium by a force that was perpendicular to the string, rather than horizontal, what would be the tension in the string?

10-16   When small oil droplets fall through (nonturbulent) air, they quickly achieve a *terminal velocity*, falling at *constant* speed downward. It is found that the terminal velocity is directly proportional to the cube of the radius of the droplet for droplets of the same liquid. How does the resistive force of the air on the droplet vary with speed?

10-17 ★ A block of mass 2.0 kg at rest on a horizontal frictionless surface is attached to a rope that passes over a frictionless massless pulley, as shown in Figure 10-20. The block is initially displaced 2.0 m horizontally from the pulley. The string makes an angle of 30° with respect to

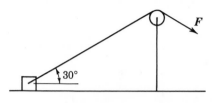

Figure 10-20

the horizontal. A constant pull of 28 nt is applied to the string. At what point relative to its starting position will the block leave the surface?

10-18   A 1.5 kg block is initially at rest at the foot of a frictionless 30° inclined plane of length 2.0 m. A constant horizontal force of 10 nt is applied to the block until it has reached the halfway mark up the incline. The applied force is then removed. (a) What is the maximum distance the block goes up the incline? (b) Find the total time the block is in motion on the incline.

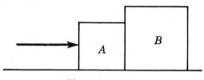

Figure 10-21

10-19   Blocks A and B, of masses 2.0 kg and 3.0 kg respectively, are in contact on a smooth horizontal surface, as shown in Figure 10-21. A force of 10 nt is applied to block A. What are (a) the acceleration of the masses, (b) the force of B on A, and (c) the force of A on B?

10-20   A 0.35-pound pitched baseball arrives at the plate from the north with a speed of 80 feet/sec. The batter hits the ball back at the same speed. If the collision time between bat and ball is 0.010 sec, what is the average force (magnitude and direction) on the ball due to the bat (a) when the ball heads back toward the pitcher and (b) when the ball is hit down the third-base line?

10-21   A 1.0 kg block moving to the right on a frictionless horizontal surface with a speed of 5.0 m/sec collides head on with a 5.0-kg block initially at rest. After the collision the 1.0-kg block is at rest. The time of collision between the blocks is 0.010 sec. (a) What is the velocity of the 5.0 kg block after the collision? (b) What is the average force acting on the 5.0 kg block during the collision?

10-22   Two light springs of force constants $k_1 = 500$ dyne/cm and $k_2 = 1000$ dyne/cm are connected to a 100 gm mass resting on a frictionless horizontal surface. How much will each spring be stretched when the external force F accelerates the mass at 10 cm/sec^2 for (a) the situation of Figure 10-22a, and (b) the situation of Figure 10-22b?

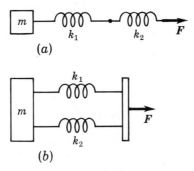

Figure 10-22

10-23   You are to measure the acceleration of gravity by means of an Atwood machine (see Figure 10-7). (a) If the mass m_1 is 1.00 kg, what should the mass m_2 be if the acceleration a of the system is to be approximately $\frac{1}{10}g$? (b) To how many significant figures must one measure the masses and the acceleration a, if one desires to find g to three significant figures?

10-24 ★   Two bodies of mass 1.5 kg and 3.5 kg are attached to opposite ends of a massless string which passes over a light frictionless pulley, as shown in Figure 10-23. (a) Assuming that $g = 10$ m/sec^2, find the maximum

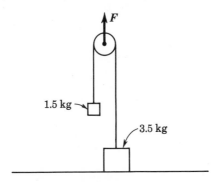

Figure 10-23

and minimum values of the upward external force F on the pulley such that the 3.5 kg mass will remain at rest on the table and the string remain taut. Find (b) the tension in the string and (c) the acceleration of the 1.5 kg mass for $F = 60$ nt. Find (d) the tension in the string and (e) the acceleration of the 1.5 kg mass for $F = 100$ nt.

10-25 ★   A 3.0-pound block, attached to one end of a horizontal spring whose force constant is 0.50 pound/inch, is initially at rest on a horizontal frictionless surface with the spring in its unstretched condition. A 2.0-pound weight is connected by means of a light string and frictionless

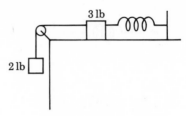

Figure 10-24

pulley to the 3.0-pound block and hangs over the side of the table. See Figure 10-24. What are (a) the acceleration of the system and (b) the tension in the string just after the 2.0-pound weight has been released? (c) Where will the 3.0-pound block be when the acceleration of the system is zero? (d) What is the tension in the string at this time?

10-26   A 3.0-pound block is at rest on a horizontal surface. The coefficients of static and kinetic friction between the block and surface are 0.50 and 0.40, respectively. If a constant pull of 7.0 pounds in a direction 30° above the horizontal is applied to the block, what is the vector displacement of the block during the first 5.0 sec?

10-27 ★ In Figure 10-25 the 200 gm block sits on top of the 500 gm block, which can slide on a frictionless surface. The coefficient of static friction between the two blocks is 0.30. What is the maximum mass m that can be attached to the string over the pulley if the 200 gm mass is *not* to slide relative to the 500 gm mass?

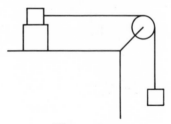

Figure 10-25

10-28   A block slides down a 2.0-foot long 30° inclined plane. The coefficient of kinetic friction between the block and incline is 0.25. Upon reaching the bottom, the block collides against a stop and rebounds with the same speed it had before hitting the stop. It then slides up the plane. To what height will the block rise before coming momentarily to rest?

10-29 ★ A 2.0-pound block is initially at rest at the top of a 37° inclined surface. The coefficients of static and kinetic friction are 0.90 and 0.85, respectively. A constant horizontal force tending to accelerate the block away from the inclined surface is then applied to the block. What are the friction force acting on the block and the acceleration of the block when the magnitude of the applied horizontal force is (a) 0.50 pound, (b) 1.0 pound, and (c) 3.0 pounds?

10-30   A 5.0 kg cart with frictionless wheels of negligible mass is initially at rest on a horizontal surface. A 1.0 kg block is placed on top of the cart, and a string connected to the block is passed over a light frictionless pulley. A mass of 2.0 kg is hung from the other end of the string. The coefficient of kinetic friction between the 1.0 kg block and cart is 0.010. See Figure 10-26. (a) What is the acceleration of the cart relative to the ground? (b) What is the acceleration of the 1.0 kg block relative to the cart?

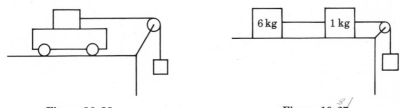

Figure 10-26   **Figure 10-27**

10-31   Two blocks having masses 6.0 kg and 1.0 kg are connected by a string of negligible mass. The two blocks are initially at rest on a horizontal surface, the coefficients of static and kinetic friction between the blocks and surface being 0.40 and 0.20, respectively. A string attached to the 1.0 kg mass passes over a frictionless massless pulley, and a body of mass m is gently hung at the other end of the string. See Figure 10-27. Assuming that $g = 10$ m/sec^2, find the tensions in the strings and the acceleration of the system when (a) $m = 2.0$ kg and (b) $m = 3.0$ kg.

10-32 ★ A cart of mass 6.0 kg is at rest on a horizontal surface. The wheels of
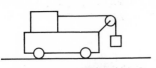
the cart are frictionless and of negligible mass. A rope passing over a light frictionless pulley connects the two blocks, both of mass 1.0 kg, as shown in Figure 10-28. (a) What is the acceleration of the cart when the coefficient of friction between the block traveling horizontally and the cart is zero? (b) What is the acceleration of the cart when the coefficient of kinetic

Figure 10-28

friction between the block and the cart is 0.50?

10-33   A 2.0 kg mass and a 4.0 kg mass are connected to opposite ends of a light spring. The masses sit at rest on a frictionless horizontal surface. See Figure 10-29. An impulse of 18 nt-sec to the right is then applied to the 2.0 kg mass, the force acting over a period of 0.020 sec. Describe the motion of the center of mass of the system composed of the two masses and attached spring for the three situations of Figure 10-29.

10-34 ★ Two blocks, each of mass m, are attached to the ends of a cord which passes over a small frictionless pulley, as shown in Figure 10-30. The horizontal surface is frictionless, and the two blocks are initially at equal distances from the pulley. What is the initial direction and magnitude of the acceleration of the center of mass of the two blocks? (*Hint:* Choose the system such that it consists of the two blocks and the string connecting them.)

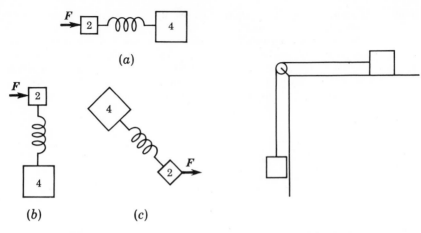

(a)

(b)   (c)

Figure 10-29   **Figure 10-30**

10-35   A body is acted on by a single force of constant *magnitude*. After 10 sec have elapsed, the body's velocity is exactly equal to its initial velocity. What is the path of the body?

10-36   A 2.0-pound puck is attached to one end of a string 1.5 feet long. The other end of the string is held fixed and the puck is constrained to move in a circle on a frictionless horizontal surface. If the breaking strength of the string is 3.0 pounds, what is the maximum tangential speed of the puck?

10-37   A 2000-pound automobile is driven at a *constant speed* of 30 miles/hour along a hilly road; see Figure 10-31. The radii of curvature at the

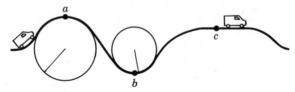

Figure 10-31

points a, b, and c are 100, 75, and ∞ feet, respectively. (a) Find the normal force of the road on the automobile at these three points. (b) What would happen if the car were to travel at a constant speed of 60 miles/hour?

10-38   In a hydrogen atom, an electron (mass 9.1×10^{-31} kg) revolves about a fixed proton, in a circular orbit of radius 5.3×10^{-11} m, the electron moving with a constant speed of 2.2×10^6 m/sec. Find the force of the proton on the electron and compare this with the weight of the electron near the Earth's surface.

10-39 A 2000-pound automobile with a 150-pound driver travels at 60 miles/hour around an unbanked curve 500 feet in radius. (a) What is the minimum coefficient of static friction, between the road and the automobile tires, that will permit the automobile to manage the curve without sliding? (b) What is the horizontal force of the *automobile* on the *driver*? (c) At what angle with respect to the horizontal would the curve have to be banked if there were to be no friction force (up or down the incline) of the road surface on the car when it takes the curve?

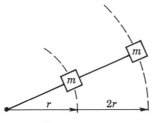

Figure 10-32

10-40 Two small blocks of equal mass are attached to two strings of equal length, as shown in Figure 10-32, and are set into rotation at constant angular speed ω. Find the ratio of the tension in the inner string to that in the outer string.

10-41 ★ A 0.50-pound block, attached to one end of a light spring whose force constant k is 6.0 pounds/ft, is set in uniform circular motion on a horizontal frictionless surface, while the other end of the spring is held fixed and is therefore serving as the center of the circle. The length of the spring when unstretched is 10 inches. What will be the spring's length when the mass rotates with a tangential speed of 8.0 feet/sec?

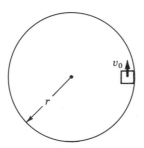

Figure 10-33

10-42 ★ A small block is constrained to move in a horizontal circular path by the rim of a circle whose radius is r. See Figure 10-33. The coefficient of kinetic friction between the block and the rim is μ; the horizontal surface is frictionless. The block's initial speed is v_0. (a) Show that the speed of the block at time t is $v_0/[1 + (\mu v_0/r)t]$. (b) How long does it take the block to come to rest?

10-43 ★ A rocket located several hundred feet above the Earth's surface ejects gas directly downward toward the Earth at an exhaust speed v_e relative to the rocket. The initial mass of the rocket and fuel is m_0. The rate at which mass is ejected by the rocket is to be such that the rocket remains at rest with respect to the Earth's surface. (a) Using the impulse-momentum theorem for the system of the rocket plus the exhaust gas, show that the mass m of the rocket at the time t is given by $m = m_0\, e^{-gt/v_e}$ where g is the acceleration due to gravity. (b) Find the rate dm/dt at which mass is ejected, in terms of m_0, g, v_e, and t. (c) What are m and dm/dt for $g = 0$ (far from any bodies)? (d) What is the force of the exhaust gas on the rocket at any instant of time? (e) Assume that a rocket is in space, free from gravitational forces, and is initially at rest with respect to an inertial system. The rocket exhausts gas particles at a speed v_e relative to the rocket. Find the rate dm/dt at which gas must be ejected such that the rocket will accelerate at constant acceleration a with respect to the inertial system. (*Hint:* Observe the motion from the point of view of a noninertial observer fixed to the rocket.)

E L E V E N

ENERGY

In this chapter we introduce the concepts of work and kinetic energy. These concepts are important because they ultimately lead to the important conservation law, the conservation of energy.

11-1 Work and kinetic energy The usefulness of the impulse-momentum relation was demonstrated in Section 9-4. There we saw that the total impulse on a body gives rise to a change in the body's linear momentum, the impulse representing the transfer of momentum from external agents to the body. The impulse changes the initial momentum p_i to the final momentum p_f according to the relation

[9-11]
$$\int_{t_i}^{t_f} F \, dt = \Delta p = p_f - p_i$$
[11-1]

The impulse gives a measure of the force integrated over *time* and describes the momentum-transfer process; the momentum on the other hand, is a property of the body itself. An analogous relation, involving the quantities work and kinetic energy, will be developed here. Work is a measure of the force applied by external agents integrated over *space*, whereas kinetic energy is the property of the body itself.

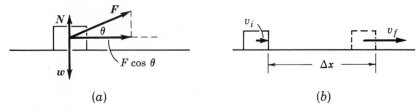

(a)   (b)

Figure 11-1. (a) A block on a horizontal surface subject to the following forces: its weight **w**, the normal force **N**, and the force **F** applied at an angle θ with respect to the horizontal. (b) The block increases its horizontal velocity from v_i to v_f over the displacement Δx under the action of the resultant force $F \cos \theta$.

Consider the situation in Figure 11-1, in which a block of mass m on a horizontal frictionless plane is initially moving to the right with speed v_i. A force **F** is applied to the block at an angle θ with respect to the horizontal over the displacement Δx, thereby increasing the block's speed to the final value v_f. The *resultant* force on the block —the vector sum of the weight **w**, the normal force **N**, and the applied force **F**—is $F \cos \theta$ to the right.

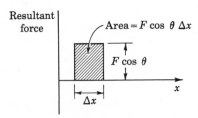

Figure 11-2. Work done by the resultant force **F** graphically represented as the area under the force-displacement graph.

We found earlier that the area under the force-*time* curve was equal to the change in the physical property of the body, i.e., the momentum. Let us inquire about the area under the force-*displacement* graph. This area is $(F \cos \theta) \Delta x$, as shown in Figure 11-2.

By Newton's second law, the resultant constant force $F \cos \theta$ produces a constant acceleration a_x to the right, which is related to Δx, v_i, and v_f by the kinematic relation

[2-11]
$$v_f^2 = v_i^2 + 2a_x \Delta x$$

$$a_x \Delta x = \frac{(v_f^2 - v_i^2)}{2}$$

$$(F \cos \theta) \Delta x = ma_x \Delta x$$

Therefore, $(F \cos \theta) \Delta x = \tfrac{1}{2}mv_f^2 - \tfrac{1}{2}mv_i^2$ [11-2]

The left-hand side, $(F \cos \theta) \Delta x$, depends only on the resultant external force and the distance over which this force acts, whereas the right-hand side gives the change in the quantity $\frac{1}{2}mv^2$, which depends only on properties of the body, namely, its mass and speed.

The quantity $(F \cos \theta) \Delta x$ is said to be the *work of the resultant force*, or the *work done by the external agents*, $W_{i \to f}$, in bringing the body from its *i*nitial to its *f*inal state of motion:

$$\text{Work} = W_{i \to f} = (F \cos \theta) \Delta x \qquad [11\text{-}3]$$

One may speak only of work done *over* a displacement in space, not of work done *at* a particular point in space, just as one may speak of an impulse *over* time but not *at* an instant.

The right-hand side of Equation 11-2 represents a *change* in the *scalar* quantity $\frac{1}{2}mv^2$ identified with the body itself. Because this quantity is related to the state of motion of the body (it is proportional to v^2), it is called the *kinetic energy* and it is symbolized by the letter K:

$$\text{Kinetic energy} = K = \tfrac{1}{2}mv^2 \qquad [11\text{-}4]$$

The kinetic energy must, of course, always be positive.

From our definitions of work and kinetic energy we may rewrite Equation 11-2 in the form

$$W_{i \to f} = \Delta K = K_f - K_i \qquad [11\text{-}5]$$

The scalar Equation 11-5 says that the work done on the body in Figure 11-1, by the resultant force, is equal to the change in kinetic energy of the body. This is the *work-energy (kinetic-energy) theorem*. We have defined the work done by a *constant* force on a body being displaced along a *straight* line; we will later extend our definition of work to include variable forces and curved paths. We will find it useful to introduce, in addition, the mathematical symbolism of the scalar product. With these general-izations, the work-energy theorem, Equation 11-5, still holds.

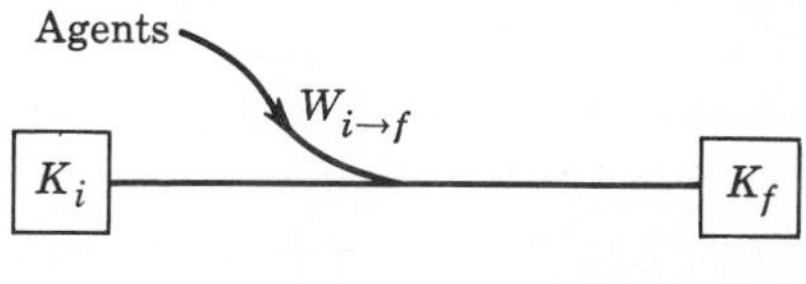

The process whereby agents trans-fer energy to the body to change its kinetic energy is symbolized in the schematic energy-flow diagram of Figure 11-3 (compare Equations 11-5 and 11-1, and Figures 11-3 and 9-9).

Figure 11-3. External agents do work $W_{i \to f}$ on a body, thereby raising the body's kinetic energy from K_i to K_f.

Let us examine the meanings of work and energy in somewhat more detail. We have defined the work done by the *resultant* force; we can equally well speak of the work done by each of the individual forces acting on the body, again using $(F \cos \theta) \, \Delta x$, where Δx is the actual displacement of the body and $(F \cos \theta)$ is the component of the individual force along the direction of the displacement.

For a force to do work on a body, (a) the body must undergo a displacement and (b) there must be a component of the force *along* the direction of the displacement. Thus, a man holding motionless a suitcase at arm's length does no work on the suitcase because the suitcase is not displaced. The man may become tired, and one muscle may do work on another muscle, but no work is done by the agent (the man) on the body (the suitcase); a statue would do the job of holding the suitcase equally well but, again, it would do no work. Also, a force that is always perpendicular to the direction of

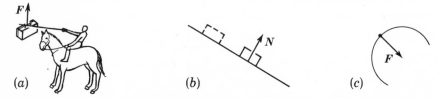

(a) (b) (c)

Figure 11-4. Examples of forces that do *not* do work: (a) an object *not* displaced by an applied force, (b) a normal force N, and (c) a resultant force acting at right angles to a body's velocity.

motion of a body does no work, because there is no component of this force along Δx. Thus, a normal force does no work. Similarly, a resultant force that acts at right angles to the velocity and maintains a body in circular motion at constant speed does no work. See Figure 11-4.

The cosine factor appearing in Equation 11-3 determines the component of F along the line of displacement. When θ is less than $90°$, the force acts along the direction of motion and *positive* work is done; when θ is $90°$, no work is done; when θ is greater than $90°$, the force component is opposite to the direction of the motion and *negative* work is done by the force. In the last situation the resultant force slows the body and reduces its kinetic energy, and *negative work is done by the agent on the body*. This is to say, the *body does (positive) work on the agent*, and energy is transferred from the body to the agent.

Suppose that a body with initial kinetic energy K_i is acted upon by a resultant retarding force $(\theta > 90°)$ and that the body is brought to rest after undergoing the displacement Δx. Then $K_f = 0$. From Equation 11-5 we have

$$W_{i \to f} = K_f - K_i = -K_i$$

or

$$K_i = -W_{i \to f}$$

The work done by the agent on the body is $W_{i \to f}$ and the work done by the body on the agent is $-W_{i \to f}$. Thus, the *kinetic energy* of a body can be thought of as the *work done on an external agent by the body as it comes to rest.* See Figure 11-5.

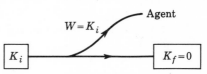

It must be emphasized that, unlike the vector linear momentum, the kinetic energy is a scalar quantity. Thus, two bodies with the same speed and of equal mass, moving in opposite directions, have *unequal momenta* but *equal kinetic energies*. The kinetic energy of a body can, however,

Figure 11-5. The work done *on* the agent *by* a body in coming to rest is equal to the body's initial kinetic energy K_i. Equivalently, the work done by the agent on the body is $W = -K_i$.

be expressed in terms of the *magnitude* of its linear momentum p:

$$K = \tfrac{1}{2}mv^2 = \frac{(mv)^2}{2m} = \frac{p^2}{2m} \qquad [11\text{-}6]$$

11-2   Units of work and energy   The units of work or energy for the three systems of units are given in Table 11-1, together with the equivalent fundamental units of mass, length, and time.

Table 11-1

SYSTEM OF UNITS	WORK OR ENERGY UNIT	EQUIVALENT FUNDAMENTAL UNITS
mks	joule	nt-m = kg-m²/sec²
cgs	erg	dyne-cm = gm-cm²/sec²
English	ft-lb	slug-ft²/sec²

Work ($F \cos \theta \, \Delta x$) is force multiplied by distance. Kinetic energy ($\tfrac{1}{2}mv^2$), given in equivalent units, is mass multiplied by the square of speed. The dimensions of both work and energy are ML^2/T^2. In the mks system one *joule* designates the work done by a force of one newton acting over a distance of one meter:

$$1 \text{ joule} = (1 \text{ nt})(1 \text{ m}) = (1 \text{ kg-m/sec}^2)(1 \text{ m}) = 1 \text{ kg-m/sec}^2$$

One joule is also the kinetic energy of a *two*-kilogram mass ($K = $ one-half mv^2) moving at a speed of one meter per second. In the cgs system, the unit of work or energy is called the *erg*; it is the work done by a force of one dyne over a distance of one centimeter; or, one erg is the kinetic energy of a two-gram mass moving at a speed of one centimeter per second. The erg is related to the joule as follows:

$$1 \text{ erg} = (1 \text{ dyne})(1 \text{ cm}) = (10^{-5} \text{ nt})(10^{-2} \text{ m}) = 10^{-7} \text{ joule}$$

The erg is only one ten-millionth of a joule.

No special name is given to the work or energy unit in the English system; the foot-pound (ft-lb) is the work done by a force of one pound acting over a distance of one foot or the kinetic energy of a two-slug mass moving at a speed of one foot per second. The relation of the foot-pound to the joule is easily obtained by recalling that one foot is 0.305 m and one pound is 4.45 nt. Therefore,

$$1 \text{ ft-lb} = (0.305 \text{ m})(4.45 \text{ nt}) = 1.36 \text{ joule}$$

The erg is a small unit for energy—approximately the kinetic energy of a mosquito in flight, whereas the joule is the energy of ten million mosquitos in flight. However, the erg is still much too large for specifying conveniently the energies of molecules, atoms, nuclei, and their constituent particles. On the atomic scale a more appropriate unit is the *electron volt* (abbreviated ev), which is defined:

$$1 \text{ ev} = 1.6 \times 10^{-19} \text{ joule} = 1.6 \times 10^{-12} \text{ erg}$$

For example, the kinetic energy of an electron (mass, 9.1×10^{-31} kg) moving at a speed of 2.2×10^6 m/sec (the speed of an electron about the nucleus of the hydrogen atom in its normal state) is

$$K = \tfrac{1}{2}mv^2 = \tfrac{1}{2}(9.1 \times 10^{-31} \text{ kg})(2.2 \times 10^6 \text{ m/sec})^2 = 2.2 \times 10^{-18} \text{ joule}$$
$$K = (2.2 \times 10^{-18} \text{ joule})(1 \text{ ev}/1.6 \times 10^{-19} \text{ joule}) = 14 \text{ ev}$$

It should be noted that there is nothing intrinsically *electrical* about atomic energies, although given in units of "electron" volts.

Table 11-2 gives the most commonly used conversion factors for energy units used in physics and engineering.

Table 11-2

1 ft-lb = 1.36 joules
1 erg = 10^{-7} joule
1 ev = 1.6×10^{-19} joule

Other energy conversion factors are given in Appendix II.

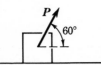

Figure 11-6. A block sliding on a horizontal surface is subject to a constant force *P* applied at 60° above the horizontal.

Example 1 A 2.0 kg block is sliding to the right at a speed of 3.0 m/sec on a smooth horizontal surface. A constant force *P* of 16 nt is then applied to the block in a direction 60° above the direction of motion of the block. See Figure 11-6. After the block has moved 2.0 m the force *P* is removed. (a) How much energy has been transferred from external agents to the block? (b) What is the change in the kinetic energy of the block? (c) What is the speed of the block after the force *P* has been removed?

(a) Because the vertical component of P upward (12 nt sin $60°$) is less than the weight downward (20 nt), the block will have no motion in the vertical direction and it is, therefore, constrained to move along the horizontal surface. The only force acting on the body which has a horizontal component is P; thus, the resultant force component along the displacement is $P \cos 60° = 8.0$ nt. The work done by the net external force over the 2.0 m distance is

$$W = (F \cos \theta) \, \Delta x = (8.0 \text{ nt})(2.0 \text{ m}) = 16 \text{ joule}$$

This is the energy transferred from the external agents to the block.

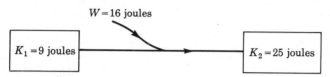

$W = 16$ joules

$K_1 = 9$ joules → $K_2 = 25$ joules

Figure 11-7. Work of 16 joules is done on a body with initial kinetic energy of 9 joules to bring its final kinetic energy to 25 joules.

(b) By the work-energy theorem, the body's change in kinetic energy ΔK is equal to W:

$$\Delta K = W = 16 \text{ joule}$$

Note that we need not and *do not* compute ΔK from the mass and the initial and final speeds; this could, of course, be done through the use of Newton's laws.

(c) We find the final speed of the block by computing first the final kinetic energy:

$$K_f = K_i + \Delta K = \tfrac{1}{2}mv_i^2 + \Delta K$$

$$K_f = (\tfrac{1}{2})(2.0 \text{ kg})(3.0 \text{ m/sec})^2 + (16 \text{ joules})$$

$$K_f = 25 \text{ joules}$$

But $\qquad K_f = \tfrac{1}{2}mv_f^2$

or $\qquad v_f = \sqrt{2K_f/m} = \sqrt{(2)(25 \text{ joules})/(2.0 \text{ kg})}$

$$v_f = 5.0 \text{ m/sec}$$

The energy transfer in this problem is shown schematically in Figure 11-7.

Example 2   A 1.0-ton satellite moves in a circular orbit close to the Earth with a speed of 2.6×10^4 feet/sec. (a) What is the satellite's kinetic energy? (b) How much work is done on the satellite by the force of gravity as the satellite completes one half-cycle?

(a) The mass of the satellite is $m = (1.0 \text{ ton})(2000 \text{ pounds/ton})/(32 \text{ feet/sec}^2) = 63$ slugs. The satellite's kinetic energy is

$$K = \tfrac{1}{2}mv^2 = (\tfrac{1}{2})(63 \text{ slug})(2.6 \times 10^4 \text{ ft/sec})^2$$

$$K = 2.1 \times 10^{10} \text{ slug-ft}^2/\text{sec}^2 = 2.1 \times 10^{10} \text{ ft-lb}$$

(b) The only force acting on the satellite is its weight. This force is constant in magnitude but not in direction, acting radially inward, always at right angles

to the velocity. This radial (centripetal) force changes the body's velocity but not its speed, and it changes the body's linear momentum but not its kinetic energy. See Figure 11-8. In short, the weight does no work on the body, and no energy is transferred from the agent (the Earth) to the body (the satellite):

$$W = (F \cos \theta) \, \Delta x = (F \cos 90°) \, \Delta x = 0$$

Figure 11-8. The force on a satellite in circular motion does *no* work.

Example 3 A 2.0 kg block is projected up a 30° inclined plane at an initial speed of 2.0 m/sec. The coefficient of kinetic friction between the block and surface is 0.30. Use the work-energy theorem to find (a) the distance the block slides up the plane and (b) the speed of the block upon its return to the bottom of the incline. (This problem was solved in Example 7, Section 10-3, by means of Newton's second law; here we solve it by the work-energy theorem.)

(a) Let the point 1 be the block when it is at the bottom and about to be projected upward, point 2 the block when it is at the highest point and momentarily at rest, and point 3 the block when it has returned to the bottom. The forces acting on the block while it slides *up* the plane are shown in Figure 11-9a. Let the distance the block is displaced up the incline be s. The angle between the force N and direction of the displacement is 90°, that between f_k and the displacement is 180°, and that between mg and the displacement 120°. Then the work done by the three forces acting on the block when it goes from state 1 to state 2 are:

$$W_{1 \to 2}(\text{by } N) = 0$$

$$W_{1 \to 2}(\text{by } mg) = (mg)(\cos 120°)s = (19.6 \text{ nt})(-0.50)s = -(9.8 \text{ nt})s$$

$$W_{1 \to 2}(\text{by } f_k) = (f_k \cos 180°)s = -(5.1 \text{ nt})s$$

where $\qquad f_k = \mu_k N = \mu_k mg \cos 30° = 5.1 \text{ nt}$

Application of the work-energy theorem gives

$W_{1 \to 2}(\text{by resultant force})$

$$= W_{1 \to 2}(\text{by } N) + W_{1 \to 2}(\text{by } mg) + W_{1 \to 2}(\text{by } f_k) = K_2 - K_1$$

$$0 - (9.8 \text{ nt})s - (5.1 \text{ nt})s = 0 - \tfrac{1}{2}mv_1^2 = -4.0 \text{ joules}$$

Therefore $s = 0.27 \text{ m} = 27 \text{ cm}$.

We notice that the work done on the block by both the weight and the friction force is *negative*, energy being transferred from the block to these external agents as the block slides up the plane.

(b) The forces acting on the block as it slides down the plane are shown in Figure 11-9b. The angle between N and the (downward) displacement is still 90° and between f_k and the displacement is still 180° (f_k always being *opposite* to the displacement direction), but the angle between mg and the displacement

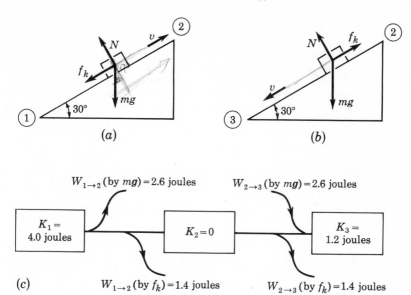

Figure 11-9. (a) A block sliding *up* a rough inclined plane from point 1 to 2 is subject to its weight $m\boldsymbol{g}$, the normal force $\boldsymbol{N}$, and the force of kinetic friction $\boldsymbol{f}_k$. (b) The block slides *down* the rough incline from point 2 to 3; note that the direction of the friction force $\boldsymbol{f}_k$ is reversed. (c) An energy flow diagram corresponding to parts (a) and (b); the net work done by the weight $m\boldsymbol{g}$ in going from 1 to 2 to 3 is zero, whereas the net work done by the friction force $\boldsymbol{f}_k$ is not.

is now 60°. The work done by the three forces as the block moves from state 2 to state 3 are:

$$W_{2\to3}(\text{by } \boldsymbol{N}) = 0$$

$$W_{2\to3}(\text{by } m\boldsymbol{g}) = (mg\cos 60°)s = (19.6\text{ nt})(0.50)(0.27\text{ m}) = 2.6 \text{ joules}$$

$$W_{2\to3}(\text{by } \boldsymbol{f}_k) = (f_k \cos 180°)s = -(5.1\text{ nt})(0.27\text{ m}) = -1.4 \text{ joules}$$

The work-energy theorem then yields

$W_{2\to3}(\text{by resultant force})$

$$= W_{2\to3}(\text{by } \boldsymbol{N}) + W_{2\to3}(\text{by } m\boldsymbol{g}) + W_{2\to3}(\text{by } \boldsymbol{f}_k) = K_3 - K_2$$

$$0 + 2.6 \text{ joules} - 1.4 \text{ joules} = K_3 - 0$$

$$K_3 = 1.2 \text{ joules}$$

Therefore, the speed of the block upon return to the bottom is

$$v_3 = \sqrt{\frac{2K_3}{m}} = \sqrt{\frac{2(1.2\text{ joules})}{(2\text{ kg})}} = 1.1 \text{ m/sec}$$

As the block slides from point 2 to point 3, energy is transferred to the block by the weight (positive work), and some of this energy is transferred from the block to the friction force (negative work). This is shown schematically in the energy-flow diagram of Figure 11-9c. The kinetic energy upon return to the bottom of the incline, $K_3 = 1.2$ joules, is *less* than the initial kinetic energy of the block projected upward, $K_1 = 4.0$ joules. This results because kinetic friction is a *dissipative* force: it always opposes the block's motion and therefore reduces its kinetic energy, whether the block goes up or down the incline. On the other hand, the weight reduces the block's kinetic energy as it goes up the plane but restores this same amount of kinetic energy as the block goes down the plane.

The difference between the initial and final kinetic energies, $K_1 - K_3$, is the total work done against the force of kinetic friction, which for this problem is $2(f_k s)$:

$$K_1 - K_3 = 2 f_k s$$

11-3 Work done by a variable force In this section we wish to extend our definition of work to include variable forces and curved paths. First

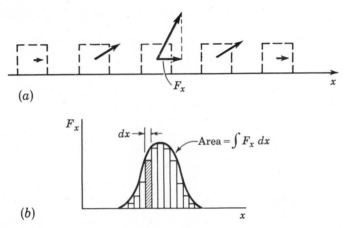

Figure 11-10. (a) A body is subject to a variable force F_x along the X-direction. (b) The total work done by the variable force is equal to the area under the force-displacement curve.

consider the work done by a force which varies in magnitude and direction while a body moves along a straight-line path. See Figure 11-10a. A graph showing the force component F_x as a function of the displacement x is given in Figure 11-10b. Over a small displacement dx, F_x is essentially constant, and we can write for the work dW done over this small displacement,

$$dW = F_x \, dx$$

The total work done over the entire displacement is the sum of contributions from each small displacement dx; therefore, we integrate $F_x \, dx$ from the initial state i to the final state f:

$$W_{i \to f} = \int_i^f F_x \, dx \qquad [11\text{-}7]$$

If the force F has a component F_x *opposite* to the direction of motion of the body, the force-displacement curve lies beneath the displacement axis, the area under the curve is negative, the work done by the agent is negative, and energy is thereby transferred from the body to the agent.

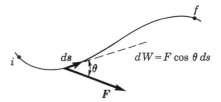

It is easy to show that the work done by the resultant of all external forces acting on a body is still equal to the change in the body's kinetic energy even when the resultant force varies. If F_x is the X-component of

Figure 11-11. The work dW done by a force F applied at an angle θ with respect to the element of displacement ds is $dW = F \cos \theta \, ds$.

the resultant force, we may use Newton's second law and write:

$$F_x \, dx = ma_x \, dx = m\left(\frac{dv}{dt}\right) dx = m\left(\frac{dx}{dt}\right) dv = mv \, dv$$

Therefore,
$$\int_i^f F_x \, dx = \int_i^f mv \, dv = \tfrac{1}{2}mv_f^2 - \tfrac{1}{2}mv_i^2$$

or, in terms of work and kinetic energy,

11-5] $$\qquad\qquad W_{i \to f}(\text{by resultant force}) = K_f - K_i$$

We now state the general definition of the work done by a force (which may vary in magnitude, direction, or both) acting on a body moving along any path. The contribution to the work over the small displacement ds is $(F \cos \theta) \, ds$, where θ is the angle between F and ds, as shown in Figure 11-11. The total work done by the force F in going along the path, or line, from point i to point f is, then,

$$W_{i \to f} = \int_i^f (F \cos \theta) \, ds \qquad [11\text{-}8]$$

Thus, the work is the *line integral* of the force over the path.

Example 4   What is the work done by a spring on a body attached to it?

An important example of a force which varies with displacement is the force applied by a stretched or compressed spring. Let us find the work done by such a variable force. Figure 11-12a shows a block of mass m resting on a horizontal surface, connected to one end of an unstretched spring of negligible mass. The other end of the spring is fastened to a wall. In Figure 11-12a the spring exerts no force on the block. Displacements of the block are measured from this equilibrium position. A positive displacement corresponds to a stretching of the spring; a negative displacement, to a compression.

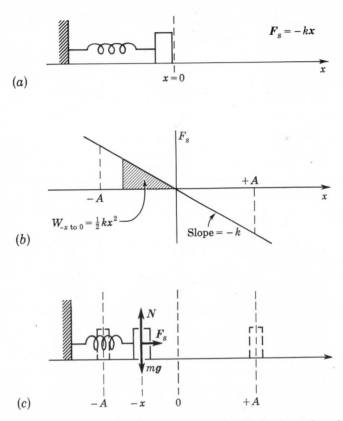

Figure 11-12. (a) A block of mass m on a smooth horizontal surface, connected to a spring of stiffness k. The spring is unstretched for $x = 0$. (b) The spring force F_s as a function of the block's displacement x. The amplitude positions are $x = \pm A$. The work $W_{-x \to 0}$, done *by the spring on the block* as the block moves from $-x \to 0$ under a force *to the right*, is $\frac{1}{2}kx^2$. (c) The forces acting on the block when it has a displacement $-x$.

We found in Section 9-3 that the magnitude of the force F_s applied by the spring to the block is directly proportional to the magnitude of the displacement x (for small elongations or compressions). Moreover, the direction of F_s is always opposite to that of the displacement; that is, when the block is to the right of the equilibrium position ($x > 0$) the spring force acts to the left ($F_s < 0$), and when the block is to the left ($x < 0$) the force is to the right ($F_s > 0$). Thus, the spring always applies a *restoring* force to the block, one which tends to restore it to its equilibrium position:

$$\boxed{F = -kx}$$

[11-9]

where the constant k (always positive) is a characteristic of the spring and gives a measure of its stiffness. The stiffness constant k has units of force per unit length (e.g., nt/m). A graph giving the spring force as a function of displacement is shown in Figure 11-12b, which we shall now discuss.

We now compute the work done by a compressed spring on the body of mass m. If a block is displaced from the equilibrium position to the left a distance A, the spring will be compressed. When the block is released, the only forces acting on the block are the weight mg, the normal force N, and the spring force F_s. The resultant force on the block is F_s, and the block initially accelerates to the right. See Figure 11-12c.

We now find the work done *by the spring force* as the block moves from the point $-x$ to the equilibrium point at $x = 0$. We have

$$W_{-x \to 0} = \int_{-x}^{0} (F_s \cos \theta)\, dx = \int_{-x}^{0} F_s\, dx$$

the angle θ being zero because F_s and dx are in the same direction. Using Equation 11-9 for F_s, we write

$$W_{-x \to 0} = \int_{-x}^{0} (-kx)\, dx = \tfrac{1}{2}kx^2$$

[11-10]

Thus, as the block moves from $-x$ to 0 an amount of energy $\tfrac{1}{2}kx^2$, the shaded area in Figure 11-12b, is transferred from the *spring* to the *block*. (Because the work depends on the *square* of x, the same amount of energy is transferred when the block goes from $+x$ to 0.)

By the work-energy theorem,

$$W_{-x \to 0} = \Delta K = K_0 - K$$

[11-11]

where K is the kinetic energy of the block at the point $-x$ and K_0 is the kinetic energy at the equilibrium position. Comparing Equations 11-10 and 11-11, we have

$$\tfrac{1}{2}kx^2 = K_0 - K$$

[11-12]

At $x = -A$, the point at which the block was released, the kinetic energy is zero. Equation 11-12 then becomes

$$\tfrac{1}{2}kA^2 = K_0 - 0 = K_0 = \tfrac{1}{2}mv_0^2$$

[11-13]

The kinetic energy at the equilibrium position is determined by A, the distance the spring is originally compressed.

When the block reaches the equilibrium position it has kinetic energy and continues to move to the right. But now the spring stretches, exerts a force F_s to the *left*, and thereby *decelerates* the block. In terms of work, the spring force opposes the motion and does negative work on the block. While the block moves to the right from $x = 0$, energy is transferred from the block to the spring. The block comes momentarily to rest at that point x_{max} to the right, for which the kinetic energy is zero. Using Equations 11-12 and 11-13 yields

$$\tfrac{1}{2}kx_{max}^2 = K_0 - 0 = \tfrac{1}{2}kA^2$$

or

$$x_{max} = A$$

The block comes momentarily to rest at the same distance A to the right as it does to the left. Then the block returns from its extreme position on the right $(x = +A)$ back to its extreme position on the left $(x = -A)$, and the motion is

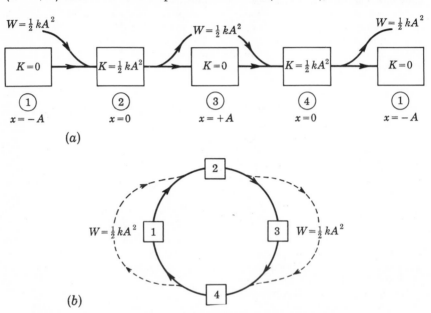

(a)

(b)

Figure 11-13. (a) Energy flow diagram for a spring of stiffness k, oscillating with an amplitude A; energy flows alternately into and out of the block as the spring does positive and negative work, respectively, on the block. (b) The energy flow diagram of part (a) drawn as a closed loop.

repeated. An energy-flow diagram illustrating the block's energy states is shown in Figure 11-13. The first and last states shown in Figure 11-13a are the same— the same kinetic energy $(K = 0)$, same momentum $(p = 0)$, and the same point in space $(x = -A)$. The motion then repeats itself indefinitely, and we represent this by the energy-flow loop of Figure 11-13b.

Note that, in Figure 11-13, the states 1 and 3 are identical in kinetic energy and momentum but not in displacement, and that states 2 and 4 are identical in kinetic energy and displacement but not in momentum.

11-4 Work and the scalar product of vectors Work is a scalar, but force and displacement, from which work is derived, are vectors. Work is an important example of the vector operation called the *scalar product of two* *vectors.* The symbolism of the scalar, or *dot*, product is useful in representing work dW done by a force F over the displacement ds.

We have defined the work (Figure 11-11) as

$$dW = (F \cos \theta) \, ds$$

where we compute the magnitude of dW by taking the product of the magnitude of the component of F, ($F \cos \theta$), along the direction of the displacement ds. We can represent this symbolically by

$$dW = F \cdot ds$$

and the total work along a path can then be written

$$W_{i \to f} = \int_i^f F \cdot ds \qquad [11\text{-}14]$$

where Equation 11-14 merely expresses Equation 11-8 in the compact form of vector notation.

The scalar product holds, of course, for vector quantities besides those of force and displacement. If A and B are the magnitudes of the vectors A and B, and θ is the (smaller) angle between the two vectors, then in general

$$A \cdot B = AB \cos \theta.$$

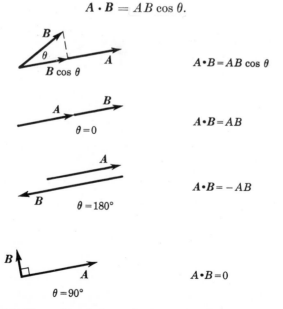

Figure 11-14. The scalar product of vectors A and B for several values of the angle θ between them.

The dimensions of $A \cdot B$ are the product of the dimensions of A and B. When A and B are aligned (that is, when $\theta = 0°$ and $\cos 0° = 1$), then $A \cdot B = AB$. When A and B are anti-aligned (that is, when $\theta = 180°$ and $\cos 180° = -1$), then $A \cdot B = -AB$. When A and B are oriented at right angles with respect to one another (that is, when $\theta = 90°$ and $\cos 90° = 0$), then $A \cdot B = 0$. See Figure 11-14.

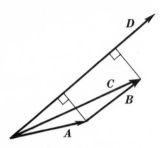

The *commutative* and *distributive laws* of the scalar product follow directly from the definition of the scalar product. Thus,

$$A \cdot B = AB \cos \theta = BA \cos \theta = B \cdot A$$

By referring to Figure 11-15, we can easily prove the distributive relationship: if $C = A + B$, then

Figure 11-15. Graphical proof of the distributive law for scalar products: $D \cdot C = D \cdot (A + B) = D \cdot A + D \cdot B$.

$$D \cdot C = D \cdot (A + B) = D \cdot A + D \cdot B$$

$$[11\text{-}15]$$

because the component of vector C along the direction of D is the sum of the components of vectors A and B along D. Thus the distributive law holds.

The distributive law for the scalar product of vectors is consistent with the fact that (a) the work done by the resultant force is equal to the sum of the work done by the separate forces acting simultaneously and that (b) the total work done along any path is equal to the sum of the work done along each segment of the path.

Example 5   A 2.0-pound ball falls freely from rest through a vertical distance of 25 feet. (a) What is the work done on the ball by gravity (that is, by the ball's weight)? (b) What is the ball's kinetic energy upon striking the ground? (c) With what speed does the ball strike the ground?

(a) The falling ball is acted on by a single constant (gravitational) force of 2.0 pounds downward: $F_g = -mg$, the positive direction of the displacement y being chosen upward. See Figure 11-16a. The work done on the ball as it goes from $y = 25$ feet to $y = 0$ is

$$dW = F \cdot ds = mg \, dy$$

$$W = \int (-mg)(-dy) = mgy$$

$$W = (2.0 \text{ lb})(25 \text{ ft}) = 50 \text{ ft-lb}$$

(b) Since the initial kinetic energy is zero ($K_i = 0$), we can find the final kinetic energy K_f immediately from the work-energy theorem:

$$W = K_f - K_i = K_f$$

$$K_f = 50 \text{ ft-lb}$$

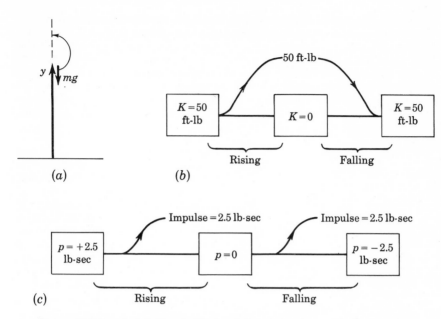

Figure 11-16. (a) A falling ball of weight mg having a displacement y above the ground. (b) Energy flow diagram for a ball thrown upward with an initial kinetic energy of 50 foot-pounds; over the round trip, the net work done by the force of gravity is zero. (c) Momentum flow diagram corresponding to parts (a) and (b); over the round trip, the net impulse by the force of gravity is *not* zero.

(c) The final speed v_f is then

$$K_f = \tfrac{1}{2}mv_f^2$$

$$v_f = \sqrt{2K_f/m} = \sqrt{(2)(50 \text{ ft-lb})/(\tfrac{1}{16} \text{ slug})}$$

$$v_f = 40 \text{ ft/sec}$$

It is easy to show that the final speed is independent of the mass (as we know already from the kinematics of falling bodies):

$$W = K_f$$

$$mgy = \tfrac{1}{2}mv_f^2$$

$$v_f = \sqrt{2gy}$$

Now suppose that the ball is thrown vertically upward with a speed of 40 feet/sec. It will attain a maximum height of 25 feet and be at rest momentarily at this point. The body will then fall downward, striking the ground with a speed of 40 feet/sec. All of this can be derived from the kinematics of falling bodies. But let us describe the motion in the language of work and kinetic energy.

When the ball is thrown upward, its initial kinetic energy is 50 foot-pounds. As the ball rises, a constant force acts on it in the direction opposite to its motion. *Negative* work is done on the ball by the force of gravity, and the body loses kinetic energy until, at its highest point, it has lost all 50 foot-pounds and is momentarily at rest. As it falls, positive work is done on the ball by the force of gravity; after falling 25 feet its kinetic energy is again 50 foot-pounds. The initial and final states of *kinetic energy* are identical, because the total amount of work done on the body over the round trip is zero. See the energy-flow diagram in Figure 11-16.

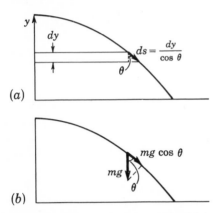

(a)

(b)

Now consider changes in the momentum. The momentum of the ball is initially positive (upward), and is negative when it strikes the ground. The ball loses momentum in the upward direction (or gains momentum in the downward direction) throughout the motion, the impulse of the constant gravitational force always acting downward. Therefore, as the momentum-flow diagram in Figure 11-16b shows, the initial and final states of *momentum* are different.

Example 6 Let us consider the 2-pound ball treated in Example 5, but this time thrown horizontally with a speed of 16 feet/sec from a height of 25 feet. (a) What is the work done on the ball as it falls to the ground? (b) What is the change in the ball's kinetic energy? (c) What is the final kinetic energy of the ball?

(a) The thrown ball traces out a path as shown in Figure 11-17a. We need *not* know that it is, in fact, a parabola. The gravitational force is constantly downward and of magnitude mg. We compute the work done by this force by

Figure 11-17. (a) Path traced out by a ball thrown horizontally from the initial displacement y. The displacement ds along the path is related to the corresponding vertical displacement dy by $ds = dy/\cos \theta$, where θ is the angle between the vertical and the direction of the ball's displacement. (b) The component of the weight mg along the direction of the displacement is $mg \cos \theta$.

taking the component of the force along an element of the path ds. The component of the weight along the path is $mg \cos \theta$, as shown in Figure 11-17b. Therefore, the work dW done over the displacement ds is

$$dW = \boldsymbol{F} \cdot d\boldsymbol{s} = (mg \cos \theta) \, ds$$

From the geometry of Figure 11-17a,

$$ds = dy/\cos \theta$$

Therefore, $dW = (mg \cos \theta)(dy/\cos \theta) = mg \, dy$, and

$$\boxed{W = mg \int dy = mgy}$$

                 [11-16]

This was precisely the work done by the force of gravity when the body was dropped rather than thrown (see Example 5a).

(b) (c) A 2-pound ball has work in the amount of 50 foot-pounds done on it as it descends 25 feet; its kinetic energy is increased by $\Delta K = 50$ foot-pounds, and the final kinetic energy K_f of the ball upon striking the ground is

$$K_f = K_i + \Delta K = \tfrac{1}{2}mv_i{}^2 + \Delta K$$

$$K_f = (\tfrac{1}{2})(\tfrac{1}{16} \text{ slug})(16 \text{ ft/sec})^2 + (50 \text{ ft-lb})$$

$$K_f = 58 \text{ ft-lb}$$

This example illustrates the remarkable utility of the work-energy theorem: we can compute both the work done and the resulting change in kinetic energy without a detailed knowledge of the path or of the horizontal and vertical components of the velocity. We concern ourselves only with the end points, the initial and final states, and not with the details of the motion between these. On the other hand, using the work-energy theorem denies us some information about the motion: we do not know where the ball strikes the ground, how long the trip takes, or the direction of the velocity upon striking. This information can be obtained by applying Newton's laws.

Example 7 A block of mass m, initially at rest at point 1, in Figure 11-18, slides down the frictionless surface, passes point 2, a distance of 9.0 feet below point 1, then passes point 3 at the bottom, a distance of 16 feet below point 1. (a) Find the speed of the block at point 2. (b) Find the speed of the block at point 3. (c) How high will the block rise along the right-hand surface? (d) What is the period of oscillation of the block?

(a) The two forces acting on the block as it slides along the surface are the weight $m\mathbf{g}$ and the normal force $\mathbf{N}$. Because $\mathbf{N}$ is always normal to the path, it does no work on the block. We know from Equation 11-16 that the amount of work done by the weight alone, along *any* path, is mgy, where y is the vertical component of the displacement. According to the work-energy theorem, we then have

$$W_{1\rightarrow 2} = K_2 - K_1$$

$$mgy = \tfrac{1}{2}mv_2{}^2 - 0$$

where v_2 is the speed at point 2 and y is 9.0 feet. Therefore,

$$v_2 = \sqrt{2gy} = \sqrt{(2)(32 \text{ ft/sec}^2)(9.0 \text{ ft})}$$

$$v_2 = 24 \text{ ft/sec}$$

(b) Similarly, the speed v_3 at point 3 is

$$v_3 = \sqrt{2gy} = \sqrt{(2)(32 \text{ ft/sec}^2)(16 \text{ ft})}$$

$$v_3 = 32 \text{ ft/sec}$$

We computed the speeds at points 2 and 3 without invoking any information on the shape or slope of the surface. The speeds depend only on the vertical displacement. If a number of different paths were constructed from point 1

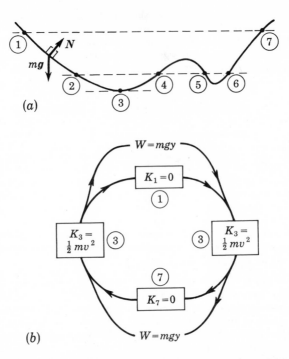

Figure 11-18. (a) A block released at point 1 on a frictionless surface slides under the influence of its weight mg and the normal force N. (b) An energy flow diagram corresponding to part (a). Note that the sliding body is returned to its initial state with no change in kinetic energy, the work done by the weight while the block slides down being exactly balanced by the (negative) work done by the weight while the block slides up.

to point 2, the block would always arrive with the same speed at point 2, although the time to travel from 1 to 2 would depend on the path.† Of course, if a friction force were present, the speed would no longer be independent of the path.

(c) To find the maximum height to which the block rises, we simply recognize that positive work is done on the block as it descends and negative work is done on the block as it ascends, the work depending only on the vertical displacement y. Therefore, the block's kinetic energy is zero at point 7, as it was initially at point 1, because the total work done in going from 1 to 7 is zero. Point 7 must, therefore, have the same vertical elevation and be on the same horizontal line as point 1.

† The question what path connecting two points not on the same elevation will lead to the least time of travel stumped many of Newton's colleagues (they referred to it as the *brachistochrone*). When he heard of the problem, Newton solved it overnight, by inventing a simple form of the calculus of variations. The answer: a cycloid.

It also follows that at points 4, 5, and 6, which are on the same horizontal line as point 2, the speed is 24 feet/sec. The *velocity* is *not*, however, the same at these points.

(d) After the block comes to rest at point 7, it reverses its direction of motion, slides down to the left, and comes to rest momentarily again at point 1. The motion is then repeated perpetually, provided, of course, that the surface is truly frictionless. Thus, the motion is periodic, the period being the time for the block to make one round trip. The work-energy theorem makes no reference to time, and consequently we cannot compute the period from it. In fact, one must know the shape of the path in detail to compute the time for one oscillation from Newton's laws.

Because this is perpetual periodic motion, the energy-flow diagram forms a closed loop, as shown in Figure 11-18b.

11-5   Power   The work done by an agent and the kinetic energy of the body itself do not involve the time t. It is often important, however, to know, for practical considerations, not only the amount of work done by an agent but also how rapidly the agent can do it. It is useful, therefore, to define a quantity called the *power*, which represents the time rate at which a machine transfers energy from the agent to the body.

The average power $\overline{P}$ over the time interval Δt is defined as the energy transferred ($W_{i \to f}$) divided by the time Δt over which the transfer takes place:

$$\overline{P} = \frac{W_{i \to f}}{\Delta t} \tag{11-17}$$

The instantaneous power P is the time rate of doing work:

$$\boxed{P = \frac{dW}{dt}} \tag{11-18}$$

Equations 11-17 and 11-18 can be written in different forms by recalling the definition of work in terms of force and displacement:

$$W_{i \to f} = \int \boldsymbol{F} \cdot d\boldsymbol{s}$$

However, $d\boldsymbol{s} = \boldsymbol{v}\, dt$, where $\boldsymbol{v}$ is the instantaneous velocity, and we can write

$$W_{i \to f} = \int (\boldsymbol{F} \cdot \boldsymbol{v})\, dt = \overline{(\boldsymbol{F} \cdot \boldsymbol{v})}\, \Delta t \tag{11-19}$$

where $\overline{(\boldsymbol{F} \cdot \boldsymbol{v})}$ is the time average of the scalar product of the instantaneous force $\boldsymbol{F}$ and velocity $\boldsymbol{v}$ over the time interval Δt. When we use Equation 11-19, Equations 11-17 and 11-18 become

$$\overline{P} = \overline{(\boldsymbol{F} \cdot \boldsymbol{v})} \tag{11-20}$$

$$\boxed{P = \boldsymbol{F} \cdot \boldsymbol{v}} \tag{11-21}$$

Power has the dimensions ML^2/T^3. The units for power in the three systems are given in Table 11-3.

Table 11.3

SYSTEM OF UNITS	POWER UNIT	EQUIVALENT FUNDAMENTAL UNITS
mks	watt (w)	joule/sec = kg-m²/sec³
cgs	erg/sec	erg/sec = gm-cm²/sec³
English	horsepower (hp)	550 ft-lb/sec = 550 slug-ft²/sec³

Some useful conversion factors among the power units are:

$$1 \text{ w} = 10^7 \text{ erg/sec}$$

$$1 \text{ hp} = 746 \text{ w} \simeq \tfrac{3}{4}\,\text{kw}$$

Work or kinetic energy can be expressed in terms of a power unit multiplied by a time unit: for example, a horsepower-hour or a kilowatt-hour. Note that horsepower-hour and kilowatt-hour are *energy* units.

Example 8 A machine raises a 300 kg mass upward at a constant speed of 0.20 m/sec. What is the power output of the machine?

If the mass is to ascend at a constant speed, the machine must apply a constant upward force equal to the weight of the raised mass. From Equation 11-20,

$$P = Fv = mgv = (300 \text{ kg})(9.8 \text{ m/sec}^2)(0.20 \text{ m/sec})$$

$$P = 0.59 \text{ kw}$$

11-6 Summary The work done by a constant force F acting on a body undergoing the displacement Δx from state i to f is

[11-3] $$W_{i \to f} = (F \cos \theta)\,\Delta x$$

where $F \cos \theta$ is the component of F along Δx.

More generally, the work done by a force F is defined as

[11-14] $$W_{i \to f} = \int_i^f F \cdot ds$$

The kinetic energy K of a body is defined as

[11-4] $$K = \tfrac{1}{2}mv^2 = \frac{p^2}{2m}$$

According to the work-energy theorem,

[11-5] $$W_{i \to f} = K_f - K$$

where $W_{i \to f}$ is the work done by the *resultant* force as a body moves from state i to f.

The force exerted by a spring is given by

[11-9] $$F = -kx$$

where x is the extension of the spring from its unstretched length and k is the spring, or stiffness, constant.

Power is the time rate of doing work:

[11-18] $$P = \frac{dW}{dt}$$

PROBLEMS

11-1   A man raises a 20-pound body 3.0 feet at the rate of 1.5 feet/sec. What is the work done by (a) the man, (b) the weight, and (c) the resultant force?

11-2   Bodies A and B have equal momenta, but the kinetic energy of A is twice that of B. What is the ratio of the mass of A to B?

11-3   The mass of a proton is 1836 times that of an electron. At what speed will a proton have (a) the same kinetic energy as a 5000 ev electron and (b) the same momentum as a 5000 ev electron? The electron mass is 9.1×10^{-31} kg.

11-4   A 50-pound trunk is pushed 6.0 feet up an incline of 30° with respect to the horizontal, by a man who applies a constant horizontal force. The trunk moves at constant speed. The coefficient of kinetic friction between the trunk and the surface is 0.20. What is the work done (a) by the man, (b) by the force of friction, (c) by the weight of the trunk, and (d) by the resultant force?

11-5   A 5.0-pound ball is thrown into the air with a speed of 30 feet/sec. What is the ball's kinetic energy when it passes a point 10 feet above the point at which it was thrown?

11-6   A 16-pound block is at rest on a horizontal frictionless surface. A constant horizontal force of 2.0 pounds to the right is applied to the block. Find the work done by this force during the first second and during the second second, (a) as measured by an observer on the ground and (b) as measured by an observer moving to the right at 4.0 feet/sec.

11-7   A constant resultant force of 20 nt to the right acts on a 2.0 kg mass initially at rest. (a) Calculate the impulse and work done by the force during the first 2.0 sec. (b) Find the impulse and work done by this force during the same time interval, from the point of view of an observer in an inertial system moving to the right at a speed of 15 m/sec with respect to the inertial system of part (a).

11-8   A constant force of 5.0 pounds to the right acts on a particle as it moves along a circular track of radius 2.0 feet. Find the work done by the constant force as the particle moves (a) from point 1 to point 2 and (b) from point 2 to point 3. See Figure 11-19.

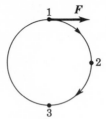

Figure 11-19

11-9   A body, connected to one end of a light rigid rod, is initially at rest on a frictionless horizontal surface and is free to rotate in a horizontal plane about the other end of the rod. A horizontal force of 5.0 pounds is applied to the body, the direction of the force always being perpendicular to the rod. Find the tension in the rod when the body has moved through one quarter of a circle.

11-10 ★   A body whose weight is 0.40 pound hangs from a 1.0-foot inextensible rope. A constant horizontal force of 0.30 pound is then applied to the body. (a) What is the maximum speed of the body? (b) What angle does the rope make with the vertical at this speed? (c) To what range of angles is the body's motion restricted?

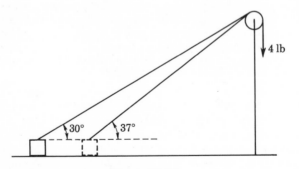

Figure 11-20

11-11 ★   A string attached to a 3.0-pound block initially at rest on a horizontal frictionless surface passes over a frictionless pulley, as shown in Figure 11-20. A force of constant magnitude, 4.0 pounds, is applied to the string, the block thereby being accelerated to the right. Find the work done by this force on the block, when the block moves from the point where the string makes an angle of 30° with the horizontal to the point where the string makes an angle of 37° to the horizontal. The pulley is 2.0 feet above the top of the block.

11-12 A body of mass m is initially at rest at the point x_1 along the positive X-axis. A force F acts on the body in the positive X-direction, the magnitude of the force varying with x as $F = c/x^2$ where c is a constant. (a) Find the work done by the force F as the body goes from point x_1 to point x_2. (b) What is the speed of the body at point x_2?

11-13 ★ Two springs having force constants k_1 and k_2 have the same length when relaxed. Both springs are fixed at their left ends and pulled together at their right ends by a single applied force, as shown in Figure 11-21. (a) What is the work done when the two springs are stretched through a distance x? (b) What is the force as a function of x?

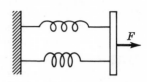

Figure 11-21

11-14 The magnitude of the attractive force, between two unlike electric charges of magnitudes q_1 and q_2 separated by a distance r, is given by kq_1q_2/r^2. How much work must be done to increase the separation of two charges from r_1 to r_2?

11-15 Consider the two vectors $A = 10$ units east and $B = 5.0$ units 60° north of east. (a) Find $A \cdot B$. (b) What is the magnitude of a vector having the direction 30° south of east which also gives the same scalar product with vector A?

11-16 Consider the three vectors $A = 10$ units east, $B = 5.0$ units 60° north of east, and $C = 15$ units north. (a) Find $(B \cdot A)C$. (b) Find $B(A \cdot C)$.

11-17 Derive the law of cosines for oblique triangles from the rules governing the scalar product, by showing that, if $C = A + B$, then $C^2 = A^2 + B^2 + 2AB \cos \theta$ where θ is the angle between the vectors A and B.

11-18 A spring is found to have a force constant k of 500 dyne/cm. Its unstretched length is 30.0 cm. (a) How much work is required to stretch the spring from a length of 35 cm to 40 cm? (b) How much work is required to stretch it from a length of 40 cm to 45 cm?

11-19 A 300 gm block is attached to a horizontal spring of force constant $k = 500$ dyne/cm and rests on a frictionless horizontal surface. The spring is compressed 4.0 cm and then the block is released. (a) What is the maximum speed of the block? (b) What is the work done by the spring force as the block goes from the position of maximum compression to maximum stretch?

11-20 A 50 gm mass is connected to two springs, as shown in Figure 11-22. The mass is displaced to the left 5.0 cm and then released. (a) What

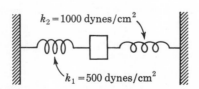

$k_2 = 1000$ dynes/cm^2

$k_1 = 500$ dynes/cm^2

Figure 11-22

is the work done by the left-hand spring as the mass goes from -5.0 cm to $+2.0$ cm? (b) What is the work done by the right-hand spring over this same displacement? (c) What is the speed of the 50 gm mass at $+2.0$ cm?

11-21   Two equal masses are connected to opposite ends of a spring whose spring constant is k. The spring is then stretched by an amount x, and then released. (a) What is the maximum speed of either mass m? (b) If one of the masses is infinite and the other is m, what is the maximum speed of the mass m?

11-22 ★ A 1.0 kg mass is initially held at rest on top of a 3.0 kg mass, the two masses being attached to one another as shown in Figure 11-23. The coefficient of kinetic friction between the surfaces of the two blocks is 0.25. The 3.0 kg block rests on a frictionless 30° inclined plane. When the system is released, the 1.0 kg block slides across the top of the 3.0 kg block, whose length is 10.0 cm. (a) Find the work done by friction on the 1.0 kg block. (b) Find the work done by friction on the 3.0 kg block. (c) Find the work done by the tension force on each block. (d) Find the work done by gravity on each block. (e) Use the work–kinetic-energy theorem to find the speed of the blocks just before the 1.0 kg block slides off the 3.0 kg block.

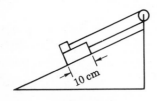   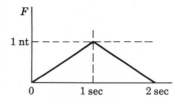

Figure 11-23   **Figure 11-24**

11-23 ★ A 1.0 kg body initially at rest at the origin on a smooth horizontal surface is acted upon by a force whose direction is fixed and horizontal but whose magnitude varies with time, as shown in Figure 11-24. How much work is done by the force during (a) the first second and (b) the second second? Find the average power during (c) the first second and (d) the second second.

11-24   A cannon fires a 2.0-pound projectile with an initial velocity of 640 feet/sec in a direction 30° above the horizontal. Find the instantaneous rate at which work is being done *on* the projectile by the gravitational force (a) 5.0 sec after firing, (b) 10.0 sec after firing, and (c) 15.0 sec after firing.

11-25   Show that it is impossible to do work at constant power on a body initially at rest.

11-26   What is the average horsepower necessary to accelerate a 2000-pound car from rest to 60 miles/hour in 10 sec?

11-27   A 160-pound man runs up a flight of stairs 10 feet high in 2.5 sec. What is the man's average power over this time interval?

11-28 An automobile of 2000 pounds coasts at a constant speed of 50 feet/sec down a hill having a slope of 20°. At what power must the automobile operate to climb the same hill at the same speed?

11-29 How much power is necessary to accelerate 2.0×10^{12} protons per second, each proton being accelerated from rest to a kinetic energy of 30 Bev (30 billion ev)?

11-30 A 1.0-ton elevator, initially at rest, is accelerated upward at a constant acceleration of 4.0 feet/sec^2 for 4.0 sec. (a) Find the average power necessary to accelerate the elevator over this 4.0 sec interval. Find the instantaneous power (b) at 1.0 sec and (c) at 4.0 sec.

T W E L V E

POTENTIAL ENERGY AND THE
CONSERVATION OF ENERGY

Up to this point we have recognized one type of energy only—the kinetic energy that a body has by virtue of its motion. In this chapter we introduce the concept of potential energy, so that we may speak of the conservation of mechanical energy. We shall give the general definition of potential energy and consider in some detail the potential energy associated with two important systems in which a conservative force acts: the Earth and a body near it, and two masses attached to a spring. The general conservation of energy law will then be treated. Collisions will be re-examined in terms of both energy and momentum conservation.

12-1 Potential energy Let us take a further look at a situation treated in Chapter 11. This situation led to a repetitive motion continuing indefinitely in the absence of a friction force: a block sliding on a frictionless surface under the influence of the constant force of gravity. See Figure 12-1. At the point 1, where the vertical displacement is y_1, or at any other

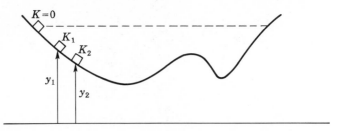

Figure 12-1. A block slides on a frictionless surface starting from rest. The block's kinetic energy is K_1 and K_2, respectively, at the vertical displacement y_1 and y_2.

position at the same elevation, the body has a kinetic energy $K_1 = \frac{1}{2}mv_1^2$; for the displacement y_2, the kinetic energy of the block is $K_2 = \frac{1}{2}mv_2^2$. The work done by the gravitational force on the block as it goes from y_1 to y_2 is $mg(y_1 - y_2)$, as was shown in Equation 11-16. Therefore, from the work-energy theorem,

$$K_2 - K_1 = W_{1 \to 2}$$

$$\tfrac{1}{2}mv_2^2 - \tfrac{1}{2}mv_1^2 = mg(y_1 - y_2) \qquad [12\text{-}1]$$

where v_1 and v_2 are the speeds at y_1 and y_2, respectively. Rearranging Equation 12-1 yields

$$\tfrac{1}{2}mv_2^2 + mgy_2 = \tfrac{1}{2}mv_1^2 + mgy_1 \qquad [12\text{-}2]$$

Equation 12-2 can be interpreted in a particularly simple way when we identify the terms mgy_1 and mgy_2 as representing a new form of energy associated with the vertical displacement y. We call this the *potential energy*. Designating the gravitational potential energy mgy by the symbol U_g, we have

$$\boxed{U_g = mgy} \qquad [12\text{-}3]$$

Equation 12-2 becomes

$$K_1 + U_1 = K_2 + U_2 \qquad [12\text{-}4]$$

Equation 12-3 applies only for vertical displacements over which g can be assumed constant. (The more general expression for gravitational potential energy is developed in Chapter 16.)

Equation 12-4 says that, when the block gains or loses kinetic energy, the gravitational potential energy changes so that the *total mechanical energy*, $E_m = K + U$, defined as the sum of the kinetic and potential energies, is *constant*. By introducing the idea of potential energy, we have a new language for describing energy transformations and a new conservation law. Whereas heretofore we could say that a falling or descending block gains kinetic energy because the Earth does work on it, we now can say, equivalently, that the descending block gains kinetic energy because it loses potential energy and that the total energy remains unchanged.

What we have done in effect, has been to choose new boundaries for our system. The old boundaries are indicated in Figure 12-2a; our new ones, in Figure 12-2b. The new system, now consisting of the block and the

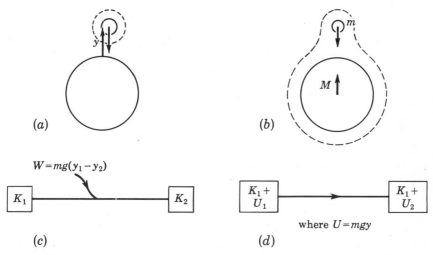

Figure 12-2. (a) A body at a vertical displacement y above the Earth; when we choose the body as our system (dotted lines), an external force mg acts on the body and does work on it. (b) Another choice of the system, the body together with the Earth; *no* external force acts on this system to do work. (c) Energy flow diagram corresponding to (a); the kinetic energy changes, because an external force does work on the body. (d) Energy flow diagram corresponding to (b); we account for changes in the kinetic energy of the system by introducing the potential energy U.

Earth, is isolated from external forces, and the force of the Earth on the block and of the block on the Earth are now *internal* forces. The effect of the internal forces is replaced by an *internal* gravitational potential energy, which is a property of the system as a whole.

Because our system now contains the Earth of mass M, we must be concerned also with its kinetic energy, $K_M = \frac{1}{2}MV^2$. It is easy to show that K_M is entirely negligible compared with the kinetic energy of the block, $K_m = \frac{1}{2}mv^2$:

$$\frac{K_M}{K_m} = \frac{\frac{1}{2}MV^2}{\frac{1}{2}mv^2} = \left(\frac{m}{M}\right)\left(\frac{MV}{mv}\right)^2 \qquad [12\text{-}5]$$

The center of mass of the Earth-block system is taken to be at rest; therefore, the total momentum of the system is zero. The momentum magnitudes of the block and the Earth are thus equal, $mv = MV$, and Equation 12-5 reduces to

$$\frac{K_M}{K_m} = \frac{m}{M} \tag{12-6}$$

The Earth's mass M is 10^{25} kg and, for a 1.0 kg block, $m/M \simeq 10^{-25}$. Therefore, $K_M/K_m \simeq 0$.

We can show from another point of view that, although the block and Earth have identical momentum magnitudes, their kinetic energies differ greatly. By Newton's third law, the forces on each of the two interacting bodies are the same. We find the work done by the block *on the Earth*—and, consequently, the resultant kinetic energy change of the Earth—by multiplying the force by the *Earth's* displacement. But this displacement is very small compared with that of the block, because momentum conservation requires that the Earth's speed be very small. It follows that the work done on the Earth is negligible and that its kinetic energy may properly be ignored. (Note, however, in Equation 12-6, that if the masses of interacting bodies are comparable, so are the respective kinetic energies.)

Let us write the *conservation of mechanical energy law* in more general form. For an isolated system consisting of two bodies a and b, having kinetic energies K_a and K_b and interacting with one another through internal forces related to the potential energy U_{ab}, the total mechanical energy E_m is

$$\boxed{E_m = K_a + K_b + U_{ab} = \text{constant}} \tag{12-7}$$

The conservation of mechanical energy law is *true by definition*; that is, potential energy is invented so that mechanical energy is conserved.

Energy-flow diagrams for both the systems are shown in Figure 12-2d. In the earth-block system, no agent does work *on the system*; the total energy of the system is constant, potential energy of the system being transformed into kinetic energy of the block.

We turn now to another illustration of potential energy: the interaction between a light block and a massive block connected to the ends of a spring. See Figure 12-3. From Equation 12-5, the massive block's kinetic energy is again negligible, and only the kinetic energy of the light block is important. The work done by the spring on the light block as it goes from x_1 to x_2 is equal, by the work-energy theorem, to the change in kinetic energy between these points:

$$\tfrac{1}{2}mv_2{}^2 - \tfrac{1}{2}mv_1{}^2 = W_{1\to 2} \tag{12-8}$$

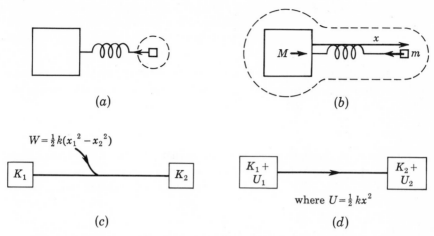

(a)   (b)

$W = \frac{1}{2}k(x_1{}^2 - x_2{}^2)$

K_1 —————————————— K_2

$K_1 + U_1$ ——————————→ $K_2 + U_2$

where $U = \frac{1}{2}kx^2$

(c)   (d)

Figure 12-3. (a) A small block acted on by the force of a spring; the system (dotted line) consists of the small block only. (b) The system is now chosen as the light and massive block, together with the spring through which they interact. (c) The light block's kinetic energy goes from K_1 to K_2 because the spring does work $W = \frac{1}{2}k(x_1{}^2 - x_2{}^2)$ on it. (d) The total mechanical energy of the system is unchanged, any changes in the kinetic energy of the light block now being accounted for by changes in the system's potential energy U.

The work $W_{1\to2}$ done by the spring is negative and equal to the area under the force-displacement graph of Figure 12-4. The area of the trapezoid is equal to that of a rectangle of height $k(x_1 + x_2)/2$ and width $(x_2 - x_1)$. Therefore,

$$W_{1\to2} = -\frac{k}{2}(x_2 + x_1)(x_2 - x_1)$$

$$= -\frac{k}{2}x_2{}^2 + \frac{k}{2}x_1{}^2$$

Then Equation 12-8 becomes

$$\tfrac{1}{2}mv_2{}^2 - \tfrac{1}{2}mv_1{}^2 = -\tfrac{1}{2}kx_2{}^2 + \tfrac{1}{2}kx_1{}^2$$

or $\tfrac{1}{2}mv_1{}^2 + \tfrac{1}{2}kx_1{}^2 = \tfrac{1}{2}mv_2{}^2 + \tfrac{1}{2}kx_2{}^2$ [12-9]

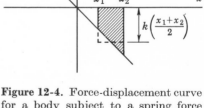

Figure 12-4. Force-displacement curve for a body subject to a spring force F_s. Over the displacement $(x_2 - x_1)$ the average force of the spring is $k(x_1 + x_2)/2$.

Equation 12-9 is of exactly the same form as Equation 12-2.

We again define a potential energy in such a way that the total mechanical energy of the block-spring-block system is constant. The potential energy

U_s associated with the spring is

$$U_s = \tfrac{1}{2}kx^2$$ [12-10]

Note that the potential energy U_s is a property of the spring alone, depending on its stiffness k and elongation x, but not on the masses or velocities of the blocks attached to it. Then Equation 12-9 may be written

$$E_m = K_1 + U_1 = K_2 + U_2$$

Suppose that the light block is set in oscillation. The block-spring-block system is then isolated from outside influence. The total mechanical energy of the block-spring-block system remains constant thereafter and, since the one block is assumed very massive, energy is continuously transformed between the kinetic energy of the light block and the potential energy of the spring. The kinetic energy of the block is a maximum as it passes through the equilibrium position $(x = 0)$; at this instant the spring is unstretched and the potential energy is zero. When the block is momentarily at rest at its greatest excursion, its kinetic energy is zero; at this instant the potential energy is a maximum. At intermediate displacements the mechanical energy of the system is partially kinetic and partially potential. An energy-flow diagram for the system is the same as that shown in Figure 12-3d.

Example 1   A stone of 3.0 pounds is thrown from a cliff 64 feet high with a speed of 20 feet/sec and at an angle of 30° with respect to the horizontal. What is the stone's kinetic energy just before striking the ground?

While the stone is in free flight, the total mechanical energy of the stone-Earth system is constant. As the stone descends, it (or, strictly, the stone-Earth system) loses potential energy, $mg\,\Delta y$ where Δy is 64 feet. Therefore, the final kinetic energy K_f is, from Equation 12-2,

$$K_f = K_i + mg\,\Delta y = \tfrac{1}{2}mv_i^2 + mg\,\Delta y$$

$$K_f = \tfrac{1}{2}(3.0 \text{ lb}/32 \text{ ft/sec}^2)(20 \text{ ft/sec})^2 + (3.0 \text{ lb})(64 \text{ ft})$$

$$K_f = 211 \text{ ft-lb}$$

The direction of the velocity does *not* enter into the energy considerations; therefore, it is not necessary to know whether the stone was thrown 30° above the horizontal or below it or, for that matter, in any other direction.

Example 2   A 0.40 kg block is pressed against, but not attached to, a light spring having a stiffness constant of 1.2×10^3 nt/m. When the spring has been compressed 0.050 m, the block is released. The block slides along a frictionless surface and up an incline, as shown in Figure 12-5. What maximum height y does the block achieve?

After the spring has been compressed and released, the total mechanical energy content of the system remains constant. First, potential energy of the spring $\tfrac{1}{2}kx_1^2$ is transformed into kinetic energy $\tfrac{1}{2}mv_2^2$ of the sliding block; then the block's kinetic energy is transformed into gravitational potential energy mgy_3 as the block comes to rest at the highest point:

$$\tfrac{1}{2}kx_1{}^2 = \tfrac{1}{2}mv_2{}^2 = mgy_3$$

$$y_3 = \frac{kx_1{}^2}{2mg} = \frac{(1.2 \times 10^3 \text{ nt/m})(0.050 \text{ m})^2}{2(0.40 \text{ kg})(9.8 \text{ m/sec}^2)}$$

$$y_3 = 0.38 \text{ m}$$

This example illustrates the usefulness of the potential energy concept and the conservation principle following from it. We merely equate the total energy of the system at the end points, taking no concern for such details of the motion as the shape of the incline or the velocity at intermediate points. We could, of course, have arrived at the same final result by applying Newton's second law. However, this would have been mathematically difficult and extremely tedious, for it would have required the following procedure. From the initial force acting on the block (and this force *varies* with position), one computes the initial instantaneous acceleration; from this acceleration one

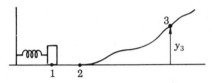

Figure 12-5. A block is pressed against a compressed spring at point 1, slides past point 2 on the same horizontal level, and finally comes to rest at point 3, where the vertical displacement is y_3.

computes the instantaneous velocity at a time dt later; from this instantaneous velocity one then computes the corresponding displacement; knowing the new displacement, one finds the new instantaneous force. The cycle is repeated over and over until finally one arrives at the position for which the velocity is zero. This procedure requires, of course, a detailed knowledge of the shape of the incline.

Example 3 A spring of stiffness constant k is attached to a ceiling. A block of mass m is attached to the lower end of the spring while the spring is unstretched, and then the block is released at this point. See Figure 12-6. (a) What is the maximum distance, say $2A$, below the point of release at which the block comes momentarily to rest? (b) At what point is the resultant force on the block zero? (c) What is the resultant force on the block at the lowest point?

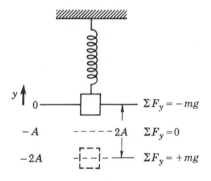

Figure 12-6. An oscillating block subject to both spring and gravitational forces. The spring is unstretched at $y = 0$; it has its maximum extension at $y = -2A$.

(a) As the block descends, the gravitational potential energy decreases and the potential energy of the spring increases. We take the vertical displacement y (positive upward) of the block, to be measured relative to the block's initial position; y then represents also the elongation of the spring. The total mechanical energy is initially *zero*, and it must remain zero at every instant thereafter. In symbols,

$$E_m = K + U_g + U_s$$

$$0 = K + mgy + \tfrac{1}{2}ky^2$$

At the lowest point, $y = -2A$ and $K = 0$. Therefore,

$$0 = 0 + mg(-2A) + \tfrac{1}{2}k(-2A)^2$$

$$2A = 2mg/k \qquad\qquad [12\text{-}11]$$

(b) The resultant force on the block is zero when the weight (downward) is equal to the spring force (upward):

$$\Sigma F_y = F_g + F_s$$

$$0 = (-mg) + (-ky)$$

(Note that $F_s > 0$ when $y < 0$.) Therefore

$$y = -\frac{mg}{k} = -A$$

where we have used Equation 12-11.

(c) The resultant force at $y = -2A$ is

$$\Sigma F_y = F_g + F_s = -mg - ky = -mg - k(-2A) = -mg + 2kA$$

By using Equation 12-11, we have

$$\Sigma F_y = -mg + 2mg = +mg$$

At the highest point ($y = 0$), the block is subject to a downward force of magnitude mg; at the lowest point ($y = -2A$), the block is subject to an *upward* force of magnitude mg; at a point midway between ($y = -A$), the resultant force is zero. Therefore, the block oscillates vertically with respect to an equilibrium position at $y = -A$.

The motion of the block can be more simply described by choosing a new origin for vertical displacement y' at the point $y = -A$, where the resultant force on the block is zero:

$$y' = y + A$$

$$\Sigma F_y = -mg - ky = -mg - k(y' - A) = -mg - ky' + kA$$

From Equation 12-11, $kA = mg$. Therefore,

$$\Sigma F_y = -ky'$$

Thus, the block undergoes simple harmonic motion with respect to an equilibrium position at $y' = 0$.

12-2   Properties of the potential energy of a system   Here we consider some important properties of the potential energy and its relation to force.†

First we have *the general definition of potential energy.* The total mechanical energy of an isolated conservative system is constant:

$$E_m = K_f + U_f = K_i + U_i$$

or
$$U_f - U_i = K_i - K_f = -(K_f - K_i)$$

where i and f represent any two states of the system. By the work-energy theorem,
$$W_{i \to f} = K_f - K_i$$

where, by definition,

[11-14]
$$W_{i \to f} = \int_i^f \mathbf{F} \cdot d\mathbf{s}$$

Therefore,
$$\boxed{U_f - U_i = -\int_i^f \mathbf{F} \cdot d\mathbf{s}}$$
[12-12]

The difference in potential energy between the final and initial states is equal to the *negative* of the work done by the *internal* forces of the system when the system goes from the initial to the final state. Thus, by evaluating the line integral in Equation 12-12, we can compute the potential-energy difference if we know the force as a function of position.

Now we list some of the general properties of potential energy.

(1) *Potential energy is a property of a system of interacting bodies as a whole.* One cannot speak of the potential energy of a single body. When, for example, a light block falls toward the Earth, it is perhaps natural to speak of the "block" as losing potential energy, inasmuch as it is the block rather than the Earth that gains most of the kinetic energy; however, it is the Earth-block *system* that gains kinetic energy as the two bodies approach one another, and it is the *system* that loses potential energy.

(2) Because one is always only concerned with differences in potential energy, *the choice of the zero of potential energy is arbitrary.* If the force associated with the potential energy is constant, as in the case of the gravitational force on a body close to the Earth, we may choose any convenient horizontal level (usually the lowest, or "ground," level) as the zero

† In this section we assume implicitly that a light body interacts with a very massive one. The general proof for the interaction of two comparable masses is given in Section 12-5.

for gravitational potential energy. If, on the other hand, the force varies with displacement, as in the case of the spring, it is customary to choose the zero of potential energy at that displacement for which the force is zero (thus, both $U_s = \frac{1}{2}kx^2$ and $F_s = -kx$ are zero at $x = 0$). There is also, in fact, an arbitrariness in the choice of the zero for kinetic energy: a body always has zero kinetic energy relative to the reference frame in which it is at rest.

Both kinetic and potential energies are scalar quantities but, unlike kinetic energy, which must always be positive, potential energy may be either positive or negative.

(3) Whereas we may speak of kinetic energy as energy of motion, *potential energy is energy of position* or, more properly, *energy of relative separation of interacting particles.* We say that a spring has potential energy when it is deformed by being stretched or compressed. The spring retains this potential energy as long as it remains deformed. Thus, if we clamp the spring while it is deformed, the spring's potential energy is locked in. No matter how long a time elapses, the spring is potentially able to do work and, if later we release the clamp, this stored energy is released.

When a spring is stretched or compressed, the atoms that comprise it must change their separation distances. Any potential energy is, in fact, related ultimately to the relative separation of particles. For example, a system consisting of two bottles holding different chemicals, each highly reactive with the other, has potential energy when the chemicals are in separate bottles. But when the contents are mixed and the two chemicals come in contact with each other and react, potential energy is released as the kinetic energy of molecules formed in the reaction.

(4) *A potential energy can be defined only for a conservative force.* By "a conservative force" is meant a force which depends only on the separation distance between the interacting bodies, *not* on the velocity or the time. For a system comprised of the Earth and a body near it, their separation distance is related to y; for the block-spring-block system, the separation distance is related to the spring elongation x.

An example of a *nonconservative force* is the force of kinetic friction. The force of friction is always in the direction opposite to that of the body's velocity and is, therefore, velocity-dependent. Such a force is a dissipative force, and a potential energy cannot be defined for it.

A conservative force is characterized by the following equivalent properties: (a) that the work done by a conservative force is independent of the path leading from the initial to the final position; (b) that the potential difference associated with a conservative force depends only on the end points, not on the route between them; (c) that the total work done by a conservative force in a round trip, or around a closed loop which brings a body back to its original location, is zero.

We may discuss this a little further, before taking up the next property. Let us, for instance, find the restriction on a force such that the assertions given be true and that the force be indeed a conservative one. From Equation 12-12,

[12-12]
$$U_f - U_i = -\int_i^f \boldsymbol{F} \cdot d\boldsymbol{s}$$

The potential energies U_i and U_f must depend only on the initial and final positions, respectively. When i and f are the same states, then clearly $U_f = U_i$. Thus, when the body is returned to its starting point along any path, U_i equals U_f and Equation 12-12 becomes

Conservative force: $\oint \boldsymbol{F} \cdot d\boldsymbol{s} = 0$ [12-13]

where the circle about the integral sign indicates that the line integral is taken around *any* closed loop.

The gravitational force and the spring force are two important examples of conservative forces. We will illustrate Equation 12-13 with these two forces.

When a ball is thrown vertically upward, the work done by the gravitational force $F_g = mg$ is negative because F_g acts in the direction opposite to that of the displacement. Along the return path downward, the work done by F_g is positive, since it now acts in the same direction as the motion. Thus, for the entire trip, up and down, we have $\oint F_g \cdot d\boldsymbol{y} = 0$.

Now consider the motion of a block fixed to the end of a horizontal spring which is set in oscillation on a smooth surface. When the block moves from the equilibrium position ($x = 0$) out to the maximum positive displacement ($x = A$), the work done by the spring force is negative because the spring force F_s acts in the direction opposite to the block's motion. On the way back, the work done by F_s is positive since it acts along the direction of motion. Inasmuch as the force depends only on the displacement, the work on the way out is equal in magnitude to the work on the way back, and $\oint F_s \cdot d\boldsymbol{x} = 0$.

We can illustrate that the work done by a conservative force on a round trip along a more complicated path is zero. Consider a particle moving around the closed path shown in Figure 12-7. Here the particle moves near the Earth in a vertical plane; we wish to find the work done by the gravitational force F_g when the particle makes a round trip by moving from point 1 to 2 to 3 and then back to 1. Along the horizontal path from 1 to 2 the work done by F_g is zero, because F_g is always perpendicular to the path:

$$W_{1 \to 2} = 0$$

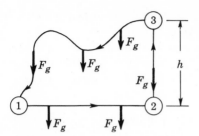

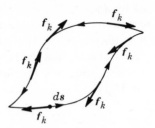

Figure 12-7. A conservative force, the gravitational force F_g, acts on a body taken around a closed path in a vertical plane from point 1 to 2 to 3 to 1.

Figure 12-8. A nonconservative force: the kinetic friction force f_k acts on a body which is taken around a closed path. Note that the force is always in a direction opposite to that of the velocity.

From point 2 to 3, the work done by F_g is negative, F_g being oppositely directed to the path element ds:

$$W_{2\rightarrow 3} = \int_2^3 F_g \cdot ds = -mgh$$

Finally, along the path from point 3 to 1, the work done by F_g will be positive and equal in magnitude to the work done between 2 and 3:

$$W_{3\rightarrow 1} = \int_3^1 F_g \cdot ds = +mgh$$

Thus, the work done in going around the closed loop is

$$W_{1\rightarrow 1} = \oint F_g \cdot ds = W_{1\rightarrow 2} + W_{2\rightarrow 3} + W_{3\rightarrow 1} = 0$$

This example is somewhat special in that the conservative force F_g has been assumed constant in magnitude and direction. However, we shall later discuss conservative forces (the electrostatic force and the general gravitational force), which vary in both magnitude and direction. For these variable conservative forces Equation 12-13 still holds.

It is easy to show that, for a

$$\boxed{\text{Nonconservative force:} \qquad \oint F \cdot ds \neq 0} \qquad \text{[12-14]}$$

Suppose that one pushes a body around a closed path on a rough horizontal surface (see Figure 12-8). The work done by the kinetic friction force f_k

will be negative for *any* segment of the path because it is always opposite in direction to that of motion. In fact, for the situation of Figure 12-8, the friction force is constant in magnitude, the angle between f_k and ds is always 180°, and the work done, then, along any path is

$$\int (f_k \cos 180°)\, ds = -f_k s$$

where s is the length of the path. The total work done by the nonconservative force f_k depends on the total distance traversed by the body and is *not* zero for a round trip of any length:

$$\oint f_k \cdot ds < 0$$

Thus, f_k is not a conservative force and we cannot associate a potential energy with this type of interaction. (Another important example of a nonconservative force is the magnetic force which acts between electric charges in motion.)

(5) *The energetics of a motion may be portrayed usefully by a graph of potential energy as a function of displacement.* Consider the plot of the gravitational potential energy U_g versus the displacement y,

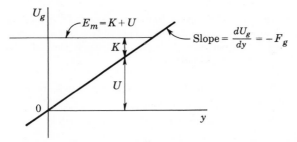

Figure 12-9. Plot of the gravitational potential energy U_g versus the vertical displacement y for a constant gravitational force F_g. The gravitational force is the negative slope of the potential-energy-displacement curve: $F_g = -dU_g/dy$.

corresponding to a body falling freely under the influence of gravity. Because $U_g = mgy$, and the potential energy is proportional to the height y, a plot of U_g versus y is simply a straight line of positive slope mg, as shown in Figure 12-9. If we draw a horizontal line to represent the total mechanical energy of the system $E_m = K + U_g$, then the vertical segment beneath the curve represents the potential energy and the vertical segment above the curve represents the kinetic energy.

The slope of a curve of potential energy versus displacement has an interesting significance. For the gravitational potential, the slope dU_g/dy is

$$\frac{d}{dy}\,(U_g) = \frac{d}{dy}\,(mgy) = mg$$

But

$$F_g = -mg$$

Therefore,

$$F_g = -\frac{dU_g}{dy}$$

The force is the negative derivative of the potential energy with respect to displacement. Therefore, the force is a measure of the steepness, or grade,

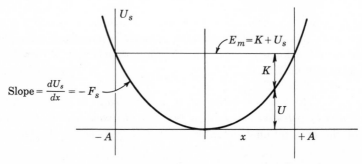

Figure 12-10. Plot of a spring's potential energy U_s versus its displacement x. The curve is a parabola. The body's motion is restricted to the displacements between $x = \pm A$, for which the total mechanical energy $E_m = K + U_s$ is positive.

of the slope. For this reason a conservative force may be referred to as the negative *gradient* of the potential energy.

A similar relation can be written for the spring force:

$$\frac{d}{dx}\,(U_x) = \frac{d}{dx}\,(\tfrac{1}{2}kx^2) = kx$$

But

$$F_s = -kx$$

Therefore,

$$F_s = -\frac{dU_s}{dx}$$

Again the negative of the slope of potential energy versus displacement gives the force. The potential-energy curve for a spring is a parabola, as shown in Figure 12-10. The motion is *bound*, the oscillating particle being confined by the "potential well" to the region between $x = -A$ and $x = +A$. Outside of this region the kinetic energy would be negative—an impossibility. When the body is initially displaced to the right or to the left of the equilibrium position at $x = 0$, a restoring force tends to return it to the lowest point in the potential-energy valley. This is in contrast to the *unbound* motion of the falling body in Figure 12-9, where the kinetic energy is positive for *all* points lower than that for which the body has zero kinetic energy.

The gravitational and spring forces are two special examples of a general relation giving the components of a conservative force in terms of the corresponding potential energy. If one has a potential energy $U(x, y, z)$ depending

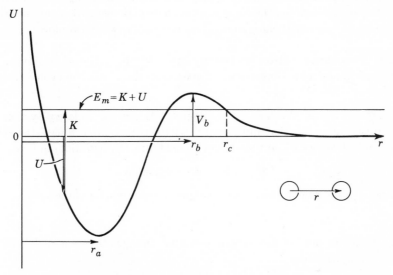

Figure 12-11. Typical graph of potential energy versus displacement for the interaction between two atoms of a diatomic molecule.

on the coordinates x, y, and z, the components of the force are F_x, F_y, and F_z and are given by

$$F_x = -\frac{\partial U}{\partial x}, \qquad F_y = -\frac{\partial U}{\partial y}, \qquad F_z = -\frac{\partial U}{\partial z} \qquad [12\text{-}15]$$

Figure 12-11 shows the potential-energy graph characterizing the interaction between two atoms of a diatomic molecule, the potential energy being given as a function of the separation distance of the two nuclei. Following the usual convention, the potential energy is chosen as zero at that location for which the interaction force is zero. Then the zero of the molecular potential energy corresponds to the two atoms infinitely separated. Classically, when the atoms are separated by a distance less than r_b, they can be bound to form a molecule provided that the total mechanical energy E_m is *less* than the potential energy U_b at r_b. For separation distances greater than r_a, the force between the atoms is one of attraction; for distances less than r_a, it is one of repulsion. For large separation distances, greater than r_c in Figure 12-11, the atoms repel one another.

Point a at the lowest point in the potential valley is a position of *stable equilibrium*, inasmuch as any small displacement from this point *increases* the potential energy and, therefore, gives rise to a restoring force. On the other hand, point b at the highest point of the potential peak is a position of *unstable equilibrium*, inasmuch as any small displacement from this position *decreases* the potential energy and gives rise to a *non*restoring force.

12-3   The conservation of energy law   We now discuss two types of systems, those with conservative forces and those with nonconservative forces.

SYSTEMS WITH CONSERVATIVE FORCES   When an isolated system is comprised of bodies that interact by strictly conservative forces, the total mechanical energy E_m of the system is constant. By definition, in fact,

$$E_m = K + U = \text{constant}$$

where K is the sum of the kinetic energies of the particles in the system,

$$K = K_1 + K_2 + K_3 + \cdots$$

and U is the sum of the various potential energies between each pair of interacting particles,

$$U = U_{12} + U_{23} + U_{31} + \cdots$$

The particles of the system may lose kinetic energy; if they do, the potential energy then must increase to keep the total mechanical energy constant. The "initial" mechanical energy $E_m(i)$ of a conservative system is exactly equal to the "final" mechanical energy $E_m(f)$ at any later time:

$$\text{Conservative system:} \qquad E_m(i) = E_m(f) \qquad \text{[12-16]}$$

If this system is no longer isolated from its surroundings and an external agent does work $W_{i \to f}$ on the system, then

$$\boxed{W_{i \to f} = E_m(f) - E_m(i)} \qquad \text{[12-17]}$$

where the energy content of the system has been increased by $W_{i \to f}$. Conversely, if the system does work on an external agent, the energy content of the system decreases.

Suppose, for example, that a man raises a block of weight mg vertically from y_1 to y_2. The man interposes himself between the Earth and the block, pushing on each to increase their separation, as shown in Figure 12-12a. He, as the agent, does work on the system, thereby increasing its mechanical-energy content.

We imagine that the man raises the block at constant velocity. Since the resultant force *on the block* must then be zero, the man will have to apply a force of magnitude mg to the block (and also to the Earth). He does negligible work on the Earth because it does not move appreciably, but he does work in the amount $mg(y_2 - y_1)$ on the block. Neither the kinetic energy of the

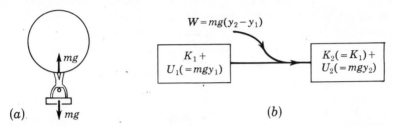

(a)

(b)

Figure 12-12. (a) An external agent increases the separation distance between a block and the Earth by applying a force of magnitude mg to both bodies. (b) The change in the potential energy of the Earth-block system is equal to the work $W = mg(y_2 - y_1)$ done by the external agent in separating the bodies at constant velocity.

block nor that of the Earth changes. The potential energy of the Earth-block system must, then, have increased by $mg(y_2 - y_1)$. This result is consistent with Equation 12-17, since

$$W_{i \to f} = mg(y_2 - y_1)$$

and

$$E_m(f) - E_m(i) = (K_f + U_f) - (K_i + U_i)$$

$$= (K_2 + mgy_2) - (K_1 + mgy_1)$$

But

$$K_2 = K_1$$

Therefore,

$$E_m(f) - E_m(i) = mg(y_2 - y_1)$$

The work done by the external agent in separating the bodies *at constant velocity* is equal to the increase in the system's potential energy. See the energy-flow diagram, Figure 12-12b.

SYSTEMS WITH NONCONSERVATIVE FORCES It is impossible to construct any large-scale system of bodies in which *all* frictional and other non-conservative forces are absent. Perpetual-motion machines are impossible. Consider an isolated system having nonconservative forces. When particles in such a system lose kinetic energy, the potential energy of the system does *not* increase in the same amount. Consequently, the initial total mechanical energy of an isolated system with nonconservative forces always *exceeds* the final mechanical energy. The total mechanical energy *decreases* with time in a nonconservative system:

$$\text{Nonconservative system:} \qquad E_m(i) > E_m(f) \qquad \text{[12-18]}$$

Mechanical energy is *not* conserved, if by "mechanical energy" is meant the kinetic energy of large-scale objects one can see and the potential energy one can identify with a discernible change in their relative separation. Thus, if energy *is* to be conserved in a system with nonconservative forces, a new form, or perhaps several new forms, of energy must be named, so that the inequality above can be replaced by an equation such as

$$E_m(f) = E_m(i) + E_{\text{non-}m} \qquad \text{[12-19]}$$

where $E_{\text{non-}m}$ represents the sum of all forms of *nonmechanical* energy, that is, energy different from the kinetic and potential energies of large-scale bodies.

One of the greatest discoveries in classical physics was that Equation 12-19 agrees with experiment. As we shall see in later chapters, physicists found that nonmechanical forms of energy exist in that they can be measured in meaningful ways, their amounts being such as to make the *total energy content* of an isolated system constant. When the nonconservative force is friction, $E_{\text{non-}m}$ is (mostly) heat, or thermal energy. But still other forms of energy are recognized: the energy associated with electromagnetic radiation (as illustrated by light or radio waves), the energy of sound, chemical energy (which can properly be called "atomic" energy), nuclear energy (which is sometimes improperly called "atomic energy"), and still others.

Experiments in all branches of physics are consistent with the *general conservation of energy law, that the total energy content of an isolated system is constant.* By an "isolated" system is now meant a collection of objects on which no work is done and into (or out of) which neither thermal energy nor radiation flows. Energy may be converted from one form to another, but it is not created or destroyed. Thus, energy conservation ranks, with the conservation laws of mass and of linear momentum, as one of the truly fundamental principles of physics. (In the theory of special relativity, the separate conservation laws of mass and energy are combined into a single conservation law, that of mass-energy, which is thus of an even greater simplicity and generality.) Physicists' confidence in the universality of energy conservation has always been vindicated by experiment.

The recognition that various forms of energy can be delineated, that energy appears as thermal energy, or as *radiation*, as well as kinetic energy and potential energy, was indeed a remarkable discovery. But even more remarkable perhaps has been the realization, coming mostly in the last fifty years, that nonmechanical forms of energy are, after all, just kinetic and potential energy on a submicroscopic scale. It is now known that thermal energy is, in fact, kinetic and potential energy associated with the disordered motion of atoms or molecules; the energy of electromagnetic radiation is the kinetic energy of particle-like photons traveling at the speed of light; the energy associated with sound is the vibrational energy of vibrating atoms and molecules; chemical energy is traceable to the kinetic energy of subatomic particles and the electric potential energy of their interaction; nuclear energy is the kinetic energy of the nuclear constituents and the potential energy associated with their interaction through the nuclear force. Macroscopically, many forms of energy must be delineated; sub-microscopically—at the level of the ultimate particles of physics—one needs only mechanical energy. At this microscopic level, *all* energy is either kinetic energy or potential energy because all of the fundamental forces between particles are *conservative forces*.

Example 4   A rigid massless rod is pivoted at one end, a body of 4.0 kg being attached to the other end of the rod. The rod is released from rest when it makes an angle of 37° with respect to the vertical, as shown in Figure 12-13. What is the tension in the rod when the body swings through the lowest point?

We find the tension T in the rod by applying Newton's second law when the body is at its lowest point, at which time its instantaneous speed along the circular arc is v:

$$\Sigma F_y = ma_y$$

$$T - mg = mv^2/r = mv^2/L$$

where the length L of the rod is also the radius of the circular arc. Therefore,

$$T = mg + mv^2/L \qquad [12\text{-}20]$$

The speed v at the lowest point is most easily found by applying the conservation of energy law. As the body falls, it loses potential energy and gains an equal amount of kinetic energy. For convenience, we take the zero of gravitational potential energy at the lowest point; then,

$$U_g = mgy = mg(L + L \cos \theta)$$

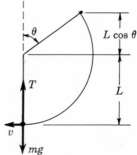

Figure 12-13.   A rigid massless rod of length L is released from rest at the angle θ to swing about a horizontal axis through one end.

from the geometry of Figure 12-13. Denoting the state when the rod is released by i, and using f to denote the state when the rod is vertical, we find that energy conservation gives

$$E_m(i) = E_m(f)$$

$$U_i + K_i = U_f + K_f$$

Here $\qquad\qquad K_i = 0 \qquad$ and $\qquad U_f = 0$

Therefore, $\qquad\qquad mg(L + L\cos\theta) = \tfrac{1}{2}mv^2$

or $\qquad\qquad\qquad v^2/L = 2g(1 + \cos\theta)$

Substituting this result into Equation 12-20 yields

$$T = mg + 2mg(1 + \cos\theta) = mg(3 + 2\cos\theta)$$

The tension does *not* depend on the rod's length L!

$$T = (4.0 \text{ kg})(9.8 \text{ m/sec}^2)(3.0 + 1.6) = 1.8 \times 10^2 \text{ nt}$$

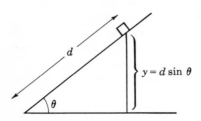

Figure 12-14. A body coasts a distance d up a rough inclined plane before coming to rest momentarily.

Example 5 A body of 5.0 kg coasts up an incline with a speed, at the lowest point, of 4.0 m/sec. It comes momentarily to rest, and then coasts down again, its speed at the lowest point on the incline being 3.0 m/sec on return. (a) How much energy is dissipated in friction? (b) If the angle of the incline is 37°, what distance does the body travel up along the incline?

(a) We find the loss in mechanical energy by comparing the initial and final mechanical energies. The potential energy is the same in the initial and final states, the body being, both initially and finally, at the base of the incline. Therefore, the decrease in the mechanical energy is simply the change in the kinetic energy. From Equation 12-19,

$$E_{\text{non-}m} = E_m(i) - E_m(f) = (K_i + U_i) - (K_f + U_f)$$

$$E_{\text{non-}m} = K_i - K_f = \tfrac{1}{2}m(v_i{}^2 - v_f{}^2)$$

$$E_{\text{non-}m} = \tfrac{1}{2}(5.0 \text{ kg})[(4.0 \text{ m/sec})^2 - (3.00 \text{ m/sec})^2] = 18 \text{ joules}$$

Eighteen joules of mechanical energy are transformed into thermal energy by friction.

(b) Now we choose as our final state that at which the body is momentarily at rest on the incline. From part (a) we know that 9.0 joules of mechanical energy have been converted into nonmechanical energy as the body increases its vertical displacement by $y = d\sin\theta$, as shown in Figure 12-14. Using Equation 12-19, we have

$$E_{\text{non-}m} = (K_i + U_i) - (K_f + U_f)$$

$$9.0 \text{ joules} = [\tfrac{1}{2}(5.0 \text{ kg})(4.0 \text{ m/sec})^2 + 0] - [0 + (5.0 \text{ kg})(9.8 \text{ m/sec}^2)(d\sin 37°)]$$

$$d = 1.0 \text{ m}$$

12-4   Collisions In Section 8-1 we examined collisions from the point of view of momentum conservation. Now we take another look at collisions—from the point of view of energy conservation as well.

When two ordinary bodies, such as billiard balls, collide, each is deformed by the interaction force during the collision. After they have separated, each object springs back, completely or partially, to its original shape.

In order that we may make the momentum and energy transformations that occur during a collision more readily visualized and interpreted, we consider the following highly idealized collision: a block sliding on a smooth horizontal surface, striking head on another block originally at rest, to which a relatively stiff spring of negligible mass has been permanently attached (see Figure 12-15). We shall assume that the only deformation occurring

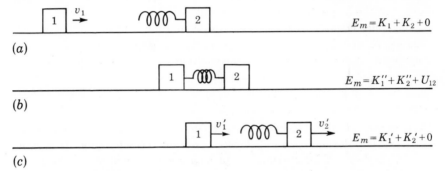

Figure 12-15. An idealized elastic collision. (a) Before the collision the bodies 1 and 2 have kinetic energies K_1 and K_2 respectively; the potential energy is zero. (b) During the collision the kinetic energies are K_1'' and K_2'' and the potential energy is U_{12}. (c) After the collision the kinetic energies are K_1' and K_2' and the potential energy is again zero.

during the collision is that of the spring, and that the force of one body on the other arises from the compressed spring alone. The body originally in motion we label 1; the struck body, 2.

First, consider momentum conservation. If no unbalanced force acts on the system (consisting of the spring and bodies 1 and 2), the total momentum of the system is constant. Whenever the bodies interact—that is, whenever the spring is compressed to any extent—the force of 1 on 2 (via the spring) is equal, by Newton's third law, to the force of 2 on 1. When body 1 first strikes the spring, the spring begins to compress. Then the momentum p_1 of body 1 (to the right) is reduced as body 1 is slowed down by the force on it (to the left). At the same time, the momentum p_2 of body 2 is increased (to the right) by precisely the same amount. In short, body 1 transfers momentum to body 2, the total momentum of the system being constant at every instant of time throughout the collision. If we denote the momenta after the collision by primes, momentum conservation gives

$$p_1 + p_2 = p_1' + p_2'$$

ELASTIC COLLISIONS   Now consider energy conservation. When the spring initially is being compressed, work is done on it and the *total* kinetic energy of the two bodies is reduced. Body 1 loses kinetic energy at a *greater* rate than body 2 gains it. At some intermediate stage in the collision the spring has its maximum compression, at which time the separation distance between the two bodies is a minimum. Both bodies may be in motion at this time, so that the total energy of the system has *three* contributions: the kinetic energy of body 1, the kinetic energy of body 2, and the potential energy of the spring. The spring then expands to its undeformed length, pushing on the bodies in opposite directions, and its potential energy is transformed into the kinetic energy of the bodies as they leave the collision.

The collision just described is an *elastic* collision, the sum of the kinetic energies K_1 and K_2 before the collision being exactly equal to the sum of the kinetic energies K_1' and K_2' after the collision:

$$\text{Elastic collision: } K_1 + K_2 = K_1' + K_2' \qquad [12\text{-}21]$$

A perfectly elastic collision occurs whenever the interaction forces are conservative, depending, by definition, only on the separation distance of the two bodies. (A detailed analysis of such a collision and of the general law of conservation of mechanical energy is given in Section 12-5.)

The force exerted by the spring is a conservative force, if the spring is perfectly elastic. An elastic spring is one that resumes its original shape and dimensions after being deformed and released. Collisions between bodies made of hard materials, such as billiard balls or ball bearings, are very nearly elastic collisions, the kinetic energy going out of such collisions being closely equal to that going into them. Such colliding bodies resume very nearly their original undeformed shapes.

Example 6   A billiard ball makes a perfectly elastic collision with a second billiard ball of the same mass but initially at rest. (a) What is the angle between the directions of motion of the two balls after the collision? (b) If the collision is head on, how does the speed of the struck ball compare with that of the ball initially in motion?

(a) From the conservation of momentum law we have

$$m\boldsymbol{v}_1 = m\boldsymbol{v}_1' + m\boldsymbol{v}_2'$$

where m is the mass of either ball, $\boldsymbol{v}_1$ and $\boldsymbol{v}_1'$ are the velocities before and after the collision, respectively, of the ball originally in motion, and $\boldsymbol{v}_2'$ is the velocity after the collision of the ball originally at rest. We may write this equation as

$$\boldsymbol{v}_1 = \boldsymbol{v}_1' + \boldsymbol{v}_2'$$

The velocity vectors form a triangle, as shown in Figure 12-16a; θ is the angle between velocities after the collision, as shown in Figure 12-16b.

The conservation of energy law requires that

$$\tfrac{1}{2}mv_1{}^2 = \tfrac{1}{2}mv_1{}'{}^2 + \tfrac{1}{2}mv_2{}'{}^2$$

or

$$v_1{}^2 = v_1{}'{}^2 + v_2{}'{}^2$$

The last equation implies, through the Pythagorean theorem, that the velocity vectors form a *right* triangle. Therefore, the angle θ between $\boldsymbol{v}_1'$ and $\boldsymbol{v}_2'$ is 90° for any non-head-on collision.

It is easy to prove that, if the ball originally at rest were more massive than the moving ball, the angle between their final velocities would be *greater* than 90°,

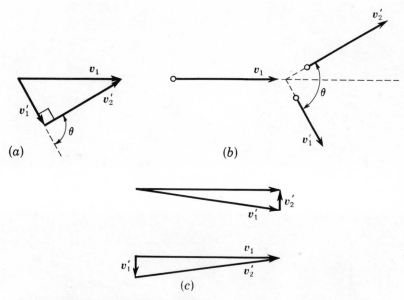

Figure 12-16. (a) Velocity vectors for the elastic collision between two bodies of equal mass. Momentum conservation requires that $\boldsymbol{v}_1 = \boldsymbol{v}_1' + \boldsymbol{v}_2'$. (b) Velocity vectors corresponding to part (a); the angle between the two velocities after the collision is θ. (c) The velocity vectors for a head-on elastic collision between two bodies of equal mass; either $\boldsymbol{v}_2' = 0$ or $\boldsymbol{v}_1' = 0$.

and that, if the ball originally at rest were less massive than the moving ball, the angle between the outgoing velocities would be *less* than 90°. Thus, if one measures the angles of each of the velocities after the collision—as shown, for example, by the tracks in a cloud chamber photograph of a collision between electrically charged particles—and if one also knows that the collision is elastic, the ratio of the masses of the colliding particles can be computed. See Figure 12-16c.

(b) We now treat the special case in which the collision is head on, neither of the two balls being deflected from the direction of $\boldsymbol{v}_1$. This implies that after the collision neither of the velocities $\boldsymbol{v}_1'$ and $\boldsymbol{v}_2'$ can have a component at right angles to the velocity $\boldsymbol{v}_1$. The condition is satisfied if we imagine the vector $\boldsymbol{v}_1$ to remain fixed and the vectors v_1' and v_2' to vary in magnitude (the angle between them remaining 90°), so that either v_2' shrinks to zero with $v_1' = v_1$ or v_1' shrinks to zero with $v_2' = v_1$, as shown in Figure 12-16c.

If $v_2' = 0$ and $v_1 = v_1'$, the ball originally in motion remains in motion at the same speed while the ball at rest remains at rest, which is to say that the one ball passes through the second ball without disturbing it (this is, of course, a bit unrealistic, but the equations implying momentum and energy conservation have no way of knowing this).

If $v_1' = 0$ and $v_2' = v_1$, the balls exchange velocities, the ball initially in motion is brought to rest, and the ball initially at rest leaves the collision site with

12-17   (a)

12-17   (b)

12-17   (c)

Figure 12-17. Cloud chamber photographs showing the elastic collision of α-particles (helium nuclei) with (a) a proton (hydrogen nucleus), (b) a helium nucleus, and (c) a fluorine nucleus. The α-particles enter from the left. In (a) the angle between the paths of the emerging particles is less than 90° since the α-particle mass is greater than that of the proton. In (b) the angle is 90°, as expected for equal masses (the angle appears to be slightly less than 90° since the tracks do not lie entirely in the plane of the photograph). In (c) the angle exceeds 90° since the α-particle is less massive than a fluorine nucleus. (From *An Atlas of Typical Expansion Chamber Photographs*, 1954, Pergamon Press, Ltd.)

velocity v_1. This exchange of velocities (as well as of momenta and kinetic energies) in an elastic head-on collision is possible only for bodies of equal mass. Only then do bodies with equal momenta also have equal kinetic energies.

When a light ball strikes a massive ball in an elastic head-on collision, as in the case of a ping-pong ball striking a billiard ball, the light ball bounces back with the same speed as that with which it approached the massive ball, the massive ball remaining at rest. On the other hand, when a massive ball strikes a light ball originally at rest in an elastic head-on collision, the massive ball continues to move forward with essentially unchanged speed and the light ball is set in motion. Although the light ball's speed exceeds that of the massive ball, its kinetic energy is very much less. Thus, a body can lose *all* of its kinetic energy in a collision only when it strikes head on a body of *equal* mass. If it strikes head on either a more massive body or a less massive body, only a fraction of its kinetic energy is transferred to the struck object.

This result is of importance when one is concerned with the problem of reducing the kinetic energies of the high-speed neutrons produced in a nuclear reactor. The neutrons are slowed down (or *moderated*) when they collide with, and transfer kinetic energy to, nuclei within the material of the nuclear reactor. This material (or *moderator*) must then consist of particles whose mass is not greatly different from that of the neutron, for the neutrons will be slowed down quickly, in a relatively small number of collisions, only if they collide elastically with nuclei of comparable mass. For this reason, the deuteron nuclei in heavy water are suitable, the deuteron mass being only twice the neutron mass.

Example 7   When a block of unknown mass and speed makes a head-on elastic collision with a 1.0 kg mass originally at rest, the 1.0 kg mass is set in motion with a speed of 15.0 m/sec. When the same block, moving at the same initial speed, collides with a 14.0 kg mass, the latter is set in motion with a speed of 2.0 m/sec. What is the unknown mass of the block?

Call the unknown mass m_1, its speed, before the collision, v_1, and after the collision, v_1'. The struck body has mass m_2 and its speed is $v_2 = 0$ before the collision and v_2' after.

From the conservation laws of energy and momentum we may write

$$\tfrac{1}{2}m_1v_1^2 = \tfrac{1}{2}m_1v_1'^2 + \tfrac{1}{2}m_2v_2'^2 \qquad [12\text{-}22]$$

and
$$m_1v_1 = m_1v_1' + m_2v_2' \qquad [12\text{-}23]$$

We wish to eliminate v_1', the speed of the unknown mass after the collision, and arrive at an expression giving v_2' in terms of the known quantities m_1, m_2, and v_1.

Equations 12-22 and 12-23 may be rewritten respectively as

$$m_1(v_1^2 - v_1'^2) = m_2v_2'^2 \qquad [12\text{-}24]$$

$$m_1(v_1 - v_1') = m_2v_2' \qquad [12\text{-}25]$$

Dividing Equation 12-24 by Equation 12-25 gives

$$v_1 + v_1' = v_2' \qquad [12\text{-}26]$$

Solving for v_1' in Equation 12-26 and substituting into Equation 12-23 yields, after a little algebra,

$$v_2' = \frac{2m_1}{m_1 + m_2}\, v_1 \qquad [12\text{-}27]$$

Now we apply Equation 12-27 to the first and second collisions in turn. In the first collision, $v_2' = 15.0$ m/sec and $m_2 = 1.0$ kg:

$$15.0 \text{ m/sec} = \frac{2m_1}{m_1 + 1.0 \text{ kg}}\, v_1$$

In the second collision, $v_2' = 2.0$ m/sec and $m_2 = 14.0$ kg:

$$2.0 \text{ m/sec} = \frac{2m_1}{m_1 + 14.0 \text{ kg}}\, v_1$$

We eliminate v_1 between the two equations given above and solve for m_1 and finally get

$$m_1 = 1.0 \text{ kg}$$

This example has an exact historical parallel in the first measurement of the mass of the neutron. J. Chadwick found in 1932 that neutrons, striking protons (atomic mass, 1.0), imparted a speed to the protons that was 7.5 times greater than the speed imparted to nitrogen nuclei (atomic mass, 14.0). In the fashion given above, Chadwick found the neutron mass to be approximately the same as that of the proton.

Let us now consider *non*elastic collisions. For this the conservation of energy law is written

$$K_1 + K_2 + Q = K_1' + K_2' \qquad \text{[12-28]}$$

where Q represents, by definition, the *excess of the total kinetic energy after the collision over the total kinetic energy before the collision.* Stated differently, Q is the amount of energy transformed, from any of various forms, into the kinetic energy of the particles leaving the collision. Thus, in an elastic collision, we have $Q = 0$ and Equation 12-28 reduces to Equation 12-21. We wish to explore two other important classes of collisions: an explosive collision, for which $Q > 0$, and an inelastic collision, for which $Q < 0$.

EXPLOSIVE COLLISIONS   One possible type of explosive collision is that shown in Figure 12-18. Here we imagine that the spring has been compressed and is held by a latch. When the collision takes place and the bodies touch, the latch is automatically released. The system's total energy before the collision consists of the kinetic energies K_1 and K_2 together with the potential energy originally stored in the spring. As the spring expands, potential energy is converted into kinetic energy, the energy released in the collision being equal to Q where $Q > 0$.

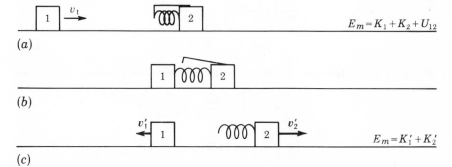

Figure 12-18. An idealized explosive collision. (a) Before the collision the total mechanical energy consists of the kinetic energy of body 1 plus the potential energy of the spring. (b) Potential energy is released during the collision, as the latch on the spring is released. (c) After the collision the total energy of the system consists of the kinetic energies of bodies 1 and 2.

A collision in which energy is released is sometimes referred to as an *exothermic* or *exoergic* collision or reaction. If a chemical explosive were to replace the latched spring and be detonated when the colliding bodies come in contact, *chemical* potential energy would be transformed into the kinetic energy of the outgoing bodies.

Example 8   When radium, a radioactive nucleus, decays, an α-particle (He^4) and a nucleus of radon (Rn^{222}), a daughter nucleus, are produced:

$$Ra^{226} \rightarrow Rn^{222} + He^4$$

The post-superscripts give the approximate masses of the particles (in amu). The alpha particle is identified as the nucleus of the helium atom. If the nuclear energy released in the decay of a radium nucleus is 4.87 million electron volts (4.87 Mev), what is the kinetic energy of the emitted α-particle?

We assume that the radium nucleus is originally isolated and at rest, its momentum and kinetic energy both being zero before the exothermic nuclear explosion. Using α and D to designate the α-particle and "daughter" nucleus, respectively, and letting Q represent the 4.87 Mev of nuclear energy released, we have, from the conservation laws of energy and momentum,

$$Q = K_\alpha + K_D \qquad [12\text{-}29]$$

$$p_\alpha = p_D \qquad [12\text{-}30]$$

The daughter nucleus and the α-particle share the energy released, but they fly off in opposite directions with equal momentum magnitudes. The kinetic energy is related to the momentum by $K = p^2/2m$. Therefore, squaring Equation 12-30 and multiplying by $\frac{1}{2}m_D$, yields

$$\frac{1}{2m_D} p_\alpha{}^2 = \frac{1}{2m_D} p_D{}^2$$

$$\frac{m_\alpha}{m_D}\left(\frac{1}{2m_\alpha} p_\alpha{}^2\right) = \frac{1}{2m_D} p_D{}^2$$

$$\frac{m_\alpha}{m_D} K_\alpha = K_D \qquad [12\text{-}31]$$

Eliminating K_D between Equations 12-29 and 12-31, and solving for K_α, we finally have

$$K_\alpha = \left(\frac{m_D}{m_D + m_\alpha}\right) Q$$

$$K_\alpha = \left(\frac{222}{222 + 4}\right)(4.87 \text{ Mev}) = 4.78 \text{ Mev}$$

Most of the nuclear energy released in the decay is carried as kinetic energy by the relatively light α-particle; the massive daughter nucleus, whose momentum magnitude is equal to that of the α-particle, has only a small fraction of the released energy.

The kinetic energy of the α-particle is precisely defined and discrete, for if the energy Q that is released is fixed, then all α-particles emerging in the decay of radium nuclei have precisely the same energy. This is *not* true if a single object decays or explodes into three or more particles. When three particles emerge from the explosion site, there are, for a given energy release, many directions in which they can move and many ways in which the total momentum of the system can be zero. Consequently, there are many ways in which the energy Q can be distributed among the three particles and thus conserve the momentum. In this way, decay into *two* particles leads to a *discrete* spectrum of particle kinetic energies, whereas decay into *three or more* particles leads to a *continuous distribution* of kinetic energies.

INELASTIC COLLISIONS   As an illustration of an inelastic collision, we imagine that a spring is originally uncompressed and that a small latch can

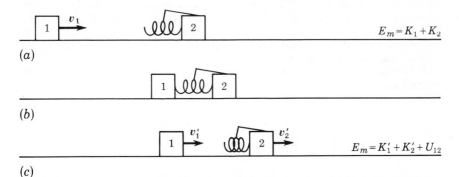

(a)

(b)

(c)

Figure 12-19. An idealized inelastic collision. (a) The spring is uncompressed before the collision. (b) During the collision bodies 1 and 2 do work on the spring, compressing it and thereby decreasing their kinetic energies. (c) After the collision the total energy of the system consists of the kinetic energies of the two bodies and the potential energy of the spring.

clamp the spring while it is deformed during collision, as shown in Figure 12-19. Since work is done on the spring in compressing it and some potential energy remains in the spring after the collision, *kinetic* energy is lost in the collision, the quantity Q in Equation 12-28 being *negative*. Some of the original kinetic energy has been transformed into potential energy. An inelastic collision is sometimes called an *endothermic* or *endoergic* collision or reaction.

Example 9   A bullet of mass m initially traveling at speed v is shot and becomes imbedded in a block of mass M originally at rest on a smooth horizontal surface. (a) What is the speed of the block (and bullet) after the collision? (b) What fraction of the bullet's kinetic energy is dissipated? (c) If the block is suspended from a thin vertical massless rigid rod pivoted at the top, and is hit by the bullet, as in the example just given, through what vertical distance would the block travel before coming to rest?

(a) The bullet and the block are subject to no net horizontal external force; therefore, the conservation of momentum requires that

$$m\boldsymbol{v} = (M + m)\boldsymbol{V}$$

where V is the block's velocity after the collision. Therefore,

$$\boldsymbol{v} = \left(\frac{M + m}{m}\right) \boldsymbol{V} \qquad \text{[12-32]}$$

One can measure the bullet's speed v indirectly through knowing the masses m and M and measuring the lower speed V.

The collision is completely inelastic. A completely inelastic collision is *not* necessarily one in which both bodies are at rest with respect to the observer; it is, rather, one in which the bodies stick together and are at rest *with respect to one another*, the kinetic energy after the collision then being the least amount consistent with momentum conservation. A nonconservative force of friction acts in stopping the bullet, mechanical energy is dissipated, and the kinetic energy out of the collision is less than the kinetic energy into the collision.

(b) The fraction of the bullet's initial kinetic energy dissipated (mostly in thermal energy) is

$$f = \frac{\frac{1}{2}mv^2 - \frac{1}{2}(m + M)V^2}{\frac{1}{2}mv^2}$$

$$f = 1 - \left(\frac{m + M}{m}\right)\left(\frac{V}{v}\right)^2 = 1 - \left(\frac{m}{m + M}\right)\left[\frac{(m + M)V}{mv}\right]^2$$

Using Equation 12-32, we find that this equation reduces to

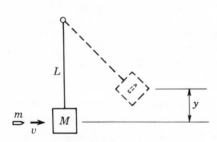

Figure 12-20. A ballistic pendulum. A bullet of mass m and velocity $\boldsymbol{v}$ strikes and becomes imbedded in a block of mass M attached to the end of a light rod of length L. The block rises a vertical distance y in coming to rest.

$$f = 1 - \frac{m}{m + M} = \frac{M}{m + M}$$

If m is much less than M (if the bullet's mass is much smaller than that of the block), the fraction f of kinetic energy lost in heat is close to 1.00, or 100 per cent. When $m \ll M$ nearly all of the kinetic energy is lost. The momentum emerging from the collision is, of course, precisely equal to the momentum going into the collision.

(c) The bullet strikes a block suspended from a rod of length L, as shown in Figure 12-20. If the bullet comes to rest in the block, its speed having been reduced from v to V in a short distance, the time interval during which the bullet is decelerated and during which the block acquires the speed V is very short indeed. The block is acted on by an impulsive force for a time interval that is much less than the time required for the block and rod to swing upward and come to rest at a height y above the lowest point. Thus, the complete motion consists of two parts: (a) the short time interval during which the bullet is brought to rest in the block and during which the block acquires the speed V without rising appreciably and (b) the much longer time interval during which the block swings to its highest point. During interval 1, momentum is conserved (no *external* force on the system of bullet and block), but kinetic energy is not conserved (a nonconservative *internal* force acts); during interval 2, mechanical energy is conserved (the block is subject only to conservative forces), but momentum is not conserved (the bullet-block system is now subject to an unbalanced external force).

During interval 2,

$$\tfrac{1}{2}(m + M)V^2 = (m + M)gy$$

$$V = \sqrt{2gy}$$

During interval 1, from Equation 12-32,

$$v = \left(\frac{M + m}{m}\right)\sqrt{2gy}$$

A bullet's speed can be measured with a device of this sort, known as a *ballistic pendulum*, simply by measuring the height y and masses m and M.

The atoms of an actual material do not, of course, interact with one another through springs. This model is, however, a useful one for visualizing their mutual interactions. When two blocks collide, the atoms in the blocks are displaced relative to one another in the collision as the blocks are deformed. If the atoms resume exactly their original relative positions after the collision, the collision is perfectly elastic. However, this is not the usual case, and a body even may be permanently deformed, as in the case of a ball of putty. In any event, the atoms of the material are usually set in random oscillation during the collision, some of the kinetic energy of the colliding bodies being transformed into disordered kinetic and potential energy of atoms. This "invisible" disordered kinetic and potential energy, occurring randomly on a submicroscopic scale, is called *thermal energy*.

Momentum is conserved in every collision because there is only one kind of momentum. *Kinetic* energy is *not* conserved in every collision because there are various forms of energy.

There are some examples of collisions in which no kinetic energy is converted into internal energy, and the collisions are consequently perfectly elastic. For example, the collisions of molecules of a gas at moderate temperatures are perfectly elastic because, by the quantum theory, a molecule can gain internal energy and have its internal structure changed only by certain discrete and finite amounts. (At moderate temperature the molecules' translational kinetic energies are not great enough to change their internal energies.) Furthermore, the collisions between such elementary particles as the proton and electron are perfectly elastic, because such particles have no internal structure.

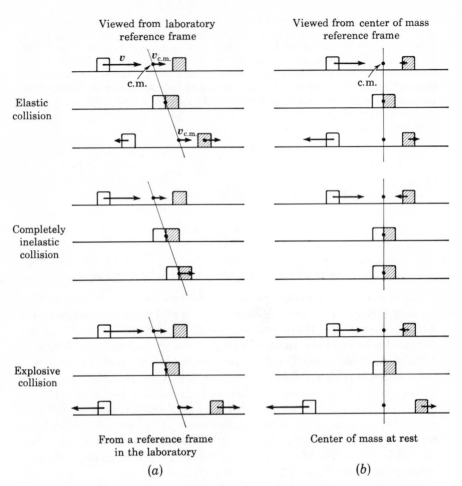

Figure 12-21. (a) From a reference frame in the laboratory, the center of mass moves to the right at constant velocity in all three collisions. (b) From a reference frame in which the center of mass is at rest.

An elastic, an inelastic, and an explosive collision are illustrated in Figure 12-21. These head-on collisions are portrayed from the point of view of two different inertial frames: that of the laboratory, in which the struck body is assumed (for simplicity) to be initially at rest, and that of the center of mass, in which the center of mass of the colliding bodies is always at rest. In Section 8-5 it was shown that the velocity v_{cm} of the center of mass relative to the laboratory is related to the masses and velocities of particles relative to the laboratory by

[8-24] $$(m_1 + m_2)v_{cm} = m_1v_1 + m_2v_2 = m_1v_1' + m_2v_2'$$

One can most easily distinguish the three types of collisions by the point of view of the center of mass reference frame. For any collision in this reference frame, the total momentum is *zero*, the two bodies approach the center of mass from opposite directions and with equal momentum magnitudes, and then recede, not necessarily along the original direction but again with equal momentum magnitudes. If we compare the speed v' of either particle after the collision with its speed v before the collision, we have the following: if $v' < v$, an explosive collision; if $v' = v$, a perfectly elastic collision; if $v' < v$, an inelastic collision; if $v' = 0$, a perfectly inelastic collision.

12-5   Proof of the general theorem of the conservation of mechanical energy

Heretofore we have considered systems of two bodies interacting through a conservative force in which one of the bodies had a *much* larger mass

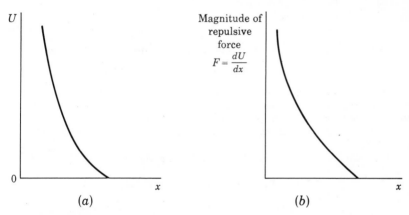

Figure 12-22. Curves for a conservative repulsive force: (a) potential energy versus displacement and (b) force versus displacement.

than that of the second body. The massive body remains at rest (or in motion at *constant* velocity), and its kinetic energy is unchanged. The changes in kinetic energy of the system can then be associated with the light body alone.

The general case, in which two bodies of comparable mass interact in a perfectly elastic collision, is treated in this section. What shall be proved is this: the total energy of the system (the sum of the kinetic energies of the two bodies and the potential energy of their interaction) is constant, depending only on the distance of separation between the two bodies.

The potential energy of the system corresponding to the conservative force between the bodies is shown in Figure 12-22a as a function of the separation distance. For convenience, the force (Figure 12-22b) is chosen as repulsive. No external force acts on the system. We assume, for simplicity, that at the instant the particles are separated by a distance x, particle a is moving to the right at speed v_{a0} and particle b is at rest, as shown in Figure 12-23. (We can arrange that b be at rest simply by choosing the appropriate inertial frame.)

At this instant, the force $\boldsymbol{F}_a$ on a by b is to the left, and the force $\boldsymbol{F}_b$ on b by a is to the right. The magnitudes of these two forces ($F = F_a = F_b$) are equal, according to Newton's third law (conservation of momentum).

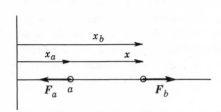

Figure 12-23. Particle a has a displacement $\boldsymbol{x}_a$ and is acted on by a force $\boldsymbol{F}_a$; particle b has a displacement $\boldsymbol{x}_b$ and is acted on by a force $\boldsymbol{F}_b$.

During the time interval Δt, particle a moves to the right a distance Δx_a; particle b moves to the right a distance Δx_b. Applying the work-energy theorem to particle a, we have

$$[11\text{-}5] \qquad \Delta W(\text{by } \boldsymbol{F}_a) = \Delta K_a$$

If Δt is small, so is the displacement Δx_a, and the repulsive force $\boldsymbol{F}_a$ on a is constant throughout the displacement Δx_a. Because $\boldsymbol{F}_a$ is opposite in direction to Δx_a, negative work is done on a. That is,

$$\Delta W(\text{by } \boldsymbol{F}_a) = \boldsymbol{F}_a \cdot \Delta \boldsymbol{x}_a$$
$$= -F\,\Delta x_a = \Delta K_a \quad [12\text{-}33]$$

A similar application of the work-energy theorem to particle b yields

$$\Delta W(\text{by } \boldsymbol{F}_b) = \boldsymbol{F}_b \cdot \Delta \boldsymbol{x}_b = +F\,\Delta x_b = \Delta K_b \qquad [12\text{-}34]$$

where positive work is done on b because $\boldsymbol{F}_b$ is in the direction of Δx_b.

Although $\boldsymbol{F}_a$ and $\boldsymbol{F}_b$ are equal in magnitude, we can *not* assume that the distances Δx_a and Δx_b will be the same in the same time interval Δt. Each distance traversed will depend on the mass of the particle and its velocity, as well as the force.

Adding Equations 12-33 and 12-34, and using the fact that $\boldsymbol{F}_a = -\boldsymbol{F}_b$, we obtain

$$\boldsymbol{F}_b \cdot \Delta \boldsymbol{x}_b + \boldsymbol{F}_a \cdot \Delta \boldsymbol{x}_a = \Delta K_a + \Delta K_b$$

$$\boldsymbol{F}_b \cdot \Delta \boldsymbol{x}_b - \boldsymbol{F}_b \cdot \Delta \boldsymbol{x}_a = \Delta K_a + \Delta K_b$$

$$\boldsymbol{F}_b \cdot (\Delta \boldsymbol{x}_b - \Delta \boldsymbol{x}_a) = \Delta K_a + \Delta K_b$$

The separation displacement $\Delta \boldsymbol{x}$ from a to b (see Figure 12-23) is

$$\Delta \boldsymbol{x} = \Delta \boldsymbol{x}_b - \Delta \boldsymbol{x}_a$$

Therefore,

$$\boldsymbol{F}_b \cdot \Delta \boldsymbol{x} = \Delta K_a + \Delta K_b \qquad [12\text{-}35]$$

The magnitude of the interaction force $\boldsymbol{F}_b$ depends only on the separation distance Δx; the direction of $\boldsymbol{F}_b$ is always to the right. Therefore, we can represent the total work done over the displacement $\Delta \boldsymbol{x}$ as a change in the potential energy ΔU_{ab} of the system of a and b. Using Equation 12-12, we obtain

$$\Delta U_{ab} = -\boldsymbol{F}_b \cdot \Delta \boldsymbol{x} \qquad [12\text{-}36]$$

The negative sign implies that the potential energy decreases when the separation distance increases. This corresponds to our initial assumption that the interaction force was repulsive. Thus we have, from Equations 12-35 and 12-36,

$$-\Delta U_{ab} = \Delta K_a + \Delta K_b \qquad [12\text{-}37]$$

An incremental decrease in the potential energy gives rise to a corresponding incremental increase in the *total* kinetic energy of the particles. Furthermore, by adding the contributions from each small displacement Δx we find that the total decrease in potential energy appears as an equal increase in kinetic energy. Thus, if the particles increase their relative separation as shown in Figure 12-24, from x_1 to x_2, the potential energy decreases and the kinetic energy increases according to Equation 12-37:

$$-(U_2 - U_1) = (K_{2a} - K_{1a}) + (K_{2b} - K_{1b})$$

Rearranging the terms yields

$$(K_{1a} + K_{1b}) + U_1 = (K_{2a} + K_{2b}) + U_2$$

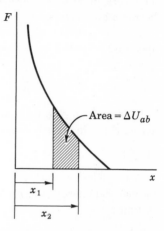

The total mechanical energy E_m is, by definition, the sum of the kinetic energy of a, the kinetic energy of b, and the potential energy U_{ab} of the system.
Therefore,

$$E_m(1) = E_m(2)$$

This is the law of the conservation of mechanical energy. The result applies for any number of interacting particles, inasmuch as the potential and kinetic energies are both scalar quantities. The assumptions were these: (a) the system is isolated and no resultant external force acts on it; (b) all internal forces are conservative; (c) observations are made from an inertial frame.

Figure 12-24. As the particles increase their separation from x_1 to x_2, the force decreases, as does the potential energy.

12-6 Summary   The total mechanical energy E_m of a system of particles consists of the sum of the particles' kinetic energies K and the potential energy U of their interaction:

[12-7] $$E_m = K + U$$

The gravitational potential energy U_g for a particle of mass m undergoing a vertical displacement y near the surface of the Earth is

[12-3] $$U_g = mgy$$

The potential energy U_s of a spring of stiffness constant k, stretched or compressed by a distance x, is

[12-10] $$U_s = \tfrac{1}{2}kx^2$$

A potential energy can be defined only for a conservative force—one whose magnitude and direction depends only on the separation distance between the interacting particles. Then the difference in potential energy between two states i and f is defined as

[12-12] $$U_f - U_i = -\int_i^f \mathbf{F} \cdot d\mathbf{s}$$

where F must be a conservative force; that is,

$$\oint F \cdot ds = 0$$

The work done by a conservative force is independent of the path leading between any two points.

The components of a conservative force may be derived from the corresponding potential energy through the relations

[12-15] $\qquad F_x = -\dfrac{\partial U}{\partial x}, \qquad F_y = -\dfrac{\partial U}{\partial y}, \qquad F_z = -\dfrac{\partial U}{\partial z}$

By definition, the total mechanical energy of a system of particles interacting through strictly conservative forces is constant in time:

[12-16] $\qquad\qquad\qquad E_m(i) = E_m(f)$

If particles interact through nonconservative forces, the system's total mechanical energy (the *macroscopic* kinetic and potential energies) decreases in time:

[12-18] $\qquad\qquad\qquad E_m(i) > E_m(f)$

The general conservation of energy law asserts that the total energy of an isolated system, consisting of both mechanical and nonmechanical forms of energy, is constant in time:

[12-19] $\qquad\qquad\qquad E_m(f) = E_m(i) + E_{\text{non-}m}$

The energetics of two-body collisions are summarized by the relation

[12-28] $\qquad\qquad\qquad K_1 + K_2 + Q = K_1' + K_2'$

where, in addition, linear momentum must be conserved according to

$$\boldsymbol{p}_1 + \boldsymbol{p}_2 = \boldsymbol{p}_1' + \boldsymbol{p}_2'$$

For elastic collisions, $Q = 0$; for explosive collisions, $Q > 0$; and for inelastic collisions, $Q < 0$.

PROBLEMS

12-1   A small ball of mass m is attached to one end of a thin rigid massless rod of length L, the other end of the rod being pivoted at the floor. If the rod is released when it is in the vertical position, with what speed does the ball strike the floor?

12-2   A ball is hung at the lower end of a string 2.0 m in length, the upper end being held fixed. If the ball is released from rest when the string makes an angle 30° with respect to the vertical, the string being kept taut, what is the speed of the ball when the string's angle with the vertical is (a) 20°, (b) 0°?

12-3   A 2.0-pound ball is thrown into the air with a speed of 25 feet/sec at an angle of 37° above the horizontal. (a) What is the maximum height the ball achieves? (b) What is the ball's minimum kinetic energy? (c) What is the ball's speed when it is 2.0 feet above the ground?

12-4   A 10.0-pound block and a 5.0-pound block are attached to opposite ends of a massless cord 6.0 feet long. The cord is hung over a small massless frictionless pulley, the 10-pound block being a distance of 2.0 feet from the floor and the pulley a distance of 4.0 feet from the floor. If the blocks are released from rest, what will be the speed of the blocks when the 10.0-pound block strikes the floor?

12-5   A meter stick of 400 gm, pivoted at one end and initially hanging vertically, is raised until it makes an angle of 60° with respect to the vertical. How much work is required?

12-6   Approximately 15 million cubic feet of water pass over the Horseshoe at Niagara Falls each minute. The water drops through a height of 158 feet. About one tenth of the water is used at the hydroelectric plant. What is the maximum output of the turbogenerators?

12-7   When the hammer of a 2000-pound piledriver falls through 8.0 feet onto a pile, it drives the pile down a distance of 4.0 inches. (a) What is the average force of the hammer on the pile? (b) If the hammer is raised to its initial position in 10 sec, what is the minimum horsepower rating required for the engine?

12-8   A 2400-pound automobile moving along a flat road at a speed of 90 feet/sec coasts over a hill 20 feet high whose radius of curvature at the crest is 250 feet. What is the force of the road on the automobile at the crest of the hill?

12-9   A block slides down a frictionless surface and makes a loop-the-loop in a circle of radius r. At what minimum height relative to the top of the loop should the block be started from rest in order that it may make the loop while remaining in contact with the surface?

12-10 ★ A small object coasts from rest at the top of a smooth spherical hill of radius r. What is the angle with respect to the vertical made by the line joining the object with the center of the spherical hill, when the object loses contact with the surface? (*Hint:* As long as the object remains on the surface, a normal force acts on it and it travels in a circle of radius r.)

12-11   A spring with a force constant of 40 nt/m has a mass of 0.20 kg attached to one end, the other end being held fixed. If the mass is released when the spring is stretched by 0.50 m, what is the speed of the mass when the spring is compressed by 0.10 m?

12-12   To pull a bowstring from its undisplaced position requires a force of 50 pounds when the middle of the string is displaced 2.0 feet. The force is closely proportional to the displacement of the middle of the string. If the bow shoots an arrow of 0.12 pound vertically upward, what is the maximum height achieved by the arrow?

12-13   A spring has an unstretched length of 8.0 inches and a stiffness constant of 19.0 pounds/inch. Two bodies, each of 3.0 pounds, are attached to the ends of the spring. The bodies are separated by 9.5 inches and then released. (a) What is the speed of each body when the length of the spring is 7.5 inches? (b) What is the minimum separation between the two oscillating bodies?

12-14   A 5.0 kg ball is dropped from a height of 2.0 m above an uncompressed vertically oriented spring of force constant 1.2×10^6 nt/m. What is the maximum amount by which the spring is compressed?

12-15   When a 4.0-pound block attached to the lower end of a spring held fixed at its upper end is lowered slowly, the spring stretches 3.0 inches. If the spring is then stretched an additional 2.0 inches and released from rest, what are (a) the maximum speed of the block and (b) the maximum height achieved by the block relative to its equilibrium position?

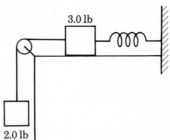

3.0 lb

2.0 lb

Figure 12-25

12-16 ★ A 3.0-pound block, attached to one end of a horizontal spring whose force constant is 0.50 pounds/inch, is initially at rest on a horizontal frictionless surface with the spring in its unstretched position. As shown in Figure 12-25, a 2.0-pound weight is connected to the 3.0-pound block and hangs over the side of the table. (a) Through what vertical distance does the 2.0-pound weight descend before coming momentarily to rest? (b) What is the maximum speed of the 2.0-pound weight?

12-17 ★ Two blocks of masses 1.0 and 2.0 kg are pressed against the ends of a spring to compress it to a length of 0.150 m. The force constant of the spring is 60 nt/m; its relaxed length is 0.180 m. If the blocks are released from rest as they sit on a frictionless horizontal surface, what are the respective speeds of the blocks after they come out of contact with the spring?

12-18   A 5.0 kg block resting on a smooth horizontal surface is attached to two identical springs, as shown in Figure 12-26. Each spring has an unstretched length of 0.20 m and a force constant of 80 nt/m. The block is released from rest at A, at which point both springs have a length of 0.30 m. What is the speed of the block as it passes point B?

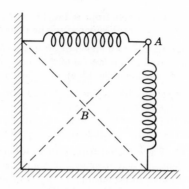

Figure 12-26

12-19   Draw graphs giving the total potential energy of the system as a function of the vertical displacements y and y' for Example 3.

12-20   The electric potential energy between two like charges q_1 and q_2 separated by a distance r is given by $U = kq_1q_2/r$, where k is a constant. What is the electric force between the charges?

12-21   The potential energy of two particles is given by $U = -(A/r)\,e^{-(r/a)}$, where r is their relative separation and A and a are constants. Find the expression giving the force between the particles. (This potential energy describes approximately the interaction between particles in a nucleus.)

12-22   A block coasts from rest down a frictionless curved surface of radius 1.5 feet and then moves along a rough horizontal surface for a distance of 8.0 feet before coming to rest. See Figure 12-27. What is the coefficient of kinetic friction between the block and the horizontal surface?

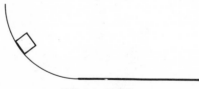

Figure 12-27

12-23   (a) What is the average resisting force acting on a 2000-pound automobile if it comes to rest from 25 feet/sec in 200 feet? (b) At what power must the automobile operate if it is to travel at a constant speed of 25 feet/sec, assuming (unrealistically) that the total resisting force arising from air friction, friction in the bearings, etc., is independent of the automobile's speed? (c) Which force does work on the automobile to maintain it at constant speed?

12-24   A 5.0-pound object falls from rest through a vertical distance of 16 feet, striking the ground with a speed of 26 feet/sec. What is the energy dissipated in friction of the air?

12-25   A 2.2-pound ball dropped from a height of 4.0 feet rebounds to 3.6 feet. What is the energy dissipated in the collision with the floor?

12-26   A block sliding initially at a speed of 30 feet/sec on a rough horizontal surface comes to rest in a distance of 200 feet. What is the coefficient of kinetic friction between the block and the surface?

12-27   A block of 6.0 pounds has a speed of 12.0 feet/sec at the base of an incline of 30°, the coefficient of kinetic friction between the block and the surface of the incline being 0.20. What is the maximum distance the block will travel up the incline before coming to rest?

12-28   A 1.0-pound block is released from rest on a frictionless incline from a height of 2.0 feet. When it passes a point at a height of 0.50 feet, what are (a) the loss in potential energy, (b) the kinetic energy of the block, and (c) the speed of the block? What are (d) the loss in potential energy, (e) the kinetic energy, and (f) the speed of the block, all for the same height as above, if the incline is rough with a coefficient of kinetic friction of 0.10 and an incline of 30°?

12-29   A 10.0 kg block is released from rest on a rough inclined plane of 30° when the block is a distance of 0.80 m along the incline from the base. The coefficient of kinetic friction between the block and the surface of the incline is 0.20. (a) With what speed will the block reach the bottom of the incline? If the block is projected up the incline with an initial speed of 10.0 m/sec, (b) how far will the block travel up the incline and (c) what will be its speed when it returns to the base?

12-30   A block resting on a rough horizontal surface is attached to one end of a spring having a force constant of 7.2×10^2 nt/m. The block, which is released when the spring has been compressed 0.048 m, undergoes a number of oscillations and comes finally to rest, the spring being stretched by 0.012 m. What is the energy dissipated in friction?

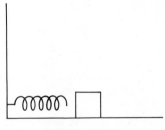

Figure 12-28

12-31   The block in Figure 12-28 is pressed against a spring whose force constant is 10 pounds/inch. The spring is compressed 3.0 inches and the block then released. The coefficient of kinetic friction between the block and the surface is 0.25. What distance will the block travel before coming to rest?

12-32   A 4.0-pound ball moving at 15 feet/sec strikes head on a 2.0-pound ball moving in the same direction with a speed of 10 feet/sec. After the collision, the 4.0-pound ball has a speed of 10 feet/sec. (a) What is the velocity of the 2.0-pound ball? (b) What is the Q of the collision?

12-33   In an elastic collision, a 10.0 kg ball traveling east at 15 m/sec strikes head on a 5.0 kg ball traveling west at 20 m/sec. What are the velocities of the two balls after the collision?

12-34   Consider the collision in Problem 12-33. (a) What is the velocity of the center of mass with respect to the observer? What are the velocities of the 5.0 kg and 10.0 kg balls, relative to the center of mass, (b) before, and (c) after, the collision?

12-35   A 2.0 kg block traveling at 1.0 m/sec strikes and sticks to a second block of equal mass initially at rest. What is the total kinetic energy (a) before, and (b) after, the collision? (c) What fraction of the initial kinetic energy is dissipated? Suppose now that the two identical blocks are both in motion in opposite directions with the speed 0.71 m/sec before they collide and stick together. What is now the total kinetic energy (a) before, and (b) after, the collision? (c) What fraction of the initial kinetic energy is now lost in the collision?

12-36   A 0.010-pound bullet traveling at 2000 feet/sec strikes and comes to rest within a 50-pound block originally at rest on a frictionless surface. (a) What fraction of the bullet's kinetic energy is dissipated in heat? (b) If the bullet comes to rest in a distance of 1.0 inch, what is the average force on the bullet? (c) Assuming that the bullet has a constant deceleration in coming to rest, what is the time interval during which the bullet comes to rest in the block?

12-37   In a determination of a bullet's speed by the ballistic-pendulum method (see Section 12-4, Example 9), the masses of the bullet and block are, respectively, 12 gm and 5.0 kg. The block rises through a distance of 2.5 cm before coming to rest. What is the speed of the bullet?

12-38   A 0.010-pound bullet traveling initially at a speed of 800 feet/sec strikes and passes through a block of 4.0 pounds originally at rest on a smooth surface. Upon emerging from the block, the bullet's speed is 600 ft/sec. What is the nonmechanical energy produced when the bullet passes through the block?

12-39   If a group of identical billiard balls are arranged in a straight line, each ball just touching its neighbors, and another billiard ball strikes the first in the line head on, it is found that the last ball in the line is set in motion with a speed identical with that of the originally moving ball. Similarly, if two billiard balls moving together at the same speed strike the line of balls at rest, the last two balls in the line are set in motion with the same speed as that of the two balls striking the line. Show that this behavior is consistent with the conservation laws of energy and momentum for head-on elastic collisions.

12-40 ★ A body of mass m_1 makes an elastic head-on collision with a body of m_2 initially at rest. Show that the fraction of the kinetic energy of m_1 transferred to m_2 in the collision is $4m_1m_2/(m_1 + m_2)^2$.

12-41   Show that, in any head-on collision of two particles of equal mass, both particles have the same velocity at the instant that their separation distance is a minimum. (*Hint:* View the motion from the center of mass reference frame.)

12-42   Show that, for (a) an elastic, (b) an explosive, and (c) an inelastic head-on collision, the relative velocities of two particles after a collision are respectively equal to, greater than, and less than, the relative velocities before the collision.

12-43   A radioactive nucleus of bismuth decays into tellurium with the emission of an α-particle according to the decay relation $Bi^{212} \rightarrow Tl^{208} + He^4$. If the α-particle has a kinetic energy of 6.20 Mev, (a) what is the kinetic energy of the tellurium nucleus and (b) what is the nuclear energy released in this decay?

12-44   A 20-pound block initially traveling east at 20 feet/sec explodes into two equal parts. One part travels at 100 feet/sec in the direction 30° north of east. How much energy is released in the explosion?

12-45   A 60-pound body, initially at rest, explodes into three equal parts. One part moves north at 50 feet/sec and a second part moves east at 50 feet/sec. What is the energy released in the explosion?

T H I R T E E N

ROTATIONAL KINEMATICS

This chapter treats of the kinematics of rotational motion. We first distinguish between the translational and rotational motion of a rigid body. The angular speed and acceleration are defined, and the kinematic formulas for rotation at constant angular acceleration are developed. The vector representations of angular velocity and acceleration are discussed.

13-1 Translation and rotation A *rigid body* is defined as an object in which the relative separations of the component particles are unchanged, the displacement of any one particle with respect to any other particle in the body being fixed. No truly rigid body exists: external forces can deform any solid. For our purposes, then, a rigid body is a solid in which the internal forces between the constituent particles change so drastically with a variation in their relative separation that large forces are required to deform it appreciably.

Up to this point we have studied the kinematics and dynamics of a particle whose position in three-dimensional space is completely specified by three coordinates. To describe, however, a change in the position of a body of finite extent, such as a rigid body, is more complicated. For convenience, it is regarded as a combination of two distinct types of motion: translational motion and rotational motion.

Purely *translational motion* occurs if every particle of the body has the same instantaneous velocity as every other particle, the path traced out by some one particle being exactly the same as the path traced out by every other particle in the body. See Figure 13-1a. Under translational motion, the change in the position of a rigid body is, therefore, specified completely by three coordinates, such as x, y, and z, giving the displacement of some one point, such as the center of mass, fixed to the rigid body.

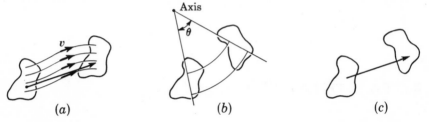

Figure 13-1. (a) Pure translational motion: every particle traces out the *same path*. (b) Pure rotational motion: every particle moves in a circle about the *same axis*. (c) Any displacement of a rigid body is equivalent to a pure translational displacement plus a pure rotational displacement.

Purely *rotational motion* occurs if *every particle* in the body *moves in* a *circle about a single line*. This line is called the axis of rotation. Then the radius vectors from the axis to all particles undergo the same angular displacement in the same time. See Figure 13-1b. The axis of rotation need not be within the body. In general, any rotation can be specified completely by the three angular displacements with respect to the rectangular-coordinate axes X, Y, and Z. Any change in the position of a rigid body is thus completely described by three translational and three rotational coordinates. We shall be concerned primarily with the simple situations in which a rigid body's translational motion is confined to the X-Y plane and its rotational motion is about the Z-axis.

Any displacement of a rigid body may be arrived at by first displacing the body translationally, without rotation, and then displacing the body rotationally, without translation; or conversely, first a rotation and then a displacement. See Figure 13-1c.

We know already that for any collection of particles—whether at rest with respect to one another, as in a rigid body, or in relative motion, as in the exploding fragments of a shell—the motion of the center of mass is completely determined by the resultant of the external forces acting on the system of particles, according to

[10-28] $$\Sigma \, \boldsymbol{F}_{\text{ext}} = M\boldsymbol{a}_{\text{cm}}$$ [13-1]

where M is the total mass of the system and $\boldsymbol{a}_{\text{cm}}$ is the acceleration of the center of mass. There remains, then, the matter of describing the rotation of the body about the center of mass and relating it to the external forces acting on the body. Rotational kinematics is discussed in this chapter; rotational dynamics, in the next. We shall find that the kinematics of rotational motion bear many similarities to the kinematics of translational motion; moreover, we shall see in the next chapter that the dynamics of rotational motion involve forms of Newton's second law of motion and of the work-energy theorem that are altogether analogous to those used in particle dynamics.

13-2 Kinematics of rotational motion   Consider first the rotation of a perfectly rigid body about a fixed axis of rotation. For this situation all particles undergo the same angular displacement θ in the same time. The angle θ, in radians, is related to the radius r and the length of the circular arc s traced out by the radius vector, by

[5-3] $$\theta \text{ (in radians)} = \frac{s}{r}$$ [13-2]

By convention, counterclockwise angular displacements are taken as positive, and clockwise angular displacements as negative.

The average angular velocity $\bar{\omega}$ is defined as the angular displacement $\Delta\theta$ divided by the corresponding elapsed time Δt:

[5-4] $$\bar{\omega} = \frac{\Delta\theta}{\Delta t}$$

The instantaneous angular velocity ω is the average angular velocity over an infinitesimal time interval, or it is the time rate of the angular displacement:

$$\boxed{\omega = \lim_{\Delta t \to 0} \frac{\Delta\theta}{\Delta t} = \frac{d\theta}{dt}}$$ [13-3]

Common units for angular velocity are radians per second, degrees per second, revolutions per minute, and revolutions per second.

The average angular acceleration $\bar{\alpha}$ is the change in the angular velocity $\Delta\omega$ divided by the corresponding elapsed time Δt, and the instantaneous angular acceleration α is the time rate of the angular velocity $d\omega/dt$:

$$\bar{\alpha} = \frac{\Delta\omega}{\Delta t}$$

$$\alpha = \lim_{\Delta t \to 0} \frac{\Delta\omega}{\Delta t} = \frac{d\omega}{dt} \qquad [13\text{-}4]$$

A positive angular acceleration implies that the rotational velocity is increasing in the counterclockwise sense (or, equivalently, decreasing in the clockwise sense). For $\alpha = 0$, the body rotates about the fixed axis at a constant rate. Angular acceleration is given in units of radians per second². Angular velocity and angular acceleration have the dimensions T^{-1} and T^{-2}, respectively.

Equations 13-3 and 13-4 relating the angular velocity ω and acceleration α to the angular displacement θ and the time t are altogether analogous to the relations between the linear displacement x, linear velocity v, and linear acceleration a. Therefore, we can arrive at the kinematic equations describing rotational motion at a constant angular acceleration from the linear kinematic equations for constant linear acceleration. We simply replace:

$$x \qquad \text{by} \qquad \theta$$

$$v = \frac{dx}{dt} \qquad \text{by} \qquad \omega = \frac{d\theta}{dt}$$

$$a = \frac{dv}{dt} \qquad \text{by} \qquad \alpha = \frac{d\omega}{dt}$$

Thus, for *constant angular acceleration*, the rotational kinematic equations for a rigid body about a fixed axis follow directly from the analogous translational kinematic equations for constant linear acceleration, as shown below.

Constant linear acceleration a		*Constant angular acceleration α*	
[2-7]	$v = v_0 + at$	$\omega = \omega_0 + \alpha t$	[13-5]
[2-8]	$x = v_0 t + \frac{1}{2}at^2$	$\theta = \omega_0 t + \frac{1}{2}\alpha t^2$	[13-6]
[2-10]	$x = (v_0 + v)t/2$	$\theta = (\omega_0 + \omega)t/2$	[13-7]
[2-11]	$v^2 = v_0^2 + 2ax$	$\omega^2 = \omega_0^2 + 2\alpha\theta$	[13-8]

Of course, one can derive Equations 13-5 through 13-8 from the definitions, Equations 13-3 and 13-4, by integration, in the same fashion as shown in Section 2-6. At the time $t = 0$, the angular displacement θ is zero, and the initial angular velocity is ω_0.

Although all particles of a rigid body will have turned through the same angle θ and have, at any instant, the same ω and α, their *linear* speeds and accelerations along the circular arcs in which they travel differ according to their relative distances from the axis of rotation. We wish to find the relations between the corresponding angular and linear quantities.

If the angular displacement θ is measured in radians, then

$$s = r\theta$$

where s is the distance traversed along a circular arc of radius r by a particle undergoing an angular displacement θ (Figure 5-7). Taking derivatives with respect to the time yields

$$ds/dt = r(d\theta/dt)$$

[5-5] $$v_t = r\omega$$ [13-9]

The tangential linear speed v_t of a particle is directly proportional to the particle's distance from the axis of rotation. It must be emphasized that Equation 13-9 holds only if ω is given in units of radians per second.

We find the *tangential* acceleration a_t, which gives the time rate of the linear speed v_t along the circular arc, by taking the time derivative of Equation 13-9:

$$dv_t/dt = r(d\omega/dt)$$

$$a_t = r\alpha$$ [13-10]

Equation 13-10 gives the tangential *component* of the body's linear acceleration; this component is nonzero only if the angular velocity changes. There is, in addition, a centripetal, or radial, component a_r of the acceleration toward the axis of rotation. The component a_r exists whenever the body is rotating, whether the angular speed is constant or changing. The radial acceleration component is related to the instantaneous tangential speed v_t and the instantaneous angular speed ω by

[5-1] $$a_r = \frac{v_t^2}{r} = \omega^2 r$$ [13-11]

The magnitude of the total linear acceleration of a particle in rotational motion is then given by

$$a = \sqrt{a_t^2 + a_r^2}$$

as shown in Figure 13-2.

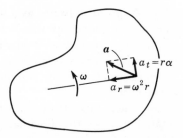

Figure 13-2. The linear acceleration a of a particle of a rotating body has a tangential component $a_t = r\alpha$ and a radial component $a_r = \omega^2 r$.

Example 1 A wheel 1.5 m in radius undergoes rotation at a constant angular acceleration of 10 radians/sec², its initial angular speed being $60/\pi$ revolutions/minute. Compute the following quantities, all for the time $t = 2.0$ sec: (a) the angular speed, (b) the angular displacement, (c) the linear speed of a point on the rim, and (d) the linear acceleration of a point on the rim.

(a) It is useful to express the initial angular speed ω_0 in units of radians:

$$\omega_0 = (60/\pi \text{ rev/min})(2\pi \text{ rad/rev})(1 \text{ min/60 sec})$$
$$\omega_0 = 2.0 \text{ rad/sec}$$

The angular speed after 2.0 sec is computed from Equation 13-5:

$$\omega = \omega_0 + \alpha t = (2.0 \text{ rad/sec}) + (10 \text{ rad/sec}^2)(2.0 \text{ sec})$$
$$\omega = 22 \text{ rad/sec}$$

(b) The angular displacement can be computed from Equation 13-6:

$$\theta = \omega_0 t + \tfrac{1}{2}\alpha t^2 = (2.0 \text{ rad/sec})(2.0 \text{ sec}) + \tfrac{1}{2}(10 \text{ rad/sec}^2)(2.0 \text{ sec})^2$$
$$\theta = 24 \text{ rad}$$

or $\theta = (24 \text{ rad})(1 \text{ rev}/2\pi \text{ rad}) = 3.8$ revolutions.

(c) We find the tangential speed from Equation 13-9:

$$v_t = r\omega = (1.5 \text{ m})(22 \text{ rad/sec}) = 33 \text{ m/sec}$$

(d) We compute the magnitude of the acceleration from its radial and tangential components, given by Equations 13-11 and 13-10, respectively:

$$a_r = \omega^2 r = (22 \text{ rad/sec})^2(1.5 \text{ m}) = 363 \text{ m/sec}^2$$
$$a_t = r\alpha = (1.5 \text{ m})(10 \text{ rad/sec}^2) = 15 \text{ m/sec}^2$$
$$a = \sqrt{a_t^2 + a_r^2} = \sqrt{(363)^2 + (15)^2} \text{ m/sec}^2 = 364 \text{ m/sec}^2$$

As time goes on, ω increases. Thus, a_r increases with time, whereas a_t remains constant, and the resultant linear acceleration points more nearly toward the axis of rotation.

13-3 Angular velocity as a vector The magnitude of ω gives the angle turned through per unit time; the sign gives the sense of rotation. Inasmuch as there is an axis associated with every rotation and two directions associated with every axis, we can associate the two possible senses of rotation unambiguously with the two opposite directions of the axis. All we need is a convention.

The rule is this: If the curled fingers of the right hand correspond to the rotational sense, the direction of the outstretched thumb points along the direction of the vector associated with the *angular velocity*. Equivalently, a right-hand screw will advance along the direction of **ω**. See Figure 13-3. The magnitude of **ω** gives the angular speed; its direction specifies the plane of rotation, as well as the sense of rotation. Thus, counterclockwise rotation in the plane of the paper corresponds to **ω** out of the paper.

Figure 13-3. The right-hand rule convention, giving the direction of the angular velocity vector.

That the angular velocity is indeed a vector is established, not merely by assigning a direction to it, but by testing whether the angular velocity obeys the rules of vector addition. We must, for example, check whether the commutative law, which requires that $\omega_1 + \omega_2 = \omega_2 + \omega_1$, holds for angular velocities.

The angular velocity is the product of a scalar, $1/dt$, and a vector, $d\theta$. We prove that $d\theta$ is a vector by showing that two infinitesimal angular displacements, $d\theta_1$ and $d\theta_2$, obey the commutative law in vector addition:

$$d\theta_1 + d\theta_2 = d\theta_2 + d\theta_1$$

The proof is obvious from an examination of Figures 13-4a and b. Here we see the arcs traced out on a spherical surface by a radius vector r undergoing, in succession, two small angular displacements. The magnitudes of $d\theta_1$

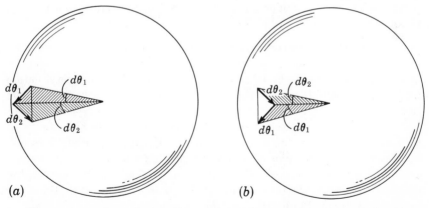

Figure 13-4. Geometrical demonstration of the vector addition of *infinitesimal* angular displacements. The angles $d\theta_1$ and $d\theta_2$ are represented by arcs on a sphere. For infinitesimal angular displacements, the arcs obey the commutative law for vector addition: $d\theta_1 + d\theta_2 = d\theta_2 + d\theta_1$.

and $d\theta_2$ are proportional respectively to the corresponding circular arcs $rd\theta_1$ and $rd\theta_2$. These circular arcs are approximately straight lines, on an essentially flat surface, when the angular displacements are very small. Figure 13-4a shows $d\theta_1 + d\theta_2$; Figure 13-4b shows $d\theta_2 + d\theta_1$. The resultant angular displacement is the same for the two cases because the resultant linear displacements are the same. *Infinitesimal* angular displacements obey the commutative law.

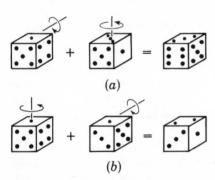

(a)

(b)

Figure 13-5. Finite angular displacements—in this case, two 90° displacements of a die—do *not* obey the commutative law: (a) $\theta_1 + \theta_2$; (b) $\theta_2 + \theta_1$. Note that $\theta_1 + \theta_2 \neq \theta_2 + \theta_1$.

Finite angular displacements, on the other hand, do not commute. Figures 13-5a and b, in which a die undergoes two successive angular displacements of 90°, indicate that *finite* angular displacements do *not commute*; that is,

$$\theta_1 + \theta_2 \neq \theta_2 + \theta_1$$

The angular velocity ω is a vector because $d\theta$ is a vector and $1/dt$ is a scalar. Similarly, the angular acceleration α is a vector because $d\omega$ is a vector and $1/dt$ is a scalar.

In general, the angular acceleration vector α is *not* necessarily along the direction of the instantaneous angular velocity vector ω, and the rotational motion is complicated. We shall consider two simple situations: (1) α always along the direction of ω and (2) α always of constant magnitude and at right angles to ω.

(1) If α and ω are along the same direction, the speed and sense of the rotational motion may change with time, but the orientation of the axis of rotation is fixed. Equations 13-5 through 13-8 hold for this situation only, where, in addition, the magnitude of α must be constant. See Figure 13-6a.

(2) If the vector α is of constant magnitude and always at right angles to ω, the direction of ω changes but its magnitude does not. See Figure 13-6b. The axis of rotation itself rotates at a constant rate in a motion known as *precession*. The angular speed of precession ω_p is $\Delta\varphi/\Delta t$, where $\Delta\varphi$ is the angle turned through by ω in the time Δt. From the geometry of Figure 13-6b, $\Delta\varphi = \alpha \, \Delta t/\omega$. Therefore,

$$\omega_p = \frac{\Delta\varphi}{\Delta_t} = \frac{\alpha}{\omega} \qquad [13\text{-}12]$$

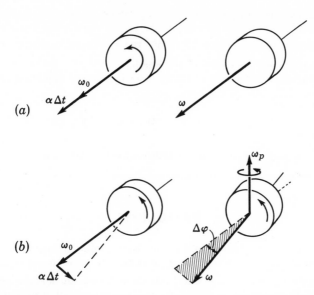

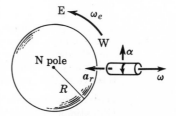

Figure 13-6. (a) When the angular acceleration $\boldsymbol{\alpha}$ is along the direction of the angular velocity $\boldsymbol{\omega}_0$, the speed of rotation changes but not the direction of the rotation axis. (b) When the angular acceleration $\boldsymbol{\alpha}$ is at right angles to the angular velocity, the direction of the rotation changes but not the speed of rotation. In time Δt the axis of rotation sweeps out an angle $\Delta\varphi$ and the body precesses at the angular velocity $\omega_p = \Delta\varphi/\Delta t$.

The two situations shown in Figures 13-6a and b are the rotational analogs, respectively, of translational motion along a straight line (in which $\boldsymbol{a}$ and $\boldsymbol{v}$ lie along the same line) and of uniform circular motion (in which $\boldsymbol{a}$ is always at right angles to $\boldsymbol{v}$).

Example 2 A cylinder is located on the Earth's surface at the Equator, as shown in Figure 13-7. It spins freely about a fixed vertical axis at an angular speed of 800 radians/sec. Calculate (a) the centripetal acceleration of the cylinder's center of mass and (b) the angular acceleration of the cylinder, both with respect to a reference frame *not* rotating with respect to the fixed stars.

(a) The radial acceleration of the cylinder's center of mass is

$$a_r = R\omega_e^2$$

where R is the radius of the Earth (6.4×10^6 m)

Figure 13-7. A cylinder at the Earth's Equator spins with an angular velocity ω. The angular velocity of the Earth's rotation is ω_e; the cylinder's angular acceleration is α; the radial acceleration of the cylinder's center of mass is a_r.

and ω_e is the angular speed of the Earth about its axis (2π radians/day $=$ 7.3×10^{-5} radians/sec). Thus,

$$a_r = (6.4 \times 10^6 \text{ m})(7.3 \times 10^{-5} \text{ rad/sec})^2 = 0.034 \text{ m/sec}^2$$

in a direction toward the center of the Earth.

(b) The angular acceleration of the cylinder is given by Equation 13-12:

$$\alpha = \omega_p \omega$$

The angular speed of precession, ω_p, is the same as the Earth's angular speed ω_e. Therefore,

$$\alpha = (7.3 \times 10^{-5} \text{ rad/sec})(800 \text{ rad/sec}) = 0.058 \text{ rad/sec}^2$$

in a direction along the Equator and to the east.

PROBLEMS

13-1   A wheel is spinning initially at 5000 revolutions/minute. What constant angular acceleration must it have to come to rest in 4.0 sec?

13-2   Starting from rest, a wheel rotates at a constant angular acceleration of 15 radians/sec². What are the magnitudes of its (a) angular displacement and (b) angular velocity, both at $t = 10$ sec?

13-3   An automobile engine increases its rotational speed from 1000 to 4500 revolutions/minute in 10 sec at constant angular acceleration. Through what angular displacement does the crankshaft turn?

13-4   A flywheel rotating initially at 4000 revolutions/minute comes to rest in 2.0 hours. (a) What is its average angular acceleration? (b) How many turns does the flywheel make before coming to rest?

13-5   A wheel makes 16 turns during a 10 sec time interval, its angular speed at the end of this interval being 15 radians/sec. Compute the average angular acceleration.

13-6   A man walks in a circle of radius 20 feet on a rotating merry-go-round, in the opposite sense to that of the merry-go-round's rotation. His speed relative to the merry-go-round is 3.0 feet/sec. The merry-go-round's angular speed is 10 revolutions/minute. (a) What is the man's angular speed relative to the ground? (b) What is his linear speed relative to the ground?

13-7   Derive the kinematic relations for constant angular acceleration (Equations 13-5 and 13-6) by integrating, with respect to time, the definitions of the angular acceleration and angular velocity (Equations 13-4 and 13-3).

13-8   Show that the magnitude of the linear acceleration of a point moving in a circle of radius r with angular velocity ω and angular acceleration α is given by $a = r(\omega^4 + \alpha^2)^{1/2}$.

13-9   Show that the ratio of the angular speeds of a pair of coupled gears is in the inverse ratio of their respective radii.

13-10   The second hand of a clock has a radius of 3.0 cm. What are (a) the
linear velocity, (b) the linear acceleration, (c) the angular velocity, and
(d) the angular acceleration, of the tip of the second hand at the time
2 hours and 30.75 minutes?

13-11   An automobile with wheels of 13-inch radius accelerates from rest at
10 (miles/hour)/sec. What are (a) the angular velocity and (b) the
angular acceleration of the wheels relative to their axles 5.0 sec after
the start?

13-12   A rope is wrapped around the circumference of a cylinder, of radius
0.75 feet, having a fixed axis of rotation and initially at rest. The
rope is unwrapped without any slipping at a constant linear acceleration of 4.0 feet/sec². Compute the following quantities, all for the time
$t = 5.0$ sec: (a) the angular speed of the cylinder, (b) the angular
acceleration, (c) the linear speed of a point on the circumference, and
(d) the linear acceleration of a point on the circumference.

13-13   A small object attached to a 1.0 m length of string swings in a vertical
plane as a simple pendulum. The object is released from rest when the
string is horizontal. What is the angular speed of the string (a) when
the string is vertical and (b) when the string makes an angle of 60°
with the vertical?

Figure 13-8

13-14 ★ One end of a string is attached to the rim of a wheel 0.50 feet in radius.
A small object hangs at the other end of the string, as shown in Figure
13-8. If the wheel is given an initial angular velocity of 9.0 radians/
sec "into the paper" and the constant angular acceleration of the
wheel is 3.0 radians/sec² "out of the paper," then (a) how many turns
does the wheel make before coming momentarily to rest, (b) what
length of string is then wrapped around the cylinder, (c) at what time
will the string again be entirely unwrapped from the cylinder, and
(d) what is the angular velocity at this instant?

13-15   What is the angular velocity of the hour hand of a clock relative to
the minute hand?

13-16   What is the difference in the periods of two satellites, both traveling
close to the Earth around the Equator—one to the east and the other
to the west—as measured by an observer on Earth?

13-17   The *mean solar day* is the time required for the Earth to make one complete rotation relative to the Sun (that is, the time interval elapsing between two successive appearances of the Sun overhead at the same longitude). The *mean sidereal day* is the time required for the Earth to make one complete rotation relative to the fixed stars. By definition, the solar day is 24 hours long. Show that the approximate length of the sidereal day is 23 hours, 56 minutes, 4 seconds.

13-18 ★ The time interval elapsing between successive transits of the Moon across a line joining the Earth and Sun is 29.5 days (the so-called *synodic month*). (a) Show that the period of the Moon's revolution about the Earth with respect to the fixed stars (the *sidereal month*) is 27.3 days (the Sun, Earth, and Moon all lie approximately in the same plane; the sense of the Earth's rotation and revolution and of the Moon's revolution are all the same—west to east). (b) The same side of the Moon is always turned toward the Earth. What is the period of the Moon's rotation relative to the Earth?

13-19   A spinning wheel initially has an angular velocity of 25 radians/sec north; 10 sec later its angular velocity is 25 radians/sec south. If the angular acceleration is constant, what are (a) the magnitude and direction of the angular acceleration, (b) the angular displacement over the 10 sec, and (c) the angular velocity at 15 sec?

13-20 ★ A cyclist riding a 26-inch bicycle (wheel diameter) at a constant speed of 15 feet/sec turns in a circle of 20 feet in radius. The axles of the wheel remain horizontal. What is the angular acceleration of the wheels?

F O U R T E E N

ROTATIONAL DYNAMICS

In this chapter we develop the rotational dynamics of rigid bodies. First is defined the moment of force, or torque, in terms of the vector, or cross, product. Then the rotational form of Newton's second law of motion is derived, the moment of inertia appearing as a measure of the rotational inertia of a rigid body. The rotational form of the work-energy theorem is then easily derived. The center of gravity is defined, and the general conditions for the equilibrium of a rigid body are treated.

14-1 Torque Suppose that a rigid body, free to rotate about a fixed axis, is acted upon by an external force that changes the body's speed of rotation. It is clear that any component of an applied force parallel to the axis of rotation has no effect on the angular speed. Thus, only force components *perpendicular* to the axis of rotation contribute to an angular acceleration about this axis. We wish to inquire into the turning effect of such an applied force in order to arrive at a measure of the *moment of force*, or *torque*.

Consider the situation shown in Figure 14-1, in which a force F lying in a plane perpendicular to the axis of rotation is applied at a point specified by the radius vector r relative to the axis of rotation. Both F and r lie in a plane perpendicular to the axis of rotation. The effect of the force is to

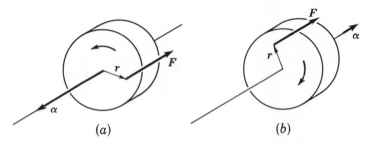

(a) (b)

Figure 14-1. A force F, applied in a plane perpendicular to the axis of rotation and at a point whose displacement from the rotation axis is r, produces an angular acceleration α. Note that the directions of α in (a) and (b) are different, the direction of α depending upon the point of application of the force F.

produce an angular acceleration α along the rotation axis, in the directions shown in Figures 14-1a and b. The force is the same in both instances; the accelerations differ, however, according to the point relative to the axis at which the force is applied. One rotational acceleration is counterclockwise, the other clockwise.

It is useful to associate a direction with the torque, represented by the vector τ, in such a way that this direction of the torque is the same as the direction of the angular acceleration it produces. The direction of τ is given by the right-hand rule: if the r vector is *imagined* to be turned through the smaller angle (less than 180°) with the fingers of the right hand until it points in the direction of the F vector, the right-hand thumb points in the direction of τ, as illustrated in Figure 14-2. Note that the vector τ is always perpendicular to the plane containing the r and F vectors. If r and F lie in the plane of the paper the force produces a counterclockwise torque τ out of the paper.

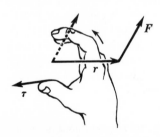

Figure 14-2. The right-hand rule convention for the direction of the torque τ: turn r into F through the small angle in the sense of the right-hand fingers; the right-hand thumb then gives the direction of τ.

Now we define the magnitude of the torque vector. <u>The angle θ is the angle between the directions in which the vectors r and F point.</u> It is clear from Figure 14-3a that if the force

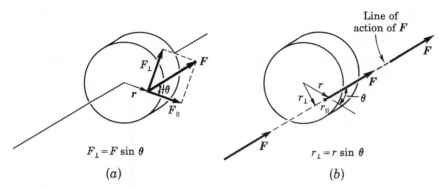

Figure 14-3. (a) The components of F, $F_\perp$ and $F_{||}$, respectively perpendicular and parallel to the direction of r: $F_\perp = F \sin \theta$. (b) The components of r, $r_\perp$ and $r_{||}$, respectively perpendicular and parallel to the direction of F: $r_\perp = r \sin \theta$.

F is replaced by two components $F_\perp$ and $F_{||}$, respectively perpendicular and parallel to the direction of r, the only component influencing the rotation of the body is $F_\perp$, inasmuch as the component $F_{||}$ passes directly through the axis of rotation. Thus, only the component $F_\perp$ at right angles to the radius vector, where $F_\perp = F \sin \theta$, should enter into the definition of the magnitude of the torque.

The same vectors r and F are shown in Figure 14-3b. Our intuition informs us that only the perpendicular component $r_\perp = r \sin \theta$ enters into the turning effect of the force for, if $r_\perp$ were zero, the force would pass through the axis and again there would be no torque. With the same distance $r_\perp$, the turning effect of a force F is the same, irrespective of the point at which the force is applied along the line of action (the line coincident with the force F).

The magnitude of the torque τ is, by definition,

$$\tau = rF_\perp = r_\perp F = rF \sin \theta \qquad \text{[14-1]}$$

This definition is in harmony with the qualitative considerations given above. In Section 14-3 it will be seen that this definition is consonant with the dynamics of rigid-body motion.

The perpendicular distance $r_\perp$ from the axis of rotation to the line of action of the applied force is called the *moment arm*, or *lever arm*.

Torque has the dimensions force multiplied by distance, ML^2/T^2. To avoid confusion with the units assigned to work or energy, which also have the units of force times distance, torque units are usually written as meter-newton (m-nt), centimeter-dyne (cm-dyne), and pound-foot (lb-ft), in the inverse order of energy units (nt-m, etc.).

It is essential to appreciate that the magnitude and the direction of the torque of a single force depends on the *choice of the axis of rotation.* One specifies completely a torque by giving, not only the magnitude and direction of the force, but also the axis relative to which the radius vector is measured and about which the torque is to be computed. Thus, a single force produces different torques for different choices of axes, and a given torque can be produced by a variety of forces applied at appropriate places.

14-2 The vector product There is a useful vector symbolism for representing both the magnitude and direction of the torque vector τ as it is derived from the magnitudes and relative directions of the vectors r and F:

$$\tau = r \times F \qquad [14\text{-}2]$$

Equation 14-2 implies that the direction of τ is related to the directions of r and F through the right-hand rule and that the magnitude of τ is given by $\tau = rF \sin \theta$. The vector multiplication in Equation 14-2 is read as "τ equals r cross F."

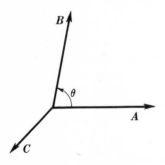

The torque is but one important example of the *cross*, or *vector*, *product* of two vectors. In general, with

$$C = A \times B$$

the direction of the vector C, representing the cross product of A and B, is arrived at by turning the first vector (A) into the second vector (B) through the smaller angle to establish the sense of rotation. Then the right-hand rule gives the direction of C, which is perpendicular to the plane containing vectors A and B. The magnitude of C is given by

Figure 14-4. Relative orientations of the vectors A, B, and C for the cross product $C = A \times B$.

$$C = AB \sin \theta$$

where θ is the angle between the vectors A and B, as shown in Figure 14-4. If vectors A and B represent the sides of a parallelogram, $A \times B$ is a vector perpendicular to the plane of the parallelogram and having a magnitude equal to its area.

The order in which the two vectors in a cross product are written is important, since $A \times B \neq B \times A$. The cross product does *not* obey the commutative law. Indeed, if the order of the vectors is reversed, so is the direction of their cross product. Therefore,

$$A \times B = -B \times A$$

The distributive law does, however, hold for cross products:

$$A \times (D + E) = (A \times D) + (A \times E)$$

If the vectors A and B are parallel or antiparallel, the angle between them being either $0°$ or $180°$, then $A \times B = 0$, inasmuch as the factor $\sin \theta$ is then zero.

The cross product and dot product (Section 11-4) must be carefully distinguished. The cross product is a vector; the dot product, a scalar. The cross product does not obey the commutative law; the scalar product does. The cross product is zero when the vectors are parallel; the dot product is zero when the vectors are perpendicular. Torque and work both involve the product of a displacement vector and a force vector; the torque (a vector) is their cross product, and the work (a scalar) is their dot product.

14-3   Newton's second law of motion for rotation   Before considering the dynamics of rotational motion, let us consider a general theorem of great importance. <u>It is this: the *sum* of the *internal torques* arising from the mutual interactions of a collection of particles is *zero*.</u>

Consider two representative particles 1 and 2 in a rigid body, as shown in Figure 14-5, and the torques arising from the forces of their interaction, $F_{2\,on\,1}$ and $F_{1\,on\,2}$. This force pair consists of equal but opposite forces, according to Newton's third law. In addition, it is assumed that the forces act along the line connecting particle 1 with 2—that is,

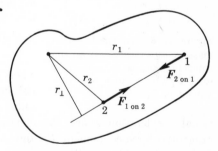

Figure 14-5. Particles 1 and 2 of a rigid body interacting through a central force; the torques of both forces have the *same* moment arm $r_\perp$.

that the interaction force is a *central force*. It is then clear from the figure that for *any* choice of axis, the moment arms for the two torques $\tau_{2\,on\,1}$ and $\tau_{1\,on\,2}$ are the same. Therefore, the *magnitudes* of the two torques are equal. Their directions are opposite, however, the direction of $\tau_{2\,on\,1}$ being into the paper for the axis shown, and the direction of $\tau_{1\,on\,2}$ being out of the paper for the same axis. Thus, $\tau_{2\,on\,1} + \tau_{1\,on\,2} = 0$.

Repeating this procedure to find the torques arising from the forces between *all* pairs of particles comprising the body, and adding together all such torque pairs, yields

$$\Sigma \, \tau_{\text{int}} = 0 \qquad\qquad [14\text{-}3]$$

provided that the internal forces are central forces. This equation applies whether the interacting particles are at rest with respect to one another, as in a rigid body, or are in relative motion with respect to one another, as are the molecules of a liquid.

We saw earlier that, if the internal forces in a system occur in pairs of equal but opposite forces, the sum of the *internal forces* is zero (Section 10-4); now we see that, if the internal forces are *central* forces, the sum of the *internal torques* is zero. Therefore, we need concern ourselves only with the *external torques.*

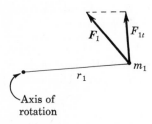

Consider the rotational motion of a rigid body about a fixed axis, the body being subjected to one or more external forces. We focus our attention first on the representative particle 1 of mass m_1, moving in a circle of radius r_1 with a linear acceleration a_1. See Figure 14-6. From Newton's second law,

$$\Sigma \, F_{\text{ext}} = m a$$
$$F_1 = m_1 a_1$$

Figure 14-6. A particle, with mass m_1 at a radius r_1 from the rotation axis, is subject to a force F_1 whose tangential component is F_{1t}.

where F_1 is the resultant of all forces, internal and external, acting on particle 1. The radial component of F_1 produces no rotational acceleration about the chosen axis. We need consider only the tangential force component F_{1t} and the corresponding acceleration component a_{1t}. Then, in magnitude,

$$F_{1t} = m_1 a_{1t} = m_1 r_1 \alpha$$

where $a_{1t} = r_1 \alpha$, according to Equation 13-10. The quantity α is the angular acceleration of particle 1 (as well as that of *all* other particles in the rigid body). The torque on particle 1 has the magnitude

$$\tau_1 = r_1 F_{1t} = m_1 r_1{}^2 \alpha$$

Similar relations can be written for all other particles of the rigid body, replacing 1 by 2, 3, etc. Taking the sums of the left- and right-hand sides yields

$$\tau_1 + \tau_2 + \tau_3 + \cdots = (m_1 r_1^2 + m_2 r_2^2 + m_3 r_3^2 + \cdots)\alpha$$

The left-hand side represents the sum of *all* torques, external and internal, on the body. However, since the sum of the *internal* torques is zero, the equation above reduces to

$$\Sigma \, \tau_{\text{ext}} = (\Sigma \, m_i r_i^2)\alpha$$

The sum of the external torques equals the quantity $\Sigma \, m_i r_i^2$ multiplied by the common angular acceleration of all particles of the rigid body. We may write this equation in vector form:

$$\boxed{\Sigma \, \boldsymbol{\tau}_{\text{ext}} = (\Sigma \, m_i r_i^2)\boldsymbol{\alpha} = I\boldsymbol{\alpha}} \qquad [14\text{-}4]$$

where

$$\boxed{I = \Sigma \, m_i r_i^2} \qquad [14\text{-}5]$$

The direction of the angular acceleration $\boldsymbol{\alpha}$ is along the direction of the resultant torque, the magnitude of the resultant torque being equal to the product of the *moment of inertia* I and the angular acceleration.

Equation 14-4 is Newton's second law for rotational motion about a fixed axis, where the moment of force replaces the force, the moment of inertia replaces the inertia, and the angular acceleration replaces the linear acceleration. It is, of course, nothing more than Newton's second law for translational motion written in a fashion that simplifies the analysis of rotational motion by the recognition that all particles in a rigid body have the same angular acceleration. In Newton's second law for translational motion we were not concerned with the point of application of the force, but in applying Equation 14-4 *we must specify the axis of rotation*; the torques, the moment of inertia, and the angular acceleration all depend on this choice.

Equation 14-4 holds when the axis of rotation is at rest. It also holds when the rotation axis of the rigid body is in motion, even with an accelerated center of mass, provided, however, that the axis passes *through the center of mass*. The motion of any rigid body moving through space can most easily be described as a combination of a translational motion of the center of mass and a rotational motion about the center of mass. To describe the translational motion of the moving rigid body we use the relation

[10-28] $$\Sigma \, \boldsymbol{F}_{\text{ext}} = M\boldsymbol{a}_{\text{cm}}$$

which relates the acceleration $\boldsymbol{a}_{\text{cm}}$ of the center of mass to the external forces. To describe the rotational motion of the rigid body relative to the center of mass, one uses Equation 14-4, where τ, I, and α are then computed relative to an axis passing through the center of mass.†

14-4 Moment of inertia Before illustrating the rotational form of Newton's second law, in which the rotational inertia, or moment of inertia $I = \Sigma \, m_i r_i^2$, appears, we shall examine in some detail the meaning of this scalar quantity and the procedure for computing the moment of inertia for bodies of various shapes.

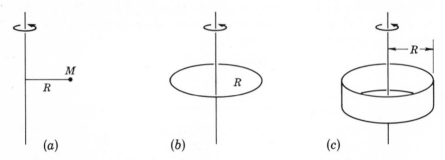

Figure 14-7. (a) A point particle, (b) a circular ring, and (c) a cylindrical shell, each of mass M and radius R, have a moment of inertia $I = MR^2$ with respect to the axes shown.

The moment of inertia depends not only on the mass but also on the distribution of the mass relative to the line that is chosen as axis of rotation. The moment of inertia, unlike the mass, is *not* an intrinsic property of the body alone; it depends on the choice of the axis. The dimensions of moment of inertia are ML^2. Its units, those of mass multiplied by the square of distance, are: kilogram-meter², gram-centimeter², and slug-foot² (kg-m², gm-cm², and slug-ft²).

For a body in which all of the mass M is at the same distance R from the axis of rotation, the moment of inertia is simply

$$I = \Sigma \, m_i R^2 = R^2 \Sigma \, m_i = MR^2$$

Thus, a small body of mass M attached to a massless rod of length R has a

† We know, of course, that we can properly apply Newton's second law to the translational motion of the center of mass when we view the motion from an inertial frame. When we apply Newton's second law for the rotational motion about the center of mass, we are viewing the motion from the reference frame of the center of mass. Even though this reference frame may be accelerating, Equation 14-4 still holds, because the inertial force, which we must add to the real forces if we wish to use Equation 14-4, may be thought of as acting at the center of mass. Therefore, any such *inertial force has no torque about an axis through the center of mass.* (See Section 10-6.)

moment of inertia MR^2 relative to an axis of rotation passing through one end of the rod and at right angles to it (Figure 14-7a). Similarly, relative to the axis through the center of symmetry, the moment of inertia of a ring (Figure 14-7b), or of a thin cylindrical shell (Figure 14-7c), of radius R and mass M is MR^2.

For a continuous distribution of mass in a solid, the moment of inertia may be written

$$I = \int r^2 \, dm = \int \rho r^2 \, dv \qquad\qquad [14\text{-}6]$$

where ρ, the density of the solid, is related to the mass element dm and the volume element dv by $dm = \rho \, dv$. If ρ is constant throughout the solid, it can be taken outside of the integral sign in Equation 14-6.

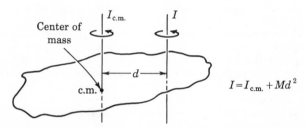

Figure 14-8. Illustration of the parallel-axis theorem. The moment of inertia about an axis through the center of mass is I_{cm}; the moment of inertia I about a parallel axis, separated a distance, d is $I_{cm} + Md^2$, where M is the mass of the body.

The moment of inertia I_{cm} of a body with respect to an axis passing through the center of mass is related in a simple way to the moment of inertia I with respect to another parallel axis:

$$I = I_{cm} + Md^2 \qquad\qquad [14\text{-}7]$$

where M is the total mass and d is the distance between the two parallel axes. See Figure 14-8. This, the so-called *parallel-axis theorem* for moments of inertia, is proved in detail in Section 14-8. As Equation 14-7 shows, the moment of inertia about an axis through the center of mass is a minimum; for any other parallel axis, clearly $I > I_{cm}$. The examples that follow will illustrate its usefulness. Formulas for the moment of inertia of several simple shapes are given in Figure 14-9.

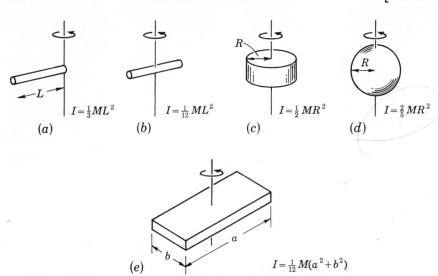

Figure 14-9. Moments of inertia for several simple shapes, all of constant density: (a) a thin rod of length L about an axis through one end and perpendicular to the axis of the rod, (b) a thin rod of length L about an axis through the center and perpendicular to the rod's axis, (c) a right circular cylinder through the symmetry axis, (d) a sphere through a diametrical axis, and (e) a thin plate with sides a and b about an axis perpendicular to the slab and passing through its center.

Example 1   Masses of 3.00 kg and 1.00 kg are attached to a thin massless rod at $x = 1.00$ m and $x = 1.80$ m, respectively. See Figure 14-10a. (a) What is the moment of inertia of the two masses relative to the Y-axis? (b) At what distance from the axis would all of the mass have to be placed in order to yield the same moment of inertia? (c) What is the location of the center of mass relative to this axis? (d) What is the moment of inertia relative to an axis passing through the center of mass and perpendicular to the rod?

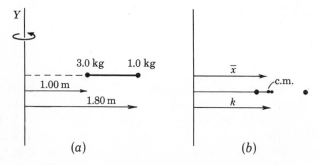

Figure 14-10. (a) A rod with masses on both ends. (b) The locations of the center of mass $\bar{x}$ and the radius of gyration (k).

(a) From Equation 14-5,

$$I = \Sigma\, m_i r_i^2 = (3.00\ \text{kg})(1.00\ \text{m})^2 + (1.00\ \text{kg})(1.80\ \text{m})^2$$

$$I = 6.24\ \text{kg-m}^2$$

(b) If all of the mass were placed at a distance k, called the *radius of gyration*, from the axis of rotation, the moment of inertia would be $I = Mk^2$. Therefore,

$$k = \sqrt{I/M} = \sqrt{(6.24\ \text{kg-m}^2)/(4.0\ \text{kg})}$$

$$k = 1.25\ \text{m}$$

(c) The location of the center of mass is given by

[8-19] $$\bar{x} = \frac{\Sigma\, m_i x_i}{\Sigma\, m_i} = \frac{(3.00\ \text{kg})(1.00\ \text{m}) + (1.00\ \text{kg})(1.80\ \text{m})}{4.0\ \text{kg}}$$

$$\bar{x} = 1.20\ \text{m}$$

Note that the center of mass and the radius of gyration are *not* at the same location (see Figure 14-10b); that is, the point at which all of the mass may be imagined to be concentrated for translational motion is not the same as the point at which all of the mass may be imagined to be concentrated for rotational motion. Furthermore, the center of mass is fixed relative to the rigid body, whereas the radius of gyration depends on the choice of axis.

(d) The moment of inertia relative to the center of mass could be computed by choosing a new origin at the center of mass and then applying Equation 14-5, but a simpler procedure is to use the parallel-axis theorem, Equation 14-7:

$$I_{\text{cm}} = I - Md^2 = (6.24\ \text{kg-m}^2) - (4.00\ \text{kg})(1.20\ \text{m})^2$$

$$I_{\text{cm}} = 0.48\ \text{kg-m}^2$$

Example 2 What is the moment of inertia of a thin rod of length L and mass M with respect to an axis of rotation that is perpendicular to the rod and passes through (a) the center of the rod and (b) one end of the rod?

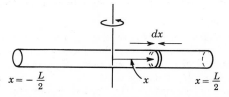

Figure 14-11. Computation of the moment of inertia of a thin rod of length L about a perpendicular axis through its center. The thin slice of thickness dx is located at x.

(a) We consider the contribution to the moment of inertia of a thin slice of thickness dx at a distance x from the axis of rotation. See Figure 14-11. For a rod of uniform density, the mass of the thin slice is $dm = M(dx/L)$. Then, with $r = x$, the moment of inertia is written

$$I_{\text{cm}} = \int r^2 \, dm = (M/L) \int_{-L/2}^{+L/2} x^2 \, dx = (M/L)(L^3/12) = \tfrac{1}{12} M L^2$$

where the integration has been extended from the left to right end of the rod, that is, from $x = -L/2$ to $x = +L/2$.

(b) We can find the moment of inertia about one end of the rod simply by choosing different limits for the definite integral given above, the rod now extending from $x = 0$ to $x = L$:

$$I_{\text{end}} = (M/L) \int_0^L x^2 \, dx = \tfrac{1}{3} M L^2$$

This result is consistent with the parallel-axis theorem:

[14-7]
$$I_{\text{end}} = I_{\text{cm}} + M d^2$$
$$I_{\text{end}} = \tfrac{1}{12} M L^2 + M(L/2)^2$$
$$I_{\text{end}} = \tfrac{1}{3} M L^2$$

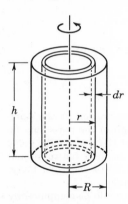

Figure 14-12. Computation of the moment of inertia of a right circular cylinder, of radius R and height h, about an axis of rotation through the cylinder's symmetry axis. A thin cylindrical shell of radius r and thickness dr is shown.

Example 3 What is the moment of inertia of a uniform right circular cylinder of mass M and radius R about the axis of symmetry?

We choose as a volume element a cylindrical shell of thickness dr. See Figure 14-12. All mass within such a shell is at the same distance r from the axis of rotation. The volume dv of the shell is the product of its height h, circumference $2\pi r$, and thickness dr; or, $dv = 2\pi h r \, dr$. Then, from Equation 14-6,

$$I = \rho \int r^2 \, dv = (M/\pi R^2 h) \int_0^R 2\pi h r^3 \, dr = \tfrac{1}{2} M R^2$$

where the density ρ has been replaced by the total mass M divided by the total volume $\pi R^2 h$, and the limits of the integral have been taken from $r = 0$ to $r = R$.

Example 4 A block A of mass M_A, resting on a smooth horizontal surface, is attached to a massless inextensible cord that passes horizontally over a uniform right circular cylinder C of radius R and mass M_C. The cord is attached to a second block B of mass M_B hanging vertically. The cylindrical pulley rotates freely about its axis of symmetry; the cord does not slip when the cylinder rotates. See Figure 14-13. (a) What is the linear acceleration of either block, and the tensions T_1 and T_2 in the upper and lower cord segments? (b) What is the speed of block B after it has descended a distance y from rest?

(a) Blocks A and B are in translational motion; their acceleration magnitude a is determined by the resultant forces on each. The cylinder C is in rotational motion; its angular acceleration α is determined by the resultant torque on it. We first isolate each of the three bodies, as indicated by the dotted loops in

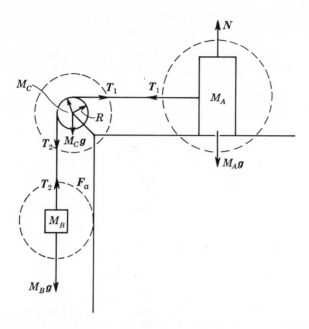

Figure 14-13. The forces acting on each of three bodies: a block on a plane, a descending block, and a rotating cylinder. The dotted lines indicate the boundaries of the respective systems.

Figure 14-13, and then show *all* the forces acting on each body. The tensions T_1 and T_2 in the two rope segments cannot be assumed to be equal in magnitude.

Applying Newton's second law to the translational motion of blocks A and B yields

$$\Sigma F_{\text{ext}} = m\boldsymbol{a}$$

Block A: $T_1 = M_A a$ [14-8]

Block B: $M_B g - T_2 = M_B a$ [14-9]

We have chosen the positive direction of B's acceleration as downward. This choice requires that the positive direction of A's acceleration be to the left and that the positive direction of C's angular acceleration be counterclockwise.

We now apply Newton's second law in its rotational form to the motion of the cylinder. The forces on the cylinder are the tensions T_1 and T_2 (both tangent to the cylinder), the force F_a exerted by the axle on the cylinder, and the weight $M_C g$ of the cylinder. The axis of rotation is taken at the cylinder's center. Therefore, the only forces on the cylinder having nonzero-moment arms are the two tensions:

$$\Sigma \tau_{\text{ext}} = I\alpha$$

Cylinder C: $RT_2 - RT_1 = I\alpha$

The tension T_2 produces a counterclockwise (positive) torque, and T_1 produces a clockwise (negative) torque. Both have the same moment arm R.

The moment of inertia of the cylinder about its center is

$$I = \tfrac{1}{2}M_C R^2$$

Because the rope does not slip on the cylinder, the tangential acceleration of a point on the rim has the same magnitude as the acceleration a of the cord and blocks. Therefore,

[13-10] $$\alpha = a/R$$

Substituting the relations for I and α in this equation yields

$$RT_2 - RT_1 = (\tfrac{1}{2}M_C R^2)(a/R)$$
$$T_2 - T_1 = \tfrac{1}{2}M_C a \qquad\qquad\text{[14-10]}$$

Curiously, the radius of the cylinder cancels out.

Equations 14-8, 14-9, and 14-10 can now be solved simultaneously for a, T_1, and T_2. The results after a little algebra, are

$$a = \frac{M_B g}{M_A + M_B + \tfrac{1}{2}M_C}$$

$$T_1 = \frac{M_A M_B g}{M_A + M_B + \tfrac{1}{2}M_C}$$

$$T_2 = \frac{(M_A + \tfrac{1}{2}M_C)M_B g}{M_A + M_B + \tfrac{1}{2}M_C}$$

If M_C is put equal to zero in the equations above—that is, if the mass of the pulley is negligible compared with the masses of the two blocks—these equations reduce to the Equations 10-9 and 10-10 found in Example 6, Chapter 10. Then $T_1 = T_2$. If, in addition, M_A is put equal to zero, $a = g$ (as it must for a freely falling body) and $T_1 = T_2 = 0$.

(b) Because block B has a constant linear acceleration and starts from rest, its speed after descending a distance y is

$$v = \sqrt{2ay}$$

$$v = \sqrt{\frac{2M_B g y}{M_A + M_B + \tfrac{1}{2}M_C}}$$

Example 5 A cylinder of mass M and radius R is projected up an inclined plane of angle θ. The cylinder rolls without slipping. The initial speed of the cylinder's center of mass is v_0. (a) What is the acceleration of the cylinder's center of mass? (b) What distance d does the cylinder travel up the plane before coming momentarily to rest?

(a) In Figure 14-14 are shown the forces acting on the cylinder: its weight $M\mathbf{g}$, the normal force $\mathbf{N}$, and the force of friction f_s. The tails of the force vectors are placed at the points where the forces are applied to the cylinder; the computation of the torques necessitates this. Notice that the static friction force is *up* the incline, in the *same* direction as the cylinder's motion.

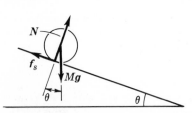

Figure 14-14. The forces acting on a cylinder rolling *up* an incline. Note that the force of static friction f_s (*up* the plane) is in the *same* direction as the velocity of the cylinder's center of mass.

The cylinder has a translational acceleration down the incline and an angular acceleration about its center of mass. Choosing up-the-incline as the positive direction for translation, counterclockwise as the corresponding positive sense for rotation, and applying Newton's second law to the translational and rotational motion in turn, gives

$$\Sigma \, \boldsymbol{F}_{\text{ext}} = M\boldsymbol{a}_{\text{cm}}$$

Along the incline: $f_s - Mg \sin \theta = Ma_{\text{cm}}$

Perpendicular to the incline: $N - Mg \cos \theta = 0$

Because the cylinder rolls but does not slip, it is always at rest momentarily at its point of contact with the plane, and a *static* force of friction acts on the cylinder where

$$f_s \leq \mu_s N$$

In considering the rotational motion, the torques, moment of inertia, and angular acceleration must all be determined relative to an axis of rotation passing through the center of mass. The forces N and Mg both pass through the axis, yielding no torques; the resultant torque on the cylinder is produced solely by the friction force $\boldsymbol{f}_s$ having a moment arm R. Therefore, Newton's second law for rotation yields

$$\Sigma \, \tau_{\text{ext}} = I_{\text{cm}}\alpha_{\text{cm}}$$

$$-Rf_s = I_{\text{cm}}\alpha_{\text{cm}}$$

But
$$I_{\text{cm}} = \tfrac{1}{2}MR^2$$

and
$$\alpha_{\text{cm}} = a_{\text{cm}}/R$$

The last relation requires justification. First we note that the acceleration a_{cm} of the cylinder's center relative to its instantaneous point of contact with the plane is equal in magnitude to the acceleration of the point of contact relative to the cylinder's center. Therefore, if we view the motion from a reference frame moving with the cylinder's center, and if the cylinder rolls without slipping, then the point of contact has the *same* tangential acceleration as the cylinder's rim, and $a_{\text{cm}} = R\alpha_{\text{cm}}$.

Using the relations for I_{cm} and α_{cm} in the equation above, we obtain

$$-Rf_s = (\tfrac{1}{2}MR^2)(a_{\text{cm}}/R)$$

$$-f_s = \tfrac{1}{2}Ma_{\text{cm}}$$

Substituting this result into the first equation gives

$$-\tfrac{1}{2}Ma_{\text{cm}} - Mg \sin \theta = Ma_{\text{cm}}$$

$$a_{\text{cm}} = -\tfrac{2}{3}g \sin \theta$$

The acceleration does *not* depend on the cylinder's mass or radius. The center of mass of *all* uniform solid cylinders, whatever their masses or radii, roll up (or down) an incline of a given angle with the *same* linear acceleration. If, however, solid uniform cylinders were replaced by cylindrical shells, the corresponding linear acceleration magnitudes would be found to be $a_{\text{cm}} = \tfrac{1}{2}g \sin \theta$ and the result for solid spheres would be $a_{\text{cm}} = \tfrac{5}{7}g \sin \theta$. The acceleration depends on the character of the mass distribution, or shape, but not on the mass or dimensions.

Note that the friction force does not enter into the relation for a_{cm}. There are, however, requirements on f_s. Combining the last two equations above yields

$$f_s = -\tfrac{1}{2}Ma_{cm} = (M/2)(\tfrac{2}{3}g \sin \theta) = \tfrac{1}{3}Mg \sin \theta$$

Unless the coefficient of static friction is large enough for the friction force to be $\tfrac{1}{3}Mg \sin \theta$, the cylinder will not roll without slipping. Of course, if the plane is frictionless, the magnitude of the linear acceleration is given by the well-known relation $a = g \sin \theta$ (see Example 5, Section 10-2).

(b) The cylinder's center of mass has a constant acceleration down the incline ($a_{cm} = \tfrac{2}{3}g \sin \theta$); therefore, the distance d it will move up the plane before coming momentarily to rest, is determined by

$$v^2 = v_0{}^2 + 2ad$$

With $v = 0$,

$$d = \frac{-v_0{}^2}{2a} = \frac{3v_0{}^2}{4g \sin \theta}$$

14-5 Work and kinetic energy in rotational motion

We first find an expression giving the work done by an external force F when a rigid body rotates an angle $d\theta$ about a fixed axis. See Figure 14-15. The force is applied at a distance r from the axis of rotation. We resolve the force into the components $F_{\parallel}$ and $F_{\perp}$ which are respectively parallel and perpendicular to the radius vector r. At the point of application of the force, the particle is displaced through a circular arc of length ds, where $ds = r\, d\theta$. Inasmuch as $F_{\parallel}$ is always perpendicular to the displacement ds, the force component $F_{\perp}$ alone does work:

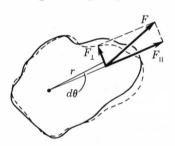

Figure 14-15. A rigid body undergoing an angular displacement $d\theta$ under the influence of force F applied at r. The perpendicular and parallel components of F are $F_{\perp}$ and $F_{\parallel}$ respectively.

$$dW = \mathbf{F} \cdot d\mathbf{s} = F_{\perp}\, ds = F_{\perp} r\, d\theta$$

But $F_{\perp}r$ is the torque τ of the force: therefore,

$$dW = \tau\, d\theta$$

If several external torques act simultaneously on the body, then τ represents their sum.

$$\boxed{dW = \tau_{\text{ext}}\, d\theta} \qquad\qquad [14\text{-}11]$$

The work done by the resultant external torque in producing an angular displacement $d\theta$ is $\tau_{\text{ext}}\, d\theta$. The work is positive when the sense of rotation of the torque and the angular displacement are alike. Then energy is transferred *to* the body, and the body's rotational kinetic energy *increases*. On the other hand, the work is negative when a braking torque acts and energy is transferred *from* the body to the agent.

We find the power, which is the rate of doing work on the rotating body, by taking the time derivative of Equation 14-11:

$$\frac{dW}{dt} = \tau_{\text{ext}} \frac{d\theta}{dt}$$

$$\boxed{P = \tau_{\text{ext}}\omega} \qquad [14\text{-}12]$$

We know from the work-energy theorem that, for a perfectly rigid body, the work done on the body by external influences is equal to the gain in kinetic energy of the body:

[11-5] $$W_{i \to f} = K_f - K_i$$

We wish to find the particularly simple form that kinetic energy assumes when work is done on a rigid body to change its angular speed about a fixed axis. (Our analysis will parallel exactly the development in Section 11-3, in which it was shown that for a single particle $\int \boldsymbol{F} \cdot d\boldsymbol{s} = \frac{1}{2}mv_f{}^2 - \frac{1}{2}mv_i{}^2$.)

From Equations 14-11 and 14-4,

$$dW = \tau \, d\theta = I\alpha \, d\theta = I\frac{d\omega}{dt} \, d\theta = I\frac{d\theta}{dt} \, d\omega = I\omega \, d\omega$$

$$W_{i \to f} = \int_i^f dW = \int_i^f I\omega \, d\omega = \frac{1}{2}I\omega_f{}^2 - \frac{1}{2}I\omega_i{}^2$$

The kinetic energy K of a body having a moment of inertia I and an angular speed ω about a fixed axis is

$$\boxed{K = \tfrac{1}{2}I\omega^2} \qquad [14\text{-}13]$$

The work-energy theorem applies equally well to translational motion and to rotational motion. When the axis of rotation is fixed, the total kinetic energy of the body, arising from the individual contributions $\frac{1}{2}mv^2$ from each of the particles, is most economically expressed by Equation 14-13.

The most general form of motion of a rigid body is that in which the body undergoes simultaneously a translational motion and a rotational motion. The total kinetic energy K of any such body, however complicated its motion, can be expressed as the sum of two contributions:

$$\boxed{K = \tfrac{1}{2}Mv_{\text{cm}}^2 + \tfrac{1}{2}I_{\text{cm}}\omega_{\text{cm}}^2} \qquad [14\text{-}14]$$

The first term represents the translational motion of the center of mass, $\frac{1}{2}Mv_{\rm cm}^2$, where M is the mass of the body and $v_{\rm cm}$ is the speed of the center of mass. The second term represents rotational motion about the center of mass, $\frac{1}{2}I_{\rm cm}\omega_{\rm cm}^2$, where $I_{\rm cm}$ is the moment of inertia of the body about an axis passing through the center of mass and $\omega_{\rm cm}$ is the angular speed of the body about this axis. A detailed proof of Equation 14-14 is given in Section 14-8.

We have seen that in rotational motion the work done by an external torque is most easily expressed by $\int \tau \, d\theta$ and that the kinetic energy of a rigid body about the center of mass is most easily expressed by $\frac{1}{2}I\omega^2$. The general conservation of energy law as developed in Section 12-5, is, however, unchanged. If external agents do work on a system, transferring energy to it, this energy gain is manifest in just three forms: <u>kinetic energy</u> (whether translational or rotational), <u>potential energy</u> (arising from any change in the relative separations of the particles of the system), and <u>thermal energy</u> (representing the nonmechanical energy within the system).

You have probably perceived that, just as the relations for rotational kinematics (Equations 13-5 through 13-8) are exactly analogous to the relations for translational kinematics (Equations 2-7 through 2-11), there is a direct parallel between the dynamical quantities in rotation and the corresponding quantities in translational dynamics. Table 14-1 lists the corresponding quantities. (The *angular* momentum and its relation to the linear momentum is discussed in Chapter 15.)

Table 14-1

TRANSLATION		ROTATION	
Force	F	Moment of force, or torque	$\boldsymbol{\tau} = \boldsymbol{r} \times \boldsymbol{F}$
Mass (inertia)	m	Moment of inertia	$I = \Sigma m_i r_i^2$
Newton's second law	$\Sigma \, \boldsymbol{F}_{\rm ext} = m\boldsymbol{a}$	Newton's second law	$\Sigma \, \boldsymbol{\tau}_{\rm ext} = I\boldsymbol{\alpha}$
Work	$\int \boldsymbol{F} \cdot d\boldsymbol{s}$	Work	$\int \tau \, d\theta$
Translational kinetic energy	$\frac{1}{2}mv^2$	Rotational kinetic energy	$\frac{1}{2}I\omega^2$
Power	$P = Fv$	Power	$P = \tau\omega$

Example 6 A block A of mass M_A resting on a smooth horizontal surface is attached to a massless inextensible cord that passes horizontally over a uniform right circular cylinder C of radius R and mass M_C. The cord is attached to a second block B of mass M_B hanging vertically. The cylinder is free to rotate about its fixed axis of symmetry. The cord does not slip when the cylinder rotates. Block B is initially at rest a vertical distance y above the floor. See Figure 14-16. With what speed will it strike the floor?

The situation here is exactly like that of Example 4 and Figure 14-13. In Example 4 we found the speed with which B strikes the floor by first finding its linear acceleration through Newton's second law. This problem can be solved more simply by applying the conservation of energy law.

When block B falls, it loses potential energy in the amount $M_B gy$. (Bodies A and C neither lose nor gain *potential* energy.) Block B gains kinetic energy $\frac{1}{2}M_B v^2$; block A gains kinetic energy $\frac{1}{2}M_A v^2$; the cylinder gains kinetic energy $\frac{1}{2}I\omega^2$, where v is the linear speed when B strikes the floor, ω is the angular speed of the cylinder at this instant, and I is the cylinder's moment of inertia. The conservation of energy law then requires that

$$M_B gy = \tfrac{1}{2}M_A v^2 + \tfrac{1}{2}M_B v^2 + \tfrac{1}{2}I\omega^2$$

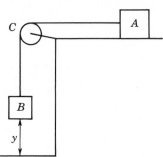

But $I = \tfrac{1}{2}M_C R^2$

and $\omega = v/R$

Substituting for I and ω into the first equation gives

$$M_B gy = \tfrac{1}{2}M_A v^2 + \tfrac{1}{2}M_B v^2 + \tfrac{1}{2}(\tfrac{1}{2}M_C R^2)(v/R)^2$$

and $$v = \sqrt{\frac{2M_B gy}{M_A + M_B + \tfrac{1}{2}M_C}}$$

This is the result found in Example 4.

Figure 14-16. As block B descends from rest at a distance y above the floor, block A moves to the left and cylinder C rotates.

Example 7 A cylinder of mass M and radius R, initially at rest, rolls without slipping down an inclined plane of angle θ. What is the linear speed of the cylinder's center of mass after it has moved down the plane a distance d? See Figure 14-17.

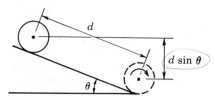

The situation here is that of Example 5 and Figure 14-14, with the motion reversed. It is easiest to find the speed by applying energy conservation.

In traversing a distance d down the plane the center of mass of the cylinder undergoes a vertical displacement $d \sin \theta$. Therefore, the cylinder loses potential energy in the amount $Mgd \sin \theta$. It acquires translational kinetic energy

Figure 14-17. A cylinder rolls, without slipping, a distance d along an inclined plane of angle θ.

$\frac{1}{2}Mv_{cm}^2$ and rotational kinetic energy $\frac{1}{2}I_{cm}\omega_{cm}^2$, where I_{cm} is the moment of inertia of the cylinder about an axis through the center of mass. Energy conservation requires that

$$Mgd \sin \theta = \tfrac{1}{2}Mv_{cm}^2 + \tfrac{1}{2}I_{cm}\omega_{cm}^2$$

But $I_{cm} = \tfrac{1}{2}MR^2$

and $\omega_{cm} = v_{cm}/R$

The last relation is justified as follows. The quantity v_{cm} represents the speed of the cylinder's center relative to the inclined plane, which is equal to the speed of a point on the plane relative to the center of the cylinder. A point on the rim of the cylinder has the speed $\omega_{cm}r$ relative to this axis and, if the cylinder rolls without slipping, this is also the speed of the plane relative to the cylinder's center.

The first equation then becomes

$$Mgd \sin \theta = \tfrac{1}{2}Mv^2 + \tfrac{1}{2}(\tfrac{1}{2}MR^2)(v/R)^2$$

$$v = \sqrt{2(\tfrac{2}{3}g \sin \theta)d}$$

The speed is independent of the mass and radius of the cylinder. The speed does, however, depend on the fact that the body is a solid cylinder, and rolls without slipping. The result here is consistent with that obtained in Example 5.

We have used, in the above, the general principle that the total kinetic energy of a rigid body is the sum of the kinetic energy of the center of mass and the rotational kinetic energy about the center of mass. There is, however, another way of looking at rolling motion.

We recall (Section 6-3 and Figure 6-11) that any body which rolls without slipping may be regarded as rotating instantaneously about an axis through the point of contact with the surface. With respect to such an *instantaneous axis of rotation*, the angular speed is $\omega_i = v_{cm}/R$, where v_{cm} is the speed of the center of the cylinder and R is its radius, as proved in Section 6-3. As the cylinder rolls down the incline, it is at every instant rotating about the point of contact with the plane. Its *total* kinetic energy is, from this point of view, $\tfrac{1}{2}I_i\omega_i^2$, where I_i is now the moment of inertia of the cylinder with respect to an axis along the point of contact with the plane. Because energy is conserved, the loss in potential energy equals the gain in the total kinetic energy, and

$$mgd \sin \theta = \tfrac{1}{2}I_i\omega_i^2$$

We compute I_i from the parallel-axis theorem, Equation 14-7:

$$I_i = I_{cm} + Md^2 = \tfrac{1}{2}MR^2 + MR^2 = \tfrac{3}{2}MR^2$$

The force of friction plays an essential role in the rolling motion of the cylinder. Without friction the body would slide. On the other hand, if the body rolls without slipping, a static friction force acts at all times. However, this force does *no work*; it is not applied over a displacement inasmuch as the point of contact between the rolling cylinder and the incline changes continuously. The friction force applies a torque to the cylinder, thereby transforming what would, otherwise, be translational kinetic energy into rotational kinetic energy.

The energy equation becomes

$$mgd \sin \theta = \tfrac{1}{2}(\tfrac{3}{2}MR^2)(v/R)^2$$

and

$$v = \sqrt{2(\tfrac{2}{3}g \sin \theta)d}$$

in agreement with our earlier result.

Example 8 The force of static friction plays an important part in the rolling motion of a body: without friction the translational motion of the center of mass and the rotational motion about the center of mass are independent of one another. On the other hand, if the body is to roll without sliding, the magnitude and direction of the static friction force f_s must be such as to insure that $a_{cm} = R\alpha_{cm}$. The *static* friction force, unlike the kinetic force of friction, does *no work* on the body. Whatever work is done by f_s in increasing the translational kinetic energy of the center of mass, an *equal* but *negative* amount of rotational work is done by f_s, thereby decreasing the rotational kinetic energy about the center of mass; and conversely. Thus, the static friction force is a nondissipative force which interchanges rotational energy and translational energy. These points are illustrated in the following example.

A solid cylinder of mass M and radius R, initially at rest on a horizontal surface, is accelerated to the right by a constant force of magnitude F. Assuming that the cylinder rolls without slipping, find the magnitude and direction of the static friction force f_s and the acceleration of the cylinder's center of mass when: (a) the external force F is applied at the axle of the cylinder (Figure 14-18a), and (b) the external force F is applied at the top rim of the cylinder (Figure 14-18b).

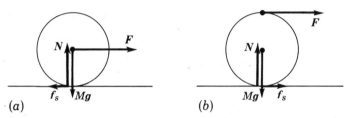

(a)   (b)

Figure 14-18. (a) The forces acting on a cylinder which rolls to the right without slipping under the action of a force F applied at the axle. (b) The forces acting on the cylinder when the force F is applied at the cylinder's top rim.

(a) Choosing the positive translational direction to be to the right and the corresponding rotational sense as clockwise, application of Newton's second law to the translational motion of the center of mass and to the rotational motion about the center of mass yields

$$\Sigma\, F_{\text{ext}} = M a_{\text{cm}} \qquad \Sigma\, \tau_{\text{cm}} = I_{\text{cm}} \alpha_{\text{cm}}$$

$$F - f_s = M a_{\text{cm}} \qquad f_s R = \tfrac{1}{2} M R^2 (a_{\text{cm}}/R)$$

$$f_s = \tfrac{1}{2} M a_{\text{cm}}$$

Solving these equations for f_s and a_{cm} gives

$$f_s = F/3, \quad \text{and} \quad a_{\text{cm}} = \tfrac{2}{3} F/M$$

We notice that our choice of direction for f_s (to the left) was correct; had we chosen its direction to be to the right, we would have found f_s to be $-F/3$.

(b) Using the same conventions for positive linear and rotational motions as in part (a), but now assuming f_s to be acting to the right, as shown in Figure 14-18b, we have

$$\Sigma\, F_{\text{ext}} = M a_{\text{cm}} \qquad \Sigma\, \tau_{\text{cm}} = I_{\text{cm}} \alpha_{\text{cm}}$$

$$F + f_s = M a_{\text{cm}} \qquad (F - f_s) R = \tfrac{1}{2} M R^2 (a_{\text{cm}}/R)$$

$$F - f_s = \tfrac{1}{2} M a_{\text{cm}}$$

Solving for f_s and a_{cm}, we find

$$f_s = F/3 \quad \text{and} \quad a_{\text{cm}} = \tfrac{4}{3} F/M$$

Here the friction force is in the *same* direction as the linear velocity of the center of mass, and f_s does *not* oppose the translational motion in this example.

When the accelerating force F in the two examples above is zero, the cylinder rolls with constant linear and angular speeds and the force of static friction is *zero*.

Problems in rolling motion can be solved equally well by using the work-energy theorem. For example, applying energy considerations to part (b) yields the following.

For translational motion: $\quad W(\text{by } \boldsymbol{F}) + W(\text{by } \boldsymbol{f}_s) = \Delta K_{\text{cm}}$

or: $\quad (Fx_{\text{cm}}) + (f_s x_{\text{cm}}) = \tfrac{1}{2}Mv_{\text{cm}}^2$

For rotational motion: $\quad W(\text{by } \boldsymbol{\tau}_F) + W(\text{by } \boldsymbol{\tau}_f) = \Delta K_{\text{rot}}$

or: $\quad (FR)\theta - (f_s R)\theta = \tfrac{1}{2}I_{\text{cm}}\omega_{\text{cm}}^2$

Because the cylinder rolls without slipping, $x_{\text{cm}} = R\theta$ and $v_{\text{cm}} = R\omega_{\text{cm}}$. Adding the two energy equations then gives

$$(Fx_{\text{cm}}) + (FR)(\theta) = \tfrac{1}{2}Mv_{\text{cm}}^2 + \tfrac{1}{2}I_{\text{cm}}\omega_{\text{cm}}^2$$

The static friction force f_s does *no net work* on the rolling cylinder. In this example f_s converts just the right amount of rotational energy into translational energy to insure that the cylinder rolls without slipping.

Using the relations $x_{\text{cm}} = R\theta$ and $v_{\text{cm}} = R\omega_{\text{cm}}$ in the last equation yields

$$2Fx_{\text{cm}} = \tfrac{1}{2}Mv_{\text{cm}}^2 + \tfrac{1}{2}(\tfrac{1}{2}MR^2)(v_{\text{cm}}/R)^2 = \tfrac{3}{4}Mv_{\text{cm}}^2$$

For motion starting from rest at constant acceleration, $v_{\text{cm}}^2 = 2a_{\text{cm}}x_{\text{cm}}$; therefore,

$$2Fx_{\text{cm}} = \tfrac{3}{4}M(2a_{\text{cm}}x_{\text{cm}})$$

$$a_{\text{cm}} = \tfrac{4}{3}F/M$$

This is the same result as that which we obtained in part (b) by using Newton's second law.

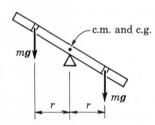

Figure 14-19. The forces acting on two symmetrically located mass elements of a thin rod rotating about a horizontal axis through the center of mass. The resultant gravitational torque for each pair of masses is zero.

14-6 Center of gravity The *center of gravity* of a rigid body is defined as that point about which the resultant of the gravitational torques on all the particles comprising the rigid body is zero. It is easy to show that the center of gravity has the same location as the center of mass, provided (as is typically the case) that the body is in a *uniform* gravitational field—that is, that the acceleration due to gravity $\boldsymbol{g}$ is the same throughout the body.

First consider the simple situation in which a uniform beam is suspended at its center of mass. We compute the torques acting on two segments of the beam, each of mass m, located at equal distances from the center of mass. See Figure 14-19. The force due to the weight on each segment is mg, and if we compute torques with respect to an axis of rotation passing through the center of mass, the moment arms of the two torques are equal. However, the one torque is clockwise, the other counterclockwise: their sum is zero. In similar fashion we find that the gravitational torques occur in equal but opposite pairs for other segments symmetrically located with respect to the center of mass. Thus, the resultant of the gravitational torques, relative to an axis of rotation through the center of mass, is zero. The center of gravity coincides with the center of mass, whether the body is at rest or in motion.

This proof is easily extended to a body of any shape. We recall that the location of the center of mass is given by the vector equation

$$[8\text{-}20] \qquad \bar{r} = \frac{m_1 r_1 + m_2 r_2 + m_3 r_3 + \cdots}{m_1 + m_2 + m_3 + \cdots} \qquad [14\text{-}15]$$

where $\bar{r}$ is the displacement of the center of mass, r_1 is the displacement of particle 1, etc., all with respect to the same origin.

Suppose that our origin is chosen to coincide with the center of mass, so that $\bar{r} = 0$. Then Equation 14-15 becomes

$$0 = m_1 r_1 + m_2 r_2 + m_3 r_3 + \cdots$$

We take the cross product of both sides of this equation with the constant acceleration due to gravity g:

$$0 = (m_1 r_1 \times g) + (m_2 r_2 \times g) + (m_3 r_3 \times g) + \cdots$$

Rearranging this equation leads to

$$0 = (r_1 \times m_1 g) + (r_2 \times m_2 g) + (r_3 \times m_3 g) + \cdots$$

Now, $m_1 g$ is the weight of particle 1 and $r_1 \times m_1 g$ is the torque due to gravity on particle 1 with respect to an axis through the center of mass. Therefore, the right-hand side in the equation above gives the resultant gravitational torque on the body. Since this resultant torque is zero about the chosen origin, this point is, by definition, the center of gravity. We have then shown that the center of mass and center of gravity coincide for a uniform gravitational field.

Our proof has assumed the constancy of g. For any object that is small compared with the radius of the Earth, g has the same magnitude and direction at all points within the object. The center of gravity and center of mass are then coincident, both being fixed relative to the body.

The existence of the center of gravity, fixed relative to the body, leads to an important consequence. We may imagine that all of the mass of an extended rigid body is concentrated at the center of gravity and that a *single* force equal to the weight of the body acts downward at this point. A rigid body under the influence of gravity only may be put into equilibrium by a single upward force equal to the weight and applied so as to pass through the center of gravity. When this is done, the resultant force and the resultant torque are both zero, and the body is in both translational and rotational equilibrium.

If a rigid body is suspended from a cord, the center of gravity must lie along a vertical line passing through the point of support. Furthermore, if the center of gravity is *below* the point of support (Figure 14-20a), the center of gravity will rise for any rotational displacement about this point of support. A body so displaced will be subject to a restoring torque, tending to lower the center of gravity, and such a situation leads to *stable equilibrium*. On the other hand, if a rigid body is supported by an upward external force equal to the weight, passing through the center of gravity, which now lies *above* the point of support (Figure 14-20b), the equilibrium is highly unstable. Any rotational displacement about the point of support will *lower* the center of gravity, and the resultant torque on the body will tend to increase the rotational displacement and thereby lead to *unstable equilibrium*.

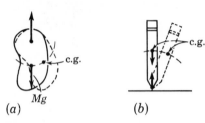

Figure 14-20. (a) An example of stable equilibrium. A body's point of support is *above* its center of gravity (c.g.). (b) An example of unstable equilibrium: the body's point of support is *below* the center of gravity.

Example 9   A 6-inch pencil, initially standing on end, falls over (Figure 14-20b). With what speed does the eraser strike the horizontal surface, assuming that the pencil point does not move?

This problem is best solved by energy-conservation methods. The pencil can be regarded as a uniform rod of mass M and length L. The pencil's center of gravity is at its center (originally a vertical distance $L/2$ above the surface). The weight of the pencil Mg can be regarded as acting as a single force applied at the center of gravity. In falling, the pencil loses potential energy $Mg(L/2)$, its center of gravity having descended $L/2$. Therefore, upon striking the surface, the gain in the rotational kinetic energy of the pencil about the fixed point equals the loss in potential energy:

$$\tfrac{1}{2}I\omega^2 = MgL/2$$

where I is the moment of inertia of the pencil and ω is the angular speed, both with respect to an axis of rotation passing through the fixed point. If v represents the linear speed of the eraser upon striking, then

$$v = \omega L$$

The moment of inertia of a uniform rod about an axis at an end (see Example 2, Section 14-4) is

$$I = \tfrac{1}{3}ML^2$$

Substituting the relations for I and ω in the energy equation above yields

$$\tfrac{1}{2}(\tfrac{1}{3}ML^2)(v/L)^2 = MgL/2$$

$$v = \sqrt{3gL}$$

$$v = \sqrt{3(32\ \text{ft/sec}^2)(0.50\ \text{ft})} = 6.9\ \text{ft/sec}$$

If the eraser had been detached and fallen freely from rest through the same vertical distance, its speed upon striking the surface would have been only $\sqrt{2gL} = 5.7$ feet/sec!

14-7 Equilibrium of a rigid body When the vector sum of the external forces on a body is zero, the linear acceleration of the body's center of mass is zero. Therefore, the body's center of mass maintains a constant linear velocity. When the vector sum of the external torques about the body's center of mass is zero, the angular acceleration is zero and the body maintains a constant angular velocity about its center of mass. When both of these conditions are fulfilled, the body is said to be in equilibrium. If, furthermore, the linear and angular velocities are initially zero, the body remains at rest and is said to be in static equilibrium. Thus, equilibrium is but a special case of dynamics and statics is a special case of equilibrium.

In mathematical terms, equilibrium implies that

$$\boxed{\begin{aligned} &\Sigma\, F_{\text{ext}} = 0; \quad \text{or } \Sigma\, F_x = 0, \quad \Sigma\, F_y = 0, \quad \text{and } \Sigma\, F_z = 0 \\ &\Sigma\, \tau_{\text{ext}} = 0; \quad \text{or } \Sigma\, \tau_x = 0, \quad \Sigma\, \tau_y = 0, \quad \text{and } \Sigma\, \tau_z = 0 \end{aligned}} \qquad [14\text{-}16]$$

where F_x, F_y, and F_z and τ_x, τ_y, and τ_z represent, respectively, the force and torque components along the X-, Y-, and Z-axes.

We shall treat only those situations in which the forces lie entirely in the X-Y plane; the torques then lie entirely along the Z-axis. A body is then in equilibrium only if

$$\Sigma\, F_x = 0, \qquad \Sigma\, F_y = 0, \quad \text{and} \quad \Sigma\, \tau_z = 0 \qquad [14\text{-}17]$$

Problems involving the equilibrium of rigid, or nearly rigid, bodies are of great importance in many branches of engineering. For example, when an engineer designs a bridge, he computes the forces acting on each member and chooses the materials and dimensions of the structural components such that these parts can withstand the forces.

If a rigid body is at rest, and therefore in static equilibrium, the resultant torque about an axis through the center of mass must clearly be zero. It is

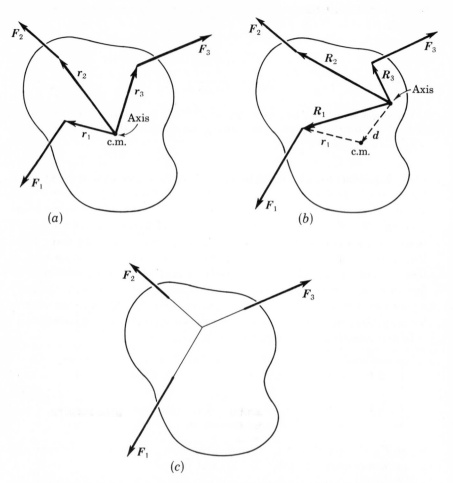

Figure 14-21. (a) A body in equilibrium under the action of the three forces F_1, F_2, and F_3 applied at the radius vectors r_1, r_2, and r_3 respectively; the origins of the latter are at the body's center of mass. (b) The same body and forces as in (a), except that now the radius vectors R_1, R_2, and R_3 give the points of application of the forces relative to a second axis of rotation; the displacement of the center of mass relative to the new rotation axis is d. (c) The lines of action of three coplanar forces, under whose influence a body is in equilibrium, always intersect at a single point.

then not difficult to prove the following theorem: if a rigid body is in static equilibrium, the resultant external torque is zero *about any axis*.

Figure 14-21a shows a body in equilibrium under the action of three coplanar forces, F_1, F_2, and F_3, the points of application of these forces relative to an axis of rotation through the center of mass being the radius vectors r_1, r_2, and r_3.

The sum of external forces is zero:

$$F_1 + F_2 + F_3 = 0 \qquad [14\text{-}18]$$

The sum of the external torques about the center of mass is zero:

$$(r_1 \times F_1) + (r_2 \times F_2) + (r_3 \times F_3) = 0 \qquad [14\text{-}19]$$

Now we compute the torques about a second axis. From Figure 14-21b we see that the radius vector R_1 from the new axis to the point of application of F_1 is given by

$$R_1 = r_1 + d \qquad [14\text{-}20]$$

where the vector displacement d represents the location of the center of mass relative to the new axis. Similar relations give R_2 and R_3.

Substituting Equation 14-20 in Equation 14-19 leads to

$$[(R_1 + d) \times F_1] + [(R_2 + d) \times F_2] + [(R_3 + d) \times F_3] = 0$$

Regrouping these terms yields

$$[(R_1 \times F_1) + (R_2 \times F_2) + (R_3 \times F_3)] + [d \times (F_1 + F_2 + F_3)] = 0$$

The left-hand bracket represents the resultant torque about the new, arbitrarily chosen, axis of rotation. Within the parentheses of the right-hand bracket is the sum of the external forces, which is zero by Equation 14-18. The left-hand bracket must then also be zero. Therefore, when a rigid body is in equilibrium,

$$(R_1 \times F_1) + (R_2 \times F_2) + (R_3 \times F_3) = 0$$

Another rule concerning rigid-body equilibrium is this: When a body subject to *three* forces is in equilibrium, these forces are coplanar and have lines of action that intersect at a *single* point, as shown in Figure 14-21c. Clearly, we can choose an axis of rotation passing through the point of intersection of the lines of action of two forces; the torques of these forces are then zero about this axis. But if the resultant torque is to be zero, the torque of the third force must be zero relative to the chosen axis, and its line of action must also pass through the intersection point.

Example 10 A uniform beam, weighing 100 pounds and making an angle of
30° with respect to the horizontal, is hinged at its lower end; a horizontal wire
is attached to its upper end, as shown in Figure 14-22. What is the tension in the
wire, and the direction and magnitude of the force of the hinge on the beam?

First we remark that, in a problem such as this, one can solve for only three
unknowns. All forces lie in a single plane, and the equilibrium conditions lead
to *three* scalar equations (Equations 14-17).

The three external forces on the beam are shown in Figure 14-22a. They are:
the weight of the beam acting at the center of gravity, a distance $L/2$ from either

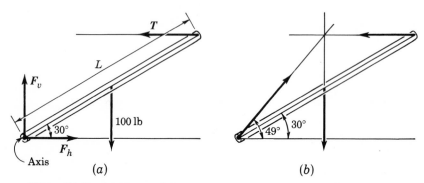

Figure 14-22. (a) External forces acting on a uniform beam. The force
on the hinge of the beam at the left end is replaced by its vertical and
horizontal components, F_v and F_h. (b) The three forces on the beam
intersect at a common point. Note that the force on the beam's left end
is *not* along the direction of the beam.

end; the force of the hinge on the beam, replaced for convenience by its vertical
and horizontal components F_v and F_h; and the tension in the wire, T. Translational equilibrium requires that

$$\Sigma F_x = 0$$

$$F_h - T = 0$$

$$\Sigma F_y = 0$$

$$F_v - 100 \text{ lb} = 0$$

A convenient choice of axis of rotation is one passing through the hinge. This
choice is made, not primarily because the hinge represents a natural point of
rotation, but rather because the forces F_v and F_h have lines of action through this
point, thereby making their torques zero relative to this axis. For this axis,
the 100-pound force produces a clockwise (negative) torque with moment arm
$L/2 \cos 30°$; the force T has a counterclockwise (positive) torque with moment
arm $L \sin 30°$. Rotational equilibrium then requires that

$$\Sigma \tau_z = 0$$

$$-(L/2) \cos 30°(100 \text{ lb}) + L \sin 30°(T) = 0$$

Solving simultaneously for F_h, F_v, and T in the equations given above yields

$$F_h = 87 \text{ lb}$$

$$F_v = 100 \text{ lb}$$

$$T = 87 \text{ lb}$$

Notice that the length L of the beam does *not* enter.

We can readily compute the magnitude F and direction θ with respect to the horizontal of the force of the hinge on the beam:

$$F = \sqrt{F_h{}^2 + F_v{}^2} = \sqrt{87^2 + 100^2} \text{ lb} = 132 \text{ lb}$$

$$\tan \theta = F_v/F_h = (100)/(87) = 1.15$$

$$\theta = 49°$$

The force of the hinge on the beam is *not* along the length of the beam. This is also obvious from Figure 14-22b, where it is seen that the three forces on the beam are collinear, their lines of action intersecting at a single point.

Example 11 A cubical box of uniform density, 3.0 feet along an edge and weighing 200 pounds, is to be tipped over along one lower edge without sliding.

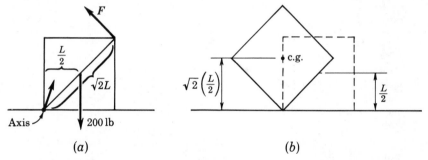

Figure 14-23. (a) A box of edge length L is tipped about an axis along the lower left edge. The direction of the applied force F is chosen (45°) as giving the maximum torque. (b) The box's center of gravity is raised to its highest point, $\sqrt{2}(L/2)$, above the floor.

(a) What is the minimum force required, where should it be applied, and in what direction? (b) How much work is done in tipping the box?

(a) First suppose that we choose an axis of rotation along the edge about which the box pivots. We see that the clockwise torque arising from the weight at the center of gravity has a moment arm of $L/2$ when the box is first raised and a smaller moment arm as the center of gravity rises. See Figure 14-23a. Therefore, if an external torque is applied and it is large enough to counterbalance the initial torque due to gravity, the box will continue to tip. The maximum external torque for a given force magnitude is achieved when the force F is applied as shown in Figure 14-23a: at 45° above the horizontal and with a moment arm of

$\sqrt{2}L$. We solve for the magnitude of F by applying the condition for rotational equilibrium:

$$\Sigma \tau_z = 0$$

$$F(\sqrt{2}L) - (200 \text{ lb})(L/2) = 0$$

$$F = 71 \text{ lb}$$

The size of the box does *not* enter.

(b) It is not convenient to solve for the work done in raising the box to its highest point by computing $\int \tau \, d\theta$, the integral of the applied torque with respect to the angle turned through (Equation 14-11). This is so because the magnitude of the force, and therefore of the torque, varies as the box pivots at constant angular speed. Instead, one easily finds the minimum work done by computing the difference in the gravitational potential energy, noting that the center of gravity of the box is raised from a distance $L/2$ above the floor to the position $\sqrt{2}(L/2)$ above the floor, as shown in Figure 14-23b:

$$W = \Delta U_g = mg \, \Delta y = mg(L/2)(\sqrt{2} - 1) = (200 \text{ lb})(1.5 \text{ ft})(\sqrt{2} - 1)$$

$$W = 124 \text{ ft-lb}$$

Example 12   A box 4.0 feet high and 2.0 feet wide sits on a rough horizontal surface in the back of a truck. The center of gravity of the box is at its center of

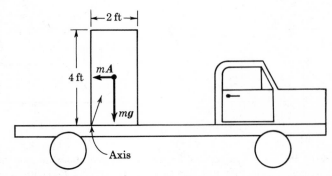

Figure 14-24. The forces acting on a box on an accelerated truck *as seen by an observer at rest on the truck*. Note the inertial force mA acting to the rear.

symmetry. See Figure 14-24. What is the maximum allowed acceleration of the truck if the box is not to tip over?

This problem is most easily analyzed from the point of view of an observer at rest in the truck. Such an observer is in an accelerated, and therefore noninertial, reference frame. As was shown in Section 10-6, we may use Newton's laws, provided that we include an inertial force which acts on the box at its center of mass, whose magnitude is mA and whose direction is opposite to the direction of the truck's acceleration A relative to the ground. If we do this, a problem in dynamics is reduced to an equivalent problem in statics.

Through the arguments given in Example 11, the force required to tip the box is a maximum when the box first begins to pivot about the rear edge. Choosing an axis of rotation along this edge, the box is then subject to two nonzero torques: the clockwise torque of the weight mg with a lever arm of 1.0 foot and the counterclockwise torque of the inertial force mA with a lever arm of 2.0 feet. Rotational equilibrium then requires that

$$\Sigma \tau_z = 0$$

$$(2.0 \text{ ft})mA - (1.0 \text{ ft})mg = 0$$

$$A = \tfrac{1}{2}g = 16 \text{ ft/sec}^2 = 11(\text{mi/hr})/\text{sec}$$

The mass of the box does not enter because both the weight and the inertial force are proportional to m.

14-8   Two proofs in rotational dynamics   In this section is given the general proof of the parallel-axis theorem and a rigorous derivation of the relation giving the kinetic energy of a rotating body.

THE PARALLEL-AXIS THEOREM   We wish to relate the moment of inertia of a rigid body, relative to an axis passing through the center of mass, to the moment of inertia of the same body relative to another parallel axis.

First consider a particle i of mass m_i having a displacement R_i relative to an arbitrarily chosen axis of rotation A. The displacement of this particle relative to the center of mass is r_i; the displacement of the center of mass relative to the axis A is d (see Figure 14-25); therefore,

$$R_i = r_i + d \qquad [14\text{-}21]$$

The three displacement vectors all lie in a plane perpendicular to the axis A.

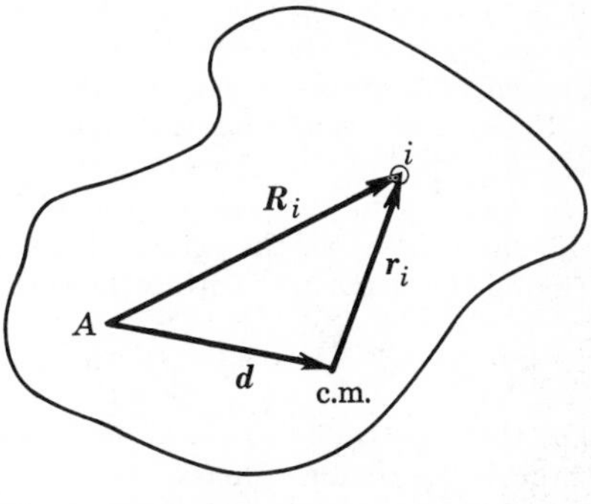

The contribution of the ith particle to the moment of inertia with respect to an axis through A is $m_i R_i^2$, which

Figure 14-25. A particle i of a rigid body has a displacement r_i relative to the body's center of mass, and a displacement R_i relative to point A. The displacement of the center of mass relative to A is d.

we may write equivalently, using the dot product, as

$$m_i R_i^2 = m_i R_i \cdot R_i = m_i(r_i + d) \cdot (r_i + d) = m_i(r_i \cdot r_i + d \cdot d + 2r_i \cdot d)$$

$$m_i R_i^2 = m_i(r_i^2 + d^2 + 2r_i \cdot d)$$

If we now add the contributions to the moment of inertia about A of all of the particles in the rigid body, we have

$$I = \Sigma m_i R_i^2 = \Sigma m_i(r_i^2 + d^2 + 2r_i \cdot d)$$

which we may write as

$$I = \Sigma m_i r_i^2 + (\Sigma m_i)d^2 + 2(\Sigma m_i r_i) \cdot d \qquad [14\text{-}22]$$

The three terms in Equation 14-22 are interpreted as follows. The first term is the moment of inertia I_{cm} of the body relative to an axis parallel to A and passing through the center of mass:

$$\Sigma \, m_i r_i{}^2 = I_{cm}$$

The second term is the body's total mass $M = \Sigma \, m_i$ multiplied by the square of the distance separating the two axes:

$$(\Sigma \, m_i)d^2 = Md^2$$

The third term contains the vector, $\Sigma \, m_i \mathbf{r}_i$, which gives, by definition (Equation 8-20), the location of the center of mass relative to the chosen origin. But the center of mass *is* at the origin of any of the displacements $\mathbf{r}_i$. Therefore, $\Sigma \, m_i \mathbf{r}_i = 0$ and the third term in Equation 14-22 is zero. Equation 14-22 then reduces to

[14-7] $$I = I_{cm} + Md^2$$

which is the parallel-axis theorem.

THE KINETIC ENERGY OF A ROTATING BODY That the total kinetic energy of a rigid body may be regarded as the sum of two terms—the translational kinetic energy of the center of mass and the rotational kinetic energy relative to the center of mass—is to be proved.

Imagine the rigid body of Figure 14-25 to be in motion. The velocity $\mathbf{V}_i = d\mathbf{R}_i/dt$ is that of the ith particle relative to the reference frame of the observer. The velocity of the ith particle relative to the center of mass is $\mathbf{v}_i = d\mathbf{r}_i/dt$ and the velocity of the center of mass relative to the observer is $\mathbf{v}_{cm} = d\mathbf{d}/dt$. Taking the derivative with respect to time, of Equation 14-21, yields

$$\mathbf{V}_i = \mathbf{v}_i + \mathbf{v}_{cm} \qquad [14\text{-}23]$$

The three velocity vectors all lie in a plane perpendicular to an axis of rotation through the center of mass.

The kinetic energy of the ith particle relative to the observer may be written, by using Equation 14-23, as

$$\tfrac{1}{2}m_i V_i{}^2 = \tfrac{1}{2}m_i \mathbf{V}_i \cdot \mathbf{V}_i = \tfrac{1}{2}m_i(\mathbf{v}_i + \mathbf{v}_{cm}) \cdot (\mathbf{v}_i + \mathbf{v}_{cm})$$

$$= \tfrac{1}{2}m_i(\mathbf{v}_i \cdot \mathbf{v}_i + \mathbf{v}_{cm} \cdot \mathbf{v}_{cm} + 2\mathbf{v}_i \cdot \mathbf{v}_{cm})$$

$$\tfrac{1}{2}m_i V_i{}^2 = \tfrac{1}{2}m_i(v_i{}^2 + v_{cm}{}^2 + 2\mathbf{v}_i \cdot \mathbf{v}_{cm})$$

The total kinetic energy K of all the particles of the system is, then,

$$K = \Sigma \, \tfrac{1}{2}m_i V_i{}^2 = \Sigma \, \tfrac{1}{2}m_i(v_i{}^2 + v_{cm}{}^2 + 2\mathbf{v}_i \cdot \mathbf{v}_{cm})$$

which we may write as

$$K = \Sigma \, (\tfrac{1}{2}m_i v_i{}^2) + \tfrac{1}{2}(\Sigma \, m_i)v_{cm}{}^2 + (\Sigma \, m_i \mathbf{v}_i) \cdot \mathbf{v}_{cm} \qquad [14\text{-}24]$$

The three terms in Equation 14-24 have the following meanings. The first term is the kinetic energy of all the particles *relative to the center of mass*. The second term is the kinetic energy of a particle having the mass of the entire system and traveling with the speed of the center of mass. The third term $(\Sigma\, m_i \boldsymbol{v}_i) \cdot \boldsymbol{v}_{\mathrm{cm}} = [d/dt\, (\Sigma\, m_i \boldsymbol{r}_i)] \cdot \boldsymbol{v}_{\mathrm{cm}}$ is zero, inasmuch as $\Sigma\, m_i \boldsymbol{r}_i = 0$, from the definition of the center of mass. Therefore, Equation 14-24 becomes

$$\boxed{K = \Sigma\, \tfrac{1}{2} m_i v_i{}^2 + \tfrac{1}{2} M v_{\mathrm{cm}}{}^2} \qquad [14\text{-}25]$$

This equation is altogether general; it gives the total kinetic energy of *any* collection of particles, whether unattached or bound together to form a rigid body. If the particles of the system form a rigid body, all particles will have the same angular velocity ω_{cm} relative to the center of mass, and

$$v_i = \omega_{\mathrm{cm}} r_i$$

Equation 14-25 can then be written

$$K = \tfrac{1}{2}(\Sigma\, m_i r_i{}^2)\omega_{\mathrm{cm}}{}^2 + \tfrac{1}{2} M v_{\mathrm{cm}}{}^2$$

But the moment of inertia I_{cm} of the body relative to an axis through the center of mass is $\Sigma\, m_i r_i{}^2$ and we have, finally,

[14-14] $$K = \tfrac{1}{2} I_{\mathrm{cm}} \omega_{\mathrm{cm}}{}^2 + \tfrac{1}{2} M v_{\mathrm{cm}}{}^2$$

14-9 Summary The moment of force, or torque $\boldsymbol{\tau}$, which gives a measure of a force's turning effect, is defined as the cross product of the radius vector $\boldsymbol{r}$ from the chosen origin and the applied force $\boldsymbol{F}$:

[14-2] $$\boldsymbol{\tau} = \boldsymbol{r} \times \boldsymbol{F}$$

For a system of particles interacting through central forces, the sum of the internal torques is zero.

Newton's second law for rotation relates the resultant external torque $\Sigma\, \boldsymbol{\tau}_{\mathrm{ext}}$ to a rigid body's angular acceleration through the relation

[14-4] $$\Sigma\, \boldsymbol{\tau}_{\mathrm{ext}} = I\boldsymbol{\alpha}$$

where the moment of inertia I is defined as

[14-5] $$I = \Sigma\, m_i r_i{}^2$$

This relation may be applied even when the rigid body's center of mass is accelerated, provided that the external torques and the moment of inertia are computed relative to an axis passing through the center of mass.

The work dW done by an external torque τ_{ext} in turning a rigid body through an angle $d\theta$ is

[14-11] $$dW = \tau_{\mathrm{ext}}\, d\theta$$

The kinetic energy of a rigid body rotating (about a symmetry axis) with the angular speed ω is

[14-13] $$K = \tfrac{1}{2}I\omega^2$$

The center of gravity of a body is that point about which the resultant gravitational torque is zero.

A rigid body is in translational and rotational equilibrium when (a) the resultant force is zero and (b) the resultant torque about any axis is zero.

The total kinetic energy of any collection of particles may be written

[14-25] $$K = \Sigma \tfrac{1}{2}m_i v_i^2 + \tfrac{1}{2}M v_{cm}^2$$

where m_i is the mass of particle i, v_i is its speed relative to the system's center of mass, M is the total mass of the system, and v_{cm} is the speed of the system's center of mass. Thus, the total kinetic energy consists of the particles' kinetic energy relative to the center of mass plus the kinetic energy of the center of mass relative to the observer.

For a rigid body,

[14-14] $$K = \tfrac{1}{2}I\omega^2 + \tfrac{1}{2}M v_{cm}^2$$

where I and ω are computed relative to the center of mass.

PROBLEMS

14-1 Vector A is 10 in the direction north. Vector B is 30 in the direction southeast. What are the magnitude and direction of (a) $A \times B$ and (b) $B \times A$?

14-2 Vectors A and B represent the sides of a parallelogram. Show that the magnitude of $A \times B$ is the area of the parallelogram and that the direction of $A \times B$ is along the normal to the plane of the parallelogram.

14-3 Vector A is 8 in the upward direction, B has a magnitude 6, and the scalar product $A \cdot B$ is zero. What are the possible directions (!) and the magnitude of $A \times B$?

14-4 Show that the direction, as well as the magnitude, of the tangential velocity of a particle having a radius vector r relative to the axis of rotation and rotating with angular velocity ω, is $v_t = \omega \times r$. (b) Show that the particle's radial acceleration has the direction and magnitude given by the vector equation $a_r = \omega \times (\omega \times r)$.

14-5 Three particles are located along the X-axis as follows: 3.0 kg at $x = -5.0$ m, 10.0 kg at $x = 5.0$ m, and 4.0 kg at $x = 2.0$ m. For this system, what is (a) the coordinate of the center of mass, (b) the moment of inertia with respect to the Y-axis, (c) the radius of gyration (defined in Example 1) with respect to the Y-axis, (d) the moment of inertia with respect to an axis perpendicular to the X-axis and passing through

$x = 2.0$ m, (e) the radius of gyration with respect to the same axis as in part (d), and (f) the moment of inertia with respect to the X-axis?

14-6 (a) Show that the moment of inertia about the center of symmetry of a uniform right circular cylindrical shell of inner and outer radii R_1 and R_2, respectively, and mass M is $(M/2)(R_1{}^2 + R_2{}^2)$. (b) Show that the moment of inertia about a diameter of a thin spherical shell of radius R and mass M is $\frac{2}{3}MR^2$. (*Hint:* Use the relations giving the moments of inertia of a solid cylinder and a solid sphere.)

14-7 Eight particles each of mass m are placed at the corners of a cube having an edge of length L. What is the moment of inertia of the system with respect to an axis of rotation (a) along one edge, (b) through the center of the cube and parallel to a cube edge, and (c) from one corner to the farthest opposite corner?

14-8 ★ What is the moment of inertia of a square nut of mass M and edge length L having a central hole of diameter $L/3$ with respect to an axis of rotation through the center of the hole?

14-9 What is the moment of inertia of a thin circular plate of mass M and radius R (a) about an axis along a diameter and (b) about an axis parallel to that of part (a) and tangent to an edge?

14-10 A dumbbell is comprised of two spheres each of radius R connected to a thin rod, the distance between the spheres' centers being L. What must be the ratio of L to R if the moment of inertia of the dumbbell with respect to an axis of rotation along the axis of the rod is to be one one-thousandth of its moment of inertia with respect to an axis perpendicular to the rod and passing through its center?

14-11 Find an approximate relation for the moment of inertia of a thin uniform rod of mass M and length L with respect to an axis through its center, by imagining the rod to be divided into four segments of equal length and, further, by imagining each segment to be replaced by a particle of equal mass at its center of mass. Compare this result with the exact relation $I = (1/12)ML^2$.

14-12 ★ A thin rod of uniform cross section, total mass M, and length L is composed of a material of nonuniform density, the density being given, as a function of the distance x along the rod from the left end, by $\rho = \rho_0 + Cx$. What is the moment of inertia of the rod in terms of ρ_0, C, M, and L for an axis of rotation passing through the left end of the rod and at right angles to the rod's length?

14-13 A 160-pound solid cylinder of 1.5-foot radius is mounted with its fixed axis horizontal. (a) What is the cylinder's moment of inertia? (b) A rope wrapped tightly around the cylinder is unwound when a constant force of 10 pounds is applied to the rope; what is the torque of the rope on the cylinder? (c) What is the angular acceleration of the cylinder after 3.0 sec? (d) What is its angular speed at this time? (e) How much work is done when 4.0 feet of rope are unwound from the cylinder? (f) What is the final kinetic energy of the cylinder?

14-14 A 200-pound right circular cylinder of 8.0 inches in radius has a fixed horizontal axis of rotation through its axis of symmetry. A cord is wrapped around the cylinder, and the cylinder is initially at rest. (a) What constant force must be applied to the cord to unwrap 2.0 feet of cord in 1.0 sec? (b) What is the cylinder's angular acceleration? (c) What weight must be hung from the rope to give the cylinder the same angular acceleration?

14-15   Two noncollinear forces having equal magnitudes but opposite directions comprise a *couple*. Show that (a) the resultant force of a couple is zero and that (b) the magnitude of the resultant torque of a couple for *any* axis of rotation perpendicular to the plane of the two forces is Fd, where F is the magnitude of either force and d is the distance separating the lines of action of the two forces.

14-16   Show that any number of forces acting on a rigid body are equivalent to: a single force equal to their resultant, acting at the center of mass of the body, and a single couple causing rotation about the center of mass equal to the resultant torque of the forces about the center of mass. (See Problem 14-15 for the definition of *couple*.)

14-17   When a constant radial force of 15 pounds is applied to the rim of a 96-pound grindstone with a radius of 2.0 feet, the grindstone comes to rest from an initial angular speed of 0.80 revolutions/sec in 5.0 sec. What is the coefficient of kinetic friction between the tool and the grindstone?

14-18   A 160-pound box, 4.0 feet high, 3.0 feet wide, and 2.0 feet deep, initially stands on a horizontal surface. The center of gravity of the box is at its geometric center. The box is tipped along a 2.0-foot edge so that its base makes an angle of 30° with respect to the surface. (a) What is the angular acceleration of the box at the instant it is released from this position? (b) Will the box tip over or tip back to its upright position?

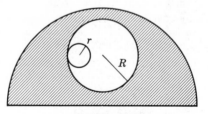

Figure 14-26

14-19   A uniform right circular cylinder of mass M and radius r rolls, without slipping, inside a fixed cylindrical shell of radius R. If the small cylinder is released from rest at the side of the shell, as shown in Figure 14-26, what is its speed at the bottom?

14-20   Show that (a) the linear acceleration of the center of mass of *all* right circular cylindrical shells rolling without slipping down an incline of angle θ is $\frac{1}{2}g \sin \theta$ and (b) that the acceleration of *all* rolling solid spheres of uniform density is $(5/7)g \sin \theta$.

14-21   A solid cylinder, a solid sphere, and a circular loop—all with the same mass and radius—roll together without slipping, their centers of mass all having the same linear speed. Which body has the largest rotational kinetic energy?

14-22 ★ A block remains at rest on an inclined plane and does not slide down as long as the angle of the incline is less than 30°. At what angle of this incline will a solid sphere begin to slide, rather than roll without slipping, assuming that the coefficient of static friction is the same for the block and the sphere?

14-23 A meter stick with a mass of 150 gm has one end on a rough floor and makes an angle of 60° with the horizontal. (a) What is the gravitational torque on the meter stick about a horizontal axis perpendicular to it and passing through the pivot? (b) What is the angular acceleration of the meter stick about this axis at the instant it is released from this position?

14-24 An electric motor rated at 20 horsepower (input) produces a torque of 13 pound-feet when rotating at 3600 revolutions/minute. What is the efficiency of the motor?

14-25 Two cords are wrapped around the ends of a solid *circular* cylinder of mass M whose axis is horizontal. The cylinder is released, the upper ends of the cords held fixed and the cords unrolling as the cylinder descends. (a) What is the linear acceleration of the cylinder's center of mass? (b) What is the tension in each cord?

14-26 A thin uniform rod of mass M and length L is pivoted at one end; a small body of mass m is attached to the other end. If the rod is released from rest when it is horizontal, what are (a) the angular speed and (b) the angular acceleration of the rod as it swings through the vertical?

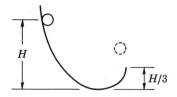

Figure 14-27

14-27 ★ A ball is released from rest from a height H and rolls along the curved track without sliding, as shown in Figure 14-27. The ball leaves the track vertically at a height $H/3$. To what maximum height does the ball rise?

14-28 ★ (a) Show that the force of static friction acting on a body (radius R) which rolls without slipping on a surface is given by $(k/R)^2 m a_{\text{cm}}$, where k is the radius of gyration (Example 1) of the body about the center of mass and a_{cm} is the linear acceleration of the center of mass. (b) What is the force of friction when the body rolls without slipping at constant speed? (c) If the coefficient of static friction is μ_s, what is the maximum value of a_{cm} which allows the body to roll without slipping on a horizontal surface?

14-29   A uniform solid sphere rolls from rest down an inclined plane. What is the maximum angle of the incline that will permit the sphere to roll without slipping, if the coefficient of static friction between the sphere and the surface is 0.25?

14-30   A 6.0-inch pencil stands initially vertically, with its point on a perfectly smooth horizontal surface. When the pencil is released, it tips over and its point slides along the surface. What is the separation distance between the point at which the pencil first rested and the point on the surface where the eraser strikes?

14-31 ★   A uniform block of finite size slides down a rough inclined plane at constant speed. Show that the normal force of the plane on the block does *not* pass through the center of gravity of the block.

14-32   What are some practical ways of determining by experiment (a) the center of gravity and (b) the moment of inertia through a chosen axis of a body of complicated shape?

14-33   The acceleration due to gravity decreases with the distance from the Earth's center. For this reason the center of gravity of an object that is comparable in size to the Earth is not coincident with the object's center of mass. Suppose that a very long, uniform, beam is oriented such that its axis is not tangent to the Earth's surface. Which is farther from the Earth's center: the beam's center of gravity or its center of mass?

14-34   Given below are the magnitudes, directions, and points of application of three forces acting on a rigid body.
        4.0 nt north, at $x = 1.5$ m and $y = 2.0$ m.
        5.0 nt southwest, at $x = 4.0$ m and $y = 0.0$ m.
        6.0 nt 30° south of east, at $x = 5.0$ m and $y = -4.0$ m.
What are the direction, magnitude, and point of application along the X-axis of a fourth force that will place the body in translational and rotational equilibrium?

14-35   When an automobile with a wheelbase of 112 inches is weighed with only its rear wheels on a scale, the scale registers 1200 pounds. With only the front wheels on the scale, it registers 1300 pounds. (a) What is the weight of the automobile? (b) Where is the center of gravity of the automobile relative to the front axle?

14-36   A uniform door, 3.0 feet wide, 7.0 feet high, and weighing 30 pounds, has an upper hinge attached at a point 1.0 feet from the top of the door. Where must the second hinge be located if the magnitude of the horizontal component of the force on each hinge is to be the same?

14-37   A uniform beam 16.0 feet long and weighing 300 pounds is placed such that it protrudes 4.0 feet over the edge of a flat roof. How far out from the edge of the roof can a 150-pound man walk on the beam without tipping the beam?

14-38   A uniform ladder 10.0 feet long and weighing 30 pounds is placed against a perfectly smooth wall, its lower end being 6.0 feet from the wall. What is the least coefficient of static friction between the lower end of the ladder and the floor that will permit a 160-pound man to stand on the uppermost rung of the ladder located 1.50 feet from the upper end of the ladder?

14-39   A uniform rod is placed such that its lower end rests on a rough floor and its upper end rests against a perfectly smooth wall. The angle between the rod and the floor is θ. Show that the minimum coefficient of static friction between the rod and the floor is $1/(2 \tan \theta)$.

14-40   When a smooth straight object, such as a meter stick, is held horizontally by two outstretched fingers and the fingers are then brought together, it is found that the object remains in equilibrium. Explain this effect, and show that it can be used to locate the object's center of gravity.

14-41 ⋆ A nutcracker stands, without sliding, on its two legs, as shown in Figure 14-28. The angle between each leg and the horizontal is 60°,

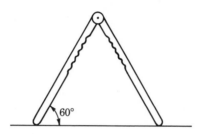

Figure 14-28

and the center of gravity of each leg is at its geometrical center. (a) What is the direction of the resultant force of the surface on each leg? (b) what is the minimum coefficient of static friction between the surface and the nutcracker?

14-42 ⋆ Ideally, a beam balance has arms of equal length, reaching left and right of the center of gravity, and a pivot that lies on a vertical line with the center of gravity of the beam. In actuality, the beam arms may not be of precisely the same length when balance is achieved with no weights on the pans. Nevertheless, one may determine an unknown mass with complete precision, using such an unequal-arm balance, by the method of double weighing. In this procedure one takes two weighings, the standard and unknown masses being interchanged. Show that the unknown mass is given by $\sqrt{M_1 M_2}$, where M_1 and M_2 are the standard masses producing balance for the two weighings. (When M_1 and M_2 are not drastically different—that is, when the arm lengths are very nearly the same—the geometric mean, $\sqrt{M_1 M_2}$, is also approximately equal to the arithmetic mean, $(M_1 + M_2)/2$.)

14-43 ⋆ A lawn roller of uniform density with a 1.0-foot radius and a weight of 200 pounds, is to be raised over an 8.0-inch curb. The handle of the roller is attached to an axle passing through the axis of symmetry of the roller. (a) What are the magnitude and direction of the minimum force required to pull the roller over the curb? (b) How much work is done in raising the roller?

14-44 ★ An automobile, whose wheel span is 60 inches and whose center of mass is 20 inches above the road, moves around a banked curve of 50 feet in radius, the road surface making an angle of 20° with respect to the horizontal. What is the maximum speed with which the automobile can travel around the curve without tipping over? (Assume that the automobile does not slide sideways along the banked surface.)

FIFTEEN

ANGULAR MOMENTUM

This chapter is concerned with angular momentum—its definition, its vector character, and its conservation. The angular momenta of particles and of rotating rigid bodies are defined. The general rotational form of Newton's second law is derived, and the rotational forms of the first and third laws are given. The conservation of the angular momentum of a particle moving under the influence of a central force is discussed. Several examples illustrate the principle of the conservation of angular momentum. Finally, we treat the motion of a spinning top.

15-1 Angular momentum In rotational dynamics the torque, or moment of force, $\tau = r \times F$, plays a role corresponding to that of the force F in translational dynamics. What corresponds in rotational dynamics to the linear momentum, $p = mv$, of a particle? By analogy we would expect the *angular momentum*, or *moment of momentum*, L of a particle to be given by

$$\boxed{\text{angular momentum:} \quad L = r \times p} \qquad [15\text{-}1]$$

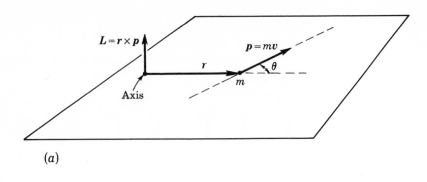

(a)

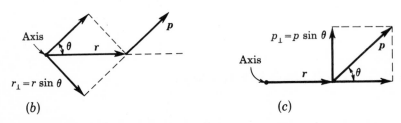

(b)   (c)

Figure 15-1. (a) The angular momentum $L = r \times p = r \times mv$ of a particle of mass m, velocity v, and displacement r, relative to an axis through the origin of r. (b) The component of r perpendicular to p is $r_\perp = r \sin \theta$. (c) The component of p perpendicular to r is $p_\perp = p \sin \theta$.

The cross product of the radius vector r (from a chosen axis) and the particle's linear momentum p gives the angular momentum vector L. We shall see that this definition is justified in rotational dynamics.

Angular momentum is a vector, its direction being given by the right-hand rule for cross products, as illustrated in Figure 15-1. The vector L points in a direction perpendicular to the plane containing the radius vector and the linear momentum (or velocity) vector. The magnitude of the angular momentum of a particle is

$$L = rp \sin \theta = r_\perp p = rp_\perp \qquad [15\text{-}2]$$

where θ is the angle between the directions in which the r and p vectors point, $r_\perp$ (the moment arm) is the component of r perpendicular to p and, similarly, $p_\perp$ is the component of p perpendicular to r. Just as it is necessary to specify the axis of rotation in computing a torque or a moment of inertia, so too, in computing the angular momentum, it is necessary to specify the axis, as well as the direction and magnitude of the linear momentum. See Figure 15-2.

A particle moving in a straight line with a constant speed has a constant linear momentum; its angular momentum is also constant in direction and magnitude with respect to any axis. Angular momentum has the dimensions of linear momentum multiplied by length (ML^2/T). Appropriate units are: kilogram-meters² per second (kg-m²/sec), gram-centimeters² per second (gm-cm²/sec), and slug-feet² per second (slug-feet²/sec).

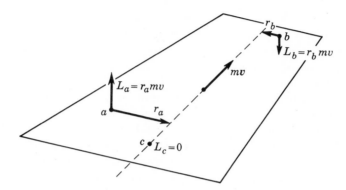

Figure 15-2. The angular momentum of a particle of linear momentum mv is described with respect to three different choices of axis, a, b, and c (in each case it is the same particle). Both the magnitude and direction of the angular momentum depend on the choice of axis.

The total angular momentum of a collection of particles is the vector sum of the individual angular momenta of the individual particles. The case of a rotating rigid body is relatively simple, inasmuch as all particles in the body have the same angular velocity. Let us find the expression giving the angular momentum for such a body.

The mass of the ith particle is m_i, the radius of its path is r_i, and its speed is v_i. The particle's velocity vector is perpendicular to its radius vector. Therefore, the magnitude of the angular momentum of this particle relative to the axis of rotation is

$$L_i = m_i v_i r_i$$

The direction of the angular momentum is the same as that of its angular velocity vector $\boldsymbol{\omega}$. See Figure 15-3. The particle's speed v_i is related to the angular speed ω by $v_i = r_i \omega$, and we may write

$$L_i = m_i r_i^2 \boldsymbol{\omega}$$

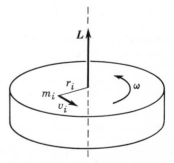

Figure 15-3. The angular momentum $L_i = m_i v_i r_i$ of particle i of a rigid body rotating at angular velocity $\boldsymbol{\omega}$.

We find the total angular momentum of the rigid body by summing the contributions to L from all particles in the body, recognizing that all particles have the same angular velocity $\boldsymbol{\omega}$:

$$L = \Sigma\, m_i r_i^2 \boldsymbol{\omega}$$

$$\boxed{L = I\boldsymbol{\omega}} \qquad\qquad [15\text{-}3]$$

where the angular momentum L, the moment of inertia I, and the angular velocity $\boldsymbol{\omega}$ are all taken with respect to the *same axis*. We shall deal only with bodies that are symmetrical with respect to the axis of rotation. (For nonsymmetrical bodies, the moment of inertia is *not* a scalar, but a tensor, and the direction of the angular momentum is not necessarily along the direction of $\boldsymbol{\omega}$, for reasons that are too recondite to be treated here.)

Any spinning or rotating body has an angular momentum along the direction of the spin axis. If the axis of rotation passes through the center of mass, then the angular momentum with respect to such an axis is known as the *spin angular momentum*. The angular momentum of a body's center of mass relative to some external axis of rotation is known as the *orbital angular momentum*. Thus, the Earth has (a) spin angular momentum by virtue of its daily rotation about a north-south axis and (b) orbital angular momentum by virtue of its annual revolution about the Sun.

It is interesting to note that the spin angular momentum of a body is independent of the choice of axis, whereas the orbital angular momentum of the center of mass depends upon this choice.

Most of the fundamental particles (electrons, protons, neutrons, etc.) of which the universe is composed possess not only orbital angular momentum but also intrinsic spin angular momentum. The angular momenta of elementary particles play a crucial role in the structure of atoms and nuclei.

Example 1   A ball of mass m is traveling east with a speed v at a height h above the ground. What is the ball's angular momentum with respect to a north-south line at ground level?

The geometry of this situation is shown in Figure 15-4. From Equation 15-2, the magnitude of L is

$$L = r_{\perp} p = hmv$$

From the right-hand rule, the direction of L is north.

Example 2   What is the total angular momentum of the Earth with respect to an axis passing through the Sun? The Earth's mass is 6.0×10^{24} kg, its mean radius is 6.4×10^6 m, and its mean distance from the Sun is 1.5×10^{11} m. The direction of the Earth's spin axis is toward the star Polaris (the North Star). This direction makes an angle of $23.5°$ with respect to a normal to the plane of the ecliptic (the plane of the Earth's orbit). See Figure 15-5.

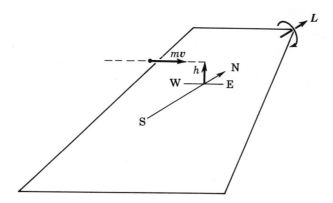

Figure 15-4. The angular momentum of a ball traveling east at an elevation h above the ground.

There are two contributions to the Earth's angular momentum: the spin angular momentum of rotation about an axis through its center of mass, and its orbital angular momentum about the Sun.

The magnitude of the spin angular momentum is given by the moment of inertia of the Earth, taken as a (near) sphere of uniform density (see Figure 14-9), multiplied by the angular speed of rotation:

$$L_{\text{spin}} = I_{\text{spin}}\omega_{\text{spin}} = (\tfrac{2}{5}mr^2)\omega_{\text{spin}}$$

$$L_{\text{spin}} = \tfrac{2}{5}(6 \times 10^{24} \text{ kg})(6.4 \times 10^6 \text{ m})^2(2\pi \text{ rad/day})$$

$$L_{\text{spin}} = 6.9 \times 10^{33} \text{ kg-m}^2/\text{sec}$$

To compute the Earth's orbital angular momentum about the Sun, the Earth is regarded as a particle moving in a circle at a distance R from the Sun:

$$L_{\text{orb}} = I_{\text{orb}}\omega_{\text{orb}} = (mR^2)\omega_{\text{orb}}$$

$$L_{\text{orb}} = (6 \times 10^{24} \text{ kg})(1.5 \times 10^{11} \text{ m})^2(2\pi \text{ rad/yr})$$

$$L_{\text{orb}} = 2.7 \times 10^{40} \text{ kg-m}^2/\text{sec}$$

Compared with the orbital angular momentum, the Earth's spin angular momentum is negligible (the L's in Figure 15-5 are *not* to scale). Therefore, the

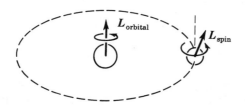

Figure 15-5. The orbital and spin angular momenta of the Earth.

total angular momentum of the Earth about the Sun is approximately 2.7×10^{40} kg-m²/sec perpendicular to the plane of the ecliptic.

The total angular momentum of the solar system about the Sun's center is comprised of the spin and orbital angular momenta of the several planets, together with the spin angular momentum of the Sun. Nearly all (98 per cent) of the angular momentum arises from the orbital angular momenta of the planets, the remainder being spin angular momenta of the Sun and planets. In atomic structure, however, the spin angular momenta of the electrons and of the nucleus are comparable to their orbital angular momentum.

15-2   Newton's laws for rotational motion   In its most general form, Newton's second law for the center of mass of a body is written

[9-8]
$$F_{\text{ext}} = \frac{dp}{dt}$$

The rate of change of the body's linear momentum p is equal to the vector sum F_{ext} of the external forces acting on the body.

It is not surprising that, by analogy, Newton's second law for rotation is written, in general, as

$$\boxed{\tau_{\text{ext}} = dL/dt}$$ [15-4]

The rate of change of the moment of momentum (angular momentum, $\Sigma\, r_i \times p_i$) is equal to the vector sum of the moments of the external forces (torques, $\Sigma\, r_i \times F_i$). It is easy to prove Equation 15-4.

Consider one of the particles comprising the system. We begin by taking the cross product of r with each side of the equation for Newton's second law:

$$r \times F = r \times \frac{dp}{dt}$$

where F represents the resultant force (external and internal) on this particle and p is the particle's linear momentum.

It remains to show that $r \times dp/dt = (d/dt)(r \times p)$. Consider the time derivative of the angular momentum,

$$\frac{d}{dt}(r \times p) = \left(\frac{dr}{dt} \times p\right) + \left(r \times \frac{dp}{dt}\right)$$ [15-5]

where we have used the rule for taking the derivative of a cross product. This rule is similar to that for the derivative of the product of ordinary scalar quantities: $d(uv) = (du)v + u(dv)$. In Equation 15-5 the derivative

$(d/dt)r$, the time rate of change of the displacement vector, is the velocity v of the particle. Therefore,

$$\left(\frac{dr}{dt}\right) \times p = v \times p = v \times mv = 0$$

inasmuch as the vector product of any two parallel vectors is zero.

It then follows that, for a single particle,

$$\tau = r \times F = \frac{d}{dt}(r \times p)$$

One can, of course, write down a similar equation for each particle in the body. Then, when we sum all such equations and recall that the sum of the internal torques is zero, we obtain Equation 15-4.

An alternative, and usually more convenient, form of Equation 15-4 is obtained when the angular momentum L is replaced by $I\omega$. Then,

$$\boxed{\tau_{\text{ext}} = \left(\frac{d}{dt}\right)(I\omega)} \qquad\qquad [15\text{-}6]$$

Differentiating the product $I\omega$ in Equation 15-6 yields

$$\tau_{\text{ext}} = \frac{dI}{dt}\,\omega + I\,\frac{d\omega}{dt}$$

Thus, an external torque can change the body's moment of inertia, or its angular velocity (direction or magnitude). This is the rotational analogue of the general form of Newton's second law for translation,

$$[9\text{-}3] \qquad\qquad F_{\text{ext}} = \frac{dm}{dt}\,v + m\,\frac{dv}{dt}$$

Whereas situations (nonrelativistic ones) in which a mass will change are uncommon, the moment of inertia of a system may change, and dI/dt is then not zero. If a rotating body is truly rigid, its moment of inertia is constant and Equation 15-6 reduces to

$$[14\text{-}4] \qquad\qquad \tau_{\text{ext}} = I\,\frac{d\omega}{dt} = I\alpha$$

as derived in Chapter 14.

We can illustrate Equation 15-4 by considering two simple examples of rotational dynamics in which I is constant: (a) the resultant torque on the rotating body is *along* the direction of the spin axis and (b) the resultant torque on the rotating body is always at *right angles* to the spin axis. These

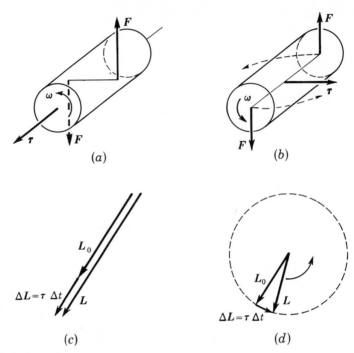

Figure 15-6. A pair of noncollinear forces of equal magnitude but opposite direction are applied to a spinning body. (a) The torque is along the spin axis, and the magnitude, but not the direction, of the body's angular momentum changes. (b) The torque is at right angles to the spin axis, and the direction, but not the magnitude, of the angular momentum changes. (c) Angular momentum vectors corresponding to (a). (d) Angular momentum vectors corresponding to (b); here the angular momentum vector undergoes *precession*.

two situations are shown in Figure 15-6, in which a pair of noncollinear forces, equal in magnitude but oppositely directed, are applied to a spinning body. Whenever an external torque acts, the change ΔL in the angular momentum over the time interval Δt is equal (in magnitude and direction) to $\boldsymbol{\tau}\,\Delta t$, called the *angular impulse*:

[15-4]
$$\Delta L = \int \boldsymbol{\tau}\,dt$$

If the torque is along the direction of L, as in Figure 15-6a, the magnitude of L changes, but not its direction. That is, the body changes its angular speed but not the direction of its spin axis. On the other hand, if the torque is constant in magnitude and always at right angles to the direction of L, as in Figure 15-6b, the direction of L changes, but not its magnitude. The spinning body then undergoes precession, changing the direction of its spin axis at a constant rate, but the angular speed about the spin axis does *not* change. (Motion of precession will be illustrated in somewhat more detail in Section 15-5.)

One can formulate Newton's first and third laws of motion for rotating bodies as follows:

(1) A body subject to no net external torque has a constant angular momentum. This means that the direction and magnitude of the angular momentum of an isolated body remain constant.

(3) When two bodies A and B interact with one another, the torque of A on B is equal in magnitude, and opposite in direction, to the torque of B on A. Stated differently, internal torques occur in pairs of equal but opposite torques, the sum of the internal torques of any system of bodies always being zero. The principle of the conservation of angular momentum (Section 15-4) follows from this law.

Table 15-1 is an extension of Table 14-1, in that it lists corresponding quantities related to momentum in translational and rotational dynamics.

Table 15-1

TRANSLATION		ROTATION	
Linear momentum	$\boldsymbol{p} = m\boldsymbol{v}$	Angular momentum	$\boldsymbol{L} = \boldsymbol{r} \times \boldsymbol{p}$ $\boldsymbol{L} = I\boldsymbol{\omega}$
Newton's second law	$\Sigma\, \boldsymbol{F}_{\text{ext}} = \dfrac{d\boldsymbol{p}}{dt}$		$\Sigma\, \boldsymbol{\tau}_{\text{ext}} = \dfrac{d\boldsymbol{L}}{dt}$
	$\Sigma\, \boldsymbol{F}_{\text{ext}} = m\boldsymbol{a}$ for constant m		$\Sigma\, \boldsymbol{\tau}_{\text{ext}} = I\boldsymbol{\alpha}$ for constant I

Example 3   Discuss the rotational and translational motion of (a) a baseball bat tossed into the air and (b) a cylindrical disc resting on a smooth horizontal surface and subject to forces at opposite sides that are equal in magnitude but oppositely directed.

(a) The resultant force on the bat is its constant weight $m\boldsymbol{g}$: the center of mass traces out a parabolic path. The resultant torque on the bat about an axis of rotation through the center of gravity is zero: the bat has a constant angular momentum about an axis through the center of gravity. See Figure 15-7a.

(b) For the situation shown in Figure 15-7b, the resultant force on the body is zero but the resultant torque on the body is *not* zero. Therefore, the center of

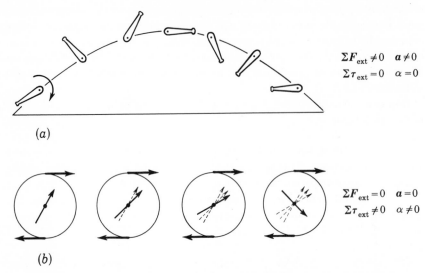

$$\Sigma F_{\text{ext}} \neq 0 \quad a \neq 0$$
$$\Sigma \tau_{\text{ext}} = 0 \quad \alpha = 0$$

(a)

$$\Sigma F_{\text{ext}} = 0 \quad a = 0$$
$$\Sigma \tau_{\text{ext}} \neq 0 \quad \alpha \neq 0$$

(b)

Figure 15-7. (a) A thrown baseball bat, an example of a body subject to a resultant force, but not to a resultant torque about the center of gravity. The angular momentum about an axis through the center of gravity is constant, while the center of gravity traces out a parabola. (b) A body subject to a resultant torque about the center of mass, but not to a resultant force. The angular momentum changes, while the center of mass moves with constant velocity.

mass moves in a straight line at constant speed, while the body has a constant angular acceleration about the center of mass.

15-3   The angular momentum of a particle subject to a central force

The angular momentum of a particle changes only if it is acted on by a resultant torque. From Equation 15-4,

$$\text{If} \quad \tau_{\text{ext}} = 0, \quad \text{then} \quad \frac{dL}{dt} = 0 \quad \text{and}$$

$$L = r \times p = \text{constant (magnitude and direction)}$$

[15-7]

In the absence of a torque the particle maintains a constant angular momentum, even though its speed and direction of motion may change.

An important situation in which a particle is acted on by an external force, but not by an external torque, is that of a particle moving under the influence of a *central force*. The situation is exemplified by a small object coasting on a smooth horizontal surface and attached to one end of a stretched rubber band that is held fixed at the other end. The force exerted by the rubber band on the object, although its dependence on the length of the band may be complicated, is a central force because it is always directed toward the same point. See Figure 15-8a.

Consider the torque on a particle relative to an axis passing through the fixed center of force. If the force F is a central one, its direction is parallel or antiparallel to the radius vector r from the center of force. Therefore,

$$\tau = r \times F = 0$$

and

$$L = r \times p = \text{constant}$$

Because the angular momentum of the particle is constant in direction, the path of the particle must lie in a *plane* perpendicular to the vector $r \times p$. Because the particle's angular momentum is constant in magnitude, the product of its linear momentum mv and the moment arm $r_\perp$ is constant:

$$r_\perp p = r_\perp mv = \text{constant}$$

Figure 15-8b shows the speeds and moment arms for two points a and b. The constancy of the particle's angular momentum then requires that

$$r_{a\perp} v_a = r_{b\perp} v_b \qquad \text{[15-8]}$$

This result is of great utility. If one knows the velocity and moment arm of a particle at one instant of time, one can predict the particle's velocity at any other time given the corresponding moment arm.

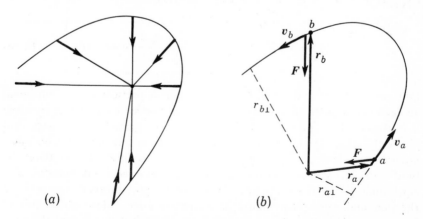

(a) (b)

Figure 15-8. (a) A body subject to a *central* force. Although varying in magnitude, the force always points to the force center. (b) The radius vectors r_a and r_b, moment arms $r_{a\perp}$ and $r_{a\perp}$, and velocities v_a and v_b for two different points (a and b).

Now consider the area swept out by the radius vector r extending from the force center to an orbiting particle moving under the influence of this central force. In a short time interval dt, the particle moves through the displacement $v\,dt$, where v is its instantaneous velocity. The area dA swept by the radius vector in this time interval dt, shown shaded in Figure 15-9, is half the area of the parallelogram with sides r and $v\,dt$. But, the area of the parallelogram has the magnitude

$$|r \times v\,dt|,$$

and thus

$$dA = \tfrac{1}{2}\,|r \times v|\,dt$$

By definition,

$$L = r \times p = r \times mv = m(r \times v)$$

Therefore,

$$dA = \frac{1}{2}\left(\frac{L}{m}\right)dt$$

or

$$\frac{dA}{dt} = \frac{L}{2m} \qquad [15\text{-}9]$$

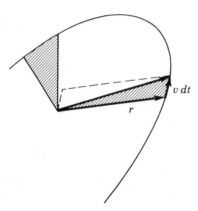

Figure15-9. The area dA (shaded) swept out by the radius vector r in time dt is equal to $dA = \tfrac{1}{2}\,|r \times v|\,dt$.

The rate dA/dt at which the radius vector sweeps out any area is equal to the particle's angular momentum divided by twice its mass. But if the force on the particle is a central one, L is constant; therefore,

$$\boxed{\text{For a } \textit{central} \text{ force:} \qquad \frac{dA}{dt} = \frac{L}{2m} = \text{constant}} \qquad [15\text{-}10]$$

Conversely, if one finds from observation that a particle sweeps out equal areas in equal times, then one knows that the particle's angular momentum is constant. This implies that the torque on the particle is zero and, consequently, that the force on the particle is a central one. Astronomical observations show that as each planet moves in an elliptical orbit about the Sun, the radius vector from the Sun to the planet sweeps out equal areas in equal times (Kepler's second law). Therefore, the gravitational force between the Sun and each planet must be a central force. More about this in Chapter 16. The electric force is also a central force in that it acts along the line joining the two interacting particles.

Example 4 A small body attached to a 5.0-foot cord slides on a frictionless horizontal surface. The other end of the cord is fixed to a pole. Initially the cord is loose and the block travels east at 10 feet/sec, as shown in Figure 15-10. Later the body is found to be traveling north with the cord taut. What is then its speed?

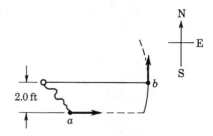

No resultant force acts on the body when the cord is relaxed; when the cord is taut it exerts a central force. Therefore, the angular momentum of the body relative to the pole is constant, and Equation 15-8 applies:

Figure 15-10. A body attached to a loose cord is traveling east from point a. The body travels north from point b when the cord becomes taut.

$$r_{a\perp}v_a = r_{b\perp}v_b$$

$$v_b = (r_{a\perp}/r_{b\perp})v_a = (2.0 \text{ ft} / 5.0 \text{ ft})(10 \text{ ft/sec})$$

$$v_b = 4 \text{ ft/sec}$$

15-4   The law of the conservation of angular momentum   When the resultant torque on a single particle or a rigid body is zero, its angular momentum is constant. Let us now consider a *system* of interacting particles or bodies. For each particle or body,

$$\tau = \frac{dL}{dt}$$

where τ is the resultant (internal and external) torque on one particle and L is its angular momentum. Taking the sum of all of the torques for the system yields

$$\Sigma\,\tau = \Sigma\,\frac{dL}{dt}$$

According to the third law of motion for rotation, the *internal torques* occur in pairs, the sum of the internal torques being zero. Therefore,

$$\Sigma\,\tau = \Sigma\,\tau_{\text{ext}} = \Sigma\,\frac{dL}{dt}$$

and

$$\boxed{\Sigma\,\tau_{\text{ext}} = \frac{d}{dt}\,(\Sigma\,L)}$$

[15-11]

The rate of change of the total angular momentum of the system is governed solely by torques external to the system.

If a system is isolated from a resultant external torque, the rate of change of the total angular momentum is zero, and *the total angular momentum of the system remains constant.* This is the fundamental law of the *conservation of angular momentum.*

If $\Sigma \tau_{\text{ext}} = 0,$ then $\dfrac{d}{dt}(\Sigma L) = 0,$ and $\Sigma L = \text{constant}$

[15-12]

The conservation law of angular momentum ranks with the conservation laws of mass, linear momentum, and energy as a basic principle of mechanics.†
Experiments in all branches of physics—mechanics, electromagnetism, atomic and nuclear physics—confirm that, when a system is isolated from a resultant external torque, its total angular momentum is constant.

Angular momentum conservation is illustrated in many familiar situations. When an ice skater spins freely on a surface of ice, his angular momentum $I\omega$ remains constant. If the skater pulls in his arms, his moment of inertia I decreases, and therefore the spin rate ω increases. A dropped cat has a constant angular momentum about its center of mass. But, while falling, the cat rearranges its limbs and tail—thereby changing its moment of inertia and thus its angular speed—so that its feet are downward when the cat strikes the ground. Similarly, a diver can change the angular speed of his body about its center of mass by rearranging the position of his arms and legs. A gyroscope, or gyrocompass, is typically a massive body set in rotation at a high angular speed to produce a large angular momentum. If the gyroscope is mounted so that no resultant torque acts on it, the direction of the angular momentum is unchanged relative to the fixed stars. Once pointed north, a gyrocompass remains pointed north, quite independent of the Earth's rotation.

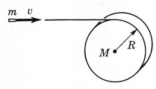

Figure 15-11. A bullet of mass m and velocity $\boldsymbol{v}$ is shot into the rim of a cylinder of mass M and radius R.

Example 5   A bullet of mass m traveling with a speed v is shot into the rim of a right circular cylinder of radius R and mass M, as shown in Figure 15-11. The cylinder has a fixed horizontal axis of rotation, and is originally at rest. What is the angular speed of the cylinder after the bullet has become imbedded in it?

We choose as our system the bullet together with the cylinder. If the axle of the cylinder is chosen as the axis for computing torques and angular momenta, and if the weight of the bullet

---

† The truly fundamental character of the conservation laws is revealed in more sophisticated analysis. It can be shown that the conservation laws of linear momentum and angular momentum are a consequence of the fact that space is isotropic for translational and rotational displacements, respectively. Furthermore, the conservation law of energy is a consequence of the isotropic nature of time.

and the frictional torque at the axle are negligible, the system is subject to no resultant torque. Therefore, the total angular momentum of the system is constant.

Before the bullet strikes the cylinder, the magnitude of its angular momentum relative to the axle is mvR, where R is the moment arm of the bullet's angular momentum. After the bullet strikes, the total moment of inertia of the cylinder and bullet is

$$I = \tfrac{1}{2}MR^2 + mR^2$$

and the conservation of angular momentum of the system gives:

Angular momentum before = angular momentum after.

$$mvR = (\tfrac{1}{2}M + m)R^2\omega$$

Therefore,
$$\omega = \frac{mv}{(\tfrac{1}{2}M + m)R}$$

Although angular momentum is conserved in this collision, linear momentum is *not* conserved, because an external force acts on the system at the axle. Furthermore, kinetic energy is *not* conserved, because energy is dissipated while the bullet is being brought to rest within the cylinder.

Example 6 A phonograph record having a moment of inertia I_r relative to an axis through its center is dropped onto a turntable having a moment of inertia I_t. The turntable is initially spinning with the angular speed ω_i as shown in Figure 15-12. What is the final angular speed of the turntable and record after the record has come to rest on the turntable?

Our system is chosen to be the record and the turntable. Assuming that the turntable spins about a frictionless axle, there is no resultant external torque on the system. Its total angular momentum remains constant. We label the *f*inal angular speed ω_f. Then angular-momentum conservation requires that

$$I_t\omega_i = (I_r + I_t)\omega_f$$
$$\omega_f = \frac{I_t}{I_r + I_t}\omega_i$$

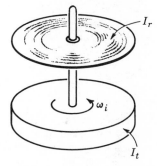

Figure 15-12. A phonograph record of moment of inertia I_r is dropped onto a turntable of moment of inertia I_t initially spinning at angular velocity $\boldsymbol{\omega}_i$.

Note that *internal* torques act within the system. The record produces a frictional torque on the turntable, slowing it, and the turntable produces a frictional torque on the record, speeding it up. The sum of these two frictional torques is zero at every instant of time. The work done by the one internal torque is *not*, however, equal to the work done by the other. During the time that the internal torques act, the angle turned through by the turntable is *greater than* the angle turned through by the record. Consequently, the gain in the rotational kinetic energy of the record is less than the loss in rotational kinetic energy of the turntable. The difference between these kinetic energies is simply the energy dissipated as thermal energy.

Example 7 Angular momentum, its representation by a vector, and its conservation are strikingly demonstrated with a stool which can rotate freely about a vertical axis. Suppose that a man sitting on such a stool, originally at rest, is handed a rotating bicycle wheel with handles at its axle. The bicycle wheel is weighted along its rim to increase its moment of inertia. The man grasps the handles so that the angular momentum vector of the rotating bicycle wheel is pointed upward. See Figure 15-13a. The moment of inertia of the man and stool is 3.00 slug-feet² and that of the bicycle wheel is 0.50 slug-feet², both with respect to the spin axes which, for simplicity, are assumed coincident. The angular speed of the wheel is 4.0 radians/sec.

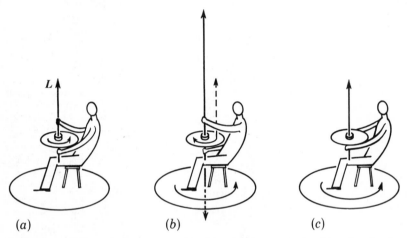

(a) (b) (c)

Figure 15-13. (a) A man on a turntable holds a spinning bicycle wheel so that the wheel's angular momentum is upward. (b) The man inverts the spinning wheel, so that the wheel's angular momentum is downward. The man and turntable thereby acquire angular momentum in the upward direction, the total angular momentum of the system remaining unchanged. (c) The man brakes the spinning wheel, while it is inverted; the angular momentum of the system remains unchanged.

(a) What is the total angular momentum of the system after the man has been handed the spinning bicycle wheel? (b) If the man turns the rotating wheel over, what is the angular momentum of the man and stool? (c) What is then the angular speed of the man and stool? (d) If the man now brings the rotating wheel to rest (while it is inverted), what are the final angular speed and the sense of rotation of the stool?

(a) When the bicycle wheel is held vertically and its angular-velocity vector points upward, the total angular momentum L of the wheel and, therefore, of the entire system of man, stool, and wheel, is

$$L = I\omega = (0.50 \text{ slug-ft}^2)(4.0 \text{ rad/sec}) = 2.0 \text{ slug-ft}^2/\text{sec upward}$$

as shown in Figure 15-13a.

(b) Inasmuch as the stool pivots freely about a vertical axis, the bearing of the stool cannot exert a *torque* in the *vertical* direction. Thus, as the man inverts the rotating wheel by applying an *internal* torque to it, the component of the wheel's angular momentum in the vertical direction decreases and finally becomes negative (vertically downward). The *total* angular momentum of the system along the vertical can then remain unchanged only if the man and stool acquire an angular momentum in the upward dirction in such an amount that the total angular momentum of the system remains 2.0 slug-feet²/sec. The man and stool must rotate in the sense opposite to that of the inverted wheel; the angular momentum vectors are shown in Figure 15-13b. It follows that the magnitude of the angular momentum L_{ms} of the man and stool is

$$\text{Total } L \text{ before } = \text{ total } L \text{ after.}$$

$$2.0 \text{ slug-ft}^2/\text{sec} = -2.0 \text{ slug-ft}^2/\text{sec} + L_{ms}$$

$$L_{ms} = 4.0 \text{ slug-ft}^2/\text{sec}$$

The magnitude of the angular momentum of the man and stool is just twice that of the wheel alone. Of course, if the man were again to reverse the direction of the wheel's axle, he and the stool would come once more to rest.

(c) The angular speed of the man and stool with the rotating wheel inverted is, then, given by

$$L_{ms} = 4.0 \text{ slug-ft}^2/\text{sec} = (3.00 \text{ slug-ft}^2)(\omega_{ms})$$

$$\omega_{ms} = 1.3 \text{ rad/sec}$$

(d) As the man presses on the spinning rim to bring the wheel to rest, he applies an internal torque to the wheel. By Newton's third law, the rim applies an internal torque of equal magnitude but opposite direction on the man. Because the total angular momentum of the system does not change, the angular velocity **ω′** of the man, stool, and wheel, after the wheel comes to rest with respect to the man, is such as to maintain the total angular momentum of the system at 2.0 slug-ft²/sec upward:

$$2.0 \text{ slug-ft}^2/\text{sec} = \omega'(3.00 + 0.50) \text{ slug-ft}^2$$

$$\omega' = 0.56 \text{ rad/sec}$$

15-5 The motion of a top We first consider the situation shown in Figure 15-14, where a top is supported at one end only and is initially in a horizontal plane. If the top is *not* spinning and its center of mass is initially at rest, as in Figure 15-14a, it falls down. The top is subject to two forces: its weight $m\mathbf{g}$ acting at the center of gravity and a force $\mathbf{F}$ acting at the point of support. These two forces produce a resultant torque $\boldsymbol{\tau}$, shown here to be out of the paper. Consequently, the angular momentum of the top, originally zero, increases along the direction of the resultant torque. This is to say, the top *falls*.

Now suppose that the top is initially spinning about its axis, as in Figure 15-14b. Again, a resultant torque (out of the paper) acts on the top. The top acquires an angular acceleration along the direction of the resultant torque. The change in the top's angular momentum is now at right angles

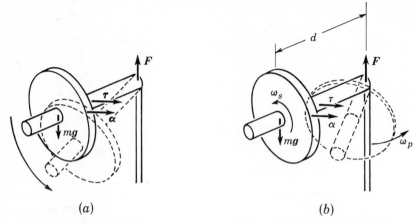

(a)   (b)

Figure 15-14. (a) A *non-spinning* top is released from rest: the top falls, the direction of the angular acceleration **α** being along the direction of the resultant torque **τ** on the top. (b) A *spinning* top is released: again the direction of the angular acceleration **α** is along the direction of the resultant torque **τ**; since the change in angular momentum is at right angles to the original angular momentum, the top undergoes precession at the angular velocity **ω**$_p$ about a vertical axis.

to the initial (spin) angular momentum. Equivalently, the angular acceleration is at right angles to the spin angular velocity. Therefore, the motion of the top is one of precession (Section 13-3).

The top precesses at a constant angular speed, *without falling*, in an equatorial plane around the point of support. The precessional angular speed ω_p is related to the spin angular speed ω_s of the top and its angular acceleration α by

[13-12] $$\omega_p = \frac{\alpha}{\omega_s}$$ [15-13]

The magnitude of the resultant torque on the top is mgd, where d is the distance from the point of support to the center of gravity. The magnitude of the top's spin angular momentum is $I\omega_s$, where I is the moment of inertia of the top about its spin axis. Therefore, from Newton's second law for rotation,

$$\Sigma \tau = I\alpha$$

$$mgd = I\alpha$$

$$\alpha = \frac{mgd}{I}$$

Substituting this result in Equation 15-13 gives

$$\omega_p = \frac{mgd}{I\omega_s} = \frac{mgd}{L_s} \qquad [15\text{-}14]$$

where L_s is the spin angular momentum. When a top precesses at a constant ω_p, it is acted upon by a torque of constant magnitude but ever-changing direction.

Actually, the top will precess at a constant speed in a horizontal plane only if it is initially set in motion along the horizontal with the precessional angular speed given by Equation 15-14. In the more general case, in which

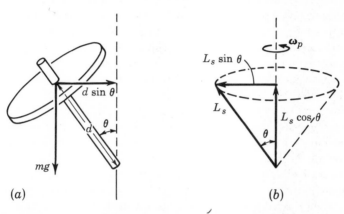

(a)   (b)

Figure 15-15. (a) A top whose spin axis makes an angle θ with respect to the vertical; the moment arm of the torque produced by the weight $m\mathbf{g}$ is $d \sin \theta$. (b) Angular momentum vectors corresponding to (a); the spin angular momentum is $\mathbf{L}_s$, $\boldsymbol{\omega}_p$ is the precession angular velocity, and the vertical component $L_s \cos \theta$ of the spin angular momentum is constant.

the top is, for example, pushed upward initially or simply released from rest, the top undergoes still another motion, that of *nutation*. Under nutation, the spin axis of the top oscillates up and down while the top precesses about the vertical.

We have treated of the rather special case in which a spinning top precesses in a horizontal plane. It is not difficult to show that the angular speed of precession given by Equation 15-14 is, in fact, independent of the angle θ between the spin axis and the vertical. From Figure 15-15a we see that the moment arm of the force $m\mathbf{g}$ about the point of support is $d \sin \theta$. From Figure 15-15b we see that only the horizontal component of the spin angular momentum $\mathbf{L}_s$ changes as the top precesses. The magnitude $L_s \sin \theta$ of the horizontal component does remain constant, but its direction changes.

Thus, Equation 15-14 applies if we replace d by $d \sin \theta$, and L_s by $L_s \sin \theta$. But $\sin \theta$ then cancels, and Equation 15-14 gives the angular speed of precession for an arbitrary angle between the spin axis and the vertical.

If there is no nutation, the spin angular momentum vector traces out a cone about the vertical: the vertical component of the spin angular momentum is constant, and the horizontal component of the spin angular momentum is constant in magnitude, but changes direction. The orbital angular momentum of the center of mass is constant in magnitude and direction about the point of support.

A top's motion appears so curious because it seems to violate our intuitive expectation that a dropped object will fall down. Most bodies are, however, *not* simultaneously spinning and being acted upon by a resultant torque. To be sure, each particle in a spinning and precessing top executes a rather complicated motion which is governed simply by Newton's laws. By using torque and angular momentum vectors, we can treat the motion of a spinning body as a whole, rather than the motions of each of the component particles in the rigid body.

The question of why a spinning top does not necessarily fall is no more (and no less) mysterious than the question, in translational dynamics, of why a body can move with constant speed even though it is acted on continuously by a force of constant magnitude. When such a resultant force is perpendicular to the body's linear momentum, the body's velocity changes direction but not magnitude—it travels in a circle at constant speed. In the same fashion, when a resultant torque of constant magnitude acts on a spinning body and is always perpendicular to the spin angular momentum, the body's spin angular velocity changes direction but not magnitude—the spinning body as a whole precesses in a circle.

15-6 Summary The angular momentum L of a particle with linear momentum p is, relative to the origin of the radius vector r,

[15-1] $$L = r \times p$$

The angular momentum of a rigid body, rotating about an axis of symmetry at the angular velocity $\boldsymbol{\omega}$, is

[15-3] $$L = I\boldsymbol{\omega}$$

In its most general form, Newton's second law for rotation is written

[15-4] $$\tau_{\text{ext}} = \frac{dL}{dt}$$

The angular momentum of a particle subject to a central force is constant, relative to the force center. Moreover, the radius vector from the force center to the particle sweeps out equal areas in equal times, following the relation

$$[15\text{-}10] \qquad \frac{dA}{dt} = \frac{L}{2m}$$

The law of conservation of angular momentum is this: if the *resultant external torque* on a system is *zero*, the *total angular momentum* of the system is *constant*.

The motion of a spinning top illustrates the fact that, when an external torque acts at right angles to a body's spin angular momentum, the body precesses, the angular momentum vector changing direction but not magnitude.

PROBLEMS

15-1 A bird of mass 0.50 kg flies east along a horizontal straight line 100 m above the ground. The bird maintains a constant speed of 10 m/sec. With respect to a north-south axis located at ground level, what are the moment of inertia, and the magnitudes and directions of the bird's angular momentum and angular velocity, when (a) the bird is 200 m from the axis and (b) the bird is directly over the axis?

15-2 Show that, relative to the X-, Y-, and Z-axes, the components of the angular momentum of a particle of mass m passing the point x, y, and z with velocity components v_x, v_y, and v_z are:

$$L_x = m(yv_z - zv_y)$$
$$L_y = m(zv_x - xv_z)$$
$$L_z = m(xv_y - yv_x)$$

15-3 In its normal state, the electron in a hydrogen atom moves in a circle of radius 0.528×10^{-10} m with a frequency of 6.58×10^{15} cycles/sec. The electron mass is 9.11×10^{-31} kg. What is the orbital angular momentum of the hydrogen atom in the normal state? (*All* angular momenta occur, according to the quantum theory, in integral multiples of 0.53×10^{-34} joule-sec.)

15-4 Show that the dimensions of angular momentum are those of energy multiplied by time.

15-5 Two bullets, each of mass m and traveling with equal speeds v in opposite directions, move in a horizontal plane along straight lines separated by a distance d. (a) What is the magnitude of the total angular momentum of the two bullets relative to *any* point? (b) What is the total angular momentum of the two bullets relative to an origin in a reference frame that moves with a speed V relative to the system described in part (a) and in the direction of one of the bullets?

15-6 ★ A dumbbell composed of two point particles of equal mass m at opposite ends of a slender massless rod 2.0 feet in length is thrown into the air. The center of mass moves from the origin in the X-Y plane with an initial velocity of 40 feet/sec at an angle of 30° with respect to the horizontal (positive X-axis). The initial angular velocity of the dumbbell about its center of mass is 12π radians/sec clockwise (along the negative Z-axis). Find the ratio of the spin angular momentum about the center of mass to the orbital angular momentum about the Z-axis, when the dumbbell's center of mass is (a) at the highest point and (b) again at the X-axis.

15-7   Refer to Example 5, Section 15-4. Find (a) the ratio of the thermal energy dissipated to the original kinetic energy of the bullet and (b) the change in the linear momentum of the system resulting from the bullet's becoming embedded in the cylinder.

15-8   Refer to Example 7, Section 15-4. (a) How much work is done in turning the rotating wheel over in part (b) of the example? (b) How much work would be done if the inverted wheel were flipped over to its original orientation? (c) How much work is done in stopping the inverted wheel in part (d) of the example?

15-9 ★   A diatomic molecule can be thought of as a dumbbell-like structure in which particles of masses m_1 and m_2 are attached to a massless rod of length r. (a) Show that the angular momentum of a molecule rotating about an axis through the center of mass and perpendicular to the interatomic axis is given by $L = \mu r^2 \omega$, where μ, the so-called *reduced mass*, is $m_1 m_2/(m_1 + m_2)$ and ω is the angular speed. (b) Show that the rotational kinetic energy is given by $K = \frac{1}{2}\mu r^2 \omega^2 = L^2/2\mu r^2$.

15-10 ★ When a hydrogen molecule, H_2, rotates at 3.6×10^{12} cycles/sec, its kinetic energy of rotation is 7.5×10^{-3} ev. What is the interatomic distance for this diatomic molecule? See Problem 15-9.

15-11   Show that for a particle moving in a straight line with constant speed, the radius vector from some arbitrary point to the moving particle sweeps out equal areas in equal times.

15-12   A 140-pound ice skater grasps a rope attached to a relatively thin, fixed post. The rope is initially 20 feet long, and the ice skater travels in a circle 20 feet in radius at a speed of 3.0 feet/sec. As the skater continues, the rope becomes wrapped around the post until its length to the skater is 8.0 feet. (a) What is then the skater's speed? (b) If the rope were attached by a loop to the post, so that it did not become wrapped around the post, and if the length of rope between the skater and the post were reduced slowly by the skater's pulling on it, what would be the skater's speed when the rope length was 8.0 feet?

15-13   A mass m slides in circle of radius r on a smooth horizontal surface. The mass is attached to a string that passes through a hole at the center of the circle, the other end of the string being attached to a mass M, as shown in Figure 15-16. (a) What is the speed of the mass m? (b) What is the angular momentum of m? (c) If the mass M is pulled down slowly through a vertical distance y, what is then the speed of m? (d) How much work was done in pulling the mass M downward in part (c)?

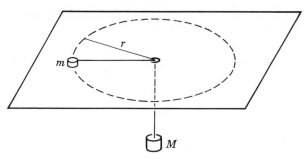

Figure 15-16

15-14 ★ The conservation of angular momentum law is often demonstrated with a freely rotating horizontal platform on which a toy train runs on a track near the circumference. Suppose that a train with a mass of 8.0 kg runs around a track of 0.75 m in radius on a platform whose moment of inertia relative to the vertical axle at the center is 3.0 kg-m². The train and the platform are initially at rest. Then the train is set in motion, its final speed relative to the tracks being 0.20 m/sec. (a) What is the angular speed of the platform relative to the ground? (b) What is the angular momentum of the platform relative to the ground? (c) What is the angular momentum of the train relative to the ground? (d) What is the angular speed of the platform relative to the ground after the motor on the train has been shut off and the train has come to rest relative to the tracks? (e) Assuming that the train's wheels do not slip as it accelerates toward its final speed, what is the work done by the electric motor of the train? (f) Is angular momentum conserved if the train's wheels do slip on the tracks as it accelerates toward its final speed?

15-15 A man sits on a stool that is free to rotate about a vertical axis. The moment of inertia of man and stool alone is 5.0 slug-feet². The man holds a 10-pound weight in each hand. With his arms first out-stretched, and with the weights a distance of 3.0 feet from the axis of the stool, the man is set in rotation at 30 revolutions/minute. The man then pulls the weights inward so that they are at the axis of rotation. (a) What is the final angular speed of the man and stool? (b) How much work does the man do in pulling the weights inward?

15-16 One of two coaxial discs is initially rotating with an angular speed of 200 radians/sec. Its moment of inertia is 10 kg-m². The second disc, having a moment of inertia of 30 kg-m² and initially at rest, is then pressed against the rotating disc in the fashion of a clutch. (a) What is the final common angular speed of the two discs? (b) How much energy is dissipated by the clutch? (c) Does the total amount of energy dissipated depend upon whether the discs are brought together slowly or quickly?

15-17 Two particles of equal mass are attached to the ends of a thin rod which rotates freely about its center at the angular speed ω. If the length of the rod is reduced to half by an internal mechanism, what is then the angular speed of the rod?

15-18 A bullet of mass m and initial speed v strikes, and is embedded in, the end of a uniform rod of mass $2m$ and length L originally at rest. See Figure 15-17. The rod pivots about a fixed axis at its center. (a) What is the angular momentum of the system of bullet and rod with respect

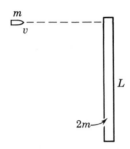

Figure 15-17

to an axis through the rod's pivot? (b) What is the angular speed of the rod after the collision? (c) Is linear momentum of the system conserved in the collision? (d) Is kinetic energy conserved?

15-19 ⋆ A bullet of mass m and initial speed v strikes and is embedded in the end of a uniform slender rod of mass $2m$ and length L originally at rest, as shown in Figure 15-17. Unlike the situation in Problem 15-18, however, the rod is free to slide on a frictionless horizontal surface. (a) What is the speed of the center of mass of the bullet and rod after the collision? (b) What is the angular momentum of the system before the collision (with respect to an axis passing through the center of mass of the system)? (c) What is the final angular speed of the rod relative to the center of mass? (d) What fraction of the original kinetic energy is lost in the collision?

15-20 A wheel of radius R and moment of inertia I relative to the vertical axis, about which it spins freely, has an initial angular speed ω. Three small pieces at the circumference, each of mass m, become detached from the wheel and fly off. Immediately after they become detached, (a) what is the speed of the three pieces, (b) what is the total angular momentum of the three pieces relative to an axis coincident with the axle of the wheel, (c) what is the angular momentum of the residual wheel, and (d) what is the angular speed of the wheel after the pieces have left it?

15-21 A bullet of mass m is shot through a weather vane having a moment of inertia I relative to its axis and originally at rest. The bullet misses the axis of the weather vane by a distance d, and its speed is reduced from v to $v/3$ in passing through. What is the angular speed of the weather vane after the bullet passes through?

15-22   A merry-go-round with a moment of inertia of 200 slug-feet^2 and a radius of 12 feet, is initially at rest. A 160-pound man walks from the center of the merry-go-round out toward the circumference; his final speed relative to the merry-go-round along the circumference is 3.0 feet/sec. What is, then, the angular speed of the merry-go-round relative to the ground?

15-23 ★ A point mass m is dropped from rest, falls through a vertical distance h, and then becomes attached to the rim of a uniform right circular cylinder of radius R and mass M having a horizontal axis. The cylinder is initially at rest. See Figure 15-18. What is the angular speed of the system when the mass m is at the lowest point?

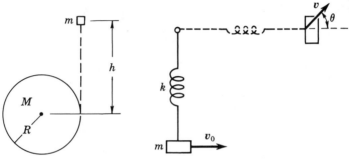

Figure 15-18   **Figure 15-19**

15-24 ★ A horizontal spring having a force constant k and relaxed length L_0 has one end fixed. The other end is attached to a mass m which slides on a frictionless horizontal surface. Initially the mass is moving to the right with a speed v_0; the length of the spring is then L_0, as shown in Figure 15-19. At some later time the spring is oriented at 90° with respect to its initial configuration, and its length is now L. What are

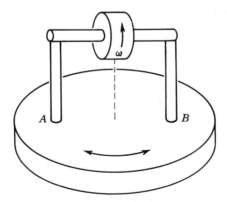

Figure 15-20

the direction and magnitude of the mass's velocity at this instant (in terms of m, L_0, L, k, and v_0)?

15-25   When its temperature rises, a freely rotating body increases all of its linear dimensions by 5 parts in 10^5. By what fraction is its angular speed of rotation reduced?

15-26   A top with a mass of 100 gm and a moment of inertia of 50 gm-cm^2 is spinning with an angular speed of 8.0 radians/sec. Its center of gravity is 6.0 cm from its point of support. (a) What is the angular speed of precession? (b) If the spin angular speed decreases because of friction, does the precessional angular speed increase or decrease?

15-27   A wheel with a moment of inertia I relative to its axis is spinning with an angular velocity ω while the ends of the axle are supported by two posts A and B, each a distance d from the axis, mounted on a rotatable platform. See Figure 15-20. At what angular velocity (magnitude and sense) must the platform be turned so that post A can be removed and the spinning wheel still maintain a fixed position relative to the platform?

S I X T E E N

GRAVITATION

This chapter is concerned with one of the fundamental forces of physics: gravity. We first consider the form of the law of universal gravitation and its demonstration through the Cavendish experiment. We then discuss the acceleration due to gravity, which is a measure of gravitational field intensity, and the gravitational lines of force, which are a representation of this field. Kepler's laws of planetary motion are related to the gravitational force. The general relation for the gravitational potential energy is derived, and the energetics of satellite motion is treated. The distinction between inertial and gravitational mass and the principle of equivalence are discussed briefly. Finally, the gravitational properties of spherical shells of matter are derived.

16-1　The law of universal gravitation　All objects near the Earth's surface experience the attractive force of the Earth. This force, called the weight, is proportional in magnitude to the object's mass and is directed toward the Earth's center. Can this force be described more fundamentally in terms of certain properties of the two interacting bodies—the object and the Earth—and, if so, is this but one example of a universal force acting for *any* pair of bodies? Sir Isaac Newton was the first to answer this in the affirmative, and to show, by carefully analyzing the motions of the planets about the Sun and of the Moon about the Earth, that their motions could be ascribed to a universal inverse-square force of gravity.

Newton found that the magnitude of the gravitational force F_g between two particles is given by the relation

$$F_g = \frac{Gm_1m_2}{r^2}$$

[16-1]

where m_1 and m_2 are the gravitational "charges," or gravitational masses, of the two particles, r is the separation distance between the bodies, and G is the proportionality constant, called the *universal gravitational constant*. The *gravitational mass*, which appears in Equation 16-1, is, as we shall see in Section 16-7, apparently identical with (or proportional to) the *inertial mass*, which appears in Newton's second law, $\Sigma F = ma$, where the inertial mass is a measure of a body's resistance to a change in its velocity. Therefore, we ordinarily need not distinguish between the gravitational and inertial masses, and hereafter m_1 and m_2 will be called simply the "masses" of the bodies.

The numerical value of G depends, of course, on the system of units used. The present accepted value for G is

$$G = 6.673 \times 10^{-11} \text{ nt-m}^2/\text{kg}^2$$
$$G = 3.436 \times 10^{-8} \text{ lb-ft}^2/\text{slug}^2$$

[16-2]

That the gravitational force is universal, that it lies along the line connecting the interacting particles, and that it is proportional to the masses and inversely proportional to the square of their separation distance, were all concluded through theoretical reasoning by Newton. That bodies of laboratory size do indeed attract one another gravitationally and that the constant G has the extraordinarily small magnitude given in Equation 16-2 were first shown through the experimental work of Henry Cavendish. We shall have more on the experiment made by Cavendish and the arguments given by Newton in Sections 16-2 and 16-4.

The gravitational force is independent of the presence of other bodies (there is no gravity "shield" or "insulator") and of other types of forces that may also be acting. Unlike the electric force between charged bodies, a force which may be either attractive

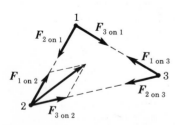

Figure 16-1. Gravitational interactions among three point particles.

or repulsive, the gravitational force is attractive only. It depends only on the mass of each of two interacting bodies and on their separation distance. Figure 16-1 shows the gravitational forces between three point particles of masses m_1, m_2, and m_3. Newton's third law applies to their interaction: the gravitational force of particle 1 on 2 is equal in magnitude but opposite in direction to the force of 2 on 1. Furthermore, the superposition principle for forces applies: the resultant gravitational force of 1 on 2 and of 3 on 2 is found by adding the two forces as vectors.

Most bodies with which we are concerned are not particles—they have a finite size. One may well ask whether the gravitational force between two *extended* bodies, such as the Earth and the Moon, can be simply interpreted, recognizing that each small part of one body attracts each small part of the second body according to Equation 16-1. Newton himself wrestled with this problem, and only after first developing the mathematical tool of the integral

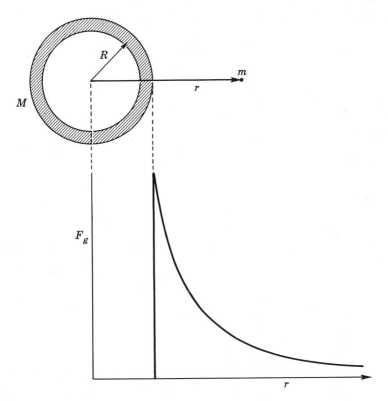

Figure 16-2. Gravitational interaction between a spherical shell and a mass point. The gravitational force is inverse-square for the particle outside the shell and zero for the particle inside.

calculus was he finally able to show that the gravitational effects produced by a spherical mass are really quite simple: if a body is spherical and if its density depends only on the distance from the center, then from an external point of view the sphere behaves gravitationally as if all of its mass were located at its center. The proof of this theorem, as well as the results stated in the next paragraph, is given in Section 16-8.

If a *spherical shell* of mass M and radius R interacts with a particle of mass m *outside* the shell, the gravitational force between them is given by GmM/r^2, where r is the distance from the shell's *center* to mass m. On the other hand, if the point mass is located at any point *inside* the shell, the gravitational force on it is exactly *zero*! See Figure 16-2. Insofar as gravitational influence goes, the shell is equivalent to a point mass M at its center when particle m is outside, and the shell is gravitationally nonexistent when the particle is inside. Inasmuch as a solid sphere consists simply of the wrapping of many shells of different radii, like an onion, in interacting with external bodies a solid sphere is equivalent in its gravitational effects to a particle of equal mass at its center. Thus, two nonoverlapping spheres interact as two particles.

Example 1 Two spherical masses of 1.0 kg and 3.0 kg, respectively, are at rest on a table. The distance between their centers is 1.0 m. With what gravitational force do they attract one another?

Equation 16-1 gives the magnitude of the gravitational force:

$$F_g = Gm_1m_2/r^2 = (6.7 \times 10^{-11} \text{ nt-m}^2/\text{kg}^2)(1.0 \text{ kg})(3.0 \text{ kg})/(1.0 \text{ m})^2$$

$$F_g = 2.0 \times 10^{-10} \text{ nt}$$

A gravitational force of this magnitude acts on each of the two spherical masses. Compared with other forces acting on either body, the gravitational force is entirely negligible.

The gravitational force is the weakest of the fundamental forces in physics, yet it is the only fundamental force readily experienced. The attractive electric force between a proton and an electron is 10^{39} times larger than the attractive gravitational force between them! The reason why the much stronger electric force is not encountered in ordinary experience is simply that all large-scale objects ordinarily are electrically neutral; they contain equal amounts of positive and negative charge. The still stronger nuclear force, which acts between the particles in the nuclei of atoms, is never evident in ordinary experience because this force is effective only over a very short range (10^{-15} m).

Example 2 Compute the ratio of the Sun's mass to the Earth's mass, given only the radii of the Moon's and the Earth's orbits (2.39×10^5 miles and 9.29×10^7 miles) and their respective periods (27.3 days and 365 days).

Let M_s, M_e, and M_m represent the respective masses of the Sun, Earth, and Moon. Furthermore, let r_{es} represent the radius, and T_{es} the period, of the Earth's orbit about the Sun, and r_{me} and T_{me} the radius and period of the

Moon's orbit about the Earth. Then we may write for the forces F_{es} on the Earth due to the Sun and F_{me} on the Moon due to the Earth:

$$F = ma = m\omega^2 r$$

$$F_{es} = \frac{GM_eM_s}{r_{es}^2} = M_e\left(\frac{4\pi^2 r_{es}}{T_{es}^2}\right)$$

$$F_{me} = \frac{GM_mM_e}{r_{me}^2} = M_m\left(\frac{4\pi^2 r_{me}}{T_{me}^2}\right)$$

Dividing the first equation by the second equation yields

$$\frac{M_s}{M_m}\left(\frac{r_{me}}{r_{es}}\right)^2 = \frac{M_e}{M_m}\left(\frac{r_{es}}{r_{me}}\right)\left(\frac{T_{me}}{T_{es}}\right)^2$$

Cancelling out the Moon's mass M_m and rearranging terms gives

$$\frac{M_s}{M_e} = \left(\frac{T_{me}}{T_{es}}\right)^2\left(\frac{r_{es}}{r_{me}}\right)^3 = \left(\frac{27.3 \text{ days}}{365 \text{ days}}\right)^2\left(\frac{9.29 \times 10^7 \text{ mi}}{2.39 \times 10^5 \text{ mi}}\right)^3$$

$$\frac{M_s}{M_e} = 3.3 \times 10^5$$

The Sun is 330,000 times more massive than the Earth. This calculation of the Sun-Earth mass ratio, which does not require a knowledge of the numerical value of the constant G, was first made by Newton.

16-2 The Cavendish experiment Newton showed, without knowing the magnitude of the universal gravitational constant G, that an inverse-square universal force of gravity accounted for the motions of the planets about the Sun and of the "falling" of the Moon and an apple toward the Earth. It remained to show that two objects of ordinary size attract one another. This was first accomplished in an historic experiment of extraordinary delicacy by Henry Cavendish in 1798, more than a hundred years after Newton had formulated the law of gravitation. The Cavendish experiment is significant, not only because it demonstrated directly that the gravitational force between two ordinary bodies exists, but also because it enabled the numerical value of the constant G to be computed.

Cavendish secured two small spheres, each of mass m_1, to the opposite ends of a light rigid rod and suspended the rod at its midpoint by a light elastic (quartz) fiber, to form a torsion balance as shown in Figure 16-3. Two large lead spheres, each of mass m_2, were then

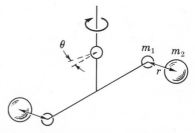

Figure 16-3. Schematic representation of the Cavendish experiment.

placed near the masses m_1, the distance between m_1 and the near-by m_2 being r. In such an arrangement each lead sphere attracts the mass m_1 close to it. This results in a clockwise torque on the rod (looking downward). (The gravitational attraction between one lead sphere and the more distant mass m_1 is ignorable: the separation distance is much greater, and the torque has a smaller lever arm.) The clockwise torque rotates the rod. As the rod rotates, the wire twists. This deformation produces a counterclockwise restoring torque which, for small angles of twist, is proportional to the twist angle θ. Equilibrium is reached when the gravitational torque equals (in magnitude) the restoring torque. By measuring the restoring torque (which is proportional to θ) one finds the attractive force between m_1 and m_2. This force, together with the masses m_1 and m_2, and their separation r, allows the constant G to be computed when Equation 16-1 is used.

The small angle θ, through which the rod is turned by the gravitational torque, is most readily measured by attaching a mirror to the fiber, shining a beam of light from a distant fixed light source on the mirror, and measuring the deflection of the light beam reflected from the mirror as the rod and mirror turn. The proportionality constant between the restoring torque and the angular displacement θ is determined (Section 17-4) by measuring the fiber's period of oscillation with the rod and attached spheres (having a known moment of inertia) suspended from it.

Cavendish's original experiment and later refinements of it not only lead to the presently accepted numerical value of G (6.673×10^{-11} nt-m^2/kg^2) but also confirm that the gravitational force varies as the product of the interacting masses and inversely as the square of their separation distance. The inverse-square nature of the gravitational force is confirmed with much higher precision through astronomical observations.

Example 3 Compute the Earth's mass.

We can write the gravitational force F_g on an object of mass m at the surface of the Earth in two equivalent ways:

$$F_g = mg$$

$$F_g = Gmm_e/r_e^2$$

where, in the second relation, the weight is attributed to the gravitational pull of the Earth of mass m_e and radius r_e.

Equating the two expressions for the weight gives

$$mg = Gmm_e/r_e^2$$

or, $m_e = gR^2/G = (9.8 \text{ m/sec}^2)(6.4 \times 10^6 \text{ m})^2/(6.7 \times 10^{-11} \text{ nt-m}^2/\text{kg}^2)$

$$m_e = 6.0 \times 10^{24} \text{ kg}$$

Cavendish is said to have measured the Earth's mass in his famous experiment, inasmuch as a knowledge of the constant G permits the mass of the Earth to be calculated.

From a knowledge of the Earth's mass and radius one can compute its average density ρ:

$$\rho = m_e/(\text{volume}) = m_e/\tfrac{4}{3}\pi r_e^3$$

$$\rho = (6.0 \times 10^{24}\,\text{kg})/\tfrac{4}{3}\pi(6.4 \times 10^6\,\text{m})^3 = 5.5\,\text{gm/cm}^3$$

The mean density of the Earth, 5.5 times that of water, exceeds that of material at the Earth's surface. One must conclude, then, that the Earth's interior consists largely of material of high density, most probably metals. Certainly, Newton and Cavendish could hardly have expected, in their basic studies of gravitation, to have arrived at a result of such great geological significance.

16-3 The meaning of g   Since we write the weight of a body as mg, the acceleration due to gravity, g, gives the gravitational force per unit mass, called the *gravitational intensity*, for any body attracted by the earth:

$$g = \frac{F_g}{m}$$

The magnitude of F_g can be written

$$F_g = \frac{Gmm_e}{r^2}$$

where m_e is the Earth's mass and r is the distance of the mass m from the Earth's center. Therefore,

$$g = \frac{Gm_e}{r^2} \qquad\qquad \text{[16-3]}$$

At the surface of the Earth, r is 2.09×10^7 feet and

$$g = (3.4 \times 10^{-8}\,\text{lb-ft}^2/\text{slug}^2)\frac{(4.11 \times 10^{23}\,\text{slugs})}{(2.09 \times 10^7\,\text{ft})^2}$$

$$g = 32\,\text{ft/sec}^2$$

The acceleration due to gravity does not have the same value at all locations; it falls off inversely as the square of the distance from the center of the Earth. At a distance of 4000 miles above the surface of the Earth, $g = (32\,\text{feet/sec}^2)/(2)^2 = 8.0\,\text{feet/sec}^2$. At the location of the Moon, $g = (32\,\text{feet/sec}^2)/(60)^2 = 8.9 \times 10^{-3}\,\text{feet/sec}^2$ (see Problem 16-4).

Because we commonly encounter vertical displacements that are small compared with the Earth's radius, the acceleration g is nearly independent of height. We can write the distance r as $r = r_e + h$, where r_e is the Earth's radius and h is the vertical height above the surface. Then Equation 16-3 becomes

$$g = \frac{Gm_e}{(r_e + h)^2}$$

which, for $h \ll r_{\mathrm{e}}$, is approximated by the relation

$$g = \frac{Gm_{\mathrm{e}}}{r_{\mathrm{e}}{}^2} \left(1 - \frac{2h}{r_{\mathrm{e}}} + \cdots\right) = (9.8 \text{ m/sec}^2)\left(1 - \frac{2h}{r_{\mathrm{e}}}\right)$$

At an altitude of 10 miles, g is only 0.5 per cent less than its magnitude at the surface; at 100 miles' altitude, g is down by 5 per cent.

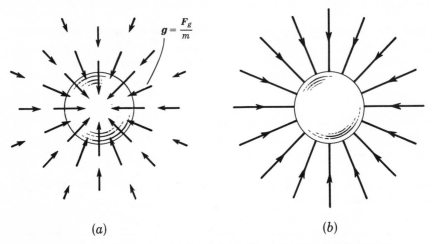

$$g = \frac{F_g}{m}$$

(a)   *(b)*

Figure 16-4. (a) The gravitational intensity **g** represented by vectors. (b) The gravitational intensity represented by gravitational lines of force.

As we shall see in Chapter 17, the magnitude of **g** can be measured to high precision (1 part in 10^6) by using various types of pendula. Such measurements show that g differs at various points on the Earth's surface. There are several causes: (a) the difference in altitude, (b) the ellipsoidal, rather than spherical, shape of the Earth (because of the equatorial bulge, bodies at low latitudes are farther from the Earth's center than bodies at the Poles), (c) local deposits in the Earth, which influence the value of g (and sometimes indicate the presence of oil or minerals), and (d) the rotation of the Earth, which causes the effective g to differ from the true g (see Example 4). At 45° latitude and at sea level, g is close to the so-called *standard acceleration*, 9.8066 m/sec² = 32.1740 feet/sec².

The magnitude of **g** is governed by Equation 16-3; its direction is always toward the Earth's center. It is useful to portray **g** by vectors, as shown in Figure 16-4a. There is a still simpler way of mapping the gravitational effect of the Earth on a body near it; this is shown in Figure 16-4b. Here lines are drawn radially inward, indicating that the gravitational force is attractive. If one surrounds the mass toward which the lines point by an imaginary sphere, the number of *gravitational lines of force* penetrating the imaginary spherical surface is the same for *any* radius. However, because the surface area of a sphere varies directly as the square of the radius ($A = 4\pi r^2$), the number of force lines penetrating a *unit* area on the imaginary sphere falls off inversely as the square of the radius. Thus, radial lines, spaced uniformly in three dimensions, may be used to indicate the magnitude as well as the direction of **g**. The magnitude of **g** is proportional to (or, by an appropriate choice of units, equal to) the number of gravitational lines of force passing through a unit area oriented perpendicular to the lines.

A *uniform* gravitational field is one in which the lines of force are uniformly spaced and parallel, **g** being constant in both magnitude and direction. For example, over a small volume near the surface of the Earth, the gravitational field is approximately uniform.

We can now describe the gravitational interaction between two masses as follows. The first mass establishes a *gravitational field* in space. The second mass, finding itself in this gravitational field, is acted upon by a gravitational force. Thus, the interaction between particles 1 and 2 may be viewed as taking place in two steps: (a) particle 1 establishes a gravitational field at all points in space, including the location of particle 2, and (b) particle 2 is subject to a force by virtue of its presence in this field. Conversely, particle 2 establishes a field which acts on particle 1.

Example 4 A plumb bob of mass m hangs from a string whose upper end is held fixed. The plumb bob is at the latitude θ. How is the true weight $m\mathbf{g}$ of the plumb bob related to its apparent weight (the tension in the cord supporting it)? How is the direction toward the Earth's center related to the "vertical" (the direction of the plumb line)?

Because the plumb bob is on the Earth's surface, it moves in a circle at the constant angular speed $\omega = 2\pi$ radians/day. As Figure 16-5 shows, the radius of the circle is $r_e \cos \theta$, where r_e is the Earth's radius. Therefore the body's acceleration must be radial, pointing toward, and being perpendicular to, the north-south axis of the Earth's rotation. The resultant of the two forces acting on the plumb bob—its weight $m\mathbf{g}$ and the tension

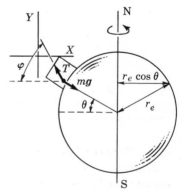

Figure 16.5. Forces on a mass suspended from a plumb bob at latitude θ.

T in the cord—must point in the direction of this centripetal acceleration. Consequently, these two forces can *not* be oppositely directed and of precisely equal magnitude: the angle φ made by the tension T with the equatorial plane exceeds the latitude angle θ, and the magnitude of $m\mathbf{g}$ exceeds that of T.

Applying Newton's second law, in turn, to the components in the north-south direction (Y-axis) and along the equatorial plane (X-axis) gives

$$\Sigma F_y = 0$$

$$T \sin \varphi = mg \sin \theta \qquad [16\text{-}4]$$

and

$$\Sigma F_x = ma_x$$

$$mg \cos \theta - T \cos \varphi = m(r_e \cos \theta)\omega^2$$

or,

$$T \cos \varphi = mg \cos \theta \,(1 - r_e\omega^2/g) \qquad [16\text{-}5]$$

The two simultaneous equations, 16-4 and 16-5, determine uniquely the angle φ and the apparent weight T for any latitude θ.

If the plumb bob is located at the North or South Pole, the true and apparent weights must be equal, and the cord must be aligned with the direction toward the Earth's center. We can verify this by putting θ equal to 90°. From Equation 16-5, when $\theta = 90°$, then $\varphi = 90°$; from Equation 16-4, when $\theta = \varphi = 90°$, then $T = mg$.

When the plumb bob is at the Equator, $\theta = 0$. Equation 16-4 then gives $\varphi = 0$, and Equation 16-5 becomes

$$\theta = \varphi = 0 \qquad \text{and} \qquad T = mg(1 - r_e\omega^2/g)$$

Thus, the ratio of the apparent weight T to the true weight mg at the Equator is

$$T/mg = 1 - r_e\omega^2/g$$

$$= 1 - (6.37 \times 10^6 \text{ m})(2\pi \text{ rad/day})^2(1 \text{ day} / 24 \times 3600 \text{ sec})^2/(9.8 \text{ m/sec}^2)$$

$$T/mg = 0.9966 = 99.66 \text{ per cent}$$

A body "weighs" less at the Equator than at the Poles because the Earth rotates. The "weight" at the Equator is smaller also because the Earth is not a perfect sphere, a body at the Equator being farther from the Earth's center than the same body located at a Pole. The effect of the equatorial bulge is comparable to that of the Earth's rotation.

16-4　Kepler's laws of planetary motion　Within our solar system are a number of examples of relatively light bodies moving in orbit about a massive body (see Table 16-1). The Moon moves in a nearly circular orbit, and artificial satellites travel in elliptical paths about the Earth. Twelve moons encircle the planet Jupiter. The planets trace out elliptical orbits about the massive Sun. It was the analysis of planetary motion that led Newton to the law of gravitation. He proved that the astronomical observations were consistent with a universal attractive force, which varied inversely as the square of the distance between the interacting bodies and whose direction was along the line connecting them.

Table 16-1

BODY	MASS (EARTH MASSES)*	MEAN DIAMETER (KILOMETERS)	MEAN DENSITY (GRAMS/CENTIMETER^3)
Sun	333,400	1,391,000	1.39
Mercury	0.0549	5,140	4.70
Venus	0.8073	12,620	4.94
Earth	1.0000	12,760	5.55
Mars	0.1065	6,860	3.92
Jupiter	314.5	143,600	1.32
Saturn	94.07	120,600	0.72
Uranus	14.40	53,400	1.22
Neptune	16.72	49,700	1.11
Pluto	—	—	—
Moon	0.01228	3,476	3.39

* Mass of Earth: 5.975×10^{24} kg.

Observations of a light celestial body moving in the vicinity of a much more massive celestial body show that:

(1) The path of the light body is a conic section—an ellipse, a parabola, or a hyperbola—depending on the injection speed. The massive body is at one focus.

(2) The area swept out per unit time by the radius vector from the massive body to the light body is constant.

(3) For elliptical orbits, the square of the period is proportional to the cube of the semimajor axis.

These empirical relations, which summarize the motions of bodies in the solar system, were first recognized by Johannes Kepler (1571–1630); they are known as *Kepler's three laws of planetary motion*. Of course, Kepler's original formulation of these laws was restricted to the motion of the then known planets of the solar system. Newton's great contribution lay in proving that Kepler's laws were the logical consequences of a universal inverse-square gravitational force. We will discuss some important features of the Keplerian laws below.†

KEPLER'S FIRST LAW   Figure 16-6 shows an elliptical orbit with the force center at one focus. The semimajor axis is a, the semiminor axis is b. At its closest and farthest distances from the Sun, a planet is at the *perihelion* and *aphelion* positions, respectively; the corresponding terms for a satellite

† For a detailed proof of the Keplerian laws, as well as other results given without derivation in this section and in Section 16-6, see, for example, U. Ingard and W. L. Kraushaar, *Introduction to Mechanics, Matter, and Waves*, Addison-Wesley Publishing Company, Inc., 1960, Chap. 10.

about the Earth are *perigee* and *apogee* (*helios*, sun; *geo*, earth). In general, the gravitational force has a tangential component F_t along the path, which changes the magnitude of the planet's velocity but not its direction, and a radial component F_r, which changes the direction of the planet's velocity but not its magnitude. Qualitatively, it is clear from Figure 16-6 that, as the planet *recedes* from the force center toward the aphelion position, the gravitational force *slows* the planet, and that, as the planet approaches the perihelion position, the gravitational force has a tangential component *along* the velocity and the planet's speed *increases*.

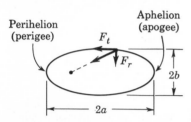

Figure 16-6. Elliptical path traced out by a planet about a sun. The tangential and radial components of the gravitational force are F_t and F_r, respectively.

For the special case of a circular path, which is closely approximated by the planets of the solar system (except Pluto) and by the moons, the two foci of the ellipse coalesce into the center of the circle. Then the force is always at right angles to the velocity ($F_t = 0$), the speed of the planet is constant, and $a = b = r$ (where r is the radius of the circle).

The gravitational force of a planet on the Sun is precisely equal, by Newton's third law, to the force of the Sun on the planet. Consequently, the force on the Sun changes with time in precisely the same fashion as the force on the planet. If the planet moves in an ellipse, so does the Sun. See Figure 16-7. Indeed, both bodies move in ellipses about their center of mass, which remains at rest. The ratio m_p/m_s of their masses is in the inverse ratio of their respective distances r_p and r_s from the center of mass: $m_p/m_s = r_s/r_p$. The total linear momentum of the system is, of course, exactly zero: the planet and Sun have momenta of equal magnitudes but opposite directions.

If a sun is very massive compared to a planet, as in the case of the solar system, the center of mass is close to the center of the sun. The sun is then

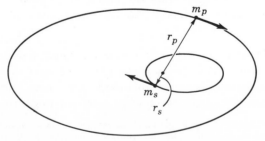

Figure 16-7. Both planet and sun trace out elliptical paths about their center of mass. The total linear momentum of the system is zero.

nearly at rest, and the total kinetic energy of the sun-planet system is equal to the kinetic energy of the planet alone. In addition, the total orbital angular momentum of the system is essentially that of the planet alone.

KEPLER'S SECOND LAW   We first recall a statement made in Section 15-3: when a body is acted upon by a *central* force—one which lies along the line joining the body to a fixed force center—its orbital angular momentum is constant. Moreover, the rate dA/dt, at which the area is swept out by the radius vector from the force center to the moving particle of mass m, is proportional to the particle's angular momentum L; that is,

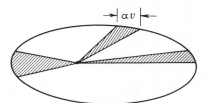

[15-9] $$\frac{dA}{dt} = \frac{L}{2m}$$

Astronomical observations show that dA/dt is a constant for planets and comets about the Sun, and for moons about a planet. This implies that the gravitational force is a *central* force, acting along the radius vector **r**.

Figure 16-8. Kepler's second law illustrated. The three shaded areas, representing the area swept out by the radius vector from the force center to the orbiting particle in equal times, are all equal.

Figure 16-8 shows the area swept out by the radius vector from the Sun to a light body for different locations relative to the Sun. Note that the body's speed is greatest at the perihelion position, and least at the aphelion position.

If v_p and v_a are the planet's speeds at the *p*erihelion and *a*phelion positions, respectively, and r_p and r_a are the corresponding distances from the Sun, the conservation of angular momentum principle requires that

[15-8] $$r_p v_p = r_a v_a$$

The direction of the angular momentum is perpendicular to the plane of the orbit and is derived from the right-hand rule.

KEPLER'S THIRD LAW   Analysis shows that the period T of a planet moving under the influence of an inverse-square force in an elliptical orbit is given by

$$T^2 = \frac{4\pi^2 a^3}{GM}$$ [16-6]

where a is the semimajor axis and M is the mass of the force center.† For a

† *Ibid.*

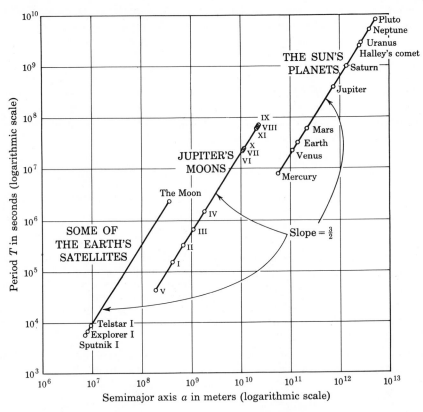

Figure 16-9. Kepler's third law illustrated for three planetary systems: the Sun and its planets, the Earth and its satellites, the planet Jupiter and its moons. The logarithm of the period is plotted against the logarithm of the semimajor axis. All three lines have the same slope, 3/2. Therefore, each system obeys the relation $\log T = \frac{3}{2} \log a + \frac{1}{2} \log K$, which is equivalent to $T^2 = Ka^3$, K being a different constant for each system.

given force center, the square of the period is proportional to the cube of the semimajor axis. This is Kepler's third law of planetary motion.

The periods and semimajor axes of the Sun's planets (including Halley's comet), some of the satellites of the Earth, and the several moons of Jupiter are given in Table 16-2. These data are portrayed graphically in Figure 16-9.

We see from the figure that, for a given force center, astronomical observations are summarized by the following relation between the period and semimajor axis:

$$T^2 = Ka^3$$

where, by Equation 16-6, the constant K is inversely proportional to the mass M of the force center. That is, $K = 4\pi^2/GM$.

It is easy to show that, for the special situation in which the elliptical orbit becomes a circle (and a becomes r), Equation 16-6 is a necessary consequence

Table 16-2

SATELLITES	SEMIMAJOR LENGTH a (METERS)	PERIOD OF REVOLUTION (SECONDS)
Planets of the Sun		
Mercury	5.79×10^{10}	7.60×10^{6}
Venus	1.08×10^{11}	1.94×10^{7}
Earth	1.49×10^{11}	3.16×10^{7}
Mars	2.28×10^{11}	5.94×10^{7}
Jupiter	7.78×10^{11}	3.74×10^{8}
Saturn	1.43×10^{12}	9.30×10^{8}
Halley's comet	2.69×10^{12}	2.39×10^{9}
Uranus	2.87×10^{12}	2.66×10^{9}
Neptune	4.50×10^{12}	5.20×10^{9}
Pluto	5.91×10^{12}	7.82×10^{9}
Some moons of the Earth		
Sputnik I	6.94×10^{6}	5.77×10^{3}
Explorer I	7.81×10^{6}	6.87×10^{3}
Telstar I	9.66×10^{6}	9.48×10^{3}
The Moon	3.84×10^{8}	2.36×10^{6}
Moons of Jupiter		
I (Io)	4.20×10^{8}	1.53×10^{5}
II (Europa)	6.70×10^{8}	3.06×10^{5}
III (Ganymede)	1.07×10^{9}	6.18×10^{5}
IV (Callisto)	1.88×10^{9}	1.44×10^{6}
V	1.81×10^{8}	4.30×10^{4}
VI	1.14×10^{10}	2.16×10^{7}
VII	1.17×10^{10}	2.24×10^{7}
VIII	2.35×10^{10}	6.38×10^{7}
IX	2.40×10^{10}	6.43×10^{7}
X	1.17×10^{10}	2.33×10^{7}
XI	2.25×10^{10}	6.35×10^{7}

of the inverse-square character of the gravitational force. A particle moving in uniform circular motion has a radial acceleration $\boldsymbol{a}_r$ of magnitude

$$[5\text{-}6] \qquad a_r = \omega^2 r = \frac{4\pi^2 r}{T^2}$$

where ω is the angular speed and T is the period of the motion. If the radial force arises from the gravitational attraction of the force center, then

$$\Sigma\, \boldsymbol{F} = m\boldsymbol{a}$$

$$\frac{GmM}{r^2} = m\left(\frac{4\pi^2 r}{T^2}\right)$$

or

$$T^2 = \frac{4\pi r^3}{GM}$$

This is precisely Equation 16-6 with a replaced by r. Kepler's *second* law requires only that the gravitational force be a *central* force; Kepler's *third* law requires, in addition, that $F_g \propto r^{-2}$.

16-5 Gravitational potential energy The gravitational force between two bodies depends only on their separation distance, not on their velocities. It is, therefore, a conservative force, and one may associate with it a gravitational potential energy (see Section 12-2). Heretofore, we considered the special case in which the gravitational force (and therefore also the acceleration due to gravity) was constant. For this situation, the difference in gravitational potential energy for a body of mass m displaced between two points separated by a vertical distance Δy was $\Delta U_g = mg\,\Delta y$. We wish now to find the more general expression for gravitational potential energy, taking into account the variation with separation distance of the gravitational force between two bodies.

By definition, the potential-energy difference $U_f - U_i$ between the points i and f is given by

[12-12]
$$U_f - U_i = -\int_i^f \boldsymbol{F} \cdot d\boldsymbol{s} = -W_{i \to f} \qquad [16\text{-}7]$$

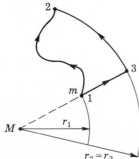

Thus, the gravitational potential difference is equal to the negative of the work done by the gravitational force when a particle is moved from some *i*nitial to some *f*inal point along *any path*.

Consider two point masses m and M, where M remains fixed. Because the gravitational force F_g between them is a conservative force, the work done on mass m as it is moved from point 1 to point 2 (see Figure 16-10) is independent of the path from 1 to 2.

Whether we take the mass m along a complicated path from 1 to 2, or along the path from 1 to 3 (along which F_g is parallel to the

Figure 16-10. The gravitational potential energy difference is computed for mass m at distances r_1 and r_2 from the mass M.

displacement) and then from 3 to 2 (along which F_g is at right angles to the displacement), the *total work done* is the *same*. Thus, we can find the gravitational potential energy difference $U_2 - U_1$ by computing the work $W_{1\to3}$ done in the path 1 to 3 and the work $W_{3\to2}$ done in the path 3 to 2. From Equation 16-7,

$$U_2 - U_1 = -W_{1\to2}$$

or, equivalently, $\qquad U_2 - U_1 = -(W_{1\to3} + W_{3\to2})$ [16-8]

Along the circular arc from 3 to 2, the gravitational force F_g is always perpendicular to the displacement ds; thus, the work done $W_{3\to2}$ in moving the mass m along this path is zero:

$$W_{3\to2} = 0$$

Along the radial path from 1 to 3 the gravitational force F_g is opposite in direction to the displacement dr, the angle θ between them being $180°$. Therefore,

$$W_{1\to3} = \int_{r_1}^{r_3} \boldsymbol{F}_g \cdot d\boldsymbol{r} = \int_{r_1}^{r_3 = r_2} F_g \cos \theta \, dr = \int_{r_1}^{r_2} \frac{GMm}{r^2}(-1)(dr)$$

Evaluating this definite integral yields

$$W_{1\to3} = GMm\left(\frac{1}{r_2} - \frac{1}{r_1}\right)$$

and substituting this result in Equation 16-8 gives

$$U_2 - U_1 = -W_{1\to2} = GMm\left(\frac{1}{r_1} - \frac{1}{r_2}\right) \qquad [16\text{-}9]$$

It is customary to choose the gravitational potential energy to be zero at the point where the force is zero—namely, at $r = \infty$. One can then speak of the gravitational potential energy U_r for two masses separated by a distance r. Equation 16-9 yields

$$U_r - U_\infty = GMm\left(0 - \frac{1}{r}\right)$$

But, by definition $U_\infty = 0$; therefore,

$$\boxed{U_r = -\frac{GMm}{r}} \qquad [16\text{-}10]$$

The negative sign in Equation 16-10 appears because zero for potential energy was chosen at $r = \infty$ and because the gravitational force is attractive. As two masses are brought closer together, their potential energy *decreases* (becomes more negative). Particles *attract* one another through the gravitational force; consequently, energy must be added to a system of particles interacting by the gravitational force to separate them and raise their potential energy to zero.

Figure 16-11a shows the gravitational potential energy between two point masses M and m as a function of their separation distance r.

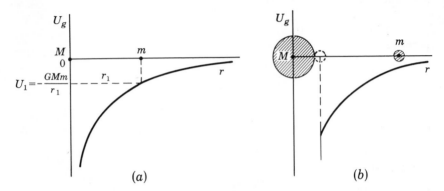

Figure 16-11. (a) Gravitational potential energy U_g as a function of the separation distance r between point particles of masses m and M. (b) Gravitational potential energy as a function of the separation distance between the centers of two spheres of masses m and M.

We can derive the gravitational force between two particles, separated by a distance r, from their gravitational potential energy $U_r = -GMm/r$. We use the general relation

[12-15]
$$F = -\frac{dU}{dr}$$

Then,
$$F = -\left(\frac{d}{dr}\right)\left(-\frac{GMm}{r}\right) = -\frac{GMm}{r^2}$$

The minus sign appearing in the term $-GMm/r^2$ simply indicates that the force of mass M on m is attractive, its direction being *opposite* to that of the radius vector extending from M to m.

Equation 16-10 expresses the potential energy of two *point* particles. It gives, as well, the potential energy between two spherical bodies. Just as the gravitational *force* between two spherical shells can be computed by regarding the entire mass of each shell as concentrated at a point at its center, so too the gravitational *potential energy* between two nonoverlapping spherical shells is computed by assuming the masses of the shells to be concentrated at their respective centers. The proof is given in Section 16-8.

The potential energy between two spherical masses M and m is illustrated in Figure 16-11b.

Because the Earth is a near sphere, we may replace it by a point mass at its center when we wish to find its gravitational potential energy with a second body. For a mass m located at the Earth's surface, we may write the potential energy as $U_g = -Gm_em/r_e$, where m_e is the Earth's mass and r_e is the Earth's radius (the separation distance between m and the center of the Earth).

Potential energy is, of course, a scalar quantity. Thus, the gravitational potential energy of a system of three or more bodies is merely the sum of the respective potential energies for each interacting pair. For the masses m_1, m_2, and m_3 shown in Figure 16-1, the total gravitational potential energy U_g of the system is

$$U_g = U_{12} + U_{13} + U_{23} = -\frac{Gm_1m_2}{r_{12}} - \frac{Gm_1m_3}{r_{13}} - \frac{Gm_2m_3}{r_{23}} \qquad [16\text{-}11]$$

Notice that introducing additional particles into the system *decreases* the system's potential energy. This reflects the fact that all particles mutually attract one another; if one is to separate them, additional energy must be added to the system.

Example 5 An object of mass m close to the Earth's surface is raised through a vertical height Δy. Show that, if Δy is small compared with the Earth's radius r_e, the general relation for gravitational potential energy reduces to the familiar relation $\Delta U = mg\,\Delta y$.

From Equation 16-9,

$$\Delta U = U_2 - U_1 = Gm_em\left(\frac{1}{r_1} - \frac{1}{r_2}\right)$$

We choose $r_1 = r_e$ and $r_2 = r_e + \Delta y$. See Figure 16-12. If $\Delta y \ll r_e$, we can write $-1/r_2$ as

$$-\frac{1}{r_2} = -\frac{1}{r_e + \Delta y} = -\frac{1}{r_e}\left[\frac{1}{1 + \Delta y/r_e}\right]$$

$$= -\frac{1}{r_e}[1 - (\Delta y/r_e) - (\Delta y/r_e)^2 \cdots] \simeq -\frac{1}{r_e} + \frac{\Delta y}{r_e^2}$$

Then Equation 16-9 becomes

$$\Delta U = Gm_em\left[\frac{1}{r_e} + \left(-\frac{1}{r_e} + \frac{\Delta y}{r_e^2}\right)\right] = m(Gm_e/r_e^2)\,\Delta y$$

But, by definition,

[16-3] $$g = Gm_e/r_e^2$$

Therefore, $$\Delta U = mg\,\Delta y.$$

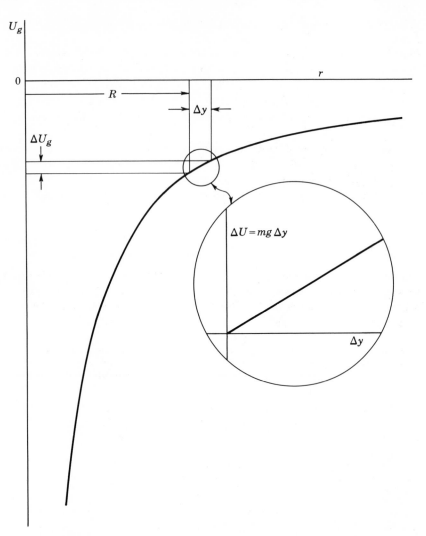

Figure 16-12. For objects close to the Earth, the gravitational potential energy difference is given by $\Delta U_g = mg\,\Delta y$.

Example 6   Masses of 400 kg and 100 kg are fixed in position and separated by 10.0 m, as shown in Figure 16-13a. (a) How much work must be done to move a 1.0 kg mass from point A, 2.0 m from the 400 kg mass, to point B, 2.0 m from the 100 kg mass? (b) With what minimum initial kinetic energy must the 1.0 kg mass be projected to the right from point A to reach point B? (c) With what minimum kinetic energy must the 1.0 kg mass be projected to the left from point B to reach point A?

(a) To find the work done in moving the 1.0 kg mass a distance 6.0 m to the right of point A, we can *not* simply multiply the resultant force on the particle at A by the 6.0 m displacement: the resultant force on the particle *varies* with distance. We can find the work done most simply by computing the difference in the gravitational potential energy of the entire system for the 1.0 kg mass, first at point A and then at point B. Using Equations 16-10 and 16-11 we have:

$$\text{Point } A: \; U_A = -G\frac{(1.0 \text{ kg})(400 \text{ kg})}{(2.0 \text{ m})} - G\frac{(1.0 \text{ kg})(100 \text{ kg})}{(8.0 \text{ m})} - G\frac{(400 \text{ kg})(100 \text{ kg})}{(10.0 \text{ m})}$$

$$\text{Point } B: \; U_B = -G\frac{(1.0 \text{ kg})(400 \text{ kg})}{(8.0 \text{ m})} - G\frac{(1.0 \text{ kg})(100 \text{ kg})}{(2.0 \text{ m})} - G\frac{(400 \text{ kg})(100 \text{ kg})}{(10.0 \text{ m})}$$

Therefore,

$$U_B - U_A = (6.7 \times 10^{-11} \text{ nt-m}^2/\text{kg}^2)(113 \text{ kg}^2/\text{m}) = 7.6 \times 10^{-9} \text{ joule}$$

Notice that the third term in the equation for U_A is the same as the third term in the equation for U_B. This term represents the gravitational potential energy arising from the interaction of the 100 kg and 400 kg masses, and it does not change, because these masses maintain the same separation distance. Therefore, when we compute $U_B - U_A$, the third terms cancel, and we need not be concerned with them hereafter.

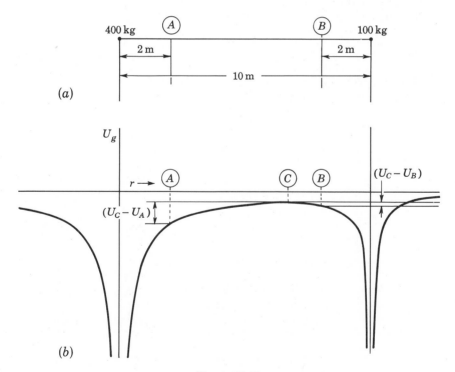

Figure 16-13

Positive work of 7.6×10^{-9} joule is done in transporting the 1.0 kg mass from A to B along *any route*. If a 2.0 kg mass were moved from A to B, twice as much work would be required. It is useful, then, to give a special name to the gravitational potential energy between a unit mass and a system of fixed masses. This quantity is called the *gravitational potential*, $V_g = U_g/m$. In our example, the difference in gravitational potential between the points A and B is 7.6×10^{-9} joule/kg, point B being at a higher gravitational potential than point A.

(b) The kinetic energy with which the 1.0 kg mass must be projected toward the right from point A to reach point B is *not* equal to 7.6×10^{-9} joule, which is the difference in the gravitational potential energy of the system for these two configurations. This is obvious when we examine a graph of the potential energy of the system as a function of the position of the 1.0 kg mass, its position to the right relative to the 400 kg mass being given by r. See Figure 16-13b.

The plot of U_g as a function of r is arrived at by taking the scalar sum of the two potential-energy terms representing the interaction of the 1.0 kg mass with the 400 kg and 100 kg masses respectively.

We see from Figure 16-13b that if a particle, beginning at point A, is to reach point B, it must traverse the potential hill. The kinetic energy with which the 1.0 kg mass must be projected from A to reach the top of, and pass over, the potential hill is $U_C - U_A$, where U_C is the gravitational potential energy at point C, the location of the maximum.

The maximum in U occurs at that point at which its rate of change with respect to r is zero; that is, $dU/dr = 0$.

The resultant force on the 1.0 kg particle is, of course, just the negative of the slope: $F = -dU/dr$, as shown in Section 12-2. Thus, U is an extremum (a maximum or minimum) at the point where the resultant force on the 1.0 kg mass is zero. The separate forces arising from the 400 kg and 100 kg masses are of equal magnitude but oppositely directed.

The forces have equal magnitude when

$$G\frac{(400 \text{ kg})(1.0 \text{ kg})}{r^2} = G\frac{(100 \text{ kg})(1.0 \text{ kg})}{(10.0 \text{ m} - r)^2}$$

This equation reduces to

$$3r^2 - 80r + 400 = 0$$

Solving this quadratic equation yields

$$r = 6.7 \text{ m, and } 20 \text{ m}$$

We discard the second solution since it corresponds to the situation in which the particle is to the *left* of the 400 kg mass. (In this location the 400 kg and 100 kg masses produce equal forces on the 1.0 kg mass, but both forces are to the *right* and do not give a zero resultant force.) The location r_C of the potential-energy maximum is, therefore, 6.7 m to the right of the 400 kg mass. When the 1.0 kg mass is at point C, the gravitational potential energy is

$$U_C = -G\frac{(1.0 \text{ kg})(400 \text{ kg})}{(6.7 \text{ m})} - G\frac{(1.0 \text{ kg})(100 \text{ kg})}{(3.3 \text{ m})} - G\frac{(400 \text{ kg})(100 \text{ kg})}{(10.0 \text{ m})}$$

The difference in gravitational energy between points C and A is then

$$U_C - U_A = (6.7 \times 10^{-11} \text{ nt-m}^2/\text{kg}^2)(123 \text{ kg}^2/\text{m}) = 8.2 \times 10^{-9} \text{ joule}$$

If the 1.0 kg mass is projected to the right from point A with kinetic energy $K_A = U_C - U_A = 8.2 \times 10^{-9}$ joule, it will reach point B. This is just enough kinetic energy to allow it, so to speak, to coast over the potential hill. The particle arrives at point B with a kinetic energy of $U_C - U_B = (8.2 - 7.6) \times 10^{-9}$ joule $= 0.6 \times 10^{-9}$ joule.

(c) The minimum kinetic energy permitting the 1.0 kg mass to pass over the potential hill starting from point B is $K_B = U_C - U_B = 0.6 \times 10^{-9}$ joule. The mass then arrives at point A with *more* kinetic energy than that with which it left point B.

The type of problem we have solved here has important applications. If one is to determine the flight pattern of a space probe, to reach the moon or a planet, one must compute the gravitational potential energy of the probe-Earth-Sun-Moon-planet system with the probe at various locations in space. The probe can reach the Moon or another planet, of course, only if it has sufficient kinetic energy to surmount the gravitational potential hills encountered en route.

16-6 The energetics of planetary motion The total linear momentum of a sun-planet system is constant. So is the total angular momentum. Here we treat the third important constant of the motion for a planet-sun system: the total mechanical energy.

We assume that one of the bodies interacting under the gravitational force is very massive and remains at rest. The total mechanical energy E_m of the system is, then, the sum of the kinetic energy K of the light body and the system's gravitational potential energy U_g:

$$E_m = K + U_g = \text{constant}$$

$$\boxed{E_m = \tfrac{1}{2}mv^2 + \left(-\frac{GMm}{r}\right)}$$ [16-12]

The conservation of energy law, Equation 16-12, together with the conservation law of angular momentum, prescribes that the motion of the light particle m be along the path of a conic section. Whether the mass m traces out an ellipse, a parabola, or a hyperbola is determined by the value of the total mechanical energy E_m:

$$E_m < 0, \quad \text{elliptical path}$$

$$E_m = 0, \quad \text{parabolic path}$$

$$E_m > 0, \quad \text{hyperbolic path}$$

We can distinguish among these paths by considering a simple situation in which a body of mass m, initially at a distance R from a massive body M, is projected at right angles to the line joining m to M. We shall imagine that the body can be launched from the same point with different initial speeds v_i.

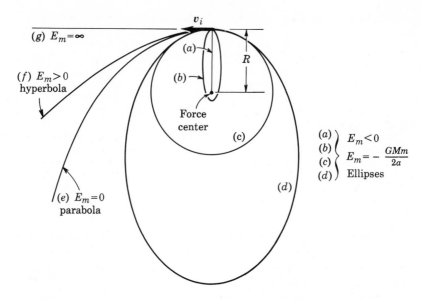

Figure 16-14. Paths of a particle projected at a distance R from a massive particle with various initial speeds v_i. The paths are (a) a straight line, (b) an ellipse, (c) a circle, (d) an ellipse, (e) a parabola, (f) a hyperbola, and (g) a straight line.

See Figure 16-14. Since R is always the same, the initial potential energy is always the same, and the value of the total energy E_m is then determined by the initial speed v_i:

$$E_m = \tfrac{1}{2}mv_i^2 - \frac{GMm}{R}$$

(a) First suppose that the body is dropped from rest. Then $v_i = 0$ and $E_m = -GMm/R$. The body falls in a straight line (but *not* at constant acceleration) toward the force center, gaining kinetic energy as it loses potential energy. It finally strikes the massive body. The total energy at *any* time is $-GMm/R$.

(b) The body is now given a small initial speed at right angles to the radius vector R. It is now a satellite as it moves in a highly eccentric elliptical orbit, being launched from the apogee position. The major axis $2a$ of the ellipse is only slightly larger than the distance R. The motion is *bound*, in that the satellite retraces its elliptical path about the force center indefinitely and can be separated from the force center only if external work is done on the system.

We can find the system's total energy at *any* time by considering the total energy at the instant the satellite is launched; $U_i = -GMm/R \simeq -GMm/2a$ and $K_i = \frac{1}{2}mv_i{}^2 \simeq 0$. Therefore,

$$E_m = -\frac{GMm}{2a}$$ [16-13]

The relation given in Equation 16-13, although obtained here for a rather special case, is, in fact, a general one that gives the total mechanical energy of any gravitationally *bound particle*.† The energy E_m depends *only* on the semimajor axis a, and *not* on the semiminor axis or the eccentricity of the ellipse.

(c) The initial speed is now large enough so that the satellite moves in a circular path. The circle is, of course, an ellipse with equal semimajor and semiminor axes, where a is now equal to the radius R. The kinetic energy, the potential energy, and E_m are all constant.

The gravitational force supplies the centripetal force on the satellite; therefore,

$$\Sigma \mathbf{F} = m\mathbf{a}$$

$$\frac{GMm}{R^2} = \frac{mv^2}{R}$$

which can be written

$$\frac{1}{2}mv^2 = \frac{\frac{1}{2}GMm}{R}$$ [16-14]

Thus, for circular orbits, the body's kinetic energy is half the magnitude of the system's potential energy. However,

$$E_m = K + U = \frac{1}{2}mv^2 + \left(-\frac{GMm}{R}\right)$$

Using Equation 16-14 yields

$$E_m = \frac{\frac{1}{2}GMm}{R} - \frac{GMm}{R} = -\frac{GMm}{2R}$$

Since the radius R is also the semimajor axis a,

$$E_m = -\frac{GMm}{2a}$$

† *Ibid.*

in agreement with Equation 16-13. The total energy for a circular orbit is just half of the potential energy.

Since the total energy of a bound system is negative, an orbiting particle can be freed, or unbound, from the force center only if energy is added to the system to bring the system's total energy to zero. The *binding energy* E_b of the system is defined as the energy which, when added to system, brings E_m to zero. When work in the amount of E_b is done on the system to separate the particles from one another by an infinite distance, then the particles will be left in a state of rest. Inasmuch as $E_m = -GMm/2a$ for a satellite in an elliptical orbit, the binding energy is $E_b = GMm/2a$. See Figure 16-15.

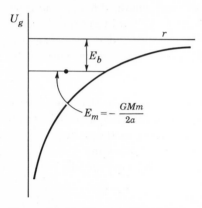

Figure 16-15. The binding energy E_b of a gravitationally bound particle moving in an elliptical orbit of semimajor axis a.

(d) Suppose now that the initial speed is larger than that for a circular orbit. The particle then moves in an elliptical path of larger semimajor axis, having been launched from the perigee position. The total energy, $E_m = -GMm/2a$, is larger than in parts (a), (b), and (c), inasmuch as E_m is less negative.

Although a number of elliptical paths, all with the *same semimajor axis* but with different semiminor axes, have the *same mechanical energy*, these orbits *differ* according to the *angular momentum* of the system. The angular momentum is a maximum for a circular orbit; it is zero for a highly eccentric orbit in which the velocity vector v is parallel to the radius vector r and in which $L = mr \times v = 0$. It can be shown that the magnitude of the angular momentum for an elliptical orbit is given, in general, by†

$$L = \sqrt{GMm^2}(b/\sqrt{a}) \qquad [16\text{-}15]$$

Thus, whereas the energy of the system depends on the *size* (the semimajor axis a) of the orbit, the angular momentum depends on the *shape* (the semiminor axis b).

(e) In parts (a), (b), (c), and (d) the initial kinetic energy was always small enough such that the system's total energy E_m was negative. Now suppose that the initial speed is large enough such that the total energy is just zero. Under these conditions the body is *not* bound to the force

† *Ibid.*

center. It moves out along a *parabolic* path, and never returns. When the body has reached a great distance (infinite) from the force center, the potential energy is zero and so is the kinetic energy.

Energy conservation requires that

$$E_m = \tfrac{1}{2}mv_e{}^2 - \frac{GMm}{R} = 0$$

or

$$v_e = \sqrt{\frac{2GM}{R}} \qquad [16\text{-}16]$$

where v_e is the *escape velocity* from the distance R.

At what speed must an object be launched from the Earth's surface to escape? Equation 16-16 shows that the object escapes from the Earth's gravitational field when launched *in any direction* (above the horizontal) with the speed $v_e \geq 7$ miles/sec. It is interesting to compare the escape velocity v_e with v_c, the speed necessary to put a satellite into circular orbit about the Earth. From Example 2, Section 5-1,

$$v_c = \sqrt{gR} = \sqrt{GM/R} = v_e/\sqrt{2}$$

Thus, the kinetic energy a satellite must have to escape from the Earth is only twice the kinetic energy it must have to be put into orbit around the Earth.

(f) If the body is launched with a higher speed than the escape velocity, it moves in a hyperbolic path with the force center at one focus of the *hyperbola*. The body is *not* bound to the force center, and $E_m > 0$. When it recedes to an infinite distance from the force center, the potential energy becomes zero. But at this infinite distance the body still has kinetic energy remaining.

(g) For the extreme situation, in which $v_i = \infty$, the body travels in a straight line. It goes so fast that the gravitational force cannot deflect or slow it.

Astronomical observations amply demonstrate that classical mechanics—Newton's laws of motion and the law of universal gravitation—adequately describe the motions of celestial bodies. Several fine points concerning planetary motion are also accounted for by the theory of gravitation:

(1) Not only is each planet attracted by the Sun, but also it is gravitationally attracted by the other planets. The planetary orbits are, consequently, not precisely ellipses about the Sun; irregularities, or *perturbations*, in these orbits arise mainly from the influences of neighboring planets. The planet Neptune was discovered through observation in 1846, when it was found that perturbations in the orbit of the planet Uranus could most easily be accounted for by assuming

the existence of a heretofore unobserved planet. In 1930, the outermost planet Pluto was discovered in similar fashion.

(2) The phenomenon of the *tides* is explainable in terms of the difference in the gravitational attraction of the Moon on various parts of the Earth which, with its mantle of oceans, is not a rigid body.

(3) The *precession of the equinoxes* (see Problem 16-41), whereby the Earth's spin axis precesses very slowly (once in 26,000 years) about a normal to the plane of the Earth's orbit, has its origin in the nonsphericity of the Earth and the resulting gravitational *torque* of the Sun on the Earth.

(4) The spin and orbital angular speeds of the Moon are equal. Thus, the same side of the Moon always faces the Earth. Similarly, the same face of the planet Mercury (and probably also of Venus) always points toward the Sun. Eventually, all planets will have equal orbital and spin rates because *tidal friction* reduces the spin kinetic energy of the planets and, therefore, their spin rates. Dissipation of energy through tidal friction, which results from the relative motion of various parts of the orbiting body, will cease only when the spin and orbital speeds are identical.

(5) The elliptical orbit of the innermost planet, Mercury, precesses very slowly (527.7 seconds of arc per century) about the Sun. This *precession of the perihelion of Mercury* is due primarily to perturbations by neighboring planets. The observed magnitude of Mercury's precession differs, however, from the theoretical value computed from classical mechanics, by 1.5 seconds of arc per century. The observed precession rate is in agreement with the theoretical value computed from the general theory of relativity.

Example 7   When fired from the Earth, a certain projectile attains an altitude of 4000 miles (equal to the Earth's radius). If the projectile is then to become an Earth satellite, its speed must be increased by the firing of a rocket. (a) What is the minimum speed the projectile must acquire at the 4000 miles altitude to be set into orbit? (b) What is then the satellite's maximum speed?

(a) The satellite's orbit, as shown in Figure 16-16, is an ellipse with the Earth's center at one focus. At the *apogee* position, the satellite's speed is v_a and its distance from the center of the Earth is r_a. The corresponding quantities for the *perigee* position are v_p and r_p, where r_p is the Earth's radius and $r_a = 2r_p$.

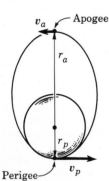

The total mechanical energy of the Earth-satellite system is, from Equation 16-13,

$$E_m = -Gm_e m/2a = -Gm_e m/(r_a + r_p)$$

where m_e and m are the masses of the Earth and satellite, respectively, and the major axis of the ellipse is $2a = r_a + r_p$.

The total energy at the apogee position may be written

$$E_m = \tfrac{1}{2}mv_a{}^2 - Gm_e m/r_a$$

Equating the two expressions for E_m above and solving for $v_a{}^2$ yields

Figure 16-16. One orbit for an Earth satellite.

$$v_a{}^2 = 2Gm_e\left(\frac{1}{r_a} - \frac{1}{r_a + r_p}\right) = 2\frac{Gm_e}{r_p}\left(\frac{r_p}{r_a} - \frac{r_p}{r_a + r_p}\right)$$

The quantity Gm_e/r_p is equal to v_c^2, where v_c is the speed of a satellite (18,000 miles/hour) in a circular orbit about the Earth near the Earth's surface. Recalling that $r_a = 2r_p$ we have, then,

$$v_a^2 = 2v_c^2(\tfrac{1}{2} - \tfrac{1}{3})$$

$$v_a = v_c/\sqrt{3} = (18,000 \text{ mi/hr})/\sqrt{3} = 10,400 \text{ mi/hr}$$

(b) We find v_p, which is the maximum satellite speed, by applying angular-momentum conservation:

$$mv_p r_p = mv_a r_a$$

$$v_p = (r_a/r_p)v_a = 2v_a = 20,800 \text{ mi/hr}$$

Notice that if the object were fired horizontally at the Earth's surface at the speed 20,800 miles/hour, it would orbit the Earth in exactly the same elliptical path as that shown in Figure 16-16.

16-7   Inertial and gravitational mass, and the principle of equivalence

In dynamics the concept of mass is used in two entirely different ways. The *inertial mass* m_i of a body is defined as the quantitative measure of the body's inertia; this is the mass that appears in Newton's second law, $\Sigma \, F = m_i a$. "Mass" is also used in another sense: as a measure of the gravitational "charge" of a body in the law of universal gravitation. It is the so-called *gravitational mass* m_g that appears in the relation $F_g = Gm_{g_1}m_{g_2}/r^2$. Thus, the inertial and the gravitational masses are quite different properties of matter.

There is no reason, a priori, why these two distinctly different types of mass should be simply related—that is, why bodies having the same gravitational charge should have the same inertial mass. Certainly, bodies having identical electric charges need not have identical inertial masses. For example, the proton and positron are particles that have precisely equal electric charges, yet their inertial masses differ by a factor of 1836. That the inertial mass of a body is, in fact, equal to its gravitational mass—or, more properly, that the ratio of the inertial to the gravitational mass is a constant—is a *result of experiment*.

Consider Galileo's simple free-fall experiment, in which a body with inertial and gravitational masses m_i and m_g, respectively, falls under the influence of the Earth's gravity. Newton's second law gives

$$\Sigma \, F = m_i a$$

$$m_g g = m_i a$$

or
$$\frac{m_g}{m_i} = \frac{a}{g}$$

The symbol g represents the constant Gm_{ge}/r_e^2 (Equation 16-3), where m_{ge} and r_e are the Earth's gravitational mass and radius. The measured acceleration of the freely falling body is a.

If we apply Newton's second law to a second body with inertial and gravitational masses M_i and M_g, falling freely at the same location with an acceleration A, we have

$$\frac{M_g}{M_i} = \frac{A}{g}$$

Experiment shows that $a = A$. *All* bodies at a given location fall with the *same* acceleration. Therefore,

$$\frac{m_g}{m_i} = \frac{M_g}{M_i} = \text{constant}$$

By choosing the same units for the inertial and gravitational masses, the constant is made equal to 1. It then follows that

$$\boxed{m_g = m_i \quad \text{and} \quad M_g = M_i}$$

The equality of the inertial and gravitational masses has been confirmed with more sophisticated experiments. Newton performed an experiment with bodies of various masses in a pendulum. The most recent results indicate that m_i equals m_g to within a few parts in 10^{12}. Clearly, the use of the single term *mass* to denote both the inertial and gravitational properties of matter is justified.

In classical physics the equality, or equivalence, of m_i and m_g must be regarded as an extraordinary coincidence. This equality is, however, taken as a basic assumption in the *principle of equivalence*, a fundamental part of the general theory of relativity, formulated by Albert Einstein (1879–1955). Because the principle of equivalence relates to accelerated reference frames, let us first recall some earlier results.

In Section 10-6 we found that an observer in an accelerated reference frame can use Newton's second law to describe a body's motion, provided that he invoke, in addition to the "real" forces acting on the body, a fictitious inertial force, $F_i = -m_i A$. The inertial force depends on the body's *inertial* mass m_i and on the acceleration A of the observer's reference frame relative to an inertial frame. The noninertial observer therefore writes Newton's second law as

[10-35] $\Sigma F + F_i = m_i a$

with $F_i = -m_i A$

Here a is the body's acceleration as measured in the accelerated frame.

Now, if the gravitational mass is precisely the same as the inertial mass, the inertial force can be written equally well as

$$F_i = -_imA = -m_gA$$

Then the "fictitious" *inertial force* is, like a gravitational force, *proportional to the observed body's gravitational mass*. *An inertial force arising in a noninertial frame is altogether equivalent to, and indistinguishable from, a gravitational force as perceived by an observer at rest in this accelerated frame.* This is the *principle of equivalence.*

As an illustration of equivalence, consider the situation experienced by a man in a closed capsule. If such an observer sees unattached objects accelerate together toward a floor, he may conclude (a) that he is in empty space and that the capsule (but not its unattached contents) is accelerating relative to the fixed stars or he may equally well conclude (b) that his capsule is at rest in an inertial frame in the vicinity of a celestial body and that the objects in the capsule are falling under the influence of this body's gravitational field. There is *no* way of telling the difference between the two alternative viewpoints by *any* experiment in physics.

Example 8   An inclined plane of 37° is attached to the floor of a truck, as shown in Figure 16-17a. (a) With what acceleration must the truck move to the right

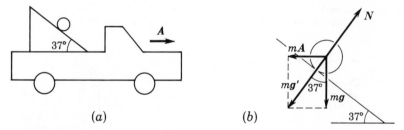

(a)   (b)

Figure 16-17. (a) A ball is at rest on an inclined plane attached to a truck which moves to the right with acceleration A. (b) The forces acting on the ball as viewed by an observer at rest on the truck.

so that a ball placed on this incline will remain at rest? (b) What is the effective acceleration due to gravity from the viewpoint of an observer on the accelerated truck?

(a) We view the ball and incline as an observer at rest on the truck. In this accelerated (noninertial) reference frame the ball is subject to *three* forces: the normal force N, which makes an angle of 37° with respect to the vertical, the weight mg vertically downward, and an inertial force $-mA$, where A is the acceleration to the right of the truck relative to the ground. From the point of view of an observer at rest in the truck, the inertial force $-m_iA$ is equivalent to, and indistinguishable from, a gravitational pull $-m_gA$. Therefore, the effective weight mg' of the ball, as seen from the truck, is the vector sum of the Earth's force mg and the inertial force $-m\mathbf{A}$. If the ball is to remain at rest on the incline, the effective weight must be perpendicular to the incline and equal in magnitude to the normal force $\mathbf{N}$.

From the geometry of Figure 16-17b, it follows that

$$\tan 37° = mA/mg = A/g$$

$$A = g \tan 37° = (9.8 \text{ m/sec}^2)(0.60)$$

$$A = 5.9 \text{ m/sec}^2$$

(b) The effective weight mg' is given by

$$mg' = mg + m\mathbf{A}$$

and the magnitude of the effective acceleration due to gravity $\mathbf{g}'$ is

$$g' = \sqrt{g^2 + A^2} = \sqrt{(9.8)^2 + (5.9)^2} \text{ m/sec}^2$$

$$g' = 11.5 \text{ m/sec}^2$$

For an accelerated observer traveling with the truck, the direction "down" (indicated by a plumb line or by the path of an object dropped from rest in this accelerated system) is along the direction of mg'. Thus, an observer on the truck finds that a dropped 1.0 kg object falls perpendicularly to the plane of the incline with an acceleration of 11.5 m/sec² and that its weight is 11.5 nt.

16-8 Gravitational potential energy of a solid sphere We first calculate the gravitational potential energy between a point mass m and a thin shell of mass M, radius R, and thickness ΔR, as shown in Figure 16-18a. The several

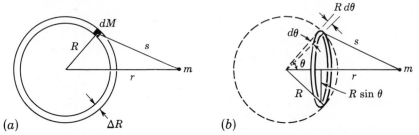

Figure 16-18. (a) A particle of mass m interacting with a spherical shell. (b) A ring of the shell interacting with the point mass.

mass elements dM composing the spherical shell are at different distances s from the point mass m and make different contributions to the potential energy. Between some one mass element dM and the point mass m there is a contribution to the potential energy of $-Gm \, dM/s$ (Equation 16-10), where s is the distance from dM to m. To find the total potential energy between the shell and the point mass m, we must add the contributions from all mass elements composing the shell.

Assume, first, that the point mass is outside the spherical shell, as shown in Figure 16-18b. All points on the thin ring, whose axis is the line joining the center of the shell and the mass m, are the same distance s from the mass m. The radius of this ring is $R \sin \theta$, its width is $R \, d\theta$, and its thickness is ΔR; therefore, the volume of the ring is

$$dV = (2\pi R \sin \theta)(R \, d\theta)(\Delta R)$$

Assuming the mass density ρ to be constant throughout the spherical shell, the mass dM of the ring is just $\rho \, dV$. We then have, for the gravitational potential energy between the ring and the point mass m,

$$dU = -Gm\rho \, dV/s = -Gm\rho(2\pi R^2 \, \Delta R) \sin \theta \, d\theta/s \qquad [16\text{-}16]$$

where $V = 4\pi R^2 \, \Delta R$ is the volume of the shell.

To find the total potential energy, we merely sum over all the rings which make up the spherical shell, the various rings differing in s and θ. We add the rings from $\theta = 0$ to $\theta = \pi$ or, equivalently, from $s = r - R$ to $s = r + R$, where r is the distance from the center of the shell to the point mass m.

The variables s and θ are related to one another through the law of cosines:

$$s^2 = R^2 + r^2 - 2Rr \cos \theta$$

Both R and r are fixed. Thus, when we take the differentials of both sides of the equation above we obtain

$$2s \, ds = 2Rr \sin \theta \, d\theta$$

$$\sin \theta \, d\theta = s \, ds/Rr$$

Using this relation in Equation 16-16 and integrating, we obtain

$$U = \int dU = -Gm\rho(2\pi R^2 \, \Delta R) \int_{r-R}^{r+R} (s \, ds/Rr)/s = (-Gm\rho 2\pi R \, \Delta R/r) \int_{r-R}^{r+R} ds$$

$$[16\text{-}17]$$

$$U = -4\pi R^2 \, \Delta R \rho Gm/r = -Gm\rho V/r$$

Since the density of the shell was assumed constant, we have $\rho V = M_s$, where M_s is the total mass of the shell. We can write the equation above as

$$U = -GmM_s/r \qquad [16\text{-}18]$$

Thus, as long as the mass m is *outside* the shell, the gravitational potential energy between it and the shell is found by considering all of the shell's mass M_s as being at the shell's center. It follows, then, that the gravitational force between an exterior point mass and a spherical shell is equivalent to that of two point masses a distance r apart.

A solid sphere is just the sum of spherical shells of different radii R. Therefore, a solid sphere is gravitationally equivalent to a particle of the same mass at its center when interacting with an external mass.

We now compute the gravitational potential energy and gravitational force between a point mass m and a spherical *shell* when the point is *inside* the shell. We merely change the limits of the variable s in Equation 16-17. Now s varies from $R - r$ to $R + r$, and

$$\int_{R-r}^{R+r} ds = 2r$$

Therefore,

$$U = -GmM_s/R$$

The potential energy is *constant* throughout the *interior* of the shell. The magnitude of the potential energy is the same as that with the point particle at the exterior surface of the shell. Since the potential energy does not change with the position of the particle within the shell, the gravitational force (equal to the negative of the space rate of change of potential energy) is *zero*.

Example 9 Imagine that a small hole is drilled diametrically through the Earth. A particle of mass m is located in this tunnel at a distance r from the center. What are the magnitude and direction of the gravitational force on the particle?

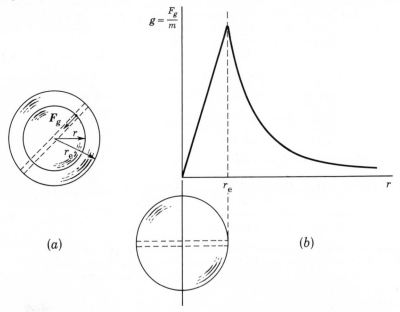

Figure 16-19. (a) Gravitational force on a particle traveling in a tunnel through the Earth. (b) Gravitational field intensity g as a function of the separation distance between a particle and the Earth's center.

The situation is shown in Figure 16-19a. We imagine the particle to be just at the outside of a sphere of radius r and inside a spherical shell with inner and outer radii of r and r_e, respectively, where r_e is the radius of the earth.

We know that there is *no* gravitational force on the particle m arising from the *surrounding* shell. Therefore, the resultant gravitational force on m arises solely from the sphere of radius r:

$$F_g = GMm/r^2$$

where M is the mass of this sphere.

If we assume that the Earth has a uniform density ρ, we may write

$$M = \rho \tfrac{4}{3}\pi r^3$$

Using the relation for M in the equation for F_g given above, we obtain

$$F_g = \frac{G(\rho\frac{4}{3}\pi r^3)m}{r^2} = Kmr$$

where K is a constant. The gravitational force on the particle is proportional to its distance r from the Earth's center.

When the particle is at the Earth's surface, $r = r_e$, and the force F_g on the particle is mg_s. Therefore,

$$mg_s = Kmr_e$$

where g_s is the acceleration due to gravity at the Earth's surface.

Eliminating K from the last two equations gives, finally,

$$F_g = (r/r_e)mg_s$$

Thus a 1.0 kg mass weighs 9.8 nt at the Earth's surface. Halfway toward the Earth's center it weighs 4.9 nt, and at the center of the Earth its weight is zero. We shall see in Chapter 17 that a particle released from rest and falling into such a tunnel executes simple harmonic motion.

Figure 16-19b shows the magnitude of the gravitational field intensity g (the gravitational force per unit mass) as a function of the distance r from the center of the Earth. The magnitude of g falls off inversely as r^2 for all points outside the Earth's surface; within the Earth, g increases linearly with r.

16-9 Summary The universal attractive force of gravitation between any two particles of masses m_1 and m_2 separated by a distance r has the magnitude

[16-1] $$F_g = \frac{Gm_1m_2}{r^2}$$

where G is a constant. The gravitational force is a central force. This relation gives, as well, the force between two nonoverlapping spherical shells whose centers are separated by r. The gravitational force on a point mass in the interior of a spherical shell of mass is zero.

The gravitational field intensity g is the gravitational force per unit gravitational mass:

$$g = \frac{F_g}{m}$$

The gravitational field may be represented by gravitational lines of force.

In their general form, Kepler's laws are written: (1) a particle under the influence of a central attractive inverse-square force moves in the path of a conic section; (2) the radius vector from the force center to the particle sweeps out equal areas in equal times; (3) for elliptical orbits, the square of the period is proportional, for a given force center, to the cube of the ellipse's semimajor axis.

The gravitational potential energy between two masses M and m separated by r is

[16-10] $$U_r = -\frac{GMm}{r}$$

When a particle moves under the influence of a fixed gravitational force center, its total mechanical energy E_m is constant and its orbital angular momentum L is constant:

[16-12] $$E_m = K + U = \tfrac{1}{2}mv^2 - \frac{GMm}{r} = \text{constant}$$

$$L = r \times p = \text{constant}$$

When $E_m > 0$, the path is hyperbolic; when $E_m = 0$, the path is parabolic; when $E_m < 0$, the particle is bound in an elliptical orbit, and

[16-13] $$E_m = -\frac{GMm}{2a}$$

where a is the semimajor axis.

Experiment shows that a body's inertial mass is equal to its gravitational mass. Therefore, by the principle of equivalence, an inertial force observed in an accelerated reference frame is equivalent to, and indistinguishable from, a gravitational force.

PROBLEMS

16-1   The Earth's mass is 81 times that of the Moon; the Earth's radius is 3.7 times that of the Moon. (a) Show that the weight of an object on the Moon's surface is approximately one sixth of its weight on the Earth's surface. (b) If a man can throw a ball vertically upward to a maximum height of 100 feet on Earth, to what height on the Moon can he throw the ball (neglect air resistance in both instances)? (c) If a block slides down a frictionless incline from rest in a time of 5.0 sec on Earth, what is the corresponding time interval with the same block and incline on the Moon?

16-2   Four particles, each of mass m, are placed at the corners of a square of edge length d. (a) What is the magnitude of the resultant gravitational force on any one mass? (b) If the four particles are released simultaneously from rest, where do they collide?

16-3   Compute the gravitational torque on a Cavendish torsional balance under the following circumstances. Two small spheres, each of 15 gm, are placed at the ends of a light rod 40 cm long. Two fixed masses of 10 kg are placed at positions to produce a maximum torque on the rod. The distance between centers for each pair of light and massive spheres is 8.0 cm.

16-4   (a) Show that the acceleration of the Moon toward the Earth is 8.9 × 10^{-3} feet/sec². The radius of the Moon's orbit about the Earth is 240,000 miles; the Moon's period is 27.3 days. (b) Show that the acceleration due to gravity, g, at the location of the Moon is smaller than that at the Earth's surface by the factor $(\frac{1}{60})^2$. (c) The radius of the Moon's orbit is 60 times the radius of the Earth. Show that the information given in parts (a) and (b) is consistent with the assumption that the force on objects attracted by the Earth varies inversely with the square of the distance from the Earth's center. Newton used such arguments to show that the universal gravitational force varies inversely as the distance squared.

16-5   Two masses of 1.0 kg and 2.0 kg are held fixed when they are separated by a distance of 1.0 m. (a) At what point (other than infinity) can a third mass of 2.0 kg be placed such that it will remain at rest? (b) What additional external force must then be applied to the 1.0 kg mass to keep it fixed?

16-6   A particle of mass m is placed midway between two fixed bodies, each of mass M. Is m in stable equilibrium with respect to a displacement (a) along the line joining the two fixed bodies and (b) along a line at right angles to the line joining the two fixed bodies?

16-7   At what distance from the Earth's center would a satellite in circular orbit above the Earth's equator revolve around the Earth with the same angular speed as that of the Earth's spin about its axis and thereby appear to be stationary as viewed from Earth?

16-8   In a hydrogen atom, an electron of mass m_e moves in a circular orbit of 0.53×10^{-10} m about a fixed proton of mass $m_p = 1836\,m_e$. The tangential speed of the electron in its orbit is 2.19×10^6 m/sec. Find and compare the magnitudes of (a) the gravitational force of the proton on the electron, (b) the gravitational force of the Earth on the electron, and (c) the centripetal force on the electron as it revolves in its circular orbit.

16-9   Before Cavendish first determined the numerical value of G, the absolute masses of the Sun and planets were not calculable from the universal law of gravitation. One could, however, find the ratio of the masses of any two bodies, each of which has an orbiting satellite. As an example, calculate, without using the numerical value of G, the ratio of Jupiter's mass to the Earth's mass from the following observations:

	Radius of orbit	*Period*
Earth–moon	2.4×10^5 miles	27 days
Jupiter–moon	4.2×10^5 miles	3.5 days

16-10   (a) Find the magnitude and direction of the additional force (other than the Earth's gravitational force) which must be applied to a satellite of mass m if it is to move in a circular orbit 4000 miles above the Earth's surface at an angular speed of 1.0 revolutions/day. (b) How might such a force be produced?

16-11 What is the ratio of the acceleration due to the Sun's gravity, g_s, to that due to the Earth's gravity, g_e, for an object on the surface of the Earth?

16-12 What is the fractional change in the acceleration due to the Earth's gravity between a point at the Earth's surface and a second point (a) 100 miles above the surface and (b) 1000 miles above the surface?

16-13 ★ The magnitude of g is less at the Equator than at the poles because of two factors: the Earth's spin, and the equatorial bulge. The distance from the center of the Earth to the Equator is 13.5 miles more than from the center to the poles. Assuming, for simplicity, that the Earth is a perfect sphere of radius 3960 miles, compute the fractional decrease in g for (a) a point 13.5 miles *above* the Earth's surface and (b) a point 13.5 miles *below* the Earth's surface (neglect the Earth's spin).

16-14 A 1.0 kg mass is located on the surface of the planet Mercury. (a) Find the magnitudes of the Sun's gravitational force and the planet Mercury's gravitational force on this 1.0 kg mass. (b) What is the acceleration due to the Sun's gravity and the acceleration due to Mercury's gravity for an object on the surface of Mercury? (The masses of Mercury and the Sun are 3.2×10^{24} kg and 2.0×10^{30} kg, respectively. The radius of the planet Mercury is 2.4×10^6 m and its distance from the Sun is 5.0×10^{10} m.)

16-15 ★ A plumb bob of mass m is suspended from a massless cord at the latitude θ. The tension in the cord is T and the angle of the cord with respect to the equatorial plane is φ. See Figure 16-5 and Example 4, Section 16-3. (a) Find the apparent weight T as a function of the true weight mg and the angle θ. (b) Find $\tan \theta$ as a function of $\tan \varphi$.

16-16 Suppose that the angular speed ω of the Earth's rotation were drastically increased such that $R\omega^2/g$ equaled 1, where R is the radius of the Earth. What would be (a) the direction and (b) the magnitude of the apparent weight of a body of mass m at the latitude θ?

16-17 ★ (a) What are the direction and magnitude of the force exerted on an object of mass m by a string from which the object is suspended, if the object is at rest with respect to the Earth's surface at the latitude 45°? (b) If one were to find that the string in part (a) made an angle of 15° with respect to the line from the Earth's center to the object, what then would be the duration, in hours, of one Earth "day"?

16-18 A projectile is fired vertically upward from the Earth's surface at a speed of 18,000 miles/hour. (a) What is its maximum distance from the Earth's surface? (Assume the Earth's radius to be 4000 miles.) (b) At what angle with respect to the vertical would the projectile have to be fired to be placed in stable orbit?

16-19 If the Moon were at rest at its present distance from the Earth, (a) with what speed would it strike the Earth's surface and (b) approximately how long would it take for the Moon to fall this distance?

16-20 How much energy is necessary to transport a 2000 kg space ship from the North Pole of the Earth to the north pole of the Moon?

16-21   Assume that the Moon is a sphere of uniform density. Find the ratio
of its spin rotational kinetic energy to the gravitational potential
energy between the Moon and Earth. (Moon's radius, 1740 km;
Moon-Earth distance, 387,000 km; Earth's mass, 5.98×10^{24} kg.)

16-22   What is the difference in gravitational potential between a point on the
Earth closest to the Sun and a second point on the Earth farthest from
the Sun? The Sun's and Earth's masses are 1.99×10^{30} kg and 5.98×10^{24} kg, respectively.

16-23   (a) At what point in space should a mass m be placed if the Sun's
gravitational force on it is to be equal in magnitude but opposite in
direction to the Earth's gravitational force on it? (b) At what point
should this mass m be placed if the gravitational force of the Sun is to
be equal in magnitude and in direction to that of the Earth's gravitational force? (c) How much work would be required to move the object
from the location of part (a) to that of part (b)?

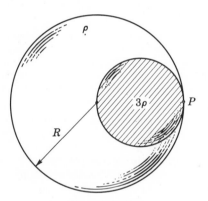

Figure 16-20.

16-24 ★   A sphere of radius R has a uniform density ρ except for the spherical
region of radius $R/2$ (see Figure 16-20), for which the density is 3ρ.
(a) What is the gravitational potential energy between the sphere and a
point mass m located at the point P? (b) What is the ratio of g, at
point P, to g at a second point on the sphere, diametrically opposite P?

16-25   Two bodies of masses m and $2m$, respectively, are a distance d apart.
(a) What must be the ratio of their speeds and the directions of their
velocities if each mass is to rotate in a circle about the system's center
of mass, which remains at rest? (b) What is the minimum energy
required to separate completely these two masses?

16-26   Upon re-entry into the Earth's atmosphere, a satellite loses energy by
virtue of the atmospheric drag. The force of drag is initially small
compared with the radial force on the satellite, and the satellite always
moves in an approximately circular orbit. (a) Show that upon re-entry
the satellite actually *speeds up*, rather than slows down. (b) Show that

the angular momentum of the satellite actually decreases, rather than remains constant.

16-27   A 200 kg satellite, initially in orbit about the Earth's equator at an altitude of 400 km, eventually re-enters the Earth's atmosphere and, because of air friction, comes to rest on the Earth's surface. Find the total thermal energy dissipated (a) when the satellite was initially moving in the same direction as the Earth was rotating in and (b) when the satellite was moving in the direction opposite to the Earth's rotation.

16-28 ★   Two 1.0 kg particles are connected to opposite ends of a massless 1.0 m rod. The rod is free to rotate about a horizontal axis through its center and perpendicular to it. Assume the Earth to be a perfect sphere. Find the difference in gravitational potential energy between the two particles and the Earth (a) when the rod is horizontal and (b) when the rod is vertical. (c) In which position is the potential energy lower?

16-29   The average speed of an oxygen molecule (mass, 32 amu) in the air near the Earth's surface is 460 m/sec. (a) Would an oxygen molecule moving at this speed have enough kinetic energy to escape from the Earth's gravitational field? (b) Would an oxygen molecule having this kinetic energy at the Moon's surface be able to escape from the Moon's gravitational field? (c) Work parts (a) and (b) for a hydrogen molecule (2 amu) and a xenon atom (129 amu), both of whose kinetic energies are the same as that of the oxygen molecule.

16-30 ★   A point mass m is at a distance d from one end, and a distance $(d + L)$ from the other end, of a long slender uniform rod of length L and total mass M. (a) Find the gravitational force between the point mass and the rod. (b) At what location can one consider all of the mass M of the rod to be concentrated, to obtain the same force?

16-31 ★   What minimum kinetic energy must a 100 kg space probe have if it is to be projected from the Earth to the Moon? (Neglect the rotation of the Earth and Moon.) See Tables 16-1 and 16-2 for the necessary data.

16-32   Find the minimum energy necessary to remove the following planets from the gravitational influence of the Sun: (a) the Earth, (b) Jupiter. See Tables 16-1 and 16-2 for the necessary data.

16-33   A satellite is observed to orbit a planet close to the planet's surface with a period T. Show that the average density of the planet is $3\pi/GT^2$.

16-34   What is the number of points on the elliptical (noncircular) path of a planet orbiting the Sun, for which the planet will have the same speed?

16-35   A satellite is observed to be moving at a speed $v = \sqrt{\frac{4}{3}Gm_e/r}$ in a direction such that v makes an angle of 30° with respect to the radius vector r from the Earth's center to the instantaneous location of the satellite. (a) Find the distance of closest approach of the satellite to the Earth. (b) What is the maximum distance between the satellite and the Earth? (c) Calculate the period of the satellite.

16-36 ★   A particle of mass m moves in an elliptical path about a gravitational center of force of mass M. Show that the total mechanical energy of the system can be written as $E_m = \frac{1}{2}mv_r^2 + L^2/2mr^2 - GMm/r$, where v_r is the component of the velocity along the direction of the radius vector $\boldsymbol{r}$ from the force center to m and L is the orbital angular momentum of the system.

16-37   A 170-pound Earth satellite (Telstar I) has a period of 158 minutes; its altitude is 593 miles when it is at the perigee position. (a) What is the satellite's altitude when it is at the apogee position? (b) What is the satellite's speed at the perigee position? (c) What is the binding energy of this satellite to the Earth?

16-38   A planet of mass m moves in an elliptical orbit about a fixed star of mass M. The closest distance between planet and star is r_{min} and the greatest distance is r_{max}. Determine the ratio of the planet's kinetic energy to the magnitude of the gravitational potential energy, (a) at the near point and (b) at the far point. (c) Show that these ratios are to one another as the inverse ratio of the respective distances.

16-39 ★ A missile is fired from the Earth's surface at an angle θ with respect to the horizontal. Its initial speed v_i is equal to that of an Earth satellite traveling close to the surface of the Earth. Show that at its highest point (the apogee position of its elliptical orbit, the Earth's center being the focus), (a) the distance of the missile from the center of the Earth is $r_e \sin^2 \theta/(1 - \cos \theta)$, where r_e is the Earth's radius, and (b) its speed is $v_i(1 - \cos \theta)/\sin \theta$.

16-40 ★ Halley's comet, which moves in a highly eccentric, elliptical orbit about the Sun, has been observed in the vicinity of the Earth every 75.5 years since the year 87 B.C. Its perihelion distance is 8.9×10^{10} m. (a) What is the greatest distance between Halley's comet and the Sun? (b) What is the comet's maximum speed?

16-41 ★ The Earth has an equatorial bulge and its spin axis is not perpendicular to the plane of its orbit about the Sun. See Figure 16-21. Because the

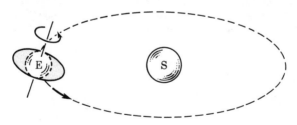

Figure 16-21.

gravitational force decreases with distance, the Sun's pull on the near protuberance of the Earth is greater than its pull on the far protuberance. These forces are *not* collinear; consequently, the Sun applies a resultant gravitational *torque* on the spinning Earth, the direction of the torque being perpendicular to the Earth's spin angular momentum. Thus, the Earth precesses, like a top. See Section 15-5. (a) What is the direction of the gravitational torque of the Sun on the Earth (with respect to the arrangement shown in Figure 16-21)? (b) What is the direction of the angular-velocity vector representing the precession of the Earth's spin axis?

This phenomenon, first explained by Newton, is known as the *precession of the equinoxes*. The period of the precession is 25,000 years. One consequence of this very slow precession is that the North Star (Polaris), toward which the Earth's spin axis presently points, will, as time goes on, no longer be found along this axis.

16-42 A 160-pound man is in an elevator traveling upward initially at 64 feet/sec. What is the man's apparent weight as indicated by the scale on which he stands, when the elevator's acceleration is (a) 8.0 feet/sec^2 up, (b) 8.0 feet/sec^2 down, (c) 64.0 feet/sec^2 down, (d) 32.0 feet/sec^2 down, and (e) 32.0 feet/sec^2 up?

16-43 ⋆ A man is on a horizontal rotating platform turning with the constant angular speed ω. The man is at a distance r from the platform's axis of rotation. (a) What is the "downward" direction as observed by this man? (b) With what initial acceleration will the man observe a dropped object to fall?

16-44 Find the "apparent" acceleration due to gravity inside a space ship (a) when the space ship is at rest at the Earth's equator and (b) when the space ship is traveling in an elliptical orbit about the Equator near the Earth's surface. Ignore the Earth's rotation.

16-45 ⋆ A point mass m initially hangs from a massless string, the other end of the string being attached to a point P about which the string can swing freely. (a) Using the principle of equivalence, describe the motion of the mass m when the point P is accelerated to the right with an acceleration $g/3$? (b) If the string is vertical before point P is accelerated, through what angle will the string oscillate when P has the acceleration $g/3$?

16-46 A space station consists of two capsules joined by a rod of 100 feet. At what angular speed must the rod and capsules rotate if artificial gravity equivalent to that at the Earth's surface is to be produced within the capsules?

S E V E N T E E N

ELASTICITY AND SIMPLE
HARMONIC MOTION

This chapter is concerned with deformable bodies. We first consider interatomic forces and the relation which governs deformations on the atomic
scale. We then treat two simple cases illustrating Hooke's law: the
stretched helical spring and the twisted torsion rod. The moduli that
summarize the elastic properties of solids are defined. We then consider the
dynamics of simple harmonic motion and arrive at formulas relating the
periods of oscillation to the inertial and elastic properties for a number of
oscillatory mechanical systems. Finally, we discuss damped simple harmonic
motion, forced oscillations, and resonance.

17-1 Hooke's law No solid is perfectly rigid. When several external
forces act on a solid at rest and the resultant of these forces is zero, the body
remains at rest. The solid's size, or shape, or both will, however, be altered
by the external forces; that is, the body will be deformed.

Any deformation, whether caused by stretching, compressing, bending,
twisting, or squeezing, has its origin in the change in the relative positions

of the atoms comprising the solid. A change in the size or shape of the solid merely reflects, on a large scale, submicroscopic changes in atomic separations.

If we are to understand the forces on a single molecule (or atom) in a solid, arising from its interaction with its neighboring molecules, then we must first know the force on one molecule due to a second molecule. Figure 17-1 shows a typical intermolecular force as a function of the separation distance between the two interacting molecules. At large separation distances the force is negligible. As this distance is decreased, the molecules

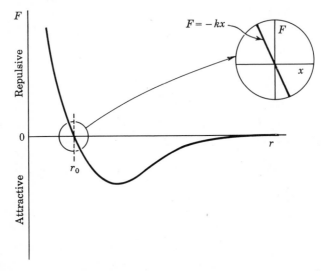

Figure 17-1. Intermolecular force as a function of the intermolecular distance. In the vicinity of the equilibrium distance r_0, the force is proportional to the displacement.

attract one another, the attractive force increasing with decreasing distance. At relatively small separation distances the intermolecular force becomes strongly repulsive.

A molecule, acted upon by a second molecule assumed fixed, is at the equilibrium position r_0 when the force on it is zero. At smaller separation distances the molecule is repelled, and at greater separation distances it is attracted. Moreover, for small displacements from the equilibrium position, the force is proportional to the atom's displacement, in the fashion of an ordinary helical spring. For such small displacements we may write

$$F = -kx$$ [17-1]

where F is the *restoring* force, as indicated by the minus sign, x is the displacement from the equilibrium position, and k is a constant dependent upon the interaction between the molecules.

Because the resultant force between atoms in a solid varies directly as the atomic displacement, all large-scale deformations of a solid follow a similarly simple relation: *for small displacements, the size of the deformation is proportional to the deforming force (or torque).* This is called *Hooke's law* after Robert Hooke (1635–1703), who first described elastic deformations through this relation.

Figure 17-2 shows two simple macroscopic structures illustrating Hooke's law: a helical spring and a torsion rod. When two equal forces are applied in

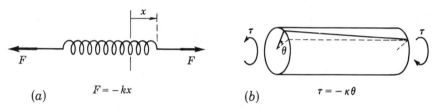

(a) $F = -kx$ (b) $\tau = -\kappa\theta$

Figure 17-2. Two simple structures illustrating Hooke's law: (a) a helical spring, for which the restoring force is proportional to the displacement x; (b) a torsion rod, for which the restoring torque is proportional to the angular displacement θ.

opposite directions to the ends of the spring, the spring is stretched (or compressed). The restoring force is equal in magnitude, and opposite in direction, to the externally applied force. Thus, for the helical spring, Equation 17-1 is again obeyed, where k, now called the force constant, or spring constant, depends on the spring's material and dimensions.

The torsion rod of Figure 17-2b is twisted by external torques (applied at its ends) of equal magnitude but oppositely directed. Experiment shows that the angular displacement θ of one end relative to the other end is, for small angles, directly proportional to the applied torque. That is, the rod, through its elastic properties, applies a *restoring torque*, this torque τ being related to θ by

$$\tau = -\kappa\theta \qquad [17\text{-}2]$$

where the torsion, or torque, constant κ depends on the rod's material and dimensions. Thus, a spring—or, in still simpler form, a wire—may be used to measure forces through its elongation, and a torsion rod, or stiff fiber, may be used to measure torques through its angular deformation.

Figure 17-3 shows the change in the length of a rod subjected to forces at its ends. The forces are *tensile* forces if they elongate the rod, and *compressive* forces if they reduce the rod's original length. Hooke's law holds for *small* relative changes in length. For sufficiently large forces, the rod is stretched or compressed beyond the so-called *elastic limit*,† the point at which the force departs from linear dependence on elongation. Still greater forces may give the rod a *permanent set*, so that if the external forces are

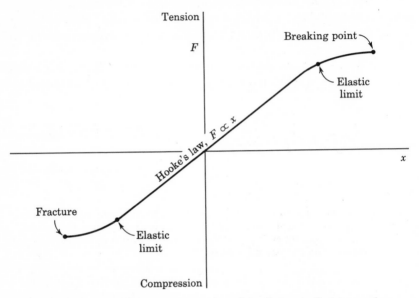

Figure 17-3. A simplified representation of the force applied to a rod as a function of the rod's length. Hooke's law is obeyed in the region between the elastic limits.

removed, the rod does not spring back to its undeformed configuration. In the limit, the rod is ripped apart by tensile forces or fractured by compressive forces.

Example 1 The rod shown in Figure 17-4 is held fixed at its left end. When a weight of 20 pounds is suspended from a wheel 0.50 feet in radius, attached to the right end of the rod, the wheel turns through 10°. What is the torsion constant of the rod?

† It is unfortunate that the term *elastic limit* is used to denote that condition at which the deformed body departs from Hooke's law. If the restoring force depends only on the elongation but not, for example, on the prior history of the body, then the force is a conservative force. Consequently, work done in deforming the body appears as elastic potential energy, energy not being dissipated. Thus, any deformation is "elastic," as contrasted with "inelastic" (or dissipative), as long as the force is conservative, even when the force is no longer strictly proportional to the elongation. For most materials, the elastic limit occurs *close to* the point where a permanent set is produced, and the work done in deforming the body is *not* recoverable as mechanical energy.

The twisting torque τ is provided by a force of 20 pounds with a moment arm of 0.50 feet. Therefore, from Equation 17-2,

$$\kappa = \tau/\theta = r_\perp F/\theta = (0.50 \text{ ft})(20 \text{ lb})/(10°)$$
$$= 1.0 \text{ lb-ft/degree} = 0.018 \text{ lb-ft/rad}$$

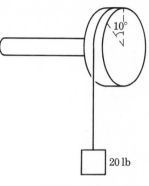

17-2   The elastic moduli   The elastic properties of a spring are characterized by the force constant k; those of a torsion rod, by the torque constant κ. The value of k or of κ depends, not only on the particular material of which the spring or rod is composed, but also on its dimensions and shape. It is, therefore, useful to define parameters describing the elastic properties of materials that are not dependent on dimensions or shape. These parameters are called the *elastic moduli*: *Young's modulus*, Y, the *shear modulus*, G, and the *bulk modulus*, B. Each modulus describes a different kind of elastic deformation.

Figure 17-4

For small deformations, whatever the type, the simple Hooke's-law relation holds,

$$\text{Elastic modulus} = \frac{\text{stress}}{\text{strain}} \qquad [17\text{-}3]$$

where the elastic moduli are constants characteristic of the material. Stress always has the units of force per unit area; strain is a dimensionless number describing relative deformation. The modulus, therefore, has the units of stress. Table 17-1 shows the deformations involved in the definitions of the Young, shear, and bulk moduli.

Young's modulus is a measure of the elastic properties of a body which is stretched or compressed. The body is subject to longitudinal tensile or compressive forces at its ends. Inasmuch as any part of the body is in equilibrium, the same longitudinal force also acts at every cross section throughout the length of the body. The longitudinal stress σ_l is defined as the *l*ongitudinal force F_l per unit cross-sectional area A; $\sigma_l = F_l/A$. The strain is the elongation (or compression) ΔL of the rod, divided by its original unstrained length L. Hooke's law, Equation 17-3, then gives

$$Y = \frac{F_l/A}{\Delta L/L} \qquad [17\text{-}4]$$

The macroscopic change in length of the rod reflects a microscopic change in separation distance between atoms comprising the rod. For small relative

Table 17-1

Macroscopic deformation	Microscopic deformation	Stress	Strain	Hooke's law	Equation number
Young's modulus = Y (change in shape and volume)		$\sigma_l = \dfrac{F_l}{A}$	$\dfrac{\Delta L}{L}$	$Y = \dfrac{F_l/A}{\Delta L/L}$	[17-4]
Shear modulus = G (change in shape only)		$\sigma_t = \dfrac{F_t}{A}$	$\tan\theta = \dfrac{\Delta w}{l}$ $\theta \simeq \dfrac{\Delta w}{l}$	$G = \dfrac{F_t/A}{\Delta w/l}$	[17-5]
Bulk modulus = B (change in volume only)		$p = \dfrac{F_n}{A}$	$\dfrac{\Delta V}{V}$	$B = -\dfrac{p}{\Delta V/V}$	[17-6]

intermolecular displacements, the force is proportional to the displacement (see Figure 17-1). Since Hooke's law holds on the atomic scale, we are not surprised to find this law—stress proportional to strain—holding on the macroscopic scale.

The stretching of a rod is accompanied by a change in its transverse dimensions, the cross section decreasing as the rod is stretched and increasing as the rod is compressed. It is found that the fractional change in a characteristic transverse dimension is *not* the same as the fractional change in longitudinal length $\Delta L/L$. Therefore, the volume of a rod changes under longitudinal stresses. In fact, the volume of a rod is decreased under tension and increased under compression.

Shear deformation is that in which the body is subject to transverse forces F_t of equal magnitude and opposite direction, applied at opposite faces, each face having an area A. For small deformations, the shape changes but the volume remains constant, a rectangle becoming a parallelogram. The *transverse stress* σ_t is defined as the shear force F_t divided by the area A over which it is applied: $\sigma_t = F_t/A$. The shear strain is $\Delta w/l = \tan \theta$. For small angles (in radians), $\tan \theta \simeq \theta$. The shear modulus G is, by Equation 17-3,

$$G = \frac{F_t/A}{\Delta w/l} \qquad [17\text{-}5]$$

Bulk modulus, the third elastic modulus, describes the elastic deformation of a solid (or a fluid) when it is squeezed. For the bulk modulus we consider only the external forces acting at right angles to all surfaces of the solid. The solid's volume is thereby reduced. Such forces are most easily produced when the solid is immersed in a liquid and the liquid is compressed (as by a piston). The stress is again the force per unit area. The bulk stress p at a particular point is defined as the *normal force F_n divided by the small perpendicular surface area A over which the normal force acts: $p = F_n/A$. For fluids (liquids and gases) the bulk stress is called the *hydrostatic pressure*. The strain is the change in volume ΔV divided by the original volume V, and Hooke's law, Equation 17-3, becomes

$$B = -\frac{p}{\Delta V/V} \qquad [17\text{-}6]$$

The bulk modulus B is always taken to be positive; the minus sign is introduced in Equation 17-6 to show that an increase in pressure produces a decrease in volume. Sometimes it is useful to use the reciprocal of the bulk modulus B. This reciprocal is called the *compressibility*. Thus, a material having a high compressibility (or small bulk modulus) is one that is easily compressed.

Table 17-2

MATERIAL	YOUNG'S MODULUS, Y (nt/m²)	SHEAR MODULUS, G (nt/m²)	BULK MODULUS, B (nt/m²)
Aluminum	7.0×10^{10}	2.4×10^{10}	7.0×10^{10}
Copper	10×10^{10}	4.2×10^{10}	12×10^{10}
Brass	9.0×10^{10}	3.5×10^{10}	6.1×10^{10}
Iron, cast	$8.4–9.8 \times 10^{10}$	—	9.6×10^{10}
Steel	20×10^{10}	8.1×10^{10}	16×10^{10}
Glass	$6.5–7.8 \times 10^{10}$	$2.6–3.2 \times 10^{10}$	$5.0–5.5 \times 10^{10}$
Quartz	5.6×10^{10}	2.6×10^{10}	2.7×10^{10}

To convert to units of pounds per square inch, multiply each entry by the factor 1.450×10^{-4}.

Experimentally determined values of Y, G, and B for several common materials are listed in Table 17-2. The larger the modulus, the greater the stress required for a given strain. All three elastic moduli carry the units of stress, i.e., force per unit area.

For an isotropic material (one that has the same properties in all directions), all elastic deformations can be related to just *two* elastic moduli. Consequently, for such a material the three moduli Y, G, and B are not independent. It can be shown that the moduli are related by[†]

$$Y = \frac{9BG}{G + 3B}$$

We remarked earlier that the constants k and κ for a helical spring and torsion rod, respectively, depend on the dimensions of these structures. Analysis shows that the torque constant κ of Equation 17-2 is given by $\kappa = \pi Gr^4/2l$, where r is the radius of the cylindrical rod and l is its length.[‡] Since the shear modulus G appears in the equation for κ, it follows that, when a rod is twisted, it undergoes a shear deformation. Note that the torsion constant is proportional to the *fourth* power of the radius. Thus, a fine torsion fiber is extraordinarily sensitive to twisting torques, a minute torque producing a sizeable angular displacement.

The force constant k of an ordinary helical spring can be shown to be given by the relation $k = Gr^4/4nR^3$, where r is the radius of the wire, n is the number of turns in the helix, and R is the radius of any turn.[§] Surprisingly, perhaps, the elastic properties of a stretched or compressed spring depends on the shear modulus G, not Young's modulus; this arises from the fact that any small segment of the wire in a helical spring is twisted as the spring is elongated.

[†] See, for example, F. H. Newman and V. H. L. Searle, *The General Properties of Matter*, 5th ed., Edward Arnold, Ltd., London, 1957, pp. 110–130.
[‡] *Ibid.*
[§] *Ibid.*

Example 2   How much mass must be suspended from the end of a steel wire 1.0 m long and 1.0 mm in diameter to stretch it 0.50 mm?

From Equation 17-4,

$$Y = \frac{F_l/A}{\Delta L/L} = \frac{F_l L}{A \, \Delta L}$$

The tensile force F_l is produced by the weight, Mg, hung at the wire's end. The cross-sectional area A is $\frac{1}{4}\pi d^2$, where d is the diameter of the wire. Therefore,

$$Y = \frac{4MgL}{\pi d^2 \, \Delta L}$$

$$M = \frac{\pi Y d^2 \, \Delta L}{4gL} = \pi \frac{(2.0 \times 10^{11} \text{ nt/m}^2)(1.0 \times 10^{-3} \text{ m})^2(0.50 \times 10^{-3} \text{ m})}{4(9.8 \text{ m/sec}^2)(1.0 \text{ m})} = 8.0 \text{ kg}$$

17-3   Simple harmonic motion   We wish to inquire into the motion occurring when a particle is subject to an elastic linear restoring force, $F = -kx$. The resulting motion —*simple harmonic motion*—is characteristic of all bodies obeying Hooke's law. There are many situations in physics illustrating this behavior: a mass attached to a spring, an object attached to a torsion rod, a simple or compound pendulum, the atoms of any solid, the atoms of a molecule, the electrons in a conductor carrying alternating current, the electric or magnetic field

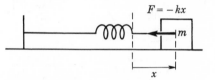

Figure 17-5. A simple harmonic oscillator. A mass m attached to a spring of force constant k, subject to a restoring force $F = -kx$, where x is the mass's displacement from its equilibrium position.

intensity in a simple electromagnetic wave, the pressure variations in a sound wave. Indeed, *any particle undergoing small oscillations about a point of stable equilibrium executes simple harmonic motion.*

As a prototype of a physical situation giving rise to simple harmonic motion, consider a body attached to a massless spring of force constant k. The body rests on a horizontal frictionless surface. See Figure 17-5. If the body is displaced from equilibrium and released, the only horizontal force acting on the mass m is the restoring force of the spring $F_s = -kx$, where x is the displacement from the equilibrium position. The minus sign indicates that the directions of the force and of the displacement are always opposite. Newton's law gives

$$\Sigma F_{\text{ext}} = ma$$

$$-kx = ma$$

which we may write as

$$a = -\left(\frac{k}{m}\right)x$$

or
$$\frac{d^2x}{dt^2} + \left(\frac{k}{m}\right)x = 0 \qquad [17\text{-}7]$$

It is easy to show that the solution of this second-order differential equation of the motion, Equation 17-7, is one in which x varies sinusoidally with respect to time. That is, the motion of a mass subject to a linear restoring force is simple harmonic motion. We need merely show that, for simple harmonic motion, the acceleration a is proportional to the negative of displacement.

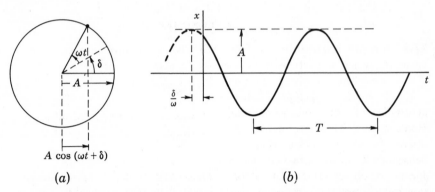

(a)   (b)

Figure 17-6. (a) Representation of the uniform circular motion corresponding to simple harmonic motion. (b) Displacement-time graph for simple harmonic motion with $x = A \cos(\omega t + \delta)$. The phase constant is δ; the angular frequency, ω; the amplitude, A; the period, T.

The kinematics of simple harmonic motion was treated in Section 5-4. There we saw that simple harmonic motion can be defined *kinematically* as the projection of uniform circular motion along a diameter. A particle's displacement x along some arbitrarily chosen X-axis at any time t is given by

[5-8] $$x = A \cos(\omega t + \delta) \qquad [17\text{-}8]$$

where A is the amplitude and ω is the angular frequency (in radians per second). The *phase constant* δ determines the particle's initial displacement; that is, when $t = 0$, then $x = A \cos \delta$. See Figure 17-6.

The instantaneous velocity and acceleration are found by taking time derivatives of Equation 17-8:

[5-8] $$v = \frac{dx}{dt} = -\omega A \sin(\omega t + \delta) \qquad [17\text{-}9]$$

[5-8] $$a = \frac{dv}{dt} = -\omega^2 A \cos(\omega t + \delta)$$

or,

$$a = -\omega^2 x$$ [17-10]

Thus, for simple harmonic motion, the acceleration *is* proportional to the negative of the displacement.

Comparing Equations 17-7 and 17-10 gives

$$\omega^2 = \frac{k}{m}$$ [17-11]

The period T, the time for one complete oscillation, and the frequency f, the number of oscillations per unit time, are then

[5-11] $$T = \frac{2\pi}{\omega} = 2\pi\sqrt{\frac{m}{k}}$$ [17-12]

[5-10] $$f = \frac{\omega}{2\pi} = \frac{1}{2\pi}\sqrt{\frac{k}{m}}$$ [17-13]

Note that the period and frequency do *not* depend on the amplitude A. The time for one oscillation depends on the body's inertia, as measured by m, and on the spring's elasticity, as measured by k, but *not* on the maximum displacement from the equilibrium position. We can say that the body's inertia makes the body overshoot the equilibrium position whereas the spring's elastic restoring force binds the body to the equilibrium position. The competing inertial and elastic effects are reflected in Equation 17-12, which shows that the period increases when the body's inertia m is increased and decreases when the spring's stiffness k is increased.

Example 3 A particle moves counterclockwise in a circle of radius A at constant angular frequency ω. The particle is at the positive X-axis at the time $t = 0$. By definition, the projection of the particle's motion along *any* diameter of the circle is simple harmonic motion. Write equations giving the displacement of the projection of the particle as a function of time for the axes (diameters) X, X', and X'' shown in Figure 17-7. The angular displacement of the X'-axis relative to the X-axis is 30°; that of the X''-axis, −90°.

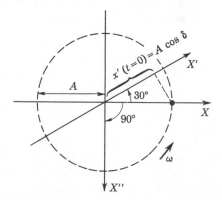

Figure 17-7. The simple harmonic motion corresponding to uniform circular motion for projection along three different diameters: X, X', and X''.

In general,

[17-8] $$x = A \cos (\omega t + \delta)$$

where $x = A \cos \delta,$ when $t = 0$

For motion along the X-axis, the phase angle δ is zero, inasmuch as the particle of the reference circle is at the $+X$-axis when $t = 0$. Relative to the X'-axis, the phase angle δ' is $-30° = -\pi/6$ radians. Relative to the X''-axis, the phase angle is $\delta'' = +90° = \pi/2$ radians. Therefore,

$$x = A \cos (\omega t + \delta) = A \cos \omega t$$
$$x' = A \cos (\omega t + \delta') = A \cos (\omega t - \pi/6)$$
$$x'' = A \cos (\omega t + \delta'') = A \cos (\omega t + \pi/2) = -A \sin \omega t$$

We note that, at a given time, the projections of the particle moving on the reference circle are not the same along the three different axes. For example: at $t = 0$ the projection along X is $x = +A$; along X', the projection is $x' = A \cos \delta' = +0.87A$; along X'', the projection is $x'' = A \cos \delta'' = 0$.

It was shown in Section 12-1 that the elastic potential energy U_s of a spring is given by

[12-10] $$U_s = \tfrac{1}{2}kx^2$$

Therefore, when a body attached to a spring oscillates in simple harmonic motion, we have, using Equation 17-8,

$$U_s = \tfrac{1}{2}kA^2 \cos^2 (\omega t + \delta)$$

The kinetic energy is given by

$$K = \tfrac{1}{2}mv^2 = \tfrac{1}{2}m\omega^2A^2 \sin^2 (\omega t + \delta) = \tfrac{1}{2}kA^2 \sin^2 (\omega t + \delta)$$

where we have used Equations 17-9 and 17-11.

The total mechanical energy E_m can then be written

$$E_m = K + U_s = \tfrac{1}{2}kA^2[\sin^2 (\omega t + \delta) + \cos^2 (\omega t + \delta)]$$

or

$$\boxed{E_m = \tfrac{1}{2}kA^2}$$ [17-14]

The energy of a simple harmonic oscillator is proportional to the *square of the amplitude*.

The total mechanical energy of an undamped simple harmonic oscillator is a constant. In the absence of dissipative forces, the oscillations persist indefinitely with undiminished amplitude. The kinetic and potential energies both vary sinusoidally with time, as shown in Figure 17-8, but their sum E_m does not change with time. The oscillating mass has a maximum kinetic energy when it passes through the equilibrium position ($x = 0$), and the spring has a maximum potential energy when the body is momentarily at rest at the amplitude position ($x = \pm A$).

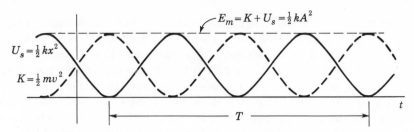

Figure 17-8. The variation with time of the kinetic energy K and the elastic potential energy U_s for a simple harmonic oscillator. Note that the total mechanical energy $E_m = K + U_s$ is constant.

Figure 17-8 shows the potential energy U_s as a function of time. It is also worth while, since simple harmonic motion is repetitive, to examine the potential energy as a function of the displacement. Figure 17-9 shows U_s as a function of x; $U_s = \frac{1}{2}kx^2$, a parabola.

Simple harmonic motion results from any physical situation in which the potential energy varies as the square of the displacement, in the fashion of $U_s \propto x^2$. This holds, for example, for an atom within a solid undergoing small excursions from its equilibrium position under the influence of inter-atomic forces. Figure 17-10 shows a typical interatomic potential-energy

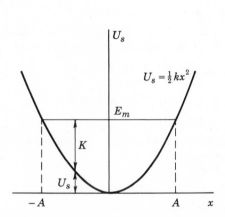

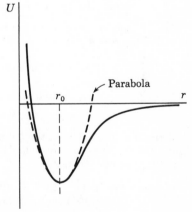

Figure 17-9. Elastic potential energy U_s as a function of displacement x for a simple harmonic oscillator. The motion is restricted to the region between the amplitude positions $x = \pm A$, for which the kinetic energy K is positive.

Figure 17-10. Interatomic potential energy as a function of separation distance. The curve is nearly parabolic in the vicinity of the equilibrium position r_0.

curve; indeed, the graph here corresponds to the force-displacement graph of Figure 17-1. In the vicinity of r_0, the distance for which U is a minimum, the curve is closely approximated by a parabola. Hence, small atomic oscillations result in simple harmonic motion. Large oscillations—occurring, for example, when a solid is heated—depart from the strictly parabolic portion of the curve. This departure from simple harmonic motion is manifest in the typical expansion of an object with a rise in temperature. More about this and other aspects of atomic oscillations in Section 19-4.

Example 4 A 2.0 kg block rests on a horizontal frictionless surface. The block is attached to the right end of a spring; the spring's left end is fixed. The block is displaced 5.0 cm to the right from its equilibrium position, and held motionless at this position by an external force of 10.0 nt. (a) What is the spring's force constant? (b) The block is then released. What is the period of the block's oscillations? What are (c) the force on the block, (d) the kinetic energy of the block, and (e) the potential energy of the spring, all at the time $t = \pi/15$ sec?

(a) From Equation 17-1,

$$k = F/x = (10.0 \text{ nt})/(0.050 \text{ m}) = 200 \text{ nt/m}$$

(b) The period is given by Equation 17-12:

$$T = 2\pi \sqrt{m/k} = 2\pi \sqrt{(2.0 \text{ kg})/(200 \text{ nt/m})} = \pi/5 \text{ sec}$$

(c) The force of the spring on the block at the time t is given by

$$F = -kx = -kA \cos (\omega t + \delta) = -kA \cos (2\pi t/T + \delta)$$

Since the motion is started from rest at the amplitude position $A = 0.050$ m, we know that $\delta = 0$. Therefore, at $t = \pi/15$ sec, the equation above becomes

$$F = -(200 \text{ nt/m})(0.050 \text{ m}) \cos \left[\frac{2\pi(\pi/15 \text{ sec})}{(\pi/5 \text{ sec})} \right]$$

$$= -(10.0 \text{ nt}) \cos 2\pi/3 = -(10.0 \text{ nt}) \cos 120°$$

$$F = +5.0 \text{ nt}$$

At the time $t = \pi/15$ sec, the 5.0 nt force of the spring on the block is to the right. The spring is compressed at this instant ($x < 0$).

(d) The kinetic energy is

$$K = \tfrac{1}{2}mv^2 = \tfrac{1}{2}m\omega^2 A^2 \sin^2 (\omega t + \delta) = \tfrac{1}{2}kA^2 \sin^2 (\omega t + \delta)$$

$$= \tfrac{1}{2}(200 \text{ nt/m})(0.050 \text{ m})^2 \sin^2 120°$$

$$K = 0.19 \text{ joule}$$

(e) We can find the spring's potential energy by using the relation $U_s = \tfrac{1}{2}kA^2 \cos^2 (\omega t + \delta)$. But, we can equally well find the spring's potential energy at $t = \pi/15$ sec by subtracting the block's kinetic energy at this instant from the total energy $E_m = \tfrac{1}{2}kA^2$ of the block-spring system:

$$U_s = \tfrac{1}{2}kA^2 - K$$

$$U_s = \tfrac{1}{2}(200 \text{ nt/m})(0.050 \text{ m})^2 - (0.19 \text{ joule}) = 0.06 \text{ joule}$$

Example 5   Show that the time averages of the kinetic and the potential energies of a simple harmonic oscillator are the same.

The proof is obvious from inspection of Figure 17-8. Over a time of one period the area under the kinetic-energy curve equals the area under the potential-energy curve. Therefore, the average kinetic energy $\overline{K}$ equals the average potential energy $\overline{U}_s$. Their sum $\overline{K} + \overline{U}_s$ is the constant $\frac{1}{2}kA^2$. Therefore, $\overline{K} = \overline{U}_s = \frac{1}{4}kA^2$.

The proof can, of course, be carried out analytically by computing the time averages of K and U_s over the time of one period T:

$$\overline{K} = \frac{1}{T} \int_0^T K \, dt = \frac{1}{T} \int_0^T \tfrac{1}{2}kA^2 \sin^2(\omega t + \delta) \, dt = \tfrac{1}{4}kA^2$$

$$\overline{U}_s = \frac{1}{T} \int_0^T U_s \, dt = \frac{1}{T} \int_0^T \tfrac{1}{2}kA^2 \cos^2(\omega t + \delta) \, dt = \tfrac{1}{4}kA^2$$

17-4   Applications of simple harmonic motion   Having analyzed the motion of a mass attached to a spring in some detail, we can now treat quite easily several other examples of simple harmonic motion. We will consider, as an example, *angular* simple harmonic motion, in which the *angular* displacement varies sinusoidally with time, following the relation

$$\theta = \theta_m \cos(\omega t + \delta)$$

where θ_m, called the angular amplitude, is the maximum angular displacement, and ω is again the angular frequency of oscillation. (The symbol ω used here does *not* denote the angular velocity $d\theta/dt$.)

We first remind the reader of the parallelism between translational and rotational quantities: for angular motion the displacement θ replaces x and the angular acceleration α replaces the linear acceleration a. Moreover, the torque replaces the force F, the moment of inertia I replaces the mass m, and the torque constant κ replaces the force constant k.

By analogy with Equations 17-8, 17-9, and 17-10, it follows that, for *angular* simple harmonic motion, the instantaneous angular acceleration, $\alpha = d^2\theta/dt^2$, is related to θ by

$$\alpha = -\omega^2\theta \qquad\qquad [17\text{-}15]$$

It is easy to derive the relation giving the peroid T of angular simple harmonic motion in terms of the inertial and elastic properties of the oscillator. If a body free to rotate about a fixed axis is subject to a restoring torque proportional to θ, then

[17-2] $\tau = -\kappa\theta$

where κ is the torque constant. By Newton's second law for rotation,

[14-4] $\Sigma\tau = I\alpha$

Table 17-3

Oscillator	Figure	Newton's Law	Acceleration-displacement relation	Period
Spring	$F = -kx$ x	$\Sigma F = ma$ $-kx = ma$	$a_x = -\left(\dfrac{k}{m}\right)x$	[17-12] $T = 2\pi\sqrt{\dfrac{m}{k}}$
Torsion pendulum	θ $\tau = -\kappa\theta$	$\Sigma\tau = I\alpha$ $-\kappa\theta = I\alpha$	$\alpha = -\left(\dfrac{\kappa}{I}\right)\theta$	[17-16] $T = 2\pi\sqrt{\dfrac{I}{\kappa}}$
Simple pendulum	θ l $l\sin\theta$ mg $\tau = -mgl\sin\theta$	$\Sigma\tau = I\alpha$ $-mgl\sin\theta = ml^2\alpha$ For small θ, $\sin\theta \simeq \theta$, and $-mgl\theta$ $\simeq ml^2\alpha$	$\alpha = -\left(\dfrac{g}{l}\right)\theta$	[17-17] $T = 2\pi\sqrt{\dfrac{l}{g}}$
Compound pendulum	L_{cm} θ mg $\tau = -mgL_{cm}\sin\theta$	$\Sigma\tau = I\alpha$ $-mgL_{cm}\sin\theta$ $= I\alpha$ For small θ, $\sin\theta \simeq \theta$, and $-mgL_{cm}\theta$ $\simeq I\alpha$	$\alpha = -\left(\dfrac{mgL_{cm}}{I}\right)\theta$	[17-18] $T = 2\pi\sqrt{\dfrac{I}{mgL_{cm}}}$

If the only torque acting on the body is the restoring torque $\Sigma\tau = \tau$, the two equations above yield

$$\alpha = -\left(\frac{\kappa}{I}\right)\theta$$

Comparing this equation with Equation 17-15 gives

$$\omega^2 = \frac{\kappa}{I}$$

The period T and frequency f are then

$$T = \frac{2\pi}{\omega} = 2\pi\sqrt{\frac{I}{\kappa}} \qquad\qquad [17\text{-}16]$$

$$f = \frac{\omega}{2\pi} = \frac{1}{2\pi}\sqrt{\frac{\kappa}{I}}$$

The equations above are analogous to Equations 17-12 and 17-13 for *linear* simple harmonic motion.

Table 17-3 shows three situations giving rise to angular simple harmonic motion: (a) an oscillating body attached to a torsion rod—a *torsion pendulum*; (b) a mass point attached to a massless string and swinging in a vertical plane—a *simple pendulum*; (c) an extended body swinging in a vertical plane about some point of support—a *compound pendulum*.

The acting forces and torques are shown in the figures. In each instance the angular acceleration α is found (for small angular displacements) to be proportional to $-\theta$; consequently, the bodies execute angular simple harmonic motion. The last column in Table 17-3 gives the periods of oscillations for the three pendula. The important aspects of linear simple harmonic motion, discussed in Section 17-3 and illustrated by a mass on a spring, are preserved: for small oscillations, the period is independent of the amplitude but depends on the characteristic inertial and elastic parameters, and the total mechanical energy is constant while the potential and kinetic energies each vary sinusoidally with time. Now we shall describe some features of these three pendula.

The torsion pendulum. Here the period depends on the torsion constant κ and on the moment of inertia I of the body attached to the torsion rod. Both κ and I are computed relative to an axis of rotation coinciding with the axis of the torsion rod. This arrangement is commonly used in such sensitive instruments as the torsion pendulum of the Cavendish experiment (Section 16-2), the galvanometer, and the hair spring of a watch. The body's angular motion is simple harmonic as long as the twisting of the rod follows Hooke's law, the elastic restoring torque being proportional to the angular displacement. Since the period is given by

$$[17\text{-}16] \qquad\qquad T = 2\pi \sqrt{\frac{I}{\kappa}}$$

the torsion pendulum may be used to measure a body's moment of inertia if the constant κ is known and the period T is determined. Conversely, knowing I and timing the oscillations permits κ to be computed, as will be shown in Example 6.

The simple pendulum. As is shown in Table 17-3, relative to a horizontal axis of rotation at the point of support of the string, the gravitational torque on the point particle has magnitude $mgl \sin \theta$, where $l \sin \theta$ is the moment arm of the weight mg. Relative to the same axis, the particle's moment of inertia is $I = ml^2$.

For small angles, the sine of θ may, to a very close approximation, be replaced by θ (in radians). For example, for $\theta = 10° = 0.175$ radians, we have $\sin \theta = 0.174$. The motion is simple harmonic, and the period T of the pendulum becomes

$$T = 2\pi \sqrt{\frac{l}{g}} \qquad\qquad [17\text{-}17]$$

Thus, for small amplitudes, the period T is independent of the amplitude θ_m.†

A pendulum is a suitable timing device, since it is *isochronous;* that is, its oscillation period is nearly independent of its amplitude. The simple pendulum provides a simple and precise basis for measuring g by using the relation $T = 2\pi\sqrt{l/g}$. One simply measures the period of a pendulum of known length.

The period of a simple pendulum does not depend on the particle's mass. All simple pendula of the same length oscillate at the same rate (an observation first made by Galileo). We have, however, made an important assumption in arriving at this result, namely, that the particle's inertial mass m_i and gravitational mass m_g are equal (see Section 16-7). The moment of inertia depends on m_i; the weight depends on m_g. As Newton found by experiment, pendula of the same length but with different masses do indeed have the

---

† The general relation giving the period for an amplitude θ_m (in radians) is

$$T = 2\pi \sqrt{l/g} \big[1 + \tfrac{1}{4} \sin^2 (\theta_m/2) + (9/64) \sin^4 (\theta_m/2) + \cdots \big]$$

With $\theta_m = 30°$, $T = 2\pi \sqrt{l/g}$ (1.017); thus, even for this large angle of swing, the actual period is greater than that given by the simple relation in Equation 17-17 by less than 2 per cent.

same period. This indicates that $m_i = m_g$, and it gives support to the principle of equivalence.

The compound pendulum. As may be seen in Table 17-3, the gravitational restoring torque depends on the weight mg of the extended body, whatever its shape, and on its moment arm $L_{\text{cm}} \sin \theta$. The length L_{cm} is the distance from the point of support to the center of mass (or center of gravity) of the body. The body's moment of inertia relative to a horizontal axis of rotation through the point of support is I. As in the case of the simple pendulum, $\sin \theta$ may be replaced by θ for small amplitudes. Then the motion is simple harmonic, the oscillations are isochronous, and the period is given by

$$T = 2\pi \sqrt{\frac{I}{mgL_{\text{cm}}}} \qquad \text{[17-18]}$$

The simple pendulum is, in fact, just a special case of the compound pendulum, in which $L_{\text{cm}} = l$ and $I = ml^2$.

One can, by using Equation 17-18, find the moment of inertia of a body of complicated shape in the following manner. Suspend the body as a physical pendulum and have it oscillate. Measuring the body's weight mg, the distance L_{cm} from the center of mass to the point of support, and the period T, allows I to be determined.

Example 6 A certain torsion pendulum consists of a thin vertical rod clamped at its upper end and a horizontal plate attached to its lower end. The period of torsional oscillations for this pendulum is found to be 50 sec. When a ring 50 gm in mass and 10 cm in radius is placed on the platform, as shown in Figure 17-11, the pendulum oscillates with a period of 150 sec. What is the torsion constant of the rod?

We designate the moment of the inertia of the plate relative to an axis of rotation along the axis of the rod by I_0. Calling the period of the unloaded torsion pendulum T_0, we have, from Equation 17-16,

$$T_0 = 2\pi \sqrt{\frac{I_0}{\kappa}}$$

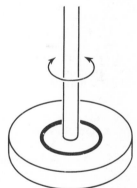

Figure 17-11. A torsion pendulum with a ring added to the platform.

The ring's moment of inertia relative to its symmetry axis is MR^2, where M and R are the ring's mass and radius. With the ring on the platform, the total moment of inertia of the torsion pendulum is $I_0 + MR^2$. The corresponding period of oscillation T is then given by

$$T = 2\pi \sqrt{\frac{I_0 + MR^2}{\kappa}}$$

Eliminating I_0 (which, then, need not be known) from the two equations above, and solving for κ in terms of the known quantities M, R, T, and T_0, yields

$$\kappa = \frac{4\pi^2 M R^2}{T^2 - T_0{}^2} = \frac{4\pi^2(0.050\ \text{kg})(0.10\ \text{m})^2}{(150\ \text{sec})^2 - (50\ \text{sec})^2}$$

$$\kappa = 9.9 \times 10^{-7}\ \text{m-nt/rad} = 0.17\ \text{cm-dyne/degree}$$

Thus, a force of only 0.17 dyne (6 micro-ounces) applied 1.0 cm from the axis will deflect the platform by 1°. For this reason, a torsion suspension can be used to measure the very small forces arising in the Cavendish experiment (Section 16-2). The torsion constant for a sensitive fiber is most easily measured by the method illustrated in this example, namely, by timing the oscillations before and after a body of known moment of inertia has been added to the torsion pendulum.

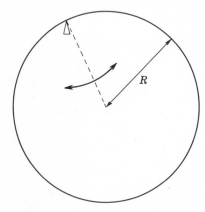

Figure 17-12. A ring of radius R oscillating as a physical pendulum about a horizontal axis at the rim.

Example 7 A thin ring of mass M and radius R is suspended as shown in Figure 17-12 and oscillates as a compound pendulum. What is the period?

We first compute the moment of inertia I_c of the ring relative to a horizontal axis of rotation at its circumference. We know that, with respect to a horizontal axis through its center, the ring's moment of inertia is MR^2. Then, from the parallel-axis theorem (Equation 14-7), $I_c = MR^2 + MR^2 = 2MR^2$. The ring's center of mass is a distance $L_{cm} = R$ from the point of support. Equation 17-18 then gives

$$T = 2\pi \sqrt{\frac{I_c}{mgL_{cm}}}$$

$$= 2\pi \sqrt{\frac{2MR^2}{mgR}} = 2\pi \sqrt{\frac{2R}{g}}$$

We notice that the period of such an oscillating ring is equal to that of a simple pendulum of length $2R$.

17-5   Damped harmonic motion   When a body is subject to an elastic restoring force only, the mechanical energy of the system remains constant and the oscillatory motion persists indefinitely with undiminished amplitude. This ideal situation is not ordinarily achieved, because of the presence of dissipative forces. For, in addition to the elastic restoring force, there is always a force which acts to oppose the motion, thereby doing negative work. As a consequence, the system's total mechanical energy decreases with time, as shown in Figure 17-13a. Such motion is called *damped motion*. For *small* dissipative forces, the body oscillates with continuously decreasing amplitude; this oscillatory motion is called *damped harmonic motion*. See Figure 17-13b.

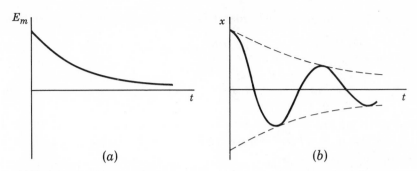

Figure 17-13. (a) Total mechanical energy E_m as a function of time for a damped simple harmonic oscillator. (b) Displacement-time graph for a damped oscillator.

An oscillator may be damped in a variety of ways. If an oscillating block is in contact with a rough surface, the kinetic force of friction damps the motion. If an object oscillates at low speeds while immersed in a liquid, a resistive force closely proportional to the body's speed opposes the motion. If the body oscillates while immersed in a gas, the dissipative force is, of course, smaller, but not zero. Even when a body oscillates in a vacuum, its motion is damped because of nonconservative internal forces within the spring.

As a specific illustration of damped harmonic motion, we consider an oscillator that is subject to a resistive force proportional to the body's speed (as is sometimes the case for a body immersed in a liquid). The resistive force F_r may be written

$$F_r = -rv$$

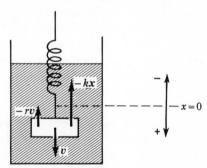

Figure 17-14. An illustration of a physical situation giving rise to damped harmonic motion: a body attached to a spring and immersed in a liquid. The body is subject to two forces: the restoring force of the spring, $-kx$, and the resistive force, $-rv$, where v is the body's velocity.

where v is the body's velocity and r is a constant. The forces acting on the body are shown in Figure 17-14.

Newton's second law then gives

$$\Sigma F_x = ma_x$$

$$-kx - rv_x = ma_x$$

$$-kx - r\frac{dx}{dt} = m\frac{d^2x}{dt^2} \qquad\qquad \text{[17-19]}$$

The solution to this second-order differential equation can be shown to be

$$x = A\,e^{-(r/2m)t} \cos{(\omega t + \delta)}$$
[17-20]

where

$$\omega = \sqrt{\frac{k}{m} - \left(\frac{r}{2m}\right)^2}$$
[17-21]

as may be verified by substitution in Equation 17-19. Figure 17-13b is a plot of Equation 17-20; Figure 17-13a gives $E_m = \frac{1}{2}mv_x{}^2 + \frac{1}{2}kx^2$ as a function of time t.

As in the case of undamped simple harmonic motion, the displacement x varies sinusoidally with time. Now, however, the constant amplitude A in Equation 17-8 is replaced by $A\,e^{-(r/2m)t}$, a quantity that decreases exponentially with time. The larger the resistive constant r, the more rapidly the motion is damped.

The angular frequency ω of the damped oscillations, given by Equation 17-21 above, is less than the natural angular frequency $\sqrt{k/m}$ in the absence of damping $(r = 0)$. This is to be expected, inasmuch as the resistive force slows the motion. It must be emphasized that Equations 17-19 and 17-20 apply only when the resistive force is *linearly* proportional to the body's speed; they do *not*, for example, apply for a speed-independent (but, of course, velocity-dependent) force of friction. Moreover, these equations apply only when the damping is relatively small, that is, when $(r/2m)^2$ is small compared with k/m.

17-6 Forced oscillations and resonance

When set into motion, a damped oscillator loses mechanical energy and eventually comes to rest. How can the mechanical energy of a damped oscillator be maintained constant? One must do work on the system, so that the energy fed into the system compensates for the energy dissipated. Energy is fed into the oscillator only when *positive* work is done by some external agent, that is, when the agent pushes in the *same* direction as the oscillator moves. For example, one can keep a damped oscillator, such as a playground swing, oscillating with constant amplitude by pushing it (at the right time) once each cycle. Then the frequency of the pushes will equal the natural frequency of the swing, and positive work will be done on the swing each time the agent pushes.

As an example of forced oscillation, consider a damped oscillator that is driven continuously by an external force varying sinusoidally with time at an angular frequency ω_e. A physical situation illustrating this behavior is shown in Figure 17-15. This is identical with that of Figure 17-14 except for the addition of a driving force $F(t)$. We suppose that the external sinusoidal force has a constant amplitude; that is, the driving force is written $F(t) = F_0 \cos \omega_e t$, where F_0 is constant.

Newton's second law, when applied to the mass m in Figure 17-15, is written

$$\Sigma F_x = m a_x$$

$$-kx - rv + F_0 \cos \omega_e t = m a_x$$

or,

$$-kx - r \frac{dx}{dt} + F_0 \cos \omega_e t = m \frac{d^2 x}{dt^2}$$

[17-22]

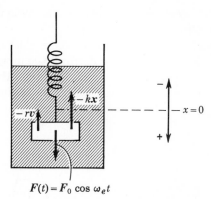

$$F(t) = F_0 \cos \omega_e t$$

Figure 17-15. A physical situation illustrating the forced oscillations of a damped oscillator. The body is subject to a restoring force $-kx$, a resistive force $-rv$, and the external driving force $F(t) = F_0 \cos \omega_e t$.

The solution of this equation and the body's motion (which this solution represents) consists of two parts: (a) the *transient* motion which ensues immediately after the driving force is first applied but quickly damps out, given by Equation 17-20, and (b) the *steady-state* solution of Equation 17-22, which can be shown to be

$$x = A_\omega \cos (\omega_e t + \delta) = \frac{F_0 / m}{\sqrt{(\omega_e{}^2 - \omega^2)^2 + (r\omega_e / m)^2}} \cos (\omega_e t + \delta) \quad [17\text{-}23]$$

where $\omega = \sqrt{k/m}$ is the natural frequency of the oscillator in the absence of damping ($r = 0$) and the phase angle δ depends upon the parameters F_0, m, r, ω, and ω_e.[†]

The driven mass undergoes simple harmonic motion *at the frequency ω_e of the external driving force.* The oscillation amplitude A_ω, given by the term preceding $\cos (\omega_e t + \delta)$ in Equation 17-23, is strongly dependent on the frequency ω_e of the external force. Indeed, the amplitude is a maximum when $\omega_e = \omega$ (assuming r to be relatively small). That is, the mass undergoes oscillations of the greatest magnitude when the oscillator is driven at its natural frequency of oscillation ($\omega_e = \omega$), as we would expect, from the qualitative arguments given above. The oscillator is said to be in *resonance* with the driving agent when the oscillator's natural frequency equals the frequency of the driving force.

The amplitude A_ω of the oscillations for the forced motion of Equation 17-23 is shown as a function of the frequency ω_e in Figure 17-16. Two curves are shown. The sharp curve corresponds to a small value of r, and

† See, for example, R. A. Becker, *Introduction to Theoretical Mechanics*, McGraw-Hill Book Company, Inc., 1954, Chap. 7.

the broader curve (whose maximum is displaced to a slightly lower frequency than ω) corresponds to larger damping. Thus, the resonance is sharp when the damping is small; the oscillator responds substantially to the driving force only over the narrow band in which the natural and driving frequencies are very nearly equal. On the other hand, if the damping is large, the resonance is broad; then the oscillator is less influenced by the external driving force, but the oscillator responds over a broad band of frequencies.

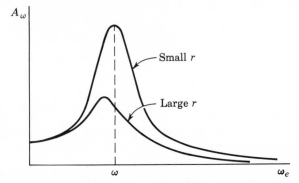

Figure 17-16. The amplitude A_ω of the forced motion of a damped oscillator as a function of the frequency of the external driving force. Resonance occurs when the driving frequency approaches the natural frequency of the oscillator. The resonance peak is narrow for small damping, broad for large damping.

The forced oscillator has a constant displacement amplitude for a given frequency ω_e. That is to say, the total mechanical energy of the oscillating mass and spring remains constant with time. Since energy is transferred out of the system continuously, through the damping, it follows that the driving force feeds energy into the system at the same rate. The resonance frequency represents that frequency at which energy is most readily transferred from the external agent to the oscillating system.

Resonance phenomena appear in many areas of physics: in resonating mechanical devices, in electric circuits, and in molecular structure. In fact, resonance occurs whenever an oscillator is acted upon by a second driving oscillator at the same frequency.

17-7 Summary Macroscopic elastic deformations reflect Hooke's law at the microscopic level: the restoring force on an atom displaced from its equilibrium position is directly proportional to the atom's displacement.

The restoring force of a helical spring is related to the spring's elongation:

[17-1] $$F = -kx$$

The restoring torque of a torsion rod is related to the rod's angular displacement by

[17-2] $$\tau = -\kappa\theta$$

Elastic moduli are defined as dimension- and shape-independent parameters describing a material's elastic properties. See Table 17-1. For small deformations, each modulus is a constant, the modulus being defined as a stress (force/area) divided by a strain (a dimensionless ratio describing the deformation):

[17-3] $$\text{modulus} = \text{stress/strain}$$

Any body subject to a Hooke's-law force executes simple harmonic motion, its acceleration being directly proportional to the negative of its displacement. For a mass m attached to a spring of force constant k,

[17-7], [17-10] $$a_x = -\left(\frac{k}{m}\right)x = -\omega^2 x$$

The period of any simple harmonic oscillator is governed by the oscillator's inertial and elastic properties.

The total mechanical energy of a simple harmonic oscillator of amplitude A is

[17-14] $$E_m = \tfrac{1}{2}kA^2$$

where k is a constant.

Torsion, simple, and compound pendula are illustrations of angular simple harmonic motion. See Table 17-3. For small amplitudes, the period of oscillation is independent of the amplitude.

The total energy and the amplitude of a damped oscillator decrease exponentially with time. A forced oscillator exhibits resonance when its natural frequency matches the frequency of the driving force. At resonance the oscillation amplitude is a maximum, as is also the energy transferred to the driven oscillator.

PROBLEMS

17-1 A helical spring having a force constant k is cut into two equal lengths. (a) What is the force constant of each half-spring? (b) What is the force constant of the composite spring formed by connecting the two half-springs in parallel, as shown in Figure 17-17?

17-2 By how much will a 30-foot steel wire having a diameter of 0.25 inches stretch, when a weight of 1.0 ton is suspended from one end?

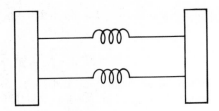

Figure 17-17

17-3   Two hundred turns of a copper wire 0.036 inches in diameter are wound tightly (no slack) around a smooth cylindrical spool of 1.0-inch diameter. What tensile force must be applied to each end of the wire to give an additional one-tenth turn of wire on the spool?

17-4   A pair of shear forces, each of magnitude 1.0×10^3 nt, are applied in opposite directions along two opposite faces of a steel cube 1.0 cm along an edge. What is the angle of shear?

17-5   A solid brass sphere has a radius of 1.0 cm when exposed to atmospheric pressure (1.0×10^5 nt/m^2). (a) By how much does the radius increase when the sphere is placed in a vacuum? (b) By how much does the radius decrease when the sphere is immersed in a liquid in which the pressure is 1.0×10^6 nt/m^2?

17-6   Experiment shows that, when the temperature of a brass rod that is free to expand is raised by 100 C°, its length increases by 2.0 parts in 10^3. If the brass rod is now fitted between two fixed supports and has its temperature raised by 100 C°, what is the stress (called *thermal stress*) produced in the brass rod?

17-7   Show that the force constant of a wire of length L, cross-sectional area A, and Young's modulus Y is YA/L.

17-8   A wire obeying Hooke's law is stretched at constant velocity until its elongation is 0.030 inches. For this elongation the tensile force is 20 pounds. (a) How much work is done in stretching the wire? (b) What is the change in the elastic potential energy of the wire?

17-9   Show that the work done in elongating a wire by ΔL is $YA(\Delta L)^2/2L$, where L is its original length, A is its cross-sectional area, and Y is the Young's modulus of the wire.

17-10   Two small spheres, each of 3.0 kg mass, are attached to the ends of a steel rod 0.40 m long and 2.0 mm in diameter. The rod rotates in a horizontal plane about a vertical axis through its center. At what constant angular speed must the rod be rotated to be stretched 1.0 mm? Neglect the mass of the rod.

17-11 ★   Figure 17-18 shows the behavior of a solid when stretched and compressed beyond its elastic limits. The restoring force is plotted as a function of the displacement from the original equilibrium position. The solid is first stretched beyond its elastic (tensile) limit by a tensile force (path A to B). When this force is gradually decreased, the solid does *not* return to its original configuration following the path B to A;

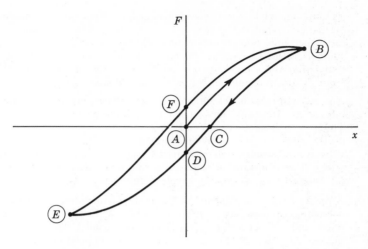

Figure 17-18. A mechanical hysteresis loop giving the force applied to a deformable body as a function of its deformation.

instead, it returns along the path B to C, retaining an elongation of magnitude AC (the *retentivity*). The compressive force required to restore the solid to its original unstretched length (the *coercive force*) has the magnitude AD. If the compressive force is increased further, the body moves along the path D to E. Then if the compressive force is removed and a tensile force is applied, the body moves along the path E to F to B, after which the cycle (or *hysteresis loop*) can be repeated. Show that the energy dissipated in taking the solid through one complete hysteresis loop is equal to the area enclosed by the loop.

17-12 ★ A rod elongates under a tensile stress, its length increasing by the fraction $\Delta L/L$. On the other hand, the rod's transverse dimensions decrease under a tensile stress, the fractional change in the width being $\Delta w/w$. For small deformations the ratio $-(\Delta w/w)/(\Delta L/L)$ is a constant, known as *Poisson's ratio* σ. For ordinary metals, σ is close to 0.3. (a) Show that the fractional change in volume $\Delta V/V$ of a body under longitudinal stress is given by $\Delta V/V = (1 - 2\sigma)(\Delta L/L)$. (b) Show that $\Delta V/V$ can also be written as $(1 - 2\sigma)(F_l/AY)$, where F_l is the longitudinal stress, A is the cross-sectional area, and Y is Young's modulus.

17-13 ★ Metallic copper contains 8.3×10^{22} copper atoms per cubic centimeter. (a) Imagining, for simplicity, that the atoms in metallic copper are densely packed cubes, each of volume d^3, compute the distance d between adjacent atoms. (b) If a copper rod is subject to a tensile stress of $4.0 \times 10^8 \, \text{nt/m}^2$, by what amount does the interatomic distance between adjacent copper atoms increase along the direction of the tensile stress? (c) What is the tensile force for a copper rod having a cross-sectional area of $5.0 \times 10^{-6} \, \text{m}^2$ and subject to the tensile stress given in (b)? (d) How many atoms will be located over the rod's cross section? (e) What is the average tensile force between adjacent copper atoms? (f) What is the atomic force constant giving the interatomic force, per unit relative elongation, between adjacent atoms? (Had symbols, rather than numerical values, been used above, we would have found that the atomic force constant is, in general, Yd, where Y is Young's modulus and d is the interatomic distance.)

17-14 A particle of mass 0.20 kg moves in simple harmonic motion along the horizontal. Its amplitude is 0.025 m and its frequency is 10 cycles/sec. The particle is at the origin and has a velocity of $\frac{1}{2}\pi$ m/sec to the right at the time $t = 0$. (a) Write expressions giving the displacement, velocity, and acceleration of the particle as a function of time. (b) What is the force constant of the spring to which the mass is attached? (c) At what time is the kinetic energy first a maximum?

17-15 A mass of 1.0 kg is attached to one end of a horizontal spring having a force constant of 1.6×10^3 nt/m. The second end of the spring is fixed, and the mass rests on a frictionless surface. The mass is then displaced 0.050 m to the right of its equilibrium position and released. (a) Write an equation giving the displacement of the mass as a function of time. (b) What is the total mechanical energy of the mass-spring system? (c) What is the mass's kinetic energy at $t = \frac{1}{60}$ sec? (d) What is the potential energy of the spring at $t = \frac{1}{60}$ sec?

17-16 The velocity of a 0.40 kg body moving in simple harmonic motion is given as a function of time by $v = 5.0 \sin(10\pi t + 1.5\pi)$, where v is in meters per second and t is in seconds. What are (a) the amplitude, (b) the frequency, and (c) the phase constant? (d) Write an expression that gives the displacement as a function of time. (e) What is the maximum resultant force on the body? (f) What is the body's kinetic energy at $t = 0.050$ sec?

17-17 When a 150-pound man stands at the end of a diving board, the end is lowered 1.0 feet from its equilibrium position. Assume that the displacement of the diving board is proportional to the force applied to it and that the mass of the board is small compared with that of the man. Compute the period of oscillation of the man on the diving board.

17-18 An automobile is lowered by 1.5 inches when a 150-pound man sits in it. When the car (driven by the man) hits a bump in the road, it oscillates with a frequency of 0.50 sec^{-1}. What is the mass of the car? Assume that the automobile has no shock absorbers that would damp the oscillations.

17-19 It was shown in Example 9, Section 16-8, that a particle falling in a hole drilled diametrically through the Earth is subject to a linear gravitational restoring force toward the Earth's center. (a) What is the period of oscillation of such a particle? (b) How does this period compare with that of an Earth satellite circling close to the Earth's surface?

17-20 Show that, for simple harmonic motion, $\tan \delta = v_0/\omega x_0$ where δ is the phase constant and v_0 and x_0 are the velocity and displacement at the time $t = 0$.

17-21   When a particle oscillates in simple harmonic motion, both its displacement and kinetic energy vary sinusoidally with time. If f is the frequency of the particle's motion, what is the frequency associated with the kinetic energy?

17-22 ★ When a 4.0-pound weight is attached to the end of an initially unloaded vertical spring and slowly released, the spring stretches by 0.20 feet. The 4.0-pound weight is then pulled down an additional 0.10 feet and released from rest. (a) What is the period of the simple harmonic oscillations? (b) What is the maximum speed of the weight? (c) Suppose that gravity is suddenly "turned off" when the weight is at its lowest point; what now are the frequency and amplitude of the oscillations?

17-23 ★ Two point masses of 1.0 kg and 3.0 kg are attached to opposite ends of a horizontal spring whose spring constant is 300 nt/m. The system rests on a frictionless horizontal surface. When the spring system is stretched by a small amount and released, both masses oscillate but the center of mass remains at rest. What is the period of oscillation of either mass?

17-24   A 10 gm coin rests on a horizontal platform that vibrates vertically in simple harmonic motion with an amplitude of 0.50 mm. (a) What is the maximum frequency of vibration that will permit the coin always to remain in contact with the platform? (b) What is the maximum force of the platform on the coin at this frequency? (c) What is the coin's maximum speed?

17-25   (a) Show that, if the X- and Y-components of a particle's displacement vary with time according to $x = a \cos \omega t$ and $y = b \sin \omega t$, where $a > b$, then the particle moves in an elliptical orbit of semimajor axis a and semiminor axis b. (This motion is illustrated by a particle at the end of string swinging as a "conical" pendulum with unequal X- and Y-amplitudes.) (b) Show that the particle's angular momentum relative to the center of the ellipse is constant.

17-26   A simple pendulum 1.0 m in length is attached to the ceiling of an elevator moving with constant acceleration near the Earth's surface. The period of the pendulum is 4.0 sec. What are the direction and magnitude of the elevator's acceleration?

17-27   In a Çavendish experiment (Section 16-2) the universal gravitational constant G is determined by means of a sensitive torsional pendulum, as shown in Figure 16-3. Two identical masses, each m, are attached to the ends of a horizontal rod (negligible mass) of a torsion pendulum having a torque constant κ. The length of the rod is l. When oscillating freely, the torsion pendulum has a period T. If two equal masses, each M, are next placed as shown in Figure 16-3, each mass M being a distance r from the closer mass m, the torsion rod is subject to a gravitational torque and the rod comes to rest when the elastic restoring torque $\kappa\theta$ equals the gravitational torque. The rod has then been turned through the angle θ. (a) Derive an expression for G in terms of m, M, r, l, κ, and θ. (b) Derive an expression for κ in terms of m, l, and T. (c) Show that $G = 2\pi^2 \theta r^2 l / M T^2$. Note that G is *independent* of the value of m!

17-28 ⋆ A small coin is placed on the horizontal plate of a torsion pendulum (see Figure 17-11) a distance of 5.0 cm from the center. The torsion pendulum's frequency of oscillation is 2.0 cycles/sec. If the coefficient of static friction between the coin and surface is 0.50, what is the maximum angular amplitude for which the coin will not slip?

17-29 When a pair of opposite torques, each of magnitude 5.0×10^{-2} m-nt, are applied to the ends of a torsion rod, the one end is displaced by $10°$ relative to the other end. When a horizontal plate is attached to the rod and set into torsional oscillation, the period is 0.080 sec. When, in addition, a ring is attached to the plate, as in Figure 17-11, the period of oscillation is 0.110 sec. What is the moment of inertia of the ring relative to a vertical axis through its center?

17-30 In Section 17-4 the period of a simple pendulum was derived by using $\Sigma \tau = I\alpha$. One may compute the period alternatively by finding the resultant force on the particle and using $\Sigma F = ma$. (a) Show that the resultant force on a particle of mass m attached to a string of length l which makes an angle θ with respect to the vertical has a magnitude $mg \sin \theta$. (b) Show that, for small θ, the ratio of the particle's linear acceleration to its linear displacement from the equilibrium position is l/g. (c) Show that the period is $2\pi \sqrt{l/g}$.

17-31 (a) What is the period of oscillation of a meter stick suspended as a physical pendulum about a horizontal axis at one end? (b) A point mass equal to that of the meter stick is attached to it at a distance y below the point of support. Find the period of oscillation T as a function of y, and sketch T as a function of y.

17-32 The physical pendulum in a certain grandfather's clock is adjusted to beat seconds (its period is exactly 2.0 sec) when the temperature is 68°F. How many seconds will this clock gain or lose in one day if, because of an increase in temperature, the dimensions of the physical pendulum increase by 1.0 part in 10^4?

17-33 A uniform flat rectangular plate of length l and width w is suspended to oscillate as a physical pendulum about a horizontal axis perpendicular to the plane of the plate. (a) At what point should the pivot be placed to give the smallest period of oscillation? (b) What is this period? (c) At what point should the pivot be placed to give the largest period of oscillation? (d) What is this period? (The moment of inertia of a rectangular plate is given in Figure 14-9e.)

17-34 The *center of oscillation* of a physical pendulum is defined to be that point C at which all of the mass of the physical pendulum can be imagined to be concentrated to give the same period of oscillation as the actual pendulum; that is, the distance L_c from P to C is the length of a simple pendulum having the same period as the physical pendulum. (a) Show that $L_c = I/mL_{cm}$, where I is the moment of inertia with respect to a horizontal axis through P, m is the mass of the physical pendulum, and L_{cm} is the distance from P to the center of mass.

(b) Show that if the physical pendulum is supported to oscillate about a horizontal axis through the center of oscillation C, the period is unchanged and the new center of oscillation is now at the point P.

17-35   A physical pendulum consists of a flat uniform circular disk of radius R, oscillating about a horizontal axis that is perpendicular to the plane of the disk and passes through a point at the disk's circumference. (a) What is the period of oscillation? (b) Where is the center of oscillation (see Problem 17-34) relative to the point of support?

17-36 ⋆ (a) Find the center of oscillation (see Problem 17-34) of a uniform thin rod of length L suspended at one end. (b) Suppose that the rod is now placed on a horizontal frictionless surface and that it is struck with an impulsive blow at the center of oscillation given in part (a). Show that the rod initially rotates about an axis at the opposite end.

The *center of percussion* of a rigid body is defined as that point at which a body may be struck impulsively to rotate freely about some chosen axis. For example, when a bat is struck by a ball at the bat's center of percussion, the bat rotates freely about the point where the bat is held; therefore, the batter feels no "sting." In general, for a chosen axis of rotation, the center of percussion and center of oscillation of a body coincide.

EIGHTEEN

FLUIDS

In this chapter we first distinguish among solids, liquids, and gases in terms of their macroscopic and microscopic properties, and then we apply the principles of mechanics (Newton's laws of motion and the conservation principles) to fluids. The continuity equation and Bernoulli's theorem—the foundations of fluid mechanics—are derived and applied to fluids in motion and at rest.

18-1 States of matter Matter as we most commonly experience it exists in one of three physical states, solid, liquid, and gas. Whether a particular material exists as a solid, a liquid, or a gas depends on the properties of the material and on such macroscopic characteristics as the pressure and temperature of the system. A familiar example is that of the substance water, at atmospheric pressure: water is a solid when its temperature is below 0° C, a liquid at temperatures between 0° and 100° C, and a gas at temperatures above 100° C.

The three states cannot always be easily distinguished; glass, for example, may be regarded as an incompletely solidified liquid. Moreover, a collection of free, electrically charged particles with equal amounts of positive and negative charge—a so-called *plasma*—is sometimes referred to as the fourth state of matter. Water, at temperatures above 2×10^5 °C is a plasma consisting of hydrogen nuclei, oxygen nuclei, and electrons.

The physical states of a material are related to other macroscopic properties—the elastic moduli. See Table 18-1, where the relative magnitudes of

Table 18-1

	SHAPE	SIZE	BULK MODULUS B	SHEAR MODULUS G
Solid	That in which it is solidified	Definite	Large	Large
Liquid	Spherical	Definite	Large	Small
Gas	That of the container	Any	Small	Very small

the elastic moduli are given, together with the shape and size for the simple but special case of matter in gravity-free space.

Liquids and solids are similar in that they are not easily compressed; both have large compressive bulk moduli. Liquids and gases are similar in that they are easily "cut" by shears; that is, both have small shear moduli.

It is also instructive to relate the states of matter to certain microscopic properties of the constituent molecules or atoms of the material. We first emphasize that, for a given material, the three states of matter do *not* differ in the *force* between interacting particles. As we saw in Figure 17-1, the interatomic or intermolecular force between a pair of atoms or molecules is zero at large separation distances, attractive for smaller separations, and repulsive for very small separations. The equilibrium distance typically is of the order of 2×10^{-10} m. For a given separation distance, the intermolecular force (and thus also the intermolecular potential energy U) between two atoms is the *same*, whether the atoms are in the gaseous, liquid, or solid state. Thus, the force between two water molecules in ice is exactly the same as the force between water molecules separated by the same distance in water vapor.

Since the intermolecular forces are the same for the three states, one must distinguish microscopically among the three states by comparing *energies*. If $\bar{K}$ represents the average kinetic energy of a particle, then that of a gas is $\bar{K} \gg U$. In a gas the total energy $(K + U)$ is positive, and the particles are *not* bound to one another. On the other hand, in a liquid or solid, $\bar{K} \simeq U$. In these states the total energy is negative (relative to the zero energy for the particles infinitely separated and at rest), and the particles are bound together. See Figure 18-1. The particle energies are related to the temperature of the material, as we shall later see.

One can thus distinguish the three states of matter simply and qualitatively from an atomic point of view. The atoms in a solid are tightly packed. Each atom is subjected to a strong interatomic force from each of its immediate neighbors. The resultant force on some particular atom in a solid is zero when the atom is at an equilibrium location. If the atom is displaced from this position, a strong resultant interatomic force acts on it to restore it to its equilibrium position. Thus, an atom in a solid is bound to a particular location. The atom possesses kinetic energy at any temperature, and vibrates about its equilibrium position. The amount of kinetic energy is not, however,

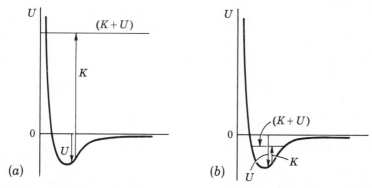

Figure 18-1. Intermolecular potential energy as a function of separation distance, for the molecules of (a) a gas and (b) a liquid or solid.

great enough to overcome the potential energy binding the atom to its neighbors. Because each atom in a solid is localized to a small region of space, this state is one in which the atoms have a relatively high degree of order.

At the other extreme is the gaseous state. Here the atoms have kinetic energies which are, on the average, much larger than the interatomic potential energies between them. The atoms are nearly free of one another, each atom now moving throughout the volume of the container. Apart from collisions, each atom moves independently of the remaining atoms. Thus, the gaseous state is one in which the atoms have a high degree of disorder. Because the atoms in a solid are tightly packed, "touching" in a liquid, but separated by great distances in a gas, a material in the gaseous state has a lower density than one in the solid or liquid states.

The liquid state is intermediate between the solid and gaseous states. An atom in a liquid has a kinetic energy that is large enough to overcome the rigid binding that characterizes atoms in a solid, but this energy is not large enough to free the atom from all other atoms. An atom in either a liquid or a solid may be thought of as being in contact with its neighbors, and so the density of a liquid is close to the density of the same material in the solid state. Very strong repulsive interatomic forces act when one attempts to pack the atoms of a liquid or solid more closely together; hence liquids and solids have large bulk moduli. The (relatively) loosely bound atoms of a liquid glide easily past one another; hence, they have small shear moduli. Liquids and gases are similar in respect to shear moduli: a *perfect liquid* has zero shear modulus, and is said to be *nonviscous*.

Liquids and gases flow, and they are referred to collectively as *fluids*. We shall concentrate on the mechanics of liquids in this chapter. The properties of gases are treated in Chapters 19 through 22.

18-2   Surface tension   A small drop of liquid has a nearly spherical shape. It is easy to show, through a consideration of surface tension, that the shape of *any* collection of molecules in the liquid state is a sphere if the collection is located in gravity-free space.

First consider a molecule in the interior of a collection of molecules. It is completely surrounded by neighboring molecules and the resultant intermolecular force on it is zero. On the other hand, if a molecule is located at the surface, it will, if it is displaced slightly outward from the surface, be acted upon by a resultant force attracting it back toward the surface. The energy E_s required to remove all *s*urface molecules out beyond the range of the attractive intermolecular force of their neighbors is proportional to the number of molecules on the surface. This is to say, the work required to remove the surface layer of molecules is proportional to the surface area A of the liquid. We may write

$$E_s = TA$$ [18-1]

where the *surface tension* T is a constant for a given liquid.† The surface tension T of water is 0.0728 joule/m²; that of mercury is 0.520 joule/m².

One may associate potential energy with the surface of a liquid through Equation 18-1. We recall that any system will always assume that configuration for which its potential energy is a minimum. Thus, a liquid will, because of the existence of surface tension, assume the shape for which its area is minimum, namely, a *sphere*.

We have assumed the sphere of liquid to be in static equilibrium in gravity-free space. Suppose, now, that the droplet is deformed from its spherical shape by external forces and is then released. The surface area, and therefore the potential energy, of the liquid will have been increased.

---

† Strictly, the surface tension is defined as the *free energy* per unit surface area. This thermodynamic term must be used because a liquid is actually cooled (unless thermal energy is added) when molecules are removed from its surface, as witness the cooling accompanying evaporation.

Intermolecular forces will act to reduce the drop's potential energy and to restore it to sphericity. Consequently, the droplet will undergo oscillations in its shape, with the sphere the equilibrium configuration. One may say that the surface tension of a liquid is equivalent, as it were, to a membrane stretched over the surface of the liquid, tending to minimize the area and maintain the droplet in the spherical shape. The surface behaves as if under tension; hence, surface "tension."

Here on the surface of the Earth we observe liquids in a gravitational field. Therefore, the weight of a liquid acts in addition to the intermolecular forces, and the situation is more complicated. For a sphere of radius r, the effects of surface tension are proportional to the surface area $4\pi r^2$, but the weight, proportional to the mass of liquid, is proportional to its volume, $\frac{4}{3}\pi r^3$. Thus, the weight varies as r^3, whereas the forces of surface tension vary as r^2. As the radius or size of the drop of liquid increases, the weight becomes increasingly more significant than surface tension. Thus, when a large drop rests on a surface, the weight and normal force deform the drop appreciably, so that it is no longer spherical. Finally, if the amount of liquid is substantial, the weight dominates and the surface tension is negligible. Then the liquid assumes the shape of the lower portion of its container and has a horizontal upper surface. The effects of intermolecular forces are evident only at the boundaries of the liquid, where a meniscus (curved surface) exists.

There is one situation in which a liquid may assume the shape of a sphere of rather large size, even in the presence of gravity. This occurs when the weight of a droplet is very much reduced by replacing most of the liquid in the droplet's interior by a gas. Then the forces of surface tension again dominate, and the shape is spherical: one has a bubble.

18-3 Density and pressure All substances are composed of discrete molecules and atoms. A typical atom is very small ($\sim10^{-10}$ m), and the number of atoms in an ordinary amount of material is very great (10^{24} to 10^{27} atoms per kilogram). Thus, from a *macroscopic* point of view, matter is essentially *continuous*, and we may define an *average density* ρ as

[7-1]
$$\rho = \frac{\Delta m}{\Delta V}$$

where Δm is the mass contained in the volume ΔV.

Table 18-2 lists the densities of some common materials. Note that, for a particular material, the densities in the *solid* and *liquid* states are comparable. Moreover, the density of a liquid or solid varies only slightly with changes in pressure and temperature. For the gaseous state, however, the density shows drastic variations with pressure and temperature. The density in the gaseous state is, of course, much less than in the liquid and solid states.

Table 18-2

MATERIAL	STATE	TEMP. (°C)	DENSITY (gm/cm³)
Air	Gas (1 atm)	0	1.29×10^{-3}
Aluminum	Solid	20	2.70
	Liquid	659	2.38
Brass	Solid	20	8.60
Gold	Solid	20	19.3
Lead	Solid	20	11.3
Mercury	Liquid	0	13.6
	Solid	−39	14.2
Oxygen	Gas	0	1.43×10^{-3}
	Liquid	−184	1.14
	Solid	−253	1.41
Silver	Solid	20	10.6
Steel	Solid	20	7.83
Ice	Solid	−10	0.9981
	Solid	0	0.9999
Water	Liquid	0	0.9999
	Liquid	4	1.0000
	Liquid	20	0.9982
	Liquid	100	0.9584

The term *specific gravity* is used to denote the ratio of the density of a particular substance to the density of water. Thus, mercury with a density 13.6 gm/cm³ = 2.63 slug/foot³ has a specific gravity of 13.6.

In Chapter 17 we defined the stress acting across any chosen area within a solid. The normal force per unit area is the normal stress; the tangential force per unit area is the shear stress. A perfect, or nonviscous, liquid cannot support a shear stress. Thus, the shear stress is zero for a perfect liquid, and the only stress that can exist within such a liquid is one of compression. This stress is called the *pressure p*.

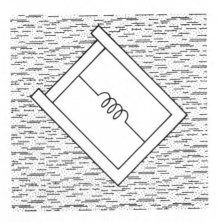

Figure 18-2. A simple pressure-measuring device.

The meaning of pressure is most easily illustrated through a definition in which one specifies the laboratory operations to be used in making a measurement of pressure. Consider the simple pressure-measuring device shown in Figure 18-2. It consists of an evacuated cylinder and a tightly fitted, weightless piston attached to the cylinder by a spring.

When the spring device is immersed in a vacuum, a vacuum then exists on both sides of the piston head, no net force acts on the piston, and the spring assumes its relaxed length. If the spring system is immersed in a fluid, the piston head is acted upon by a compressive force arising from the fluid, and the spring is compressed until the inward force of the fluid is balanced by the outward force of the compressed spring. Knowing the force constant of the spring one can compute the force of the fluid on the piston head simply by measuring the amount by which the spring has been compressed (and applying $F = -kx$).

Let ΔF represent the magnitude of the force on the piston head, as measured by the spring, and ΔA the area of the piston. Then the pressure p of the fluid is, by definition,

$$p = \lim_{\Delta A \to 0} \left(\frac{\Delta F}{\Delta A} \right)$$ [18-2]

Note that we take the limit of the ratio of $\Delta F / \Delta A$ as the area of the piston is made very small. This defines the pressure at a *point* within the fluid. If ΔA is sizable, $\Delta F / \Delta A$ gives the *average* pressure over the chosen area.

One finds by experiment that, at any one point within a fluid, the compression of the spring is the *same* for *all* orientations of the spring device. Pressure is a *scalar* quantity, not a vector. If one chooses a surface of area ΔA, a compressive force $\Delta F = p \, \Delta A$ acts perpendicular to the surface. We can write this equation in vector form: $\Delta \boldsymbol{F} = p \, \Delta \boldsymbol{A}$, where the area element $\Delta \boldsymbol{A}$ is a vector whose direction is *normal* to the surface and whose magnitude is ΔA. When the surface is reoriented, both the force $\Delta \boldsymbol{F}$ on the surface and the area $\Delta \boldsymbol{A}$ change direction, but the ratio of their magnitudes, p, is the same.

Inasmuch as the forces within a nonviscous gas or liquid can only be those of compression, the spring shown in Figure 18-2 is always compressed, never elongated. The lowest possible pressure it registers is zero—a vacuum. We have been discussing the so-called *absolute pressure*, whose zero corresponds to a vacuum. It is sometimes convenient, however, to speak of the pressure of a fluid *relative* to the atmospheric pressure p_0 which arises from the Earth's atmosphere of nitrogen and oxygen. This relative pressure is called the *gauge pressure* p_g, which is related to the absolute pressure p and atmospheric pressure p_0 by

$$p_g = p - p_0$$ [18-3]

The ordinary pressure gauge used in measuring the pressure of an inflated automobile tire indicates the gauge pressure: if p_g is positive, the tire is inflated; if $p_g = 0$, the tire is flat; and if p_g is negative, the tire is at least partially evacuated.

Standard atmospheric pressure is defined as

$$1 \text{ std. atm} = 1.013250 \times 10^5 \text{ nt/m}^2 = 1{,}013{,}250 \text{ dyne/cm}^2$$

Atmospheric pressure has its origin in the gravitational pull of the Earth on the gases surrounding it. In fact, atmospheric pressure (approximately 10^6 dyne/cm^2 = 10 nt/cm^2) represents the weight of all the air in a column 1.0 cm^2 in cross section, extending from the Earth's surface to the top of the atmosphere. Inasmuch as the weight of the air in this column is 10 nt, the total mass of air in such a column is approximately 1 kg.

The commonly used units for pressure in engineering practice are pounds per square inch; written in these units, one standard atmosphere is 14.70 pounds/inch^2. Atmospheric pressure near sea level never differs much from that of a standard atmosphere. Thus, a fifteen-pound force acts on every exposed area of one square inch. This substantial force is evident, however, only if the reverse side of any surface is at least partially evacuated.

We shall later (Section 18-7) discuss pressure-measuring devices that depend on the height of a column of liquid. In a mercury barometer, standard atmospheric pressure corresponds to a height of exactly 76 cm. Although spring devices of the sort shown in Figure 18-2 ordinarily are not used in measuring pressure, the *aneroid barometer* operates on the same basic principle. This device employs an evacuated flexible metal chamber, one of whose walls is displaced by pressure changes. The elasticity of the walls replaces the spring of Figure 18-2, and the displacement of the flexible wall indicates the absolute pressure.

Example 1 Two halves of a cubical box are placed together and form an airtight enclosure. The box is partially evacuated so that the pressure in its interior is one tenth of the atmospheric pressure p_0 at the box's exterior. The area of one side of the box is A. See Figure 18-3. (a) What is the gauge pressure within the box? (b) What force is required to separate the two halves? (c) If the box were moved into empty space (where no atmosphere exists), what force would be required to hold the two halves together?

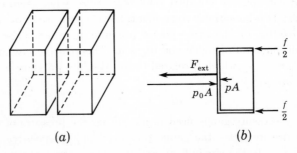

(a)   (b)

Figure 18-3. (a) The two halves of a partially evacuated cubical box. (b) The forces acting on the left half.

(a) From Equation 18-3,

$$p_g = p - p_0 = \tfrac{1}{10}p_0 - p_0 = -\tfrac{9}{10}p_0$$

(b) We concentrate on the horizontal forces acting on one of the two halves of the box, as shown in Figure 18-3b. The force of the right half on the left half is f; the applied external force is F_{ext}. At the point of separation, $f = 0$. Therefore, if the left half is in equilibrium,

$$F_{ext} = p_0 A - pA = \tfrac{9}{10}p_0 A$$

(c) In empty space the smallest external force, now directed inward, that will hold the box together is $F_{ext} = pA = \tfrac{1}{10}p_0 A$.

Example 2 A device like that shown in Figure 18-2 is to be used for measuring the pressure in the atmosphere, and also for that under water. The area of the piston is $2.00\,cm^2$; the spring's force constant is $4.00 \times 10^3\,nt/m$. When it is immersed in the atmosphere, the device's spring is compressed 5.10 mm. (a) What is the atmospheric pressure? (b) When the device is placed under water to a depth of 10.0 m, the spring is compressed an additional 4.60 mm. What is the absolute pressure of the water at this depth?

(a) $$p = \Delta F/\Delta A = kx/\Delta A$$

$$p = (4.00 \times 10^3\,nt/m)(5.10 \times 10^{-3}\,m)/(2.00 \times 10^{-4}\,m^2)$$

$$p = 1.02 \times 10^5\,nt/m^2$$

(b) The spring is now compressed a total distance of $(5.10 + 4.60)\,mm = 9.70\,mm$. Therefore, the pressure at this depth is

$$p = kx/\Delta A = (4.00 \times 10^3\,nt/m)(9.70 \times 10^{-3}\,m)/(2.00 \times 10^{-4}\,m^2)$$

$$p = 1.94 \times 10^5\,nt/m^2 = 1.92\,atm$$

18-4 Streamline flow Hydrodynamics is that branch of physics which treats of the dynamical motion of liquids and gases; hydrostatics is a special case of hydrodynamics, one in which the fluid is at rest.

The most general motion of particles in a fluid may be very complicated. Although it is possible to trace out in detail the path of some one particle in a turbulent sea, for example, by knowing the acting forces and applying Newton's laws, the problem is forbiddingly difficult. One can analyze fluid motion only when it is relatively simple. We shall restrict ourselves here to the special case of the *steady flow* of a *nonviscous fluid* of *constant density* in *irrotational streamline motion*.

Fluid motion is *steady* if the velocity of all particles passing any given point does not change with time. Examples of steady motion are the flow of fluid through a pipe and the flow of water past the side of a boat *as viewed by an observer on the boat*. Instead of concentrating our attention on some one particle as it travels through space, we focus on the velocity of *all* particles passing through any chosen point. For steady motion, the velocity is always the same at a given location. Therefore, the velocity is a function of location but not of time. *Nonsteady* motion is more common: it is illustrated, for example, by the rapid, chaotic, and turbulent motion of particles in a pounding surf, or by the flow of water past the side of a moving boat *as viewed by an observer on the bank.*

We will take the fluid to be *nonviscous.* This implies that the fluid's shear modulus is zero and that no energy is dissipated by frictional forces within

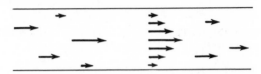

Figure 18-4. Velocity vectors for the viscous flow of liquid through a pipe.

the fluid. We also will assume that there is no frictional force between the fluid and the constraining tube through which it flows. In actuality, when water flows through a pipe, the water in contact with the pipe sticks to the walls and is at rest there. The velocity increases toward the center of the pipe, as shown in Figure 18-4. The finite viscosity of liquids arises from a nonzero shear force between layers of the liquid, and the energy dissipated when one layer of liquid moves past an adjoining layer appears as thermal energy.

Most liquids (and gases under certain circumstances) are nearly incompressible. If, furthermore, there is no cavitation in the fluid, the density of the fluid can be assumed constant.

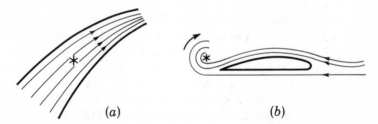

(a)   (b)

Figure 18-5. Examples of (a) irrotational and (b) rotational fluid flow.

Irrotational motion is best illustrated by an experimental test. Suppose that a small paddle wheel, free to turn on its axis, is inserted into a moving fluid. If the wheel does *not* rotate, the motion at that point is *irrotational.* When the paddle wheel is placed in a whirlpool or eddy, the wheel turns and the motion is rotational. See Figure 18-5.

One can distinguish between rotational and irrotational motion differently. If the angular momentum of any small volume of liquid, relative to its center of mass (the *spin* angular momentum), is zero, the motion is irrotational. On the other hand, if the spin angular momentum of the liquid is not zero, as indicated by the angular momentum acquired by a paddle wheel inserted into the liquid, the motion is rotational.

Now we consider steady streamline motion. Figure 18-6 shows the path traced out by particles which begin at point A and later pass through points B and C. Every particle starting at A follows the same path, or *streamline*. At each point the direction of the velocity is tangent to the streamline. Therefore, we can construct streamlines indicating the direction of the fluid's

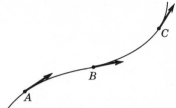

Figure 18-6. A streamline. The vectors represent the velocities of the fluid particles at A, B, and C.

velocity at various points. It is also possible to indicate the *magnitude* of the velocity by choosing the *number* of streamlines, passing through any small

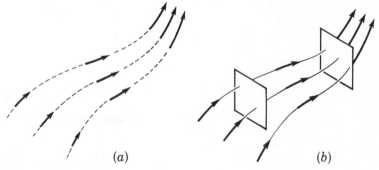

(a)   (b)

Figure 18-7. (a) A collection of streamlines representing a velocity field. (b) The magnitude of the velocity is given by the number of streamlines passing through a unit area oriented at right angles to the streamlines.

area oriented perpendicular to the streamlines, to be proportional to the speed, or magnitude of the velocity, at that point. Thus, a collection of streamlines constitutes a *velocity field*: their density and direction give, respectively, the magnitude and direction of the velocity of the fluid.† See Figure 18-7.

† Fluid motion is a second example of a *vector field*. Here we map the direction and magnitude of the velocity by the direction and density of the streamlines. Our first example of a vector field was the gravitational force field (Section 16-3), where gravitational lines of force were used to represent the direction and magnitude of the gravitational force on a small mass placed in the field. Other examples of vector fields are the electric and magnetic fields of electromagnetism.

Streamlines cannot cross. If they did, particles reaching an intersection would *not* have a *unique* velocity at that point in space.

18-5 The equation of continuity   We define the *mass flux* of a fluid at some point as the mass Δm passing per unit time across an area $A_\perp$ perpendicular to the fluid's velocity at that point. See Figure 18-8a. Thus,

$$\text{Mass flux} = \frac{\Delta m / \Delta t}{A_\perp} \qquad [18\text{-}4]$$

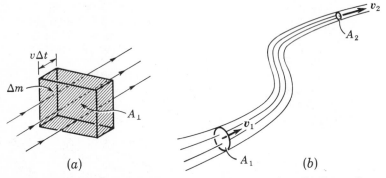

Figure 18-8. (a) The mass flux through the area $A_\perp$. (b) Streamline flow through a tube of varying cross section.

Similarly, the *volume flux* is the volume ΔV of fluid passing through $A_\perp$ in the time Δt:

$$\text{Volume flux} = \frac{\Delta V / \Delta t}{A_\perp} \qquad [18\text{-}5]$$

Inasmuch as $\Delta m = \rho \, \Delta V$, where ρ is the mass density at the point P at which Δm and ΔV are measured, we can write

$$\text{Mass flux at } P = \rho \times \text{volume flux at } P$$

The conservation of mass principle leads to a useful relation, known as the *equation of continuity*, between the velocity and the cross-sectional area for ideal fluid flow. Consider the situation shown in Figure 18-8b, where a fluid moves in streamline flow through a tube of varying cross section. The tube may be an actual pipe constraining the fluid or it may simply be a collection of adjacent streamlines within a fluid. No fluid passes through the sides of the tube.

At point 1 the cross-sectional area is A_1, the mass density is ρ_1, and the velocity of all particles crossing A_1 is v_1; at point 2 the area is A_2, the density is ρ_2, and the velocity is v_2. Both ρ_1 and ρ_2 are assumed to remain constant in time. In the time interval Δt the mass entering the tube at point 1 is Δm_1:

$$\Delta m_1 = \rho_1 \, \Delta V_1 = \rho_1(A_1 v_1 \, \Delta t)$$

The mass of fluid emerging from the tube at point 2 during the same time interval Δt is

$$\Delta m_2 = \rho_2 \, \Delta v_2 = \rho_2(A_2 v_2 \, \Delta t)$$

Since fluid cannot leak through the walls and there are no "sources" or "sinks" within, the total mass of fluid in the tube between points 1 and 2 must remain constant. Because of the conservation of mass principle, this implies that the mass Δm_1 entering must equal the mass Δm_2 emerging:

$$\Delta m_1 = \Delta m_2$$

and

$$\boxed{\text{Mass flux} = \rho_1 A_1 v_1 = \rho_2 A_2 v_2} \qquad [18\text{-}6]$$

The quantity $\rho A v$, which represents the mass per unit time of fluid crossing the area A perpendicular to v, is the same at all points along the tube. Equation 18-6 is called the *equation of continuity*.

If the fluid is incompressible, the density ρ is constant. Then Equation 18-6 reduces to

$$\boxed{\text{Volume flux} = A_1 v_1 = A_2 v_2} \qquad [18\text{-}7]$$

Thus, for constant density, the volume flux Av is conserved. This implies that the speed of the fluid is great where the cross section is small, and conversely. Equation 18-7 is also consistent with the use of streamlines to represent the direction and magnitude of the fluid velocity. Since v indicates the number of streamlines passing through a unit cross-sectional area, the quantity vA represents the total number of streamlines at any cross section. Equation 18-7 then shows that the total number of streamlines within the tube is conserved, the streamlines crowding together at a constriction and dispersing where the cross section is large.

Example 3 Water (density, 2.0 slugs/feet³) moves in a steady flow through the system of pipes shown in Figure 18-9. The cross-sectional areas of pipes 1, 2, and 3 are all equal to 1.44 inch²; pipe 4 has twice this cross-sectional area, namely, 2.88 inch². Water enters pipe 1 at the rate of 2.0×10^{-2} feet³/sec. (a) Compute the volume and mass fluxes through each pipe. (b) What is the speed of flow through each pipe?

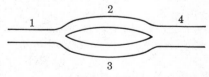

Figure 18-9

(a) The volume flux through pipe 4 is the same as that through pipe 1, namely, 2.0×10^{-2} feet^3/sec. In pipe 2 or 3 the volume flux is half that of pipe 1, namely, 1.0×10^{-2} feet^3/sec. The mass flux is equal to the volume flux multiplied by the mass density of water, 2.0 slugs/feet^3. Thus in pipe 1 or 4, the mass flux is 4.0 slugs/sec; in pipe 2 or 3, it is 2.0×10^{-2} slugs/sec.

(b) From Equation 18-7,

$$\text{Volume flux} = Av$$

Thus, for pipe 1,

$$v_1 = (\text{volume flux})/A_1 = (2.0 \times 10^{-2} \text{ ft}^3/\text{sec})/(1.0 \times 10^{-2} \text{ ft}^2) = 2.0 \text{ ft/sec}$$

It similarly follows that the speeds through pipes 2, 3, and 4 are

$$v_2 = v_3 = v_4 = 1.0 \text{ ft/sec}$$

18-6 Bernoulli's theorem

When the conservation of mass principle is applied to fluid motion we arrive at the equation of continuity. The conservation of energy principle also leads to a useful relation of great generality

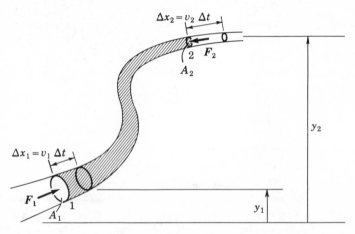

Figure 18-10. Irrotational flow of an incompressible nonviscous fluid through a nonhorizontal pipe of varying cross section.

among the quantities pressure, speed, and elevation. This relation, first derived by Daniel Bernoulli in 1738, is known as *Bernoulli's theorem.*

We consider an incompressible nonviscous fluid moving in streamline flow through a pipe, as shown in Figure 18-10. The cross-sectional area of the pipe at any point is assumed to be small enough for all particles crossing a given cross section to have the same velocity at that cross section. At point 1 the tube's cross-sectional area is A_1, the fluid's speed is v_1, the pressure is p_1, and the vertical height, or elevation, of the fluid above some arbitrary horizontal reference line is y_1. The corresponding quantities at point 2 are designated A_2, v_2, p_2, and y_2. Because we have assumed the fluid to be incompressible, the density ρ is the same at all points. We concentrate our attention on the fluid between points 1 and 2, shown shaded in Figure 18-10a.

The work-energy theorem (Equation 12-17) requires that, during any small time interval Δt, the work ΔW done on the fluid by external forces (other than gravity) must equal the increase in the total mechanical energy, i.e., the kinetic energy plus the gravitational potential energy ($\Delta K + \Delta U_g$), during this same time interval:

$$\Delta W = \Delta K + \Delta U_g \qquad [18\text{-}8]$$

The only two forces which have components parallel or antiparallel to the motion, and thus do work on the system, are the force F_1, arising from the fluid to the left of point 1 and acting to the right on the fluid shown shaded in the figure, and the force F_2, arising from the fluid to the right of point 2 and acting to the left on the fluid to the left (shaded). Force F_1 is in the *same* direction as the fluid's motion, and thus does *positive* work; F_2, being *opposite* to the fluid motion, does *negative* work. See the figure. In the time Δt, the left end of the shaded fluid advances a distance $\Delta x_1 = v_1\,\Delta t$ to the right, while the right end moves a distance $\Delta x_2 = v_2\,\Delta t$, also to the right. The net work done by external forces on the system is then

$$\Delta W = F_1\,\Delta x_1 - F_2\,\Delta x_2 = (p_1 A_1)(v_1\,\Delta t) - (p_2 A_2)(v_2\,\Delta t) \qquad [18\text{-}9]$$

where we have replaced F_1 by $p_1 A_1$ and F_2 by $p_2 A_2$.

Using the equation of continuity,

[18-7] $$A_1 v_1 = A_2 v_2$$

and the fact that the mass Δm of fluid within the displaced volume element $A_1(v_1\,\Delta t)$, or within $A_2(v_2\,\Delta t)$, is given by

$$\Delta m = \rho(A_1 v_1\,\Delta t)$$

we may write Equation 18-9 more simply as

$$\Delta W = (A_1 v_1\,\Delta t)(p_1 - p_2) = (\Delta m/\rho)\,(p_1 - p_2) \qquad [18\text{-}10]$$

We now consider the changes ΔK and ΔU_g in the kinetic and gravitational potential energies of the system. Fortunately, we need concern ourselves only with the fluid entering the system at point 1 in time Δt and the fluid leaving the system at point 2 in the same time. We may ignore the energy of the fluid within the region between points 1 and 2 because the total kinetic and potential energies of this fluid remain constant. This is so because the kinetic energies and potential energies of fluid within any small volume element are unchanged, even though matter flows continuously into and out of each volume element. Thus, the change in energy of the system is identical with that arising from the transfer of the mass element

$$\Delta m = \rho A_1 v_1 \, \Delta t = \rho A_2 v_2 \, \Delta t$$

from point 1 to 2.

The kinetic energy changes by

$$\Delta K = \tfrac{1}{2}\Delta m(v_2{}^2 - v_1{}^2) \qquad\qquad [18\text{-}11]$$

and the gravitational potential energy changes by

$$\Delta U_g = \Delta mg(y_2 - y_1) \qquad\qquad [18\text{-}12]$$

Substituting Equations 18-10, 18-11, and 18-12 into Equation 18-8 yields

$$(\Delta m/\rho)(p_1 - p_2) = \tfrac{1}{2}\Delta m(v_2^2 - v_1^2) + \Delta mg(y_2 - y_1)$$

Cancelling Δm from all terms, multiplying by ρ, and rearranging, gives *Bernoulli's theorem*:

$$\boxed{\; p_1 + \rho g y_1 + \tfrac{1}{2}\rho v_1{}^2 = p_2 + \rho g y_2 + \tfrac{1}{2}\rho v_2{}^2 \;} \qquad [18\text{-}13]$$

This relation and the equation of continuity are the foundations of the hydrodynamics of incompressible nonviscous fluids, whether a fluid is in motion or at rest. The continuity equation and Bernoulli's theorem are nothing more than the principles of mass and energy conservation, now expressed as the conservation of the quantities Av and $p + \rho g y + \tfrac{1}{2}\rho v^2$, respectively.

We can immediately deduce some qualitative results from the Bernoulli relation. Suppose, first, that fluid flows along the horizontal, such that y_1 equals y_2 in Equation 18-13. Then $p + \tfrac{1}{2}\rho v^2$ is constant. Thus, when fluid flows through a horizontal pipe of varying cross section, the pressure is least where the cross-sectional area is smallest (by the equation of continuity, the fluid speed is large where the cross section is small). This decrease in pressure with an increase in fluid speed is manifest even in situations for which the flow is not strictly streamline and for which the fluid is somewhat compressible and viscous. For example, when a high wind blows over the roof of a building, the pressure above is less than the pressure under the roof. As a result, the roof may be blown off—or, more properly, exploded off.

The deflection (hence, the curving) of a spinning baseball can also be explained qualitatively through the Bernoulli relation. Figure 18-11a shows the motion of air past a spinning baseball, as viewed by an observer moving translationally with the pitched baseball and looking down at it. The air is assumed to be nonviscous, and there is no friction between the air and ball. Clearly, the speed of the air relative to the ball's center is the same at the left and at the right of the ball. Figure 18-11b shows the motion of air relative to the ball's center, now arising from the ball's spinning in viscous air. Here the air is dragged along with the spinning ball. Figure 18-11c, a superposition of Figures 18-11a and 18-11b, indicates that the air speed, again as seen by an observer traveling with the ball, differs at the left and right. By Bernoulli's principle, the air pressure is relatively high where the speed is low; and conversely. Consequently, the ball is subject to a deflecting force acting at right angles to the ball's translational velocity, as shown in Figure 18-11d.

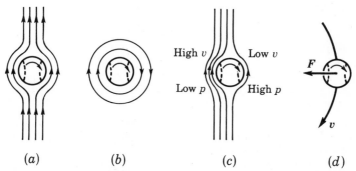

$$(a) \qquad\qquad (b) \qquad\qquad (c) \qquad\qquad (d)$$

Figure 18-11. The curving of a spinning baseball. (a) Streamlines for air past a spinning baseball in the *absence* of viscosity, as viewed by an observer traveling with the ball. (b) Streamlines for viscous air about a spinning ball. (c) Streamlines for a pitched and spinning ball through viscous air, as viewed by an observer traveling with the ball. (d) Deflecting force and path of a pitched and spinning ball, as viewed from the ground.

One must be careful about units when applying Equation 18-13 to numerical problems. Each of the terms p, $\rho g y$, and $\frac{1}{2}\rho v^2$ has the dimensions of pressure (M/LT^2); all three terms must also have the *same units* of pressure. For example, in the mks system, with ρ in kilograms per cubic meter, g in meters per square second, y in meters, and v in meters per second, the pressure p *must* be expressed in newtons per square meter. Similarly, in the English engineering system, with ρ in slugs per cubic foot, g in feet per square second, y in feet, and v in feet per second the corresponding unit for pressure is pounds per square foot (*not* pounds per square inch, centimeters of mercury, or atmospheres).

Example 4   A large tank containing liquid of constant density ρ has a small hole a vertical distance y below the liquid surface. With what speed will the liquid emerge from the hole?

The situation is shown in Figure 18-12. We designate a point at the surface as 1 and a point in the emerging stream as 2. Vertical heights are measured from the horizontal plane of the hole. Bernoulli's theorem, Equation 18-13, then becomes

$$p_1 + \rho g y + \tfrac{1}{2}\rho v_1{}^2 = p_2 + 0 + \tfrac{1}{2}\rho v_2{}^2$$

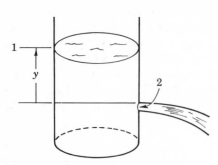

Figure 18-12. Liquid escaping from a hole in the side of a container.

Inasmuch as p_1 and p_2 are both atmospheric pressure, they cancel. The equation of continuity requires that $A_1 v_1 = A_2 v_2$, where A_1 is the cross-sectional area of the tank and A_2 is that of the hole. We see that $A_1 \gg A_2$; therefore, $v_1 \ll v_2$. The liquid level then descends very slowly, and can be regarded as at rest ($v_1 = 0$). The equation above becomes

$$\rho g y = \tfrac{1}{2}\rho v_2{}^2$$

or,

$$v_2 = \sqrt{2gy}$$

This result is known as Toricelli's principle. Note that the liquid emerges with the same speed (but *not* the same velocity) that droplets would attain after falling freely from rest through a height y in a gravitational field alone.

Example 5 Water (density, 1.0×10^3 kg/m³) flows through a horizontal pipe which narrows to one half of its original cross section. The water's speed at the constriction is 6.0 m/sec. By how much does the pressure drop from the original cross section to the constriction?

We label the wide portion of the pipe "1" and the narrow portion "2," as shown in Figure 18-13. Since the elevations y_1 and y_2 are the same at both points, Bernoulli's theorem reduces to

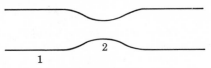

Figure 18-13.

$$p_1 + \tfrac{1}{2}\rho v_1{}^2 = p_2 + \tfrac{1}{2}\rho v_2{}^2$$
$$p_1 - p_2 = \tfrac{1}{2}\rho(v_2{}^2 - v_1{}^2) = \tfrac{1}{2}\rho v_2{}^2(1 - v_1{}^2/v_2{}^2)$$

From the equation of continuity, $v_1/v_2 = A_2/A_1$. Therefore,

$$p_1 - p_2 = \tfrac{1}{2}\rho v_2{}^2[1 - (A_2/A_1)^2]$$
$$p_1 - p_2 = \tfrac{1}{2}(1.0 \times 10^3 \text{ kg/m}^3)(6.0 \text{ m/sec})^2[1 - (\tfrac{1}{2})^2] = 1.4 \times 10^4 \text{ nt/m}^2$$
$$= 0.14 \text{ atm}$$

18-7   Hydrostatics   For a fluid of constant density ρ at rest in a uniform gravitational field g, Bernoulli's theorem, Equation 18-13, reduces to

$$p_1 + \rho g y_1 = p_2 + \rho g y_2$$

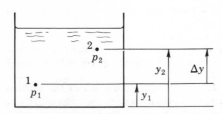

Figure 18-14. Pressure at two points in a static fluid.

See Figure 18-14. The pressure of a static fluid is the *same* at all points on the *same horizontal level*, quite apart from the shape or size of the containing vessel. The difference in pressure ($p_2 - p_1$) between two horizontal planes is proportional to the vertical separation $(y_1 - y_2)$ of the planes:

$$p_2 - p_1 = \rho g(y_1 - y_2) = -\rho g(y_2 - y_1)$$

or
$$\boxed{\Delta p = -\rho g\, \Delta y}$$ [18-14]

A minus sign appears in Equation 18-14, because the hydrostatic pressure increases as the elevation decreases. The ratio $\Delta p/\Delta y$ is called the *pressure gradient*.

Observe that Equation 18-14 does *not* give the absolute pressures, p or p_0, at two levels, but only the pressure *difference* between these horizontal planes. For example, if the absolute pressure at the horizontal surface of a liquid is p_0 (the atmospheric pressure), then the absolute pressure p at a depth h below the surface is, from Equation 18-14,

$$\boxed{p = p_0 + \rho g h}$$ [18-15]

where h is measured as positive downward.

The difference $p - p_0 = \rho g h$ is the gauge pressure at the depth h.

We may construct simple pressure-measuring devices by making use of the fact that, for a given density of liquid, the pressure difference between two points within the liquid depends only on their vertical separation. Consider the U-tube manometer shown in Figure 18-15. We wish to relate the pressure p_i inside the vessel to the difference in height of liquid between the two sides of the tube. Inasmuch as the hydrostatic pressure is the same at all points at the same level, the pressure p_A at the point A within the right-hand tube is the same as p_i. Using Equation 18-15, we can also write $p_A = p_0 + \rho g h$. Therefore, $p_i = p_0 + \rho g h$; which is to say, the pressure in the vessel exceeds atmospheric pressure by an amount $\rho g h$.

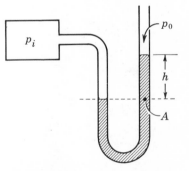

Figure 18-15. An open U-tube manometer.

Because one arm of the U-tube in Figure 18-15 is open to the atmosphere, the device is called an open-tube manometer. If the right-hand surface were to lie *below* the left-hand surface, the pressure within the vessel would be *less* than that outside, by the magnitude $\rho g h$.

A more common barometer, a closed-tube manometer, is that shown in Figure 18-16. The liquid used in a manometer is usually mercury because at room temperature (a) it is liquid, (b) it has a high density, its specific

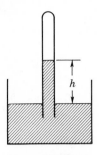

Figure 18-16. A closed-tube ma- nometer, or ba- rometer.

gravity being 13.6, (c) it is chemically stable, and (d) it has a relatively low vapor pressure. The tube is closed at the upper end, and a near vacuum exists within this region above the liquid surface. Thus, the pressure existing at the outside liquid surface, which is equal to that within the tube at the same elevation, is $\rho g h$, where h is the height of the mercury column. Standard atmospheric pressure corresponds to a mercury height of exactly 76 cm. Therefore,

$$1 \text{ std. atm} = \rho g h = (13.595 \times 10^3 \text{ kg/m}^3)$$
$$\times (9.80665 \text{ m/sec}^2)(0.760000 \text{ m})$$
$$1 \text{ std. atm} = 1.013250 \times 10^5 \text{ nt/m}^2$$

The density ρ of the liquid and the gravitational acceleration g are constants. Therefore, one may measure pressures directly in units of centimeters of mercury (cm Hg), as well as in atmospheres, newtons per square meter, or pounds per square inch.

Example 6   A concrete dam holds a reservoir of water to a depth H, as shown in Figure 18-17a. The dam has a length L. (a) Find the horizontal force F_w of the water on the dam. (b) Find the horizontal force F_a of the air on the dam.

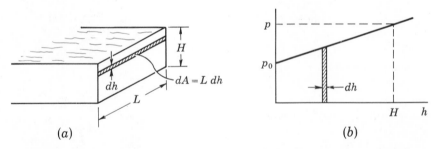

(a) (b)

Figure 18-17. (a) The dam at the end of a reservoir. (b) Pressure at the dam as a function of depth h.

(a) On the water side of the dam the pressure p at a depth h below the surface is, from Equation 18-15,

$$p = p_0 + \rho g h$$

where p_0 is atmospheric pressure at the surface, ρ is the density of water, and h is the depth.

The pressure increases linearly with the depth h. Consequently, on a small strip of area $dA = L \, dh$, the force dF is

$$dF = p \, dA = pL \, dh$$

The variation with depth is shown in Figure 18-17b, where the total force F_w of water on the dam is equal to the area under the pressure-depth curve multiplied by the length L; that is,

$$F_w = \int dF = L \int_0^H p \, dh = LH\left(\frac{p_H + p_0}{2}\right)$$

where the pressure at depth H is $p_H = p_0 + \rho g H$. Substituting in the relation above gives

$$F_w = LH(p_0 + \tfrac{1}{2}\rho g H)$$

It is interesting to note that the force of water on the dam does *not* depend at all on the amount of water restrained by the dam!

(b) We assume that the atmospheric pressure p_0 is constant over the vertical distance H. Then the horizontal force F_a of the air on the dam is merely the pressure p_0 multiplied by the *projection* of the area of the dam onto the vertical plane:

$$F_a = p_0 LH$$

The difference in the forces acting on the two sides of the dam is simply $F_w - F_a = \tfrac{1}{2}gLH^2$. The dam must be able, through its structural rigidity, to withstand this force. Inasmuch as the horizontal shearing force within the dam increases with depth, the dam must be structurally stronger at the bottom than at the top.

18-8 Archimedes' principle   Eighteen hundred years before Newtonian mechanics was developed Archimedes discovered that any body, partially or wholly immersed in a fluid, is acted upon by an upward, or buoyant, force which is equal in magnitude to the weight of the fluid displaced by the body.

One proof of Archimedes' principle is simple, nonanalytical, but altogether rigorous. We focus our attention on an arbitrary volume V within a liquid at rest, as shown in Figure 18-18a. The liquid within V is at rest because the resultant force of the surrounding liquid on it just annuls the downward weight of the liquid contained in V. Thus, the liquid in V is subject to an upward force arising from the surrounding liquid which equals the weight of the liquid within V. Now suppose that our imaginary volume of liquid V is replaced by a solid of exactly the same shape and volume. The same forces act at the boundary of V, since the density and other properties of the solid do not affect the surrounding liquid. Thus, this solid is subject to a force arising from the surrounding liquid which equals the weight of the liquid it displaces. See Figure 18-18b.

Now let us arrive at the same result by using the relations for hydrostatic pressure. For simplicity, we consider a solid parallelepiped of height H, horizontal area A, and mass M; see Figure 18-19 (any irregularly shaped object can, of course, be represented by a large collection of such small parallelepipeds). The block is completely immersed in a liquid of constant density ρ_l.

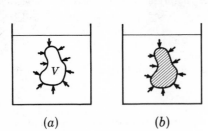

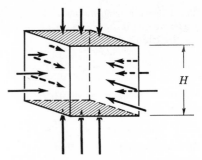

Figure 18-18. Archimedes' principle illustrated: (a) hydrostatic forces on the surface of an arbitrary volume V of liquid within a liquid, (b) hydrostatic forces on a solid of volume V replacing the liquid.

Figure 18-19. Hydrostatic forces on the faces of a parallelepiped of height H.

Two external influences act on the block: the Earth exerts a downward force Mg, and the normal forces of the liquid act on each exposed surface of the block (Archimedes' principle is just a statement concerning the net effect of these normal forces).

We notice first that the *horizontal* forces of the liquid on the vertical sides cancel. This follows because the pressure at any point depends only on the depth, the horizontal forces acting on opposite vertical sides adding to zero. On the other hand, the upward force on the bottom surface of area A *exceeds* the downward force on the upper surface by virtue of the increase in pressure with depth. By Equation 18-15, the pressure p_l and p_u at the *lower* and *upper* surfaces, respectively, are related by

$$p_l = p_u + \rho_l g H$$

The resultant force F_b, the *buoyant* force, of the liquid on the block is upward; its magnitude is

$$F_b = p_l A - p_u A = (p_l - p_u)A = \rho_l g A H$$

Now, AH is the volume V of the block, as well as of the fluid displaced by the block, $\rho_l A H$ is the mass of the displaced fluid, and $\rho_l g A H = \rho_l g V$ is the weight of the displaced fluid. Thus this equation yields Archimedes' principle:

$$\boxed{F_b = \rho_l g V} \qquad\qquad [18\text{-}16]$$

Whether a body immersed in a fluid will be accelerated upward, downward, or not at all, depends on the resultant of *all* of the acting vertical forces, of which the buoyant force is but one. Clearly, if the only external forces acting are the buoyant force and the weight of the body, the body will be accelerated upward if the buoyant force exceeds the weight. This is to say, a body totally immersed in a fluid will be accelerated upward toward the surface if the body's density is less than that of the fluid. Conversely, a body with a density greater than that of the fluid will sink.

Example 7 A cylindrical buoy of mass M and cross-sectional area A is partially immersed in water, its lower end being a distance h from the water surface, as shown in Figure 18-20. (a) What is the resultant upward force on the buoy? (b) To what depth h_0 does the buoy float when in equilibrium? (c) What is the buoy's motion if it is released from a nonequilibrium position within the water?

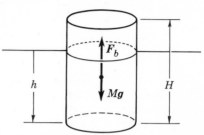

Figure 18-20. Forces on a cylindrical buoy of height H immersed to a depth h within a liquid.

(a) The buoy is subject to a downward force, its weight Mg, and to an upward force, the buoyant force F_b. The buoy displaces a volume of water Ah; the mass of this water is $\rho_w Ah$ and its weight $\rho_w Ahg$, where ρ_w is the density of water. Therefore, the resultant upward force F_r on the buoy is

$$F_r = F_b - Mg = \rho_w Ahg - Mg$$

(b) The buoy floats at rest when the resultant force on it is zero ($h = h_0$). The equation above becomes

$$0 = \rho_w Ah_0 g - Mg$$

$$h_0 = Mg/\rho_w Ag$$

We can write this result in simpler fashion by replacing the mass M of the buoy by $\rho_b AH$, where ρ_b is the average density of the buoy and H is its over-all height. Then we have:

$$h_0 = \rho_b AHg/\rho_w Ag = H(\rho_b/\rho_w)$$

That is, the fraction h_0/H of the buoy's volume beneath the surface is equal to the (average) specific gravity ρ_b/ρ_w of the buoy. Therefore, if the buoy's density is, for example, 80 per cent that of water, it will float 80 per cent submerged.

(c) The relation for the resultant force may be written

$$F_r = \rho_w Ahg - \rho_w Ah_0 g = \rho_w Ag(h - h_0)$$

The resultant force on the buoy is, in general, proportional to its displacement $(h - h_0)$ from its equilibrium position. Thus, if the buoy is released from a nonequilibrium position, it will, with negligible friction, oscillate vertically in simple harmonic motion.

Example 8 A ping-pong ball is immersed in a liquid and attached to the bottom of the vessel by a string. See Figure 18-21a. (a) What is the force of the string on the ping-pong ball when the vessel is at rest in an inertial frame? (b) Suppose that the vessel is now accelerated to the right at the constant acceleration a.

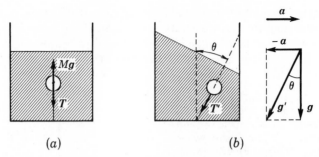

Figure 18-21. (a) Forces on a ping-pong ball attached by a string and immersed in a liquid. (b) The container is moved to the right with acceleration **a,** and the effective acceleration due to gravity, as viewed by an observer at rest with the container, is **g'**.

What is the angle between the vertical and the string? (c) What is the tension in the string? (d) What is the angle of inclination of the liquid surface under these circumstances?

(a) Neglecting the weight of the ping-pong ball, the only forces acting on the ball are: the tension T downward and the buoyant force Mg upward, where M is the *mass of liquid* having the same volume as that of the ball. Because the resultant force on the ball is zero,

$$\Sigma F = Mg - T = 0$$
$$T = Mg$$

The direction of the tension T in this static situation is, of course, along the direction of the acceleration due to gravity, g.

(b) Let us view the accelerated motion as an observer who travels with the vessel. We may then apply the principle of equivalence (Section 16-7) to arrive at the direction of the effective acceleration g' due to gravity in this noninertial reference frame. The acceleration g' has two components: g downward, arising from the true weight, and a horizontal component a, arising from making observations in a noninertial system. The horizontal component is opposite in direction to the acceleration a of the vessel, relative to the inertial frame. See Figure 18-21b.

The ping-pong ball is at rest in the accelerated reference frame. Thus, the direction of the tension T' in the string must be along the direction of g', and the angle θ between the vertical and the string is given by

$$\tan \theta = a/g$$

(c) The magnitude of the tension T' is

$$T' = Mg' = M\sqrt{g^2 + a^2}$$

(d) The free surface of any liquid at rest is horizontal. More precisely, the surface of a liquid in equilibrium is perpendicular to the direction of the acceleration due to gravity. Thus, the surface of the liquid in the accelerated vessel, which we see as an observer accelerating with the vessel, must be perpendicular to g', which is "down." The angle between the "apparent horizontal" (represented by the surface of the liquid) and the true horizontal is also θ.

Note that, if one takes into account the change in the direction and magnitude of the acceleration due to "gravity," the situations portrayed in Figures 18-21b and 18-21a are alike.

An interesting alternative interpretation can be given to the behavior of a ping-pong ball, or a similar "bubble" in a fluid, by attributing a *negative* gravitational mass to the "hole" in the liquid. See Problem 18-39.

18-9 Summary The molecules of a solid or liquid are more or less tightly bound to their neighboring molecules. The molecules of a gas are essentially free.

The surface energy of an exposed area A of a liquid is given by

[18-1] $$E_s = TA$$

where T is a constant, the surface tension.

The pressure p is defined by

[18-2] $$p = \lim_{\Delta A \to 0} \left(\frac{\Delta F}{\Delta A} \right)$$

Standard atmospheric pressure is 76 cm Hg $\simeq 10^5$ nt/m^2 $\simeq 10^6$ dyne/cm^2.

Streamlines are used to represent the velocity field of a fluid in streamline flow, the direction and magnitude of the velocity at points in space being given thereby.

The simplest type of fluid motion is the steady flow of a nonviscous fluid of constant density in irrotational streamline motion.

The equation of continuity, which expresses the conservation of mass law, is

[18-6] $$\text{Mass flux} = \rho_1 A_1 v_1 = \rho_2 A_2 v_2$$

Bernoulli's theorem, which expresses the conservation of energy law, is

[18-13] $$p_1 + \rho g y_1 + \tfrac{1}{2}\rho v_1{}^2 = p_2 + \rho g y_2 + \tfrac{1}{2}\rho v_2{}^2$$

For a static liquid of density ρ, the pressure p at a depth h below the surface is given by

[18-15] $$p = p_0 + \rho g h$$

where p_0 is the pressure at the surface.

PROBLEMS

18-1 An evacuated pressure-measuring device similar to that of Figure 18-2 is used to measure pressures in fluids near the Earth's surface. The cross-sectional area of the piston is 10 cm^2; the spring constant is

200 nt/m. The spring is compressed a distance 0.90 cm from its unstretched length when the device is oriented so that the open end of the cylinder is straight down. If the cylinder is turned until the open end points straight up, the spring is compressed 1.00 cm from its unstretched length. (a) Find the mass of the piston. (b) What is the pressure of the fluid?

18-2 If the Earth's atmosphere had the same density at all distances above the Earth's surface as at the surface (1.29×10^{-3} gm/cm³), what would be the height of the atmosphere when the pressure at the Earth's surface was 1 standard atmosphere?

18-3 What is the magnitude of the total weight of the atmosphere surrounding the Earth (radius, 4000 miles)?

18-4 What is the decrease in energy of surface tension when two spherical water droplets, each of radius 2.0 mm, amalgamate into one spherical droplet? The surface tension coefficient of water at room temperature is 73 ergs/cm².

18-5 How much work must be done to separate a droplet of mercury (surface tension, 0.52 joule/m²) of 2.0 mm diameter into two droplets of equal size?

18-6 The surface tension has been defined as the surface energy per unit area of a liquid. The surface tension T also is equal to the force per

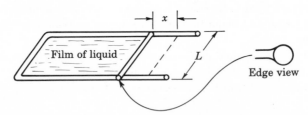

Figure 18-22. A liquid film on a U-shaped wire and a moveable wire.

unit length exerted by the liquid at any boundary. Consider the situation shown in Figure 18-22a, where a film of liquid is bounded by a fixed U-shaped wire and a movable wire. (a) How much work (in terms of T) is required to displace the wire a distance x and thereby increase the exposed area of the liquid on each of the two sides of the film by Lx? (b) What constant force must be applied to the wire to displace it by x? (c) Show that the force per unit length of interface between the liquid and the movable wire is equal to the surface tension T. (Note that the liquid joins the wire along *both* the top and bottom, as shown in Figure 18-22b.)

18-7 ★ The rise of liquid in a tube of small cross section, the phenomenon of *capillarity*, is a result of surface tension. Figure 18-23 shows a liquid of density ρ rising to a height h in a capillary tube of radius r by virtue of the forces of surface tension. The forces at the uppermost liquid-tube boundary act vertically upward when the angle of contact

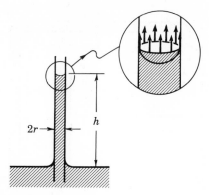

Figure 18-23. A capillary tube with the forces of surface tension at the upper meniscus.

between the liquid surface and the wall is zero, as is very nearly the case for water and glass. (a) Using the fact that the surface tension is the force per unit length of interface (Problem 18-6), show that $h = 2T/r\rho g$. (b) What must the radius of a capillary tube be to make water rise 10 cm? (For water, $T = 73$ dyne/cm.)

18-8   Water flows through the pipe system shown in Figure 18-24 at the rate of 4.0 feet³/minute. The pipe diameters are 4.0 inches and 2.0

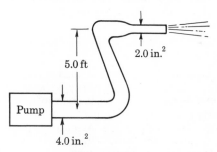

Figure 18-24.

inches at the lower and upper sections, respectively. The water is discharged into the atmosphere at the right end of the upper section, this section being 5.0 feet above the lower pipe. Assume atmospheric pressure to be 15 pounds/inch². (a) What are the speeds of flow in the lower and upper sections of the pipe? (b) What are the pressures in the lower and upper sections? (c) A pump having 80 per cent efficiency is used to take water, originally at rest, and discharge it into the system of pipes at 4.0 feet³/minute. What is the horsepower rating of the pump?

18-9   One device, commonly used for transferring a liquid from one container to another at a lower level, is the *siphon*, shown in Figure

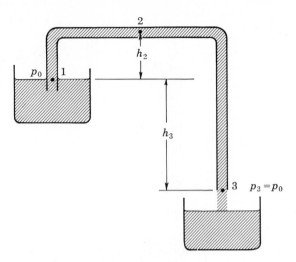

Figure 18-25.

18-25. Assume that the cross-sectional area of the siphon tube is 2.0 inches^2 and that the lower end of the tube (point 3) discharges water into the atmosphere ($p_3 = p_0$). If the heights h_2 and h_3 are 8.0 feet and 16.0 feet, respectively, what are: (a) the pressure at point 1, (b) the pressure at point 2, (c) the speed of the water at points 1, 2, and 3, and (d) the rate, in pounds per cubic foot, at which water flows through the tube.

18-10   See Problem 18-9. What will be the discharge rate if the height h_3 is increased to 25.0 feet?

18-11   Water flows through a 1.0-inch-diameter pipe at the rate of 4.0 feet^3/minute, the absolute pressure in the pipe being 30 pounds/inch^2. What must be the diameter of a constriction in the pipe if the pressure at this point is to be 4.0 pounds/inch^2? (A partial vacuum exists at the constriction, inasmuch as the absolute pressure there is less than atmospheric pressure. Thus, a tube connected to such a constriction acts as a pump, called an *aspirator*.)

18-12   Water moves in streamline flow through the horizontal pipe system shown in Figure 18-26. The diameter of the large pipe is 15 cm; the diameter of the constriction is 5.0 cm. The height of the mercury in the left-hand tube of this *Venturi meter* is 16 cm; in the right-hand tube, the height is 80 cm. (a) What is the speed of the water in the large pipe? (b) Find the mass rate of flow through the pipe. (c) What is the maximum mass rate of flow measurable with this particular Venturi meter?

18-13   A short section of 1.0-inch (inside diameter) pipe is joined to a long horizontal 3.0-inch (inside diameter) pipe. Water flows through the pipe at the rate of 0.10 feet^3/sec. What is the difference in pressure between the 1.0-inch constriction and the 3.0-inch pipe?

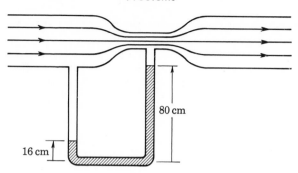

Figure 18-26. A Venturi meter.

18-14 ⋆ A cubical vessel 20 cm on a side is completely evacuated and then submerged in a large amount of mercury, until the top of the cube is 2.0 cm below the mercury surface. The mercury surface is exposed to the atmosphere. Find the total time required to fill the cubical vessel if a circular hole of cross-sectional area 0.10 cm² is located (a) on the top surface of the cube and (b) on the bottom surface of the cube.

18-15 A small hole of cross-sectional area 0.50 inch² is made in the side of a tank holding water at a depth of 10 feet below the water surface. (a) Find the initial volume discharge rate, in cubic feet per second, through the hole. (b) Find the initial mass discharge rate, in slugs per second, through the hole.

18-16 Two large open tanks hold different liquids. The liquid in the first tank has three times the density of the liquid in the second tank. Suppose that a small hole is punched in each tank at the same depth, h, below the surface. What is the ratio of the area of the hole in the first tank to that in the second tank if (a) the mass fluxes emerging from the two tanks are equal and (b) if the volume fluxes emerging from the two tanks are equal?

18-17 ⋆ A large tank, open to the atmosphere at the top, contains a liquid of density ρ to a depth h. The liquid is slowly discharged into the atmosphere through a tapered vertical pipe of length l connected to the bottom of the tank. The cross-sectional area of the pipe at its upper end is A_u. (a) What is the area of the pipe as a function of distance y below the tank bottom such that the pressure and density *both* remain constant at all points along the pipe? (b) What is the discharge rate?

18-18 ⋆ A large tank, open at the top, contains water to a depth H. Water flows through a hole in the bottom of the tank, then down a vertical tube of constant cross section, and finally into the atmosphere. Assume that the cross section of the tube is much less than that of the tank. (a) At what point within the tube is the pressure atmospheric? (*Note:* The water will *not* fill the tube completely, and *cavitation* will occur at any points below that at which the pressure becomes atmospheric.) (b) Show that the average density of the water-air mixture within the tube is given by $\rho = \rho_w[(H + y')/(H + y)]^{1/2}$, where ρ_w is the density of water, y is that distance below the bottom of the tank at which ρ is measured, and y' is defined in part (a).

18-19   The lower end of a hose is submerged in a lake; the upper end is connected to a vacuum pump located 50 feet above the lake surface. (a) To what height above the lake surface will the water rise in the hose when the pressure in the upper end of the hose is one-half atmospheric pressure? (b) What is the height when the pressure in the upper end is one-thousandth atmospheric pressure?

18-20   Figure 18-27 shows a side view of a tank filled with water to a depth of 3.0 feet. The sides of the tank are vertical, parallel, and separated

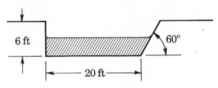

Figure 18-27.

by 10 feet. (a) What is the force of the water on the bottom of the tank? (b) What is the force of the water on the vertical end? (c) What is the force of the water on the inclined end?

18-21   Assuming the density of air to be approximately constant near the Earth's surface, compute the barometric pressure at an elevation of 200 feet above sea level. The pressure at sea level is 76 cm Hg.

18-22   Assuming the density of sea water to be constant, 2.1 slugs/feet^3, what is the absolute pressure, in atmospheres, at a depth of 1.0 mile below the ocean surface?

18-23   A U-tube, open to the atmosphere on both sides, contains mercury (density, 13.6 gm/cm^3) in both arms to a height of 5.0 cm above the bottom of the tube. Water is slowly poured into the left tube until the interface between the mercury and the water in the left tube is 4.0 cm above the tube bottom. (a) What is the height of the water column? (b) By how much will the water-mercury interface be lowered if the air is removed from both sides of the U-tube?

18-24   Two hemispheres are placed together, and the interior space is completely evacuated. The minimum force applied to each of the two hemispheres that will separate them when they are immersed in air is 50 pounds. Atmospheric pressure is 15 pounds/inch^2. What is the minimum force required to separate the evacuated hemispheres when they are immersed in water at a depth of 20 feet?

18-25   The hydraulic brake system of an automobile is an example of the *hydraulic press* and of *Pascal's principle*. According to Pascal's principle, a pressure change in one portion of an incompressible liquid in a closed container is transmitted to all parts of the liquid. Suppose that the pressure in an automobile's brake fluid is increased by the application of a force of 20 pounds at the brake pedal over an area of

0.25 inch^2 (at the master cylinder). What force is applied to a wheel's brake shoe if the area over which it is applied (at the wheel cylinder) is 2.0 inches^2?

18-26 A 200 gm sphere has a diameter of 6.0 cm. When dropped into water the sphere is observed to descend, after a short time, at constant velocity. What is the upward resistive force of the water on the sphere when it is descending at constant velocity?

18-27 An object made of copper (density, 8.9 gm/cm^3) hangs at the end of a vertical spring. When the object is immersed in air, the spring is elongated by 2.0 cm from its unstretched length. What will be the spring's elongation when the object is immersed in water?

18-28 A cylindrical cork floats on water, the axis of the cork being vertical. The specific gravity of the cork is 0.150. If the atmosphere above the water is removed, what additional fraction of the cork will be submerged?

18-29 ★ A 100 gm cubical vessel, 20 cm on a side and initially floating in a large sea of mercury, is pushed down until the mercury surface almost reaches the top of the vessel. (a) What downward force is necessary to hold the vessel in this position? (b) Find the total work done on the vessel in shoving it down to this position. (Ignore frictional forces.)

18-30 ★ A cube of oak wood (density, 0.80 gm/cm^3) 2.0 cm on a side floats in water. How much work must be done on the cube to push it down very slowly until it is just submerged?

18-31 At the Earth's surface, ice (specific gravity, 0.92) floats on water. (a) What fraction of the ice is submerged? (b) What fraction of the ice would be submerged in water at the Moon's surface?

18-32 ★ A *hydrometer* is a device that floats in a liquid and indicates the density of the liquid in which it is immersed by the fraction of its volume above the surface. A typical hydrometer consists of a relatively large bulb and a long slender stem attached to it. Show that the graduations on the stem indicating the density are linear (uniformly spaced) if the stem's volume is a small fraction of the bulb's volume.

18-33 A 300 gm balloon is filled with helium until the volume of the balloon is 1.5 m^3. The density of the contained helium is 0.178 kg/m^3 and the density of the surrounding air is 1.29 kg/m^3. What downward force must be applied to the balloon to prevent it from rising?

18-34 ★ A cylinder of brass (density, 8.6 gm/cm^3) having a mass of exactly 1 kg hangs from a spring balance at the Earth's equator. Calculate the difference between the weight of the brass and the tension in the supporting spring. The density of air is 1.29×10^{-3} gm/cm^3.

18-35 A block of wood (specific gravity, 0.60) floats on water. What is the minimum mass of wood necessary to support a 160-pound man standing on the block?

18-36 A 10-pound block of wood is to be loaded with a lead weight so that it floats with its top surface at the surface of water. What weight is required if the lead is attached (a) to the top side of the block and

(b) to the bottom side of the block? The specific gravities of the wood and of lead are 0.70 and 11.3, respectively.

18-37   A certain object weighs 25 pounds in air, 18 pounds when immersed in water, and 20 pounds when immersed in another liquid of unknown density. What is (a) the density of the object and (b) the density of the second liquid?

18-38   An iron casting is suspected of having internal cavities. Its weight in air is found to be 32.2 pounds; in water, 27.5 pounds. What is the volume of the cavities? (Density of water, 2.0 slugs/feet³; density of iron, 15.6 slugs/feet³.)

18-39 ⋆   In Example 8 it was shown that the resultant force on a ping-pong ball immersed in a liquid, or on any other bubble of negligible weight, is upward in direction and equal in magnitude to the weight of liquid displaced by the ball. The hole in the liquid rises, rather than falls, when released, and one may attribute a *negative* effective gravitational mass and a negative effective weight to the hole. At the same time, one attributes a zero effective weight to the surrounding liquid. Thus, a hole in a sea of liquid is equivalent to a sphere of negative weight in a vacuum, and one may analyze certain problems in hydrodynamics from this point of view.

Suppose that a pipe, closed at the lower end, is immersed in a liquid until the closed end is 16 feet below the surface of the liquid. The lower end is then opened suddenly to allow the liquid to rise in the pipe. How long does it take, after the lower end is opened, for the pipe to be filled with liquid?

18-40   The two vertical arms of an open U-tube containing a liquid are separated horizontally by 10.0 cm. When the U-tube is at rest, the height of liquid in the two arms is, of course, the same. Suppose that the U-tube is moved horizontally with a constant acceleration of 4.0 m/sec². What is the difference in heights of the liquid in the two arms?

18-41 ⋆   Show that when a liquid in a bucket is rotated about a vertical axis at constant angular speed, the surface of the liquid assumes the shape

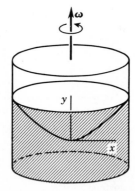

Figure 18-28. The paraboloidal surface of a liquid in a rotating bucket.

of a paraboloid (a cross section through the center is a parabola). See Figure 18-28. (*Hint:* View the liquid as a rotating observer at rest with respect to the liquid. In this reference frame each particle of liquid is subject to, in addition to its weight mg, an outward centrifugal force $m\omega^2x$. The effective weight of a particle on the surface of the liquid must be perpendicular to the surface. To show that $y = Kx^2$, the equation for a parabola, we need merely show that $dy/dx = 2Kx$, where K is a constant.)

18-42 $\star$ A long vertical tube of cross-sectional area 0.20 inch^2 contains mercury to a height of 10 feet and is open to the atmosphere at the top. This tube is placed alongside a large open tank containing water to a height of 10 feet. The horizontal area of the large tank is 75 feet^2. A short horizontal tube of cross section 0.050 inch^2 connects the tube of mercury and the tank of water at their bottoms. (a) What is the initial mass discharge rate of mercury into the water tank when the connecting tube is opened? (b) What fraction of the mercury will finally be found in the water tank?

NINETEEN

TEMPERATURE AND THERMAL EXPANSION

This is the first of several chapters on the general topic of heat, including the kinetic theory of gases and the laws of thermodynamics. We set forth here not only a preview of the contents of this chapter but also a brief outline of the succeeding chapters as well.

Historically, the subject of heat developed quite separately from that of mechanics. Heat was first thought to be a substance (called the *caloric*), and the units devised for measuring the amount of heat (calories) were quite distinct from those in mechanics. Moreover, the temperature of a body was not thought to be related in any simple way to its mechanical properties. The single most profound discovery concerning heat was the recognition, emerging about 1840, that *heat and temperature*—indeed, *all thermal phenomena—can be interpreted in mechanical terms.*

The key is the molecular theory of gases. In this theory, ordinary Newtonian mechanics is applied to the microscopic motions of molecules of a gas. One finds that thermal phenomena are merely mechanical phenomena taking place on a microscopic scale, that thermal energy is simply the disordered mechanical energy of atoms and molecules, that temperature is a measure of the translational kinetic energy of gas molecules, and that heat is nothing more than a thermal-energy transfer caused by a temperature difference.

We shall not follow the historical development of ideas concerning heat and thermodynamics. Instead, our strategy will be as follows.

We shall first consider the measurement of temperature, the meaning of thermal equilibrium, and the task of finding reliable thermometers. Several varieties of thermometers and the expansion of liquids and solids arising from temperature change will be discussed. Then (Chapter 20) we shall investigate the properties of an ideal gas, the general-gas law, ideal-gas thermometers, and several types of transformations taking place in the state of a gas.

We turn then (Chapters 21 and 22) to the molecular model, or kinetic theory, of the simplest of all many-particle systems—an ideal gas. Here we apply mechanics to molecular collisions, deduce the general-gas law from a mechanical model, and interpret temperature in terms of molecular behavior. We shall interpret the meanings of the words *heat, internal energy,* and *specific heat* in terms of the molecular behavior and discuss the first and second laws of thermodynamics.

Next (Chapter 23), we extend the molecular model to more complicated systems—solids and liquids. We interpret the thermal behavior of solids and liquids, and the meanings of heat, temperature, and the first and second laws of thermodynamics for these systems. We also consider changes in state and the modes of thermal-energy transfer.

Finally (Chapter 24), we consider formal thermodynamics. Here we avoid details of the molecular behavior and concentrate on the very general and powerful laws of thermodynamics. The Carnot engine, the most efficient of all heat engines, is discussed, and also a procedure for measuring temperatures altogether independent of the thermometric substance. The second law of thermodynamics is treated in terms of entropy.

19-1   Temperature and the zeroth law of thermodynamics   The most rudimentary conception of temperature arises from our sense of touch. We can tell by touch, although only qualitatively and roughly, whether two bodies have the same temperature or whether one is relatively hot or cold compared with the second. What are needed are a means of asserting that two bodies have the *same* temperature and a quantitative measure of *difference* in temperature. That is, we need a thermometer.

Suppose that we bring two bodies together, place them in contact, isolate them (that is, insulate them) from external influences—and wait. After a sufficiently long time has elapsed, the bodies are said to be in *thermal equilibrium*, and the property the two bodies then have in common—whatever differences there may be in their size, mass, material, and past history—is *temperature*. Two bodies in thermal equilibrium have the same temperature, by definition.

Suppose now that we have three bodies: vessel A, vessel B, and a thermometer. The thermometer is first placed in vessel A. After these two objects have come to thermal equilibrium, we read their common temperature on the thermometer. (A thermometer reads not only its own temperature but also that of a body with which it is in equilibrium.) Suppose that the thermometer is then placed in vessel B and we find the same final temperature as that of vessel A. The thermometer has the same temperature as that of vessels A and B because it has achieved thermal equilibrium with each in turn. Do A and B have the same temperature? Are A and B in thermal equilibrium? According to the *zeroth law of thermodynamics*, they are. That is, *if bodies A and B are separately in thermal equilibrium with a third body C, then A and B are in thermal equilibrium with each other.* The zeroth law of thermodynamics, which is fundamental to all thermodynamics, is so named because it has priority over the first and second laws of thermodynamics.

19-2 Thermometry Just as a physicist defines length as the quantity that one measures with a meter stick, and time as the quantity that one reads on a clock, so too one must first say that temperature is simply what one reads on a thermometer. But what is a thermometer? *A thermometer is any device having some measurable physical property that changes with the degree of relative hotness or coldness of the body.* For example, the change in the volume of a liquid with temperature is the basis of the common liquid-in-glass thermometer. We will consider this type of thermometer in some detail, to see how the temperature scales are defined and the thermometers calibrated, and also to see some important problems in thermometry that apply to all thermometers.

Our liquid-in-glass thermometer consists of a spherical bulb of glass filled to the brim with the dense liquid mercury. If the temperature is then raised, the mercury expands more rapidly than the glass container. Some of the liquid overflows. One can, in principle, read the temperature by measuring the amount of mercury overflow. A simpler procedure, however, is to attach a cylindrical stem of uniform cross section to the bulb so that, when the mercury overflows from the bulb into the stem, one can measure this overflow by noting the position of the meniscus along the stem.

Next we calibrate the thermometer. The thermometer may be placed in a mixture of ice and water under standard atmospheric pressure. We make a mark at the position of the meniscus and label it "0." By definition, the *ice point* at standard pressure has a temperature of 0° on the *Celsius* (also known as the *centigrade*) temperature scale. The thermometer is then brought into thermal equilibrium with a mixture of water vapor and boiling water, again under standard atmospheric pressure. We make a second mark at the new position of the meniscus and label it 100° C. By definition, the *steam point* of water at standard pressure is 100° Celsius. The calibration is completed when we add uniformly spaced graduations between 0° and 100° C, to place 100 graduations (centigrade) between the two chosen *fixed points*.

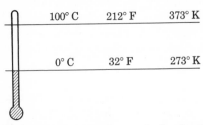

See Figure 19-1. We can extend the scale by adding graduations of the same size below the 0° and above the 100° marks.

In the familiar *Fahrenheit* scale of temperature, the ice point is defined as 32° F and the steam point as 212° F. Thus, 180 graduations separate the two fixed points on the Fahrenheit scale, as against 100 graduations on the Celsius scale. Not only are the temperatures different

Figure 19-1. Definition of the fixed points for the Celsius, Fahrenheit, and Kelvin temperature scales.

at the fixed points on the two scales, but the sizes of the degrees differ as well. As Figure 19-1 shows, any temperature t_C on the Celsius scale is related to the same temperature t_F registered on the Fahrenheit scale, by

$$\frac{t_C}{100} = \frac{t_F - 32}{180} \qquad [19\text{-}1]$$

Room temperature is approximately 20° C or 68° F. Although there is no upper limit on temperature, the lowest possible temperature is −273.15° C.

In order to distinguish temperature differences from temperatures, it is customary to represent temperature *differences* as Celsius degrees (C°) rather than as degrees Celsius (°C). Thus, 60° C differs from 40° C by 20 C°. Furthermore, 100 C° = 180 F°, although 100° C is *not* the same as 180° F. In general, the relative sizes of degrees on the two scales is given by 1 C° = $(\frac{9}{5})$ F°.

How do we know that the mercury in our thermometer expands uniformly between 0° and 100° C? We don't know—in fact, can't know—since we can test for uniform thermal expansion only with a thermometer. Therefore, let us now define a first thermometer. Suppose that we construct two thermometers using *different* liquids. For example, our first thermometer might contain mercury and our second thermometer might contain alcohol (colored with a pink dye). We calibrate this second thermometer in the same fashion as the first, using the two fixed points of water and uniformly spaced graduations.

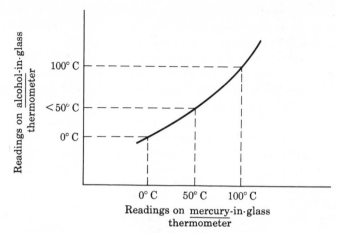

Figure 19-2. Readings of a uniformly graduated alcohol-in-glass thermometer against the corresponding readings for a mercury-in-glass thermometer. (The departure from linearity is greatly exaggerated.)

How do the readings on the two thermometers compare when we bring both thermometers into thermal equilibrium with a third body? At the two fixed points the thermometers agree perfectly. They must, of course. But, if we compare the readings at other temperatures, we find that the two readings, although they are very nearly the same, do *not* agree precisely. See Figure 19-2. Thus, the behavior of the thermometer depends on the

Table 19-1

THERMOMETER AND PHYSICAL PROPERTY OR EFFECT	TEMPERATURE RANGE
Magnetic properties of paramagnetic salts	$-273°$ to $-272°$ C
Pressure of helium vapor in equilibrium with liquid helium	$-272°$ to $-269°$ C
Resistance thermometer (electrical resistance of substances).	$-261°$ to $600°$ C
Thermocouple (electromotive force of two wires of dissimilar materials, the junctions maintained at different temperatures)	$-250°$ to $1000°$ C
Liquid-in-glass thermometers (difference in expansion properties)	$-196°$ to $500°$ C
Gas thermometers (constant pressure or constant volume, ideal gas of very low density)	$> \sim 300°$ C
Optical pyrometer (visible electromagnetic radiation from body to be measured—the color of an incandescent filament is compared with that of the body)	$> 600°$ C

thermometric substance (here, mercury or alcohol). We cannot, at this stage, say which of the two thermometers is more nearly correct, but only that the thermal expansion of mercury differs from that of alcohol.

Thermometers may be based on other physical effects than thermal expansion. Some properties that change with temperature are the electrical resistance (resistance thermometer), the electromotive force developed by a pair of unlike wires with their junctions at different temperatures (thermocouple), the color of light emitted from a solid, or from a gas, as in the case of a star (pyrometer), and the pressure of a gas (gas thermometer). Table 19-1 lists several different types of thermometers, the physical property or effect on which each is based, and the temperature ranges over which each is most commonly used.

19-3   The constant-volume gas thermometer   Can one devise a thermometer that would be independent of the thermometric substance?

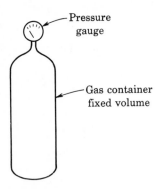

Yes, if one uses a gas of very low density. Here we discuss the *constant-volume gas thermometer*. The constant-pressure gas thermometer, which is similar to it, will be taken up later.

A simple type of constant-volume gas thermometer is shown in Figure 19-3. The pressure-measuring device may, of course, be a manometer, in which the pressure is registered by the difference in mercury heights. *The pressure of the gas* is the physical quantity we use *to register the temperature* of the gas. The temperature of the gas must be high enough, and its pressure low enough, for the gas to have a very low density; that is, the gas must not be close to the condition under which it condenses into a liquid.

Figure 19-3. A constant-volume gas thermometer.

Our calibration procedure is just like that used with the liquid-in-glass thermometers. Maintaining the volume of the gas constant, we record the pressures at the ice point and at the steam point. Then, *assuming* the pressure to vary linearly with temperature, we mark the pressures corresponding to 0° C and 100° C on graph paper, and draw a *straight* line through the two points, to establish temperatures between 0° and 100° C. By extrapolation, we extend to temperatures beyond this range, as shown in Figure 19-4. (The drawing of a straight line corresponds here to the marking of *uniform* graduations on the stem of the mercury thermometer.)

We have not specified what gas is to be placed in the constant-volume gas thermometer. Experiment shows that it does *not* matter! All low-density gases show exactly the same behavior. Two thermometers with different gases agree, not only at the fixed points, but also at *all* other temperatures when we assume a linear pressure-temperature relation. This is, of course, why a gas thermometer is a good thermometer.

For example, if a low-density gas has a pressure of 0.100 atmosphere at the ice point (0° C) and a pressure of 0.136 atmosphere at the steam point (100° C), the temperature 50° C corresponds, by definition, to a pressure exactly midway between: $(0.100 + 0.136)/2 = 0.118$ atmosphere. Furthermore, if the pressures

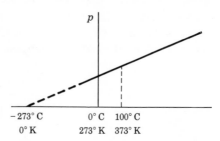

Figure 19-4. A pressure-temperature graph for a constant-volume gas thermometer.

at the fixed points of a *second* low-density gas maintained at constant volume are measured, these pressures will *not*, in general, be the same as those of the first gas, but again 50° C will correspond precisely to the mean pressure. These two thermometers, or any other constant-volume gas thermometers, will agree at *all* temperatures for which the gas density is relatively low. See Figure 19-5.

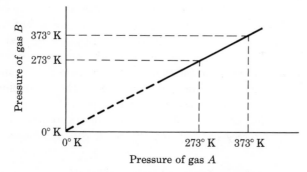

Figure 19-5. Pressure (that is, absolute temperature) for one constant-volume gas thermometer against the corresponding pressure (temperature) for a second constant-volume gas thermometer. Compare with Figure 19-2.

Figure 19-4 implies a temperature scale in which the pressure p_t at any temperature is directly proportional to the temperature. When we extrapolate the straight line to low temperatures, we find that the pressure is zero when the Celsius temperature is $-273.15°$. More properly, if the behavior of the gas at elevated temperatures persisted unchanged to the lowest temperatures (which it does not, because gases liquefy), its pressure would be zero at approximately $-273°$ C. The temperature $-273.15°$ C provides a *possible* lower limit of temperature. It is, therefore, convenient to introduce a new temperature scale with its zero at this point. The *Kelvin temperature scale* is so chosen that its zero is at $-273.15°$ C, the size of the Kelvin degree being the same as the Celsius degree. Kelvin temperatures are represented by T. Then, through the *constant-volume gas thermometer*, the *Kelvin temperature* is given by

$$T = \left(\frac{p_T}{p_{273}}\right) 273.15° \text{ K}$$

with $T = t_C + 273.15°$

[19-2]

where p_{273} is the pressure of the gas at the ice point.

We have referred to the ice and steam points of water under standard atmospheric pressure as the bases of temperature scale determinations. We could equally well choose the zero of the Kelvin scale and the triple point of water as the two fixed points to define the Kelvin scale. The *triple point* of water, which occurs at a pressure of 4.58 mm Hg and a temperature of $273.16°$ K, corresponds to that unique condition under which water can exist simultaneously in the liquid, solid, and vapor states.

Zero on the Kelvin scale, the so-called *absolute zero*, is the lowest possible temperature. That this is indeed the case must be proved through thermodynamic arguments (Chapter 24); it is suggested by, but *not* deduced from, Figure 19-4. We shall see that the Kelvin, or *absolute*, scale of temperature has a simple interpretation in terms of the mechanics of molecular motion. Suffice it to say here that the independence of the thermometric substance found for low-density gases is not entirely unexpected. In low-density gases the molecules are very distant from one another, and interact by intermolecular forces only during the small periods of time that they collide.

19-4   Thermal expansion of solids and liquids   Most (but not all) solids and liquids, when free, expand as their temperatures rise. A change in the external dimensions of a body implies, of course, corresponding changes in the average separation distances between the atoms or molecules composing the body. Therefore, thermal expansion is intimately related to the interatomic and intermolecular forces, which determine, in turn, the separation distances between the atoms.

Figure 19-6 shows a typical interatomic potential energy of two neighboring atoms as a function of their separation distance r. (See Section 18-1 and Figures 18-1a and b.)

In the vicinity of the equilibrium position r_0, the potential curve is parabolic, the restoring force is proportional to the atomic displacement $(r - r_0)$ from equilibrium, and the atomic vibrations are simple harmonic oscillations about r_0. At low temperatures the atoms vibrate, with relatively low energies, near the minimum in the potential-energy curve. Then, any one atom spends as much time at positions for which $r > r_0$ as at positions for

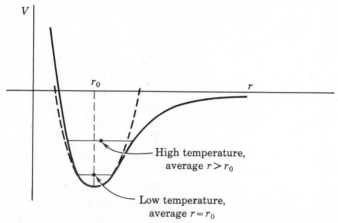

Figure 19-6. A typical interatomic–potential-energy curve. The potential curve is nearly parabolic (dotted line) in the vicinity of the equilibrium position r_0.

which $r < r_0$. On a time average, the separation distance between adjacent atoms is just r_0.

As we shall see in Chapter 23, when the temperature of a solid or liquid rises, so does the energy of the atomic vibrations. At high temperatures the atoms make excursions into the nonparabolic portions of the potential curve. As we can see in Figure 19-6, this curve bends downward for $r > r_0$ and upward for $r < r_0$ both relative to the parabola (dotted line) that describes the potential curve near its minimum. Inasmuch as the intermolecular force is proportional to the slope of the potential-energy–displacement curve ($F_r = -dU/dr$ from Equation 12-15), the interatomic restoring force is less than that arising from a parabolic potential for $r > r_0$ but greater for $r < r_0$. Consequently, the atom's restoring acceleration is relatively small at large r compared with its acceleration at small r. The atom still oscillates periodically, but *not* in simple harmonic motion. Moreover, the atom spends more time at large than at small separation distances. On a time average, the separation distance is then *larger* than r_0. Thus, the distances between adjacent atoms increase with temperature, and the body as a whole expands.

(Bodies which contract with a temperature rise have potential curves that depart from a parabolic shape in the opposite sense.)

A body changes dimensions with a change in its temperature, not because of increased oscillation amplitude, but because the interatomic forces depart from Hooke's law. If the interatomic potential remained strictly parabolic at all energies, then a rise in temperature would cause the atoms to oscillate with greater amplitude about their equilibrium positions. However, the average interatomic distance would remain r_0, and the body would neither expand nor contract with temperature change.

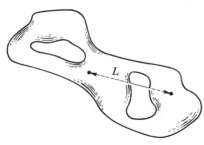

We now consider the quantitative aspects of thermal expansion. Suppose that we have a body of any shape (including cavities and holes), free to expand under an increase in temperature. See Figure 19-7. Let L represent the distance between *any* two points in the body. When the temperature changes, L changes slightly by an amount ΔL. Experiment shows that, for a given body, $\Delta L/L$ is the *same* for all pairs of points of the body. That is, thermal expansion is like photographic en-

Figure 19-7. Thermal expansion of a body of arbitrary shape. The distance between an arbitrary pair of points is L.

largement: the size changes, but not the shape. The length increase ΔL is strictly proportional to the original length L.

In addition, over a small enough range of temperatures the length L is found to vary *linearly* with temperature, as shown in Figure 19-8. The

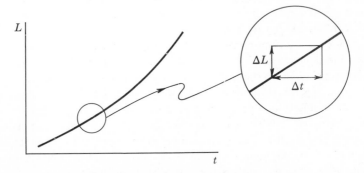

Figure 19-8. Length as a function of temperature for a typical thermal expansion. Over a small range, the change in length, ΔL, is directly proportional to the temperature difference Δt.

fractional increase in length follows the rule

$$\frac{\Delta L}{L} \propto \Delta t$$

This proportionality can be expressed as an equation when we introduce α, the *linear coefficient of thermal expansion*. Over a small temperature range, the expansion coefficient is essentially constant, dependent only on the particular material of the body:

$$\boxed{\frac{\Delta L}{L} = \alpha \, \Delta t}$$ [19-3]

The units of α are those of reciprocal temperature difference: $(C°)^{-1}$ or $(F°)^{-1}$. For steel the value of α is $12 \times 10^{-6}(C°)^{-1}$; this means that the distance between any two points of a steel object increases by twelve parts in one million for every one Celsius degree rise in its temperature.

Table 19-2 lists experimentally determined values of α for several solids. As Figure 19-8 shows, the expansion coefficient for a given substance changes with temperature. For example, copper has an α of 14.1×10^{-6} $(C°)^{-1}$ at $-90°$ C, but 18.2×10^{-6} $(C°)^{-1}$ at $250°$ C. A negative value for α implies that the body shrinks with a temperature rise.

Table 19-2

MATERIAL	TEMPERATURE RANGE (C°)	COEFFICIENT OF LINEAR THERMAL EXPANSION, (C°)⁻¹	COEFFICIENT OF VOLUME THERMAL EXPANSION, (C°)⁻¹
Aluminum	20 to 600	28.7×10^{-6}	
Copper	-25.3 to 10	11.7×10^{-6}	
Copper	0 to 100	$\cdot 20.3 \times 10^{-6}$	
Glass (Pyrex)	20 to 100	3.3×10^{-6}	
Ice	-250	-6.1×10^{-6}	
Ice	0	52.7×10^{-6}	
Invar (64% Fe, 36% Ni)	0 to 100	$\sim 1 \times 10^{-6}$	
Platinum	0 to 100	9.0×10^{-6}	
Silver	0 to 100	19.4×10^{-6}	
Steel (average carbon)	20 to 100	12×10^{-6}	
Tungsten (wolfram)	0 to 100	4.4×10^{-6}	
Carbon (diamond)	27		3.2×10^{-6}
Alcohol (ethyl, 30%)	18 to 39		293×10^{-6}
Mercury	0 to 100		182×10^{-6}

It is sometimes useful to write Equation 19-3 in a different form. Let L be the length of an object at some temperature. Then, if L_t is the length of the object at a temperature t, which is Δt above that for which its length is L, we have

$$L_t = L + \Delta L = L + \alpha L \, \Delta t$$

$$L_t = L(1 + \alpha \, \Delta t) \qquad\qquad [19\text{-}4]$$

It is easy to define area and volume coefficients of thermal expansion in terms of the linear coefficient. We consider a square of edge length L, which becomes $L + \Delta L$ when its temperature rises by Δt. (Any area, whatever its shape, can be constructed with small squares, so that the expansion of an object of any shape follows the same behavior as that of a square.) It is clear from Figure 19-9 that the area A of the square has increased by $\Delta A = 2L \, \Delta L$. (The area of the tiny square may be neglected.) Thus, the fractional change in area is

$$\frac{\Delta A}{A} = \frac{2L \, \Delta L}{L^2} = 2\left(\frac{\Delta L}{L}\right)$$

Using Equation 19-3, we have

$$\frac{\Delta A}{A} = (2\alpha) \, \Delta t \qquad\qquad [19\text{-}5]$$

Thus, the coefficient of area expansion, 2α, is twice the coefficient of linear expansion.

We now find the coefficient of volume expansion for a solid in similar fashion, considering the change ΔV in the volume of a cube of an edge

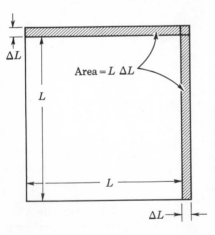

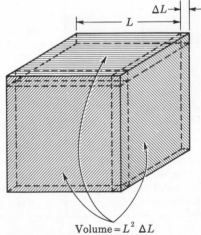

Figure 19-9. Thermal expansion of a square of edge length L.   **Figure 19-10.** Thermal expansion of a cube of edge length L.

length L. As Figure 19-10 shows,

$$\Delta V = 3L^2 \, \Delta L$$

$$\frac{\Delta V}{V} = \frac{3L^2 \, \Delta L}{L^3} = 3\left(\frac{\Delta L}{L}\right)$$

From Equation 19-3,

$$\frac{\Delta V}{V} = (3\alpha) \, \Delta t \qquad\qquad [19\text{-}6]$$

The volume coefficient of thermal expansion (sometimes also called the "cubical" coefficient) is three times the linear coefficient for the same material. If the volume coefficient is represented by the symbol $\beta = 3\alpha$, Equation 19-5 is written

$$\boxed{\frac{\Delta V}{V} = \beta \, \Delta t} \qquad\qquad [19\text{-}7]$$

A liquid at the Earth's surface has a definite volume, but not a definite shape. One can define a thermal coefficient of volume expansion β for a liquid, but not linear or area expansion coefficients. Equation 19-7 applies to liquids. Volume expansion coefficients are typically larger for liquids than for solids. This is illustrated by the mercury-in-glass thermometer: mercury overflows the glass bulb and expands into the stem because β for mercury, $180 \times 10^{-6} \, (\text{C}°)^{-1}$, is much larger than the β for glass, which is about $10 \times 10^{-6} \, (\text{C}°)^{-1}$.

The thermal expansion of water is particularly interesting. Indeed, water contracts with a temperature rise over a small range of temperatures. Figure 19-11 shows the volume of a 1 gm mass of water as a function of its temperature. The line is curved, not straight; which is to say, the change in the volume of water is *not* proportional to the temperature difference, and one cannot define a *single* coefficient of volume expansion for water over the range 0° to 100° C. Moreover, from the ice point to 4° C, the volume of water *decreases* as the temperature increases. Between 0° and 4° C, β is then *negative*. Equivalently, the density of water, which is inversely proportional to the volume for a given mass, increases from 0° C to a maximum at 4° C, and then decreases for higher temperatures. The maximum density of water is 0.999973 gm/cm³.

The anomalous expansion properties of water are responsible for the fact that lakes freeze first at the upper surface, leaving water for the fish beneath. As the temperature of water in a lake is reduced by a colder atmosphere, the most dense water goes to the bottom. As the temperature drops from 4° C

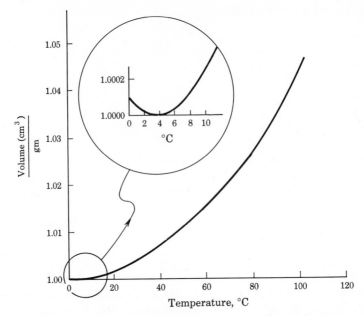

Figure 19-11. Thermal expansion of water, the volume of a one-gram mass as a function of temperature.

to zero, the most dense (and warmest) water remains at the lake bottom. Therefore, the water that first reaches the ice point is at the top.

Example 1   When its temperature is 20° C, a steel ring has an inner diameter of 10.00 cm and an outer diameter of 10.10 cm. What are (a) the fractional change in the inner diameter, (b) the change in the inner diameter, (c) the fractional change in the inner circumference, and (d) the fractional change in the area of the hole, all when the ring's temperature rises to 30° C?

(a) (c) From Equation 19-1, the fractional change in *any linear* dimension is

$$\Delta L/L = \alpha \, \Delta t = [11 \times 10^{-6} \, (C°)^{-1}](10 \, C°) = 11 \times 10^{-5}$$

Thus, the inner diameter—as well as the circumference, which may be thought of as a length of steel rod bent into a circle—changes by 11 parts in 10^5.

(b) The diameter, originally 10.00 cm, increases by

$$\Delta L = (10.00 \, \text{cm})(11 \times 10^{-5}) = 1.1 \times 10^{-3} \, \text{cm}$$

(d) The hole *expands* with an area coefficient 2α, and its fractional change $\Delta A/A$ is

$$\Delta A/A = 2\alpha \, \Delta t = 22 \times 10^{-5}$$

That the hole must expand with a temperature rise, rather than contract, is shown not only by the fact that the circumference of the ring has increased but also by the following argument. Suppose that one has, also, a solid disc with a diameter equal to the outer diameter of the ring, and further, that one marks with chalk the location of the ring's inner diameter. Then clearly, the chalked circle expands with a temperature rise. If one now cuts along the chalk line to produce a ring and a tightly fitting disc within the ring, both the ring and the disc will expand with a temperature increase. Finally, if the ring and disc are separated, and we again increase the temperature of both, the disc and the hole of the ring expand. In short, all holes, cavities, and indentations *expand* when the temperature of the material is raised (provided, of course, that the material has a positive expansion coefficient).

Example 2 A steel rod 50 cm long and 4.0 mm in diameter is clamped at its ends to two fixed supports. At room temperature there is no tension in the horizontal rod. (a) If the temperature of the rod is increased 30 C°, what is the *thermal compressive stress* produced in the rod? (b) What is the magnitude of the horizontal force of either clamp on the rod?

(a) This problem is most easily done in two steps. First, assume that the clamps at the ends are removed and the rod expands freely by virtue of an increase Δt in its temperature. The fractional increase in length is given by Equation 19-3:

$$\Delta L / L = \alpha\,\Delta t$$

Next, we imagine that compressive forces are applied to the ends of the rod, which return the rod to its original length. By Equation 17-4, the longitudinal stress F_l/A necessary to compress the rod by ΔL is

$$F_l/A = Y(\Delta L/L)$$

where Y is Young's modulus. Equating the fractional decrease in length, arising from compression, to the fractional increase in length arising from thermal expansion, we obtain the thermal compressive stress:

$$F_l/A = Y(\alpha\,\Delta t)$$

For the steel rod we have

Thermal stress $= (2.0 \times 10^{11}\ \text{nt/m}^2)(12 \times 10^{-6}\ /\ \text{C}°)(30\ \text{C}°) = 7.2 \times 10^7\ \text{nt/m}^2$

(b) The compressive force F of either clamp on the rod is

$$F = (\text{stress})(A) = (7.2 \times 10^7\ \text{nt/m}^2)(1.26 \times 10^{-5}\ \text{m}^2) = 910\ \text{nt}$$

19-5 Summary After a sufficiently long time has elapsed, a collection of bodies isolated from external influence achieves thermal equilibrium. The property that all the bodies in the collection then have in common is temperature.

Any physical property which varies with temperature can be used as a basis for constructing a thermometer. All low-density gases at constant volume show the same pressure variation with temperature. The Kelvin, or absolute, temperature T registered on all constant-volume ideal-gas thermometers is then related to the pressure p_T of the gas by

[19-2] $$T = \left(\frac{p_T}{p_{273}}\right) 273.16°\ \text{K}$$

where p_{273} is the pressure corresponding to the triple point of water. The Kelvin temperature T is related to the Celsius temperature t_C by $T = t_C + 273.15°$; one hundred degrees separate the ice and steam points of water on both the Kelvin and Celsius temperature scales.

Thermal expansion of solids and liquids arises because of departures from Hooke's law at the atomic level. The fractional change in length of a solid, $\Delta L/L$, is the same for all pairs of points in the solid. Furthermore, for small temperature changes Δt,

[19-3] $$\frac{\Delta L}{L} = \alpha \, \Delta t$$

where α, the linear coefficient of thermal expansion, is a constant, characteristic of the material.

The fractional change in volume $\Delta V/V$ is given in terms of the temperature change Δt by

[19-7] $$\frac{\Delta V}{V} = \beta \, \Delta t$$

where β is the volume coefficient of thermal expansion.

PROBLEMS

19-1   The following temperatures, all at standard atmospheric pressure, are among the fixed points which are used to calibrate thermometers: (a) boiling point of helium, $-268.98°$ C; (b) boiling point of oxygen (O_2), $-182.97°$ C; (c) temperature of freezing lead, $327.3°$ C; (d) temperature of freezing gold, $1063.0°$ C; (e) temperature of melting tungsten, $3380°$ C. What are the corresponding Kelvin temperatures for (a), (b), and (c), and the corresponding Fahrenheit temperatures for (d) and (e)?

19-2   (a) At what temperature will the reading on a Celsius thermometer be the same as the reading on a Fahrenheit thermometer? (b) At what temperature will the readings on a Fahrenheit thermometer and a Kelvin thermometer be the same?

19-3   At what temperature will the Kelvin and Celsius temperatures be the same to within 0.10 per cent?

19-4   For what fundamental reason is water an unsuitable thermometric substance in a liquid-in-glass thermometer?

19-5   A constant-volume gas thermometer registers a pressure of 24.4 cm Hg at 100° C. What is the temperature of the gas when its pressure is 35.6 cm Hg?

19-6   A bicycle tire is inflated to a gauge pressure of 40 pounds/inch² (often referred to, improperly, as "40 pounds") when the temperature is 68° F. What is the gauge pressure when the temperature of the tire and the air within has been raised to 90° F? Atmospheric pressure is 14.7 pounds/inch². Assume, for simplicity, that the tire does not expand.

19-7 Sketch the intermolecular potential as a function of distance for a material, such as rubber, which shrinks when its temperature rises and, consequently, has a *negative* linear coefficient of thermal expansion.

19-8 The linear coefficient of thermal expansion of steel is 11×10^{-6} (C°)$^{-1}$. What is this coefficient in units of reciprocal Fahrenheit degrees?

19-9 What is the change in length (in inches) of a 50-foot steel beam, taking place between a cold day in winter ($-5°$ F) and a hot day in summer (95° F)?

19-10 Because the alloy Invar has a particularly small linear thermal expansion coefficient, 0.7×10^{-6} (C°)$^{-1}$, this material can be used to make measuring rods which are relatively insensitive to errors arising from temperature changes. By how much does the distance between the graduations corresponding to 10 cm and 20 cm change when the temperature of an Invar scale rises by 20 C°?

19-11 A steel wire 1.0 m long and 0.50 mm² in cross section hangs vertically, a weight attached to its lower end. The temperature of the wire drops 20 F°. What additional weight must be added to the wire to restore it to its original length?

19-12 ⋆ A simple-pendulum clock is calibrated to run correctly at a temperature of 20° C, the period of the clock being exactly 2 sec at this temperature. The pendulum arm is made of steel. (a) When this clock is at a temperature of 60° C over a one-year period, how many seconds does it lose (or gain) during the true year? (b) When it is maintained at $-20°$ C, how many seconds does it lose (or gain) in one year? (c) When it is maintained at 60° C for one half of the year and $-20°$ C for the other half, by how many seconds (to the nearest second) would it lose (or gain)?

19-13 The length of a solid is given approximately by the relation $L_t = L(1 + \alpha \, \Delta t)$, where α is the linear coefficient of thermal expansion. Apply this relation to compute the area and volume of an expanding solid and thereby deduce that the area and volume coefficients of thermal expansion are given approximately by 2α and 3α, respectively.

19-14 A steel ball has a diameter of 1.000 cm at room temperature. The temperature of the ball is raised 50 C°. (a) What is the increase in the ball's diameter? (b) By what fraction is the ball's density decreased?

19-15 An aluminum ring, having an inner diameter of 1.125 inches, is to be slipped over a steel rod whose diameter is 1.128 inches. Both ring and rod are initially at 20° C. (a) By how much must the temperature of the ring be raised? (b) Alternatively, by how much should the temperature of the rod have been lowered? (c) To what common temperature must both the ring and rod be brought so that the ring slips over the rod?

19-16 ⋆ A uniform thin rod of length L and mass M is pivoted at one end about a horizontal axis. The material of the rod has a linear thermal expansion coefficient α. Suppose that the temperature of the rod is increased by Δt. What is the change, relative to the pivot, in the rod's (a) center of mass and (b) moment of inertia? (c) Suppose that the rod swings with a small amplitude as a physical pendulum; is the period of oscillation increased or decreased? (d) By what amount?

19-17   A rectangular plate of a nonisotropic material, such as wood, has length L and width W. The linear coefficients of thermal expansion along the length and width are α_l and α_w, respectively. What is the area coefficient of thermal expansion?

19-18   A mercury barometer will indicate 1 standard atmosphere when its column length is 760 mm and the temperature of the mercury is 0° C. By how much will the height of the mercury column increase in a barometer having an inside diameter of 5.0 mm when the temperature is 30° C, assuming that the barometer tube does not expand?

19-19   The bulb of a mercury-in-glass thermometer is made of Pyrex glass. The interior volume of the bulb is 4.0 mm^3. (a) If the bulb is filled to the brim with mercury at some temperature, how much mercury overflows when the temperature rises by 10 C°? (b) Suppose that a glass stem with an interior cross-sectional area of 3.5×10^{-4} mm^2 is attached to the bulb; by what distance does the mercury column advance along the stem when the temperature changes by 10 C°?

19-20 ★ The volume V_t of a given mass of material as a function of the temperature can be closely approximated by a relation of the type $V_t = V_0(1 + at + bt^2 + ct^3)$, where a, b, and c are constants chosen to give the best fit with the observed thermal behavior of the material. The temperature t may be chosen to have its zero at *any* convenient point, not merely at 0° C or 0° F. Suppose that we use a relation of the type given above to describe the thermal expansion of water. At what temperature should we choose $t = 0$ such that the constant a is zero?

19-21   The electrical resistance of a standard platinum resistance thermometer is given as a function of temperature by the formula $R_t = R_0(1 + At + Bt^2)$, where R_0, A, and B are constants. At how many temperatures must the resistance be measured in order to calibrate such a thermometer?

19-22 ★ A liquid with a volume coefficient of thermal expansion β and a bulk modulus B fills completely a sealed container. Assuming that the container's volume does not change, by how much is the pressure of the liquid increased when its temperature is changed by Δt?

19-23   Suppose that a steel rod 0.15 m in length and 4.0 cm^2 in cross section fits exactly when placed between the jaws of a vice. What longitudinal thermal stress exists within the steel rod when its temperature rises by 100 F°? Assume that the vice does not change its dimensions.

T W E N T Y

IDEAL GASES: MACROSCOPIC PROPERTIES

This chapter treats the relationships among the pressure, temperature, volume, and mass of an ideal gas. We also consider changes or transformations in the state of an ideal gas, particularly as represented on a pressure-volume graph.

20-1 The general-gas law We are concerned here with an *ideal*, or *perfect*, gas. Any gas behaves as an ideal gas if its density is very low. This requires, in effect, that the gas's temperature be relatively high and its pressure relatively low, so that the gas is not close to the conditions under which it condenses into a liquid. Most gases at room temperature and atmospheric pressure can be regarded as ideal gases.

The general-gas law is concerned with the relationship among the macroscopic measurable properties of a gas: the absolute temperature T, the pressure p, the volume V, and the mass m. We have already seen, through the definition of the absolute temperature, that the pressure is related to the temperature of an ideal gas by

$$\frac{p_1}{T_1} = \frac{p_2}{T_2}, \qquad \text{for constant } V \text{ and } m \qquad [20\text{-}1]$$

where the subscripts 1 and 2 refer to a gas of fixed volume under two different conditions of temperature and pressure.

Consider now the thermal expansion of an ideal gas at constant pressure. Experiment shows that, for a fixed mass of gas maintained at constant

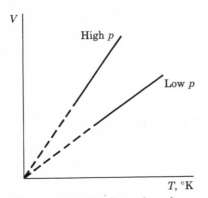

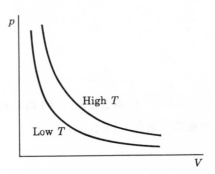

Figure 20-1. Graphs of volume versus absolute temperature for an ideal gas for two different constant pressures.

Figure 20-2. Pressure-volume graphs for an ideal gas. The isotherms are hyperbolas.

pressure, the volume† is directly proportional to the absolute temperature, as shown in Figure 20-1. This implies that

$$\frac{V_1}{T_1} = \frac{V_2}{T_2}, \qquad \text{for constant } p \text{ and } m \qquad [20\text{-}2]$$

All low-density gases at constant pressure show the same behavior as that expressed in Equation 20-2; that is, for any ideal gas, the ratio of volume to temperature remains constant. Therefore, one may use Equation 20-2 as the basis of a *constant-pressure gas thermometer*. This relation is sometimes referred to as the law of J. L. Gay-Lussac and J. A. C. Charles, its discoverers.

Now suppose that the temperature and mass of an ideal gas are kept constant while the pressure and volume change. The experimental results, shown in Figure 20-2, are summarized by the relation known as Boyle's law:

$$p_1 V_1 = p_2 V_2, \qquad \text{for constant } T \text{ and } m \qquad [20\text{-}3]$$

† Since a gas fills any container completely, the "volume" of a gas is strictly the interior volume of the container holding it.

The lines of constant temperature (called *isotherms*) are rectangular hyperbolas.

Equation 20-3 can be expressed in an interesting alternative form. Recalling that the density ρ of any material is the ratio m/V, we may write Equation 20-3 as

$$\frac{p_1}{\rho_1} = \frac{p_2}{\rho_2}, \qquad \text{for constant } T \text{ and } m \qquad [20\text{-}4]$$

Equations 20-1, 20-2, and 20-3 can be combined into a single relation for p, V, and T:

$$\frac{p_1 V_1}{T_1} = \frac{p_2 V_2}{T_2} = K, \qquad \text{for constant } m \qquad [20\text{-}5]$$

The constant K differs according to the kind of gas and its mass. Experiment shows, however, that we can express Equation 20-5 in still simpler form. If we express the mass in terms of the number of moles n of the gas, the form of the equation becomes *independent* of the particular type of gas. By definition,

$$n = \frac{m}{w} \qquad [20\text{-}6]$$

where m is the mass of gas in grams, w is the atomic weight of the gas molecules, and n is the number of *gram-moles*. Thus, *one gram-mole* of any material contains w grams. For example, oxygen has a molecular weight of 32; therefore, one mole of oxygen consists of 32 grams.

When the constant K of Equation 20-5 is measured for various kinds of gases, it is found that

$$\frac{pV}{T} = K = nR$$

where a single, universal constant R, called the *universal gas constant*, can be used for *all* low-density gases. The relation between p, V, T, and n is summarized by a single formula known as the *general-gas law*, applicable to all ideal gases:

$$\boxed{pV = nRT} \qquad [20\text{-}7]$$

Clearly, Equations 20-1, 20-2, 20-3, 20-4, and 20-5 are but special cases of Equation 20-7.

The numerical value of R will depend on the units used for p and V (T must be in degrees Kelvin, and n is always in gram-moles). One determines the value of R by measuring p, V, n, and T under a given condition. For example, one mole of diatomic hydrogen gas (2.0160 gm) at *s*tandard *t*emperature

($T = 273.15°$ K) and standard atmospheric pressure (1.013250×10^5 nt/m²), abbreviated "STP," is found to occupy a volume of 22.415×10^{-3} m³. Therefore, from Equation 20-7,

$$R = pV/nT$$

$$= (1.013250 \times 10^5 \text{ nt/m}^2)(22.415 \times 10^{-3} \text{ m}^3)/(1 \text{ mole})(273.15° \text{ K})$$

$$R = 8.314 \text{ joules/mole-K}°$$

Indeed, under STP, one mole of *any* low-density gas has a volume of 22.415×10^{-3} m³ $\simeq 22.4$ liters (one liter is defined as 10^{-3} m³).

It is sometimes useful to express R in other units. For example, the calorie is an energy unit commonly used to measure thermal energy or heat. (We shall see in Chapter 23 that the calorie has a simple meaning in terms of the thermal properties of water.) By definition,

$$1 \text{ cal} = 4.1840 \text{ joules}$$

Using this conversion factor, we have

$$R = 1.986 \text{ cal/mole-K}°$$

One often has occasion to use the value of R appropriate for pressure expressed in atmospheres and volume in liters. For these units of p and V,

$$R = 0.08207 \text{ liter-atm/mole-K}°$$

Example 1   What is the density of helium under STP?

We compute ρ directly by recalling that, for a pressure of one atmosphere and a temperature of zero degrees Celsius, the volume of one gram-mole of any gas is 22.415×10^{-3} m³. Since helium is monatomic and has an atomic weight of 4.003,

$$\rho = (4.003 \times 10^{-3} \text{ kg})/(22.415 \times 10^{-3} \text{ m}^3) = 0.1786 \text{ kg/m}^3$$

Example 2   A tank having a volume of 30 liters contains nitrogen gas at 20° C at a gauge pressure of 3.00 atmospheres. The tank's valve is opened momentarily and some nitrogen escapes. After the valve is closed and the gas has returned to room temperature, the tank's pressure gauge reads 2.40 atmospheres. How much nitrogen has leaked out?

We designate the number of moles of gas and the pressure before and after the leak by subscripts 1 and 2, respectively. Then, from Equation 20-7,

$$n_1 - n_2 = \frac{p_1 V}{RT} - \frac{p_2 V}{RT} = \frac{V}{RT}(p_1 - p_2)$$

$$n_1 - n_2 = \frac{(30 \text{ l})(0.60 \text{ atm})}{(0.082 \text{ l-atm/mole-K}°)(293° \text{ K})} = 0.75 \text{ mole}$$

Since nitrogen has an atomic weight of 14, one mole has a mass of 28 gm. The mass escaping is, then,

$$m = nw = (0.75 \text{ mole})(28 \text{ gm/mole}) = 21 \text{ gm}$$

20-2 The equation of state   When we use instruments that measure the large-scale, or macroscopic, properties of a gas, we use the three obvious and commonly used quantities p, V, and T (there are others). We may ignore variations in the mass of gas by assuming it always to be 1 mole; alternatively, we may use V to indicate the volume per unit mass, or *specific volume*, of gas.

The *state* of a gas is completely specified by a knowledge of p, V, and T (and m). The state of a gas does *not* depend, for example, on its past history.

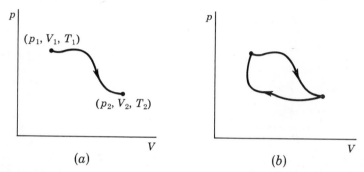

Figure 20-3. (a) A process involving the change in state of a gas from (p_1, V_1, T_1) to (p_2, V_2, T_2). (b) A cycle.

Of course, if a gas is ideal, $pV = nRT$. Then we need specify only two of the three variables, inasmuch as the general-gas law permits the third variable to be computed. Thus, the general-gas law is the *equation of state* of an ideal gas. If a certain gas is not ideal and the general-gas law is inapplicable, a more complicated relation between p, V, and T, again known as "the equation of state," describes the gas's behavior.

We can portray the state of a gas as a point on a diagram, giving the pressure as a function of the volume, a so-called *p-V diagram*. Two different points on a p-V diagram correspond to two states of the gas—for example, (p_1, V_1, T_1) and (p_2, V_2, T_2), which differ in at least *two* of the variables p, V, and T.

A continuous change in the state of a gas is called a *process*. On the p-V diagram it appears as a line, or "path," going from the initial to the final state. See Figure 20-3a. Clearly, there are many possible paths or processes which connect a given pair of initial and final states. A process in which a gas is returned to its initial state is called a *cycle*; this appears as a closed loop on a p-V diagram (Figure 20-3b).

20-3 Work done by a gas   We choose to show changes in the state of a gas on a p-V diagram, because the area under the curve describing a process has a simple interpretation in such a diagram. Suppose that a gas undergoes an expansion. For example, the expanding gas may displace a piston fitted into a cylindrical container. The gas's volume increases by dV. See Figure 20-4. The gas does work dW *on* the piston as it applies a force F over an infinitesimal displacement dx. The force on the piston is $F = pA$, where p is the pressure of the gas and A is the area of the piston. From the definition of work,

$$dW = F \, dx = (pA) \, dx = p(A \, dx)$$

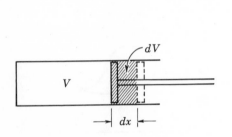

Figure 20-4. Work done by a gas in expanding through a volume change ΔV as the piston is displaced dx.

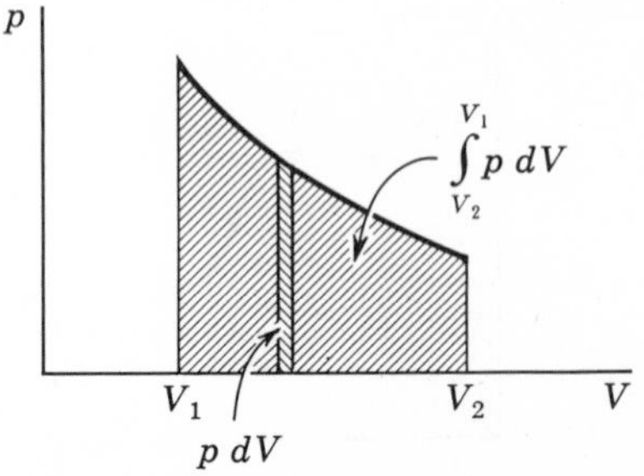

Figure 20-5. Work done by an expanding gas, as represented by the area under the pressure-volume graph.

But $A \, dx$ is dV, the volume swept out by the displaced piston, and also the change in gas volume. We may then write

$$dW = p \, dV \qquad \text{[20-8]}$$

The work dW done *by* an expanding gas is $p \, dV$. We write the work in differential form to allow for the possibility that the pressure changes as the gas expands. The total amount of work $W_{1 \to 2}$ done as the volume goes from V_1 to V_2 is, then,

$$W_{1 \to 2} = \int_{V_1}^{V_2} p \, dV \qquad \text{[20-9]}$$

The integral in Equation 20-9 can be evaluated and the work computed when p is known as a function of V.

We have taken the work done *by the gas* on the piston to be positive. If the gas were compressed by the piston, the gas would do *negative* work; that is, work would be done *on the gas* by the piston.

Figure 20-5 shows an expansion process. The work done by the gas as it expands is equal in magnitude to the area under the curve on the p-V diagram. This area depends on the path between the end points. Suppose that a gas is compressed. Then the path is to the left on the p-V diagram, and the area under the curve is the work done *on the gas*. Therefore, when a gas is taken through a cycle, the *net* amount of work done by the gas over the cycle is represented by the area enclosed by the loop, as shown in Figure 20-6. (Strictly, the area of the loop gives the net work done by the gas only if the loop is traversed in the clockwise sense.)

In undergoing a complete cycle, a gas is returned to its initial state of pressure, volume, and temperature. Therefore, the total energy of the gas, whatever its form, cannot have changed. Yet the gas *has* done work over

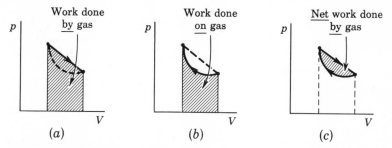

Figure 20-6. Graphical representation on a pressure-volume diagram of the work done by and on a gas. (a) Work done *by* the gas in expanding. (b) Work done *on* the gas as it is compressed. (c) Net work done *by* the gas over the cycle.

the cycle. This implies that energy is *not* conserved unless a new form of *energy transfer*, in addition to the work done by the gas, is introduced. This new form of energy transfer, about which much will be said in subsequent chapters, is called *heat*.

20-4 Changes in the state of a gas Several types of change in the state of a gas are particularly simple, inasmuch as one variable in the equation of state remains constant. Each process is briefly described below, for the simple case of an ideal gas.

In an *isothermal process* the *temperature* is constant. Lines of constant T, corresponding to $pV = $ constant, are called *isotherms*. The pressure increases in an isothermal compression and decreases in an isothermal expansion. See Figure 20-7a.

An *isobaric process* is one in which the *pressure* remains constant. We see from Figure 20-7b that when a gas expands isobarically, its temperature rises; and conversely.

In an *isovolumetric process* the *volume* remains constant. Figure 20-7c shows that the temperature of a gas in a container of fixed size drops as its pressure falls.

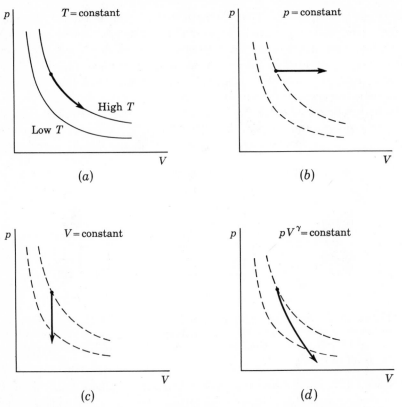

Figure 20-7. Several important changes in the state of a gas. The dotted lines represent two isotherms. (a) Isothermal process. (b) Isobaric process. (c) Isovolumetric process. (d) Adiabatic process.

An *adiabatic process*, which we will study in more detail in Example 5, in Section 21-6, is one in which there is *no heat* into or out of the gas. A gas will undergo an adiabatic process under two simple circumstances: when the container is a heat insulator, which isolates the gas thermally from its surroundings, and when a process takes place so rapidly that there is not enough time for energy to be transferred to or from the gas through the container walls. As we shall prove later, an adiabatic process is described for an ideal gas by the relation

$$pV^\gamma = \text{constant} \qquad [20\text{-}10]$$

where γ is a constant. The numerical value of γ depends on the nature of the gas, but is always greater than 1. Therefore, adiabatic lines on a *p-V* diagram are more steeply inclined than isotherms, for which pV is constant. Figure 20-7d shows that the temperature falls in an adiabatic expansion.

Example 3 One mole of an ideal gas, initially at standard temperature and pressure, expands *isothermally* until its volume is doubled. (a) How much work is done by the expanding gas? (b) Suppose, instead, that the gas were to expand *isobarically* to twice its initial volume; how much work would be done by the gas?

(a) From Equation 20-9 the work done by the gas in going from state 1 to 2 is

$$W_{1\to 2} = \int_{V_1}^{V_2} p\, dV$$

Since the gas is ideal and $p = nRT/V$,

$$W_{1\to 2} = nRT \int_{V_1}^{V_2} \frac{dV}{V} = nRT \ln \frac{V_2}{V_1} \qquad [20\text{-}11]$$

Note that T could be brought to the left of the integral sign only because the temperature is constant in an isothermal process. We are given that $n = 1$, $T = 273°$ K, and $V_2 = 2V_1$. Therefore,

$$W_{1\to 2} = (1 \text{ mole})(8.314 \text{ joules/mole-K}°)(273° \text{ K})(\ln 2)$$
$$W_{1\to 2} = 1.54 \times 10^3 \text{ joules}$$

(b) The work done by the gas when expanding isobarically is

$$W_{1\to 2} = \int_{V_1}^{V_2} p\, dV = p \int_{V_1}^{V_2} dV = p(V_2 - V_1)$$

Here p can be brought to the left of the integral sign because it remains constant in the isobaric process. We are given $p_1 = p = 1.00$ atmosphere, $V_1 = 22.4$ liters. Therefore,

$$W_{1\to 2} = p(2V_1 - V_1) = pV_1 = (1.00 \text{ atm})(22.4 \text{ liters}) = 22.4 \text{ liter-atm}$$
$$W_{1\to 2} = 2.26 \times 10^3 \text{ joules}$$

20-5 Summary The equation of state for any low-density gas, the so-called general-gas law, is

[20-7] $$pV = nRT$$

where n is the number of moles of gas and R is the universal gas constant (8.314 joules/mole-K°). At STP one mole of any ideal gas occupies a volume of 22.4 liters.

The work $W_{1\to 2}$ done by an expanding gas on its surroundings in going from volume V_1 to V_2 is

[20-9] $$W_{1\to 2} = \int_{V_1}^{V_2} p\, dV$$

On a p-V diagram this work is equal to the area under the curve describing the expansion process.

PROBLEMS

20-1 A filled aerosol bomb has a gauge pressure of 5 atmospheres at 20° C. The bomb will burst when the internal gauge pressure reaches 15 atmospheres. To what temperature must the aerosol bomb be raised for the bomb to burst?

20-2 A bubble of air has a diameter of 3.0 mm when it is 4.0 m below the surface of a lake. What is the bubble's diameter as it reaches the surface, assuming no change in temperature?

20-3 ★ A tightly fitting, circular piston 5.0 kg in mass and 10.0 cm in diameter is placed in the top of an upright cylinder 1.0 m high containing air at STP. The piston is lowered slowly, to maintain a constant gas temperature until it floats over the gas trapped below in the cylinder. What is the distance from the bottom of the cylinder to the lower face of the piston?

20-4 A tumbler with an internal diameter of 5.0 cm and a height of 15.0 cm is immersed, while inverted, in a container of water, trapping air within it. What is the difference in the elevations of the water surfaces between the inside and outside of the tumbler when the tumbler is half-immersed in the container? Assume the air to be at STP initially.

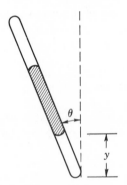

Figure 20-8.

20-5 ★ The closed tube in Figure 20-8 is evacuated at its upper end and has a column of mercury above an ideal gas in the section below. The tube can be tilted about a pivot at its lower end. Show that, if the temperature of the gas does not change, the vertical elevation y of the lower end of the mercury column above the pivot does *not* depend on the angle θ.

20-6 An ideal gas is contained in an upright right circular cylinder, into which a tightly fitting piston, free to slide vertically without leaking gas, has been placed so that it floats in equilibrium. Show that the distance from the bottom of the cylinder to the lower face of the piston is directly proportional to the absolute temperature of the gas within, provided that the region outside the container is evacuated.

20-7   (a) Show that the volume coefficient of thermal expansion at constant pressure of any ideal gas at $0°$ C is $(1/273)$ $(C°)^{-1}$. (b) Does an ideal gas have the same isobaric volume coefficient of thermal expansion at other temperatures?

20-8   Air at standard atmospheric pressure and $20°$ C is trapped in a closed container. The oxygen (20 per cent of air by weight) is removed through oxidation with materials within the container, and no gases are evolved in the chemical reaction. What is the pressure of the remaining gas (nearly all nitrogen) after all the oxygen has been removed?

20-9   A gas occupies a volume of 6.0 liters when its temperature is $60°$ F and its pressure is 76 cm Hg. What volume must this gas occupy when its temperature has been raised to $212°$ F and its pressure increased to 240 cm Hg?

20-10   An evacuated tank with a capacity of 20 liters is filled with helium at room temperature $(20°$ C). The mass of the tank is thereby increased by 0.10 kg. What then is the pressure registered on the tank's pressure gauge?

20-11   Two grams of a monatomic gas occupy a volume of 1.49 liters when the temperature is $0°$ C and the pressure is 8 atmospheres. What is the gas?

20-12   What numerical value must be used for the universal gas constant R in the general-gas law when pressures are given in centimeters of mercury and volumes in cubic meters?

20-13   A certain ideal gas exerts a pressure of 10 atmospheres when its temperature is $20°$ C and its volume is 5.0 liters. (a) How many moles of gas are there? (b) What is the mass density if the gas is molecular hydrogen, H_2? (c) What is the mass density if it is oxygen, O_2?

20-14   The gas in Problem 20-13 is compressed such that its volume is reduced to 0.050 liter, its pressure is 400 atmospheres, and its temperature is $-170°$ C. Can the gas be regarded as an ideal gas under these circumstances?

20-15   A low-density gas has been placed in a tank at $20°$ C. The gauge pressure is initially 3.0 atmospheres. Half of the gas is then released from the tank and thermal equilibrium is again established. What will the pressure gauge read when the temperature of the tank has been raised to $313°$ C?

20-16   Compute the density of air at STP, assuming the air to consist of N_2 and O_2 in the ratio of 5/1 by weight. The atomic weights of nitrogen and oxygen molecules are 28 and 32, respectively. According to the law of partial pressures, the pressure of each of the two gases is independent of the presence of the other.

20-17   Helium gas (atomic weight, 4) is contained in a spherical balloon of a 1.0 m diameter. The mass of the balloon alone is negligible. (a) How much helium is contained if the balloon just floats in the atmosphere? Under the conditions of part (a), what is (b) the density of the helium, and (c) the pressure of the helium gas?

20-18   The gauge pressure of air inside the tires of an automobile is found to be 26 pounds/inch^2 when the temperature is 20° C. After the automobile has been running on a hot highway, it is expected that the temperature of the tires and air within will rise to 30° C. (a) What fraction of the air in the tires should be released at 20° C if the gauge pressure of the hot tires is not to exceed 26 pounds/inch^2? (b) What will then be the gauge pressure in the tires at 20° C? Take atmospheric pressure as 15 pounds/inch^2 and assume that the volume does not change.

20-19   The equation of state for gases of relatively high density can be approximated by the *van der Waals equation*, $(p + a/V^2)(V - b) = nRT$ where a and b are constants. Sketch isothermal lines on a p-V diagram for temperatures at which the contribution arising from the terms containing a and b are not negligible.

20-20   In an isothermal compression, how much work must be done on 1 mole of an ideal gas, initially at STP, to reduce the volume to one half?

20-21   One mole of helium gas, initially at STP, undergoes an isovolumetric process in which its pressure falls to half its initial value. (a) What is the work done by the gas? (b) What is the temperature of the gas? (c) The helium gas then expands isobarically to twice its volume; what is the work done by the gas? (d) What is the gas's final temperature? (e) Suppose that the gas undergoes a process from the initial state in (a) to the final state in (c) by an isothermal expansion; what is the work done by the gas?

20-22   An ideal gas undergoes an isobaric expansion to twice its volume, followed by an isovolumetric change to half its pressure. A second gas having the same initial state undergoes an isovolumetric change to half its pressure, followed by an isobaric expansion to twice its volume. (a) How do the final temperatures for the processes of each of the two gases differ? (b) For which of the two processes does the gas do a greater amount of work? (c) What is the difference in work done?

20-23 ⋆   An ideal gas is to go from the initial state (p_1, V_1, T_1) to a final state (p_2, V_2, T_2). It is assumed (unrealistically) that the equation of state for an ideal gas holds at *all* temperatures. (a) What processes must the gas undergo if it is to be taken from the initial to the final state without any net work being done by or on the gas? (b) What temperature must the gas achieve in going from the initial to the final state?

20-24 ⋆   (a) Show that the work done by a gas expanding adiabatically from the state (p_1, V_1, T_1) to the state (p_2, V_2, T_2) is $(p_1V_1 - p_2V_2)/(\gamma - 1)$. (b) Does the temperature rise or fall in this process? (c) Suppose that, starting from the same initial state, the gas expands isothermally to the same final pressure p_2 as in the adiabatic transformation; is more work or less work done by the gas?

TWENTY-ONE

IDEAL GASES: MICROSCOPIC PROPERTIES AND THE KINETIC THEORY OF GASES

The general-gas law describes an ideal gas in terms of its macroscopic properties: pressure, volume, temperature, and total mass. In this chapter we consider a gas to be composed of a large number of microscopic particles. Through the kinetic theory, we will relate the microscopic properties of gas molecules—their speeds, diameters, masses, kinetic energies, and their number—to the macroscopic behavior of ideal gases. We will thereby be led to a mechanical interpretation of the concept of the temperature of a gas; indeed, we shall see that the temperature is merely a measure of the average translational kinetic energy of the molecules. We shall define the internal energy of a system of particles and identify the thermal energy of a gas with the disordered energy of the molecules.

We shall then explore further consequences of the kinetic theory: the concept of heat, the first law of thermodynamics, and the specific heats of gases.

21-1   The molecular hypothesis   That all matter consists of atoms is the fundamental assumption of chemistry. Here we are concerned with molecules, which consist of one or more atoms bound together.

We first recall that one gram-mole of any element is the element's atomic weight in grams. Thus, one gram-mole of *any* pure substance contains the same number of atoms or molecules. This number is called *Avogadro's number*, N_0. By experiment,

$$\text{Avogadro's number} = N_0 = 6.023 \times 10^{23}/\text{gm-mole}$$

By its definition, Avogadro's number is measured by counting (indirectly) the number of atoms or molecules in a pure element or compound *whose mass in grams* is equal to the corresponding atomic or molecular weight.[†] Thus, 2 gm of H_2, 32 gm of O_2, and 4 gm of He, all contain 6×10^{23} molecules. Avogadro's number gives, as well, the number of atoms per gram-mole for solids existing as pure elements; for example, 197 gm of solid gold (atomic weight, 197), or 2 gm of solid H_2, contains N_0 atoms.

We wish to find the approximate size of a typical molecule and the average distance between neighboring molecules in a gas. Consider oxygen. At STP one gram-mole (32 gm) is known to occupy a volume of 22.4 liters $= 2.24 \times 10^{-2}$ m^3. The gas is, of course, easily compressed.

If we lower the temperature of this oxygen to 90° K while maintaining the pressure constant, the gas will condense into a nearly incompressible liquid. Now in the liquid state the 32 gm of oxygen is found to have a volume of only 3.2×10^{-5} m^3. Thus, the volume in the liquid state is smaller than the original volume by a factor of 1400. We have, of course, the same number of oxygen molecules, 6.023×10^{23}, in both the gaseous and the liquid states. Since the volume of liquid oxygen can be reduced appreciably only by relatively large external pressures, we can assume that in the liquid state the oxygen molecules are in contact with one another. Every molecule exerts strong repulsive intermolecular forces on its neighboring molecules when compressive external forces are applied to the liquid.

Let us compute the volume associated with each oxygen molecule. We know that in the liquid state, 1 mole of oxygen (6.023×10^{23} oxygen molecules) occupies a volume of $(3.2 \times 10^{-5}$ m$^3)/(6.023 \times 10^{23}) = 5.3 \times 10^{-29}$ m^3. We can find the approximate diameter d of the molecule through the relation $d^3 \simeq 5.3 \times 10^{-29}$ m^3, or $d \simeq 4 \times 10^{-10}$ m. Thus, the diameter of an oxygen molecule is close to 4×10^{-10} m $= 4$ Å (the *Ångström* unit of distance, abbreviated Å, is defined as 1 Å $= 10^{-10}$ m). All molecules are found to have diameters of the order of several Ångströms.

† One method of measuring N_0 is by electrolysis. The total electric charge Q carried by the ions of one gram-mole can be measured directly. Since the electric charge q carried by each ion can be determined independently, the total number of ions is $N_0 = Q/p$.

We know, of course, that a molecule is itself a porous structure. It consists of atoms which consist, in turn, of electrons surrounding nuclei. It might, therefore, be thought that the diameter of a molecule is an ill-defined quantity. But this is not so, for we have computed the molecular diameter by using precisely the same procedure that one might employ to find the diameter of a large-sized sphere, such as a billiard ball. One can define the diameter of identical billiard balls as the distance between the centers of a pair of such balls in contact with one another; that is, the diameter is that separation distance below which the force between the balls becomes strongly repulsive. In like fashion, we have found the molecular diameter to be the separation distance between adjacent molecules marking the onset of a strongly repulsive intermolecular force.

Now that we know the approximate size of an oxygen molecule (4×10^{-10} m), we can find the average separation distance between molecules of oxygen under STP. The available volume per molecule in the gaseous state is 1400 times larger than the available volume per molecule in the liquid state. Thus, the average distance between molecular centers for oxygen under STP is $(1400)^{1/3} \simeq 11$ times the distance between molecular centers in liquid oxygen. For oxygen at STP, the molecules are, therefore, separated on the average by 11 molecular diameters, or by about 4.4×10^{-9} m = 44 Å. Of course, for still smaller densities, for which the general-gas law is even more applicable, the molecules are separated even farther. Thus, the molecules in a low-density gas may be regarded as mass points in a vacuum.

21-2 The assumptions of the kinetic theory We list below the assumptions of the kinetic theory of gases. These assumptions are amply justified, not only because they lead to a successful interpretation of the macroscopic properties of ideal gases in terms of the microscopic properties of gas molecules, but also because the microscopic properties are verified directly by experiment.

(1) The molecules of a gas are, on the average, separated by distances that are large compared with the molecular diameters. In fact, for ideal gases we assume the *molecules* to *have a negligible volume* compared with the volume of the container of the gas.

(2) The molecules are in constant *random motion*. Because the number of molecules is enormous, we assume that this motion is utterly chaotic: the molecules move in all directions with equal probability and with a variety of speeds. The center of mass of the gas as a whole remains at rest, the *total* vector momentum of all molecules being zero.

(3) The collisions of the molecules with one another and with the walls are *perfectly elastic*.

(4) Between collisions the molecules are free of forces and move with a constant speed.† A collision takes place when one molecule is within the short-range intermolecular force of a second molecule. The *duration of any collision is assumed to be very small compared with the time between collisions.* Thus, although a pair of molecules will lose kinetic energy and gain potential energy during a collision, the potential energy can be ignored because a molecule spends a negligible fraction of its time in collisions.

(5) *Newtonian mechanics applies* to molecular collisions.

21-3 Pressure of an ideal gas As our first application of the kinetic theory, we compute the pressure (a macroscopic property) of an ideal gas in terms of the microscopic properties of the gas molecules: N, the number of molecules in the container; m, the mass of each molecule; and v, the (average) molecular speed.

We attribute the pressure of the gas to the bombardment of the container walls by molecules. We imagine that N molecules are contained in a cubical box of edge length l. In reality, the molecules move in all directions and have a variety of speeds. However, to expose the physical arguments clearly, we shall, at first, assume that all molecules have the *same* speed v and that one third of them, $\frac{1}{3}N$, move along each of the directions X, Y, and Z. Moreover, we assume initially that the molecules collide only with the container walls and not with one another. We will later remove these simplifying restrictions and generalize the analysis.

We focus our attention on the $N/3$ molecules moving back and forth parallel with the X-axis and colliding elastically with the container walls in the YZ-plane. See Figure 21-1: the average pressure on the right-hand, shaded wall arising from the molecular bombardment is the total average force per unit area. This total force is $N/3$ times the *average* force F_{av} resulting from the collision of a single molecule. By Newton's second law,

$$F_{\text{av}} = \frac{\Delta(mv)}{\Delta t} \qquad [21\text{-}1]$$

where $\Delta(mv)$ is the magnitude of the momentum change of the molecule at the struck wall occurring in the time Δt.

We choose Δt to be the time required for any molecule to make one complete round trip between the end walls, traveling a distance $2l$ at a

† Strictly, the molecular speeds are constant between collisions only if the molecules move in gravity-free space. All molecules in a gas at the Earth's surface are subject to a constant acceleration **g** downward. But we shall see that the change in velocity arising from gravity is small compared with the molecular velocities and can be ignored. Stated differently, the change in the kinetic energy of a molecule arising from its rise or fall in a gravitation field is negligible compared with the kinetic energy of a typical molecule.

speed v. Therefore,

$$\Delta t = \frac{2l}{v} \qquad [21\text{-}2]$$

During the time interval Δt, the molecule has made a single collision with the right-hand wall, and in so doing has transferred to it momentum $\Delta(mv)$, a quantity given by

$$\Delta(mv) = mv - (-mv)$$

$$\Delta(mv) = 2mv \qquad [21\text{-}3]$$

Using Equations 21-1, 21-2, and 21-3, we have, for the average pressure on the right-hand wall,

$$p = \left(\frac{N}{3}\right) \frac{F_{\text{av}}}{l^2} = \left(\frac{N}{3l^2}\right) \frac{\Delta(mv)}{\Delta t}$$

$$p = \left(\frac{N}{3l^2}\right) \frac{(2mv)}{(2l/v)} = \left(\frac{1}{3}\right) \frac{Nm}{l^3} v^2$$

The volume of the box l^3 is the volume V of the gas in it, and we may write the above equation as

$$pV = \tfrac{1}{3}Nmv^2 \qquad [21\text{-}4]$$

Before discussing the physical significance of Equation 21-4, we shall remove the simplifying assumption that one third of the molecules move in

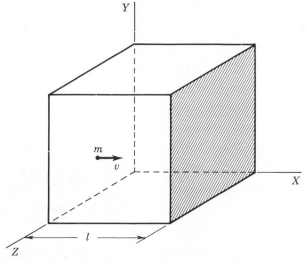

Figure 21-1. Molecule of mass m and speed v striking the YZ-wall of a cubical container of edge length l.

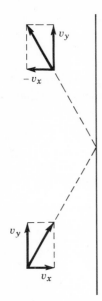

Figure 21-2. A molecule collides obliquely with a container wall. Only the velocity component at right angles to the surface changes.

each of three directions and that the molecules all travel at the same speed. Although we shall allow for motion in all directions with a variety of molecular speeds, we shall still neglect collisions between molecules. It will be later shown that this does not change the results.

We again consider the collision of a molecule with the right-hand YZ-wall of the cubical container of edge length l. Now, however, a molecule may approach the wall from any direction. Let its rectangular velocity components be v_x, v_y, and v_z. Inasmuch as the molecule collides elastically with the wall, it rebounds with the same speed. The v_y and v_z components are *not* changed, while the v_x component becomes $-v_x$ after the collision. See Figure 21-2. In the collision, the molecule loses momentum $2mv_x$ to the right while the wall gains momentum $2mv_x$ to the right. Thus, Equation 21-1 is now written

$$F = \frac{\Delta(mv)}{\Delta t} = \frac{2mv_x}{2l/v_x} = \frac{mv_x^2}{l} \qquad [21\text{-}5]$$

Each time a molecule strikes the container wall it imparts an impulsive force to it, and the total force on the wall is the resultant of a very large number of discrete and abrupt molecular collisions. See Figure 21-3. The molecular speeds vary, and the molecules strike the wall from different directions; consequently, the individual impulses differ in size. But because of the large number of molecules, the total force on the wall is essentially constant and the pressure of the gas is essentially continuous. Equation 21-5 gives the average force on the YZ-wall from one molecule.

Since the force of one molecule is given, by Equation 21-5, as $F = mv_x^2/l$, the pressure p on the wall, arising from all molecules striking it, is

$$p = \frac{\Sigma F}{l^2} = \frac{F_1 + F_2 + F_3 + \cdots}{l^2}$$

$$p = \frac{m(v_{x1}^2 + v_{x2}^2 + v_{x3}^2 + \cdots)}{l^3}$$

where the subscripts 1, 2, 3, etc., refer to the various individual molecules.

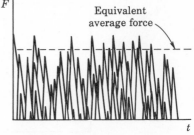

Figure 21-3. Force on container wall, arising from discrete molecular collisions, as a function of time. The equivalent average force is constant.

The *speeds* of the molecules are distributed over a continuous range of values. So are the *X-components* of the velocities. If we define $\overline{v_x^2}$ as the average of the squares,

$$\overline{v_x^2} = \frac{v_{x1}^2 + v_{x2}^2 + v_{x3}^2 + \cdots}{N}$$

then the pressure on the right-hand wall becomes

$$p = \frac{N m \overline{v_x^2}}{l^3} \qquad [21\text{-}6]$$

We can, of course, define similar averages for the *Y-* and *Z-*components of the velocities, as well as for the velocity itself. Then,

$$\overline{v_y^2} = \frac{v_{y1}^2 + v_{y2}^2 + v_{y3}^2 + \cdots}{N}$$

$$\overline{v_z^2} = \frac{v_{z1}^2 + v_{z2}^2 + v_{z3}^2 + \cdots}{N}$$

Since, by definition,

$$\overline{v^2} = \frac{v_1^2 + v_2^2 + v_3^2 + \cdots}{N}$$

and

$$v_1^2 = v_{x1}^2 + v_{y1}^2 + v_{z1}^2$$

it follows that

$$\overline{v^2} = \overline{v_x^2} + \overline{v_y^2} + \overline{v_z^2} \qquad [21\text{-}7]$$

Now, if the molecules move in truly random directions, one direction is like any other. Thus,

$$\overline{v_x^2} = \overline{v_y^2} = \overline{v_z^2}$$

and Equation 21-7 can be written

$$\overline{v^2} = 3\overline{v_x^2}, \quad \text{or} \quad \overline{v_x^2} = \tfrac{1}{3}\overline{v^2}$$

Equation 21-6 then becomes

$$pV = \tfrac{1}{3} N m \overline{v^2} \qquad [21\text{-}8]$$

It is useful to introduce the *root-mean-square velocity*, v_{rms}, which is the square *r*oot of the *m*ean of the *s*quares of the molecular velocities. By definition,

$$v_{\text{rms}} \equiv \sqrt{\overline{v^2}}$$

Then Equation 21-8 may be written

$$\boxed{pV = \tfrac{1}{3} N m v_{\text{rms}}^2} \qquad [21\text{-}9]$$

Note that Equation 21-9 is identical with Equation 21-4, the root-mean-square speed v_{rms} replacing the constant speed v.

Here we show that the analysis leading to Equation 21-9 is not changed when we take into account the very frequent collisions between molecules. We note first that there is no delay in the motion of any one molecule by virtue of intermolecular collisions, inasmuch as the duration of any one collision is assumed to be negligible compared with the time between collisions. (This will be directly proved in Section 22-5.) The velocity of any one molecule will, of course, change both in magnitude and direction during a collision. Suppose that molecules 1 and 2 have velocities v_1 and v_2 before they collide, and velocities v_1' and v_2' after they collide. Momentum conservation requires that

$$m v_1 + m v_2 = m v_1' + m v_2'$$

$$\text{or} \qquad v_1 + v_2 = v_1' + v_2'$$

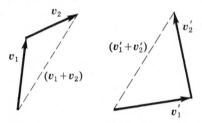

Figure 21-4. Velocity vectors for the collision between two molecules of equal mass. Before collision the molecules have velocities of v_1 and v_2; after collision, v_1' and v_2'.

Figure 21-4 shows the results of the above equation in graphical form. We see that the *sum* of the velocities of two molecules of equal mass colliding is unchanged, both in magnitude and direction, in a collision. Consequently, the component of the velocity sum in *any* direction is the same before and after the collision. It follows that if molecule 1 loses velocity in some direction, say the X-direction, then the X-component of molecule 2's speed is enhanced by the same amount. This means that the total number of collisions per second made by molecules 1 and 2 with the wall is the same, whether we consider intermolecular collisions or not.

Now, because the conservation of momentum law holds, the component of the momentum sum along the X-direction is the same before and after the intermolecular collision. This implies that the total momentum transferred to the YZ-wall by molecules 1 and 2 is the same, whether or not they collide. Therefore, Equation 21-9, although it was derived on the assumption of no intermolecular collisions, applies equally well when such collisions occur.

The analysis given above was based on Newtonian mechanics applied to molecular collisions, and through it we have related the macroscopic properties of a gas (the pressure p and volume V) to the microscopic molecular properties N, m, and v_{rms}. Equation 21-9 can be written more compactly by introducing the mass density of gas, ρ, where ρ is the total mass Nm of molecules within the container divided by the volume V that they occupy. Since $\rho = Nm/V$, Equation 21-9 can be written

$$p = \tfrac{1}{3} \rho v_{\text{rms}}^2 \qquad\qquad [21\text{-}10]$$

Equation 21-10 is a fundamental result of the kinetic theory of gases. It permits us to compute the root-mean-square speed of the molecules by knowing merely the pressure and density of the gas. For example, under conditions of STP, molecular hydrogen has a density

$$\rho = (2.016 \text{ gm}/22.4 \text{ liters}) = 9.00 \times 10^{-2} \text{ kg/m}^3$$

and a pressure $p = 1.013 \times 10^5 \text{ nt/m}^2$. From Equation 21-10,

$$v_{\text{rms}} = \sqrt{\frac{3p}{\rho}} = \sqrt{\frac{3(1.013 \times 10^5 \text{ nt/m}^2)}{(9.00 \times 10^{-2} \text{ kg/m}^3)}} = 1.84 \times 10^3 \text{ m/sec}$$

A typical hydrogen molecule at STP has a speed of nearly 2 km/sec $\simeq$ 4000 miles/hour! This does not mean that, in one second, such a molecule will travel along a straight line for 2 km, nor, for that matter, that it will travel directly from one end of a small box to the opposite end. A molecule in a gas of moderately low density makes very frequent collisions with other molecules. These collisions change both the magnitude and direction of the molecule's velocity (more about this in Section 22-5). What Equation 21-10 *does* say is that, between collisions, a typical hydrogen molecule at STP travels at a speed of 2 km/sec.

21-4   The meaning of temperature and internal energy It is now easy to relate the macroscopic concept of the temperature of an ideal gas, as defined through the general-gas law,

[20-7] $$pV = nRT$$ [21-11]

to the average kinetic energy of the molecules comprising the gas. From the kinetic theory we have

[21-9] $$pV = \tfrac{1}{3}Nmv_{\text{rms}}^2 = \tfrac{1}{3}Nm\overline{v^2}$$ [21-12]

We may write the total number of molecules N as the product of the number of moles, n, and the number of molecules per mole, N_0 (Avogadro's number); that is, $N = nN_0$.

Equating Equations 21-11 and 21-12, we obtain

$$\tfrac{1}{2}m\overline{v^2} = \frac{3}{2}\left(\frac{R}{N_0}\right)T$$

The *average translational kinetic energy* of a molecule of an *ideal gas* is *directly proportional* to the *absolute temperature* of the gas. Thus, temperature is, from the point of view of the kinetic theory, simply a measure of the average *translational* kinetic energy per molecule in an ideal gas. If gases followed the general-gas law to very low temperatures—which they do not—the molecules would be at rest at the absolute zero of temperature.

The ratio of the universal gas constant R to Avogadro's number N_0 is called the *Boltzmann constant* k:

$$\text{Boltzmann constant} = k = \frac{R}{N_0} = 1.380 \times 10^{-23} \text{ joule/molecule-K}^\circ$$

The Boltzmann constant may be regarded as the universal gas constant *per molecule*.

Our equation above can then be written:

$$
\boxed{
\begin{array}{c}
\text{Average translational kinetic energy per molecule} \\[6pt]
= \tfrac{1}{2}m\overline{v^2} = \dfrac{3}{2}\left(\dfrac{R}{N_0}\right)T = \tfrac{3}{2}kT
\end{array}
}
\qquad \text{[21-13]}
$$

This equation has profound consequences. For instance, suppose that we bring together two gases, initially at different temperatures, within a single container. Through intermolecular collisions the molecules of the hotter gas will transfer energy to the molecules of the cooler gas until thermal equilibrium is established. All of the gas molecules will then have a single final temperature. Equation 21-13 also implies that, at any fixed temperature, *all* molecules, whatever their masses, have the *same* average translational kinetic energy. Therefore, in a mixture of different gases, the molecules of small mass move at relatively high speeds and massive molecules move at low speeds.

Still another result of Equation 21-13 is this: for a given gas (given mass m) the root-mean-square speed is directly proportional to the square root of the absolute temperature. The molecular speed depends on neither the pressure nor the density singly; it depends only on their ratio p/ρ which, as can be seen from the general-gas law, is proportional to T.

For *any* type of gas at room temperature (300° K), the average translational kinetic energy per molecule is

Average translational kinetic energy per molecule at 300° K

$$= \tfrac{3}{2}kT$$

$$= (\tfrac{3}{2})(1.380 \times 10^{-23} \text{ joule/molecule-K}^\circ)(300^\circ \text{ K})(1 \text{ ev} / 1.6 \times 10^{-19} \text{ joule})$$

$$= \tfrac{1}{25} \text{ ev}$$

Only for the molecules of an *ideal* gas is the absolute temperature directly proportional to the average translational kinetic energy per molecule. For liquids and solids, the relation between temperature and particle energy is more complicated. Indeed, gases follow the relation $\tfrac{1}{2}m\overline{v^2} = \tfrac{3}{2}kT$ only to the extent that the assumptions of the kinetic theory apply. Thus, only if the gas density is low is it proper to assume that the finite molecular size is negligible compared with the volume of the container, and only then can the potential energy of molecules during a collision be neglected entirely.

Example 1   What is the rms molecular speed and average kinetic energy per molecule for hydrogen and oxygen molecules at (a) 300° K and (b) 30,000° K?

(a) At the end of Section 21-3 we found the rms speed for hydrogen molecules at 0° C to be 1.84 km/sec. From Equation 21-13, the rms speed for a fixed molecular mass is

$$v_{rms} \propto \sqrt{T}$$

Therefore, the rms speed of hydrogen molecules at 300° K is

$$v_{rms} = (1.84 \text{ km/sec}) \sqrt{\frac{300}{273}} = 1.93 \text{ km/sec}$$

We can easily compute the rms speed for O_2 at 300° K by recognizing that molecules of all gases at the same temperature have the same average kinetic energy. Thus,

$$\tfrac{1}{2}m_H v_H{}^2 = \tfrac{1}{2}m_O v_O{}^2$$

where the subscripts H and O refer to hydrogen and oxygen, respectively. Then, for O_2 at (300° K),

$$v_O = v_H \sqrt{m_H/m_O} = (1.93 \text{ km/sec}) \sqrt{2.016/32.00} = 0.484 \text{ km/sec}$$

As shown above, the average translational kinetic energy per molecule of any gas, including H_2 or O_2, is $\tfrac{1}{25}$ ev at 300° K.

(b) To find the speeds and kinetic energies at 30,000° K we simply recognize that, since the temperature is up by a factor of 100, the energies increase by the factor of 100, and the speeds by a factor of 10, over the corresponding values at 300° K. Therefore,

$$\tfrac{1}{2}m\overline{v^2} \text{ for } H_2 \text{ or } O_2 \text{ at } 30,000° K = (\tfrac{1}{25} \text{ ev})(100) = 4.0 \text{ ev}$$

$$v_{rms} \text{ for } H_2 \text{ at } 30,000° K = (1.93 \text{ km/sec})(10) = 19.3 \text{ km/sec}$$

$$v_{rms} \text{ for } O_2 \text{ at } 30,000° K = (0.484 \text{ km/sec})(10) = 4.84 \text{ km/sec}$$

Example 2   Hydrogen gas at 0° C is contained in a box 1.0 m along an edge. (a) What is the maximum change in the gravitational potential energy of a hydrogen molecule within the box? (b) Compare the change in gravitational potential energy of a molecule with its average kinetic energy.

(a) We are to find the difference in gravitational potential energy for a hydrogen molecule when at the top and at the bottom of the box. We use the relation

[12-3] $$\Delta U = mg \, \Delta y$$

where Δy is 1.0 m.

The mass of a single hydrogen molecule is the molecular weight of hydrogen divided by Avogadro's number:

$$(2.016 \text{ gm})/(6.023 \times 10^{23} \text{ molecules/gm-mole}) = 3.4 \times 10^{-27} \text{ kg}$$

Therefore,

$$\Delta U = (3.4 \times 10^{-27} \text{ kg})(9.8 \text{ m/sec}^2)(1.0 \text{ m})/(1.6 \times 10^{-19} \text{ joule/ev})$$
$$= 2.1 \times 10^{-7} \text{ ev}$$

(b) The average translational kinetic energy of an H_2 molecule at $0°$ C is $\frac{1}{25}$ ev; this is larger than the change in gravitational potential energy by a factor of 10^5. Thus, the change in a molecule's speed under the influence of gravity is negligible and may properly be neglected.

It is useful to use the term *internal energy* to designate the total energy content of a system. Thus, if a system consists of a spring with attached masses, the internal energy U of the system is the sum of the kinetic energies of the masses and the potential energy of the spring. If a system consists of an ideal gas composed of N particles† in thermal equilibrium, this system's internal energy U is just the average kinetic energy per particle, $\frac{3}{2}kT$, multiplied by the number of particles N; that is,

$$U = \tfrac{3}{2}NkT = \tfrac{3}{2}nRT \qquad\qquad [21\text{-}14]$$

Equation 21-14 implies that, for an *ideal gas*, the internal energy of the system is a function of the absolute temperature only.

(a)   (b)

Figure 21-5. (a) Molecules with the same velocity display *ordered* motion. (b) Molecules with randomly distributed velocities display *disordered* motion.

The internal energy of an ideal gas is energy arising from the *disordered* motion, or molecular chaos, of many small particles. Because the molecular motion is random, the molecules have kinetic energy, but the total linear momentum of the system as a whole is *zero*. Figure 21-5 shows two systems, both of which have the same total kinetic energy. In Figure 21-5a the motion of the particles is ordered and the total momentum of the system is just N times the momentum of each particle; in Figure 21-5b the motion of particles is disordered and the center of mass of the system remains at rest.

Thus, the internal energy of a system of particles may be either ordered or disordered (or a combination of the two). When the motion is ordered, it is manifest macroscopically as recognizable kinetic and potential energy. When the motion is disordered, as in an ideal gas, one "sees" no energy on a

† We here assume for simplicity that the molecules are monatomic. Then no energy is associated with the vibration of atoms within the molecule, and there is no kinetic energy of rotation of the molecule as a whole. We shall remove these restrictions in Section 21-7.

macroscopic scale, although it exists microscopically as kinetic or potential energy. This disordered, chaotic, internal energy of a system is called *thermal energy*.

The thermal energy is always measured by an observer at rest with respect to the system's center of mass. Suppose that a container of gas were to be in motion relative to us. The speeds and kinetic energies of the molecules would then be higher, as compared with their values for the container at rest. But, simply because we are in motion relative to the container, we do *not* find the temperature of the gas to have increased. For a container of gas in motion, there are two contributions to the total internal energy: the disordered thermal energy of the gas molecules relative to the center of mass of the system (which determines the temperature) and the ordered kinetic energy arising from the motion of the container relative to the observer.

21-5 The meaning of heat and the first law of thermodynamics

Here we are concerned with the ways in which the internal energy of a gas can change. Assume that we have a gas in thermal equilibrium with its container; that is, the temperature of the collection of gas molecules is the same as that of the container. As time goes on, the total internal energy, and therefore the temperature, of the gas remains unchanged. The collisions are perfectly elastic, and no energy is lost or gained. This implies that, when a molecule strikes a wall, it rebounds with the same kinetic energy, so that the gas molecules neither gain nor lose energy in such collisions.

It is, however, unrealistic to imagine the container wall as a perfectly smooth, hard surface. Indeed, the wall consists of atoms bound to one another in a solid, each atom oscillating continuously about some fixed position. When a molecule strikes a wall, it hits an atom which is, in general, moving. Therefore, the gas molecule may leave the wall with a greater or lesser kinetic energy. For thermal equilibrium, the *average* energy of molecules rebounding from the wall equals the *average* energy of molecules striking the wall.

There is only one way in which the internal energy, or thermal energy, of a gas in a container can change: the molecules must, on the average, either gain or lose kinetic energy in their collisions with atoms in the container walls. (Here we suppose, for simplicity, that the molecules are monatomic and also that no electromagnetic radiation enters or leaves the container.) We may distinguish *two modes of energy transfer* to or from the gas molecules: *work* and *heat*.

Suppose that a gas is in a container with a movable, freely sliding piston, as shown in Figure 21-6a. The molecules bombard the piston and the walls. Suppose, further, that the pressure on the outside of the container is zero. Then the piston is moved outward by the molecular bombardment; that is,

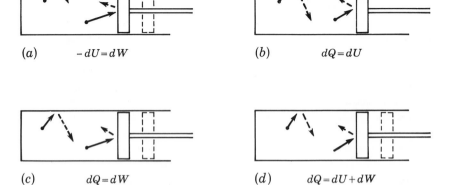

(a) $-dU = dW$

(b) $dQ = dU$

(c) $dQ = dW$

(d) $dQ = dU + dW$

Figure 21-6. Changes in internal energy, work, and heat for a gas, illustrated by collisions of molecules with container walls. (a) The internal energy dU decreases and work dW is done by the gas when, on the average, a molecule rebounds from the piston at a lower speed. (b) The gas is heated dQ and its internal energy increased dU when, on the average, a molecule rebounds from the container wall at a higher speed. (c) The gas is heated dQ, does work dW, but has no change in its internal energy when, on the average, a molecule rebounds with increased speed from the container and with corresponding decreased speed from the piston. (d) The gas is heated dQ, its internal energy increased dU, and it does work dW.

the contained gas does work on the piston and the piston gains ordered kinetic energy. We can compute the amount of work done by the gas through the relation

[20-8] $$dW = p\, dV$$

where p is the gas pressure and dV is the additional volume arising from the expansion.

The temperature of the gas falls as the piston is moved outward. Let us imagine that the container walls are always maintained at the same temperature as the gas. Then any molecule striking a fixed container wall (excluding the moving piston), will rebound, on the average, with unchanged kinetic energy. But what about the molecules hitting the piston? Each molecule does work on the piston in striking it. Each molecule rebounds with a reduced speed (and reduced kinetic energy), as shown in Figure 21-6a. Consequently, the total internal energy of the gas is lowered, the decrease in internal energy, $-dU$, being exactly equal to the work done by the gas on the piston:

$$-dU = dW$$

or $$0 = dU + dW$$

In this process, some of the disordered thermal energy of the gas molecules is converted into the ordered kinetic energy of the piston.

We can, of course, reverse the process described above. An external agent compresses the gas, the temperature of the walls again being maintained at the same temperature as that of the gas. Then, when the piston is displaced inward, work is done *on* the gas, the molecules leave the piston wall with a *larger* kinetic energy, and the total internal energy of the gas is *increased*.

Is it possible to change the internal energy of the gas, even if no work is done? We now imagine that the container is initially at a higher temperature than the gas within; that is, we start with a cool gas in a hot container. The piston is locked in position. Because the atoms in the wall are oscillating energetically, when molecules strike the wall they rebound, on the average, with a *higher* kinetic energy. See Figure 21-6b. This process of energy-transfer, which has its origin in the temperature difference between the gas and the container, is called *heat*. The gas has been heated because there is a difference in temperature between it and the container. The internal energy of the gas increases by dU. This gain in internal energy is equal to the thermal energy dQ transferred into the system through heat; that is,

$$dQ = dU$$

The process may also be reversed. If the gas is initially at a higher temperature than that of the container walls, a typical molecule *loses* energy upon striking the wall. Then the internal energy of the gas changes by $-dU$, the amount of heat *to* the gas being $-dQ$. Again, $dQ = dU$.

Heat and work both describe energy transfer processes. *Work* is identified with the *macroscopic* displacement of an object having *ordered* kinetic energy; no temperature difference need be involved. *Heat*, on the other hand, is identified with the transfer of thermal energy, energy of *disordered* motion, arising from a temperature difference. When a system is heated, work is done, to be sure, but it occurs on a microscopic scale and in disordered fashion. It involves the interaction between individual atoms and molecules and it can be described macroscopically in terms of a temperature difference.

Heat may be expressed in any units of work or energy: joules, ergs, foot-pounds, electron-volts. By tradition, heat is often given in terms of the energy units *calories* or *British thermal units* (BTU), where 1 cal = 4.18 joule and 1 BTU = 778 foot-pounds.

On a microscopic scale, where one deals with the interaction and collision of individual particles, there is no such thing as heat, or "thermal energy." At this level the kinetic energy and potential energy of individual particles change, because one particle does work on a second particle. On the other hand, heat and thermal energy are macroscopic properties which permit us to preserve and use the conservation of energy principle without regard for the detailed motions of the many interacting particles.

Unfortunately, the term *heat* is sometimes used not only to describe an energy-transfer process itself but also to denote the thermal energy content of a system. But one cannot properly speak of the *heat* "content" of a system any more than one can speak of the "work content" of a system. Moreover, it is misleading to describe heat as a "form" of energy, or to speak of the "flow" of heat. These phrases are left over from the notion, now rejected, that heat (or "caloric") is a substance. They are, unhappily, thoroughly entrenched in the parlance of thermodynamics.

Figure 21-6a shows a process in which there is no heat; work is done and the internal energy changes. Figure 21-6b shows a process in which no work is done; the gas is heated and the internal energy changes. Now consider the situation of Figure 21-6c, in which the gas is heated and does work without, however, changing its internal energy. Energy flows into the system through heat dQ; the same amount flows out, as work dW done on the piston:

$$dQ = dW$$

The internal energy of the gas (therefore, its temperature) is unchanged. On a molecular scale the following occurs for this process: a typical molecule gains kinetic energy when striking a fixed wall, but loses kinetic energy when striking the piston. Inasmuch as heat occurs only when a temperature difference exists, the container walls must, strictly, be at an infinitesimally higher temperature than the gas. The "direction" of temperature difference always gives, so to speak, the direction of net thermal-energy flow.

Figure 21-6d shows a process involving changes in all three—the heat, internal energy, and work done by the system. If the heat exceeds the work done—that is, if the thermal energy into the system exceeds the ordered energy leaving the system—the internal energy will increase. The relation governing such a process is

$$dQ = dU + dW \qquad [21\text{-}15]$$

This is the *first law of thermodynamics*. It is simply the conservation of energy principle expressed in its most general form. It recognizes transfer of energy through either work or heat, and it includes in the internal energy of the system *all* forms of energy, whether ordered or disordered.

Note the convention for the signs in Equation 21-15: $+dQ$ represents the thermal energy *entering* the system through heating, $+dW$ represents the energy *leaving* the system by virtue of work done *by* the system, and dU is the change in internal energy of the system. Figure 21-7 is a symbolic representation of the first law.

Although we have arrived at the first law of thermodynamics by considering the microscopic behavior of molecules in an ideal gas, this relation is of complete generality. We shall later consider its applications to systems of liquids and solids and its complete confirmation in experiment.

Let us consider one more example of thermal-energy transfer through heat. Suppose that an insulated container is divided into two parts by a removable partition. A hot gas is on the left side, and a cooler gas of the same type is on the right. Then the partition is removed and the gas molecules mix. Both $dQ = 0$ and $dW = 0$ in this process. The mixture attains thermal equilibrium, and a single temperature, intermediate between the initial high and low temperatures, describes the final collection of gas molecules. According to the first law of thermodynamics, the total thermal-energy content of the gas is unchanged, the energy lost by the hot gas in cooling being exactly equal to the energy gained by the cold gas in heating. Alternatively, we may say that the hot gas has heated the cold gas, bringing both to the same common temperature.

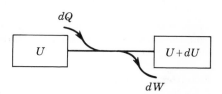

Figure 21-7. Schematic representation of the first law of thermodynamics. Energy enters the system as heat dQ, leaves as work done dW, and the internal energy increases by dU.

What happens on a microscopic scale? When the partition is removed, the fast-moving molecules of the hot gas move into the region of the cold gas at a higher rate than do the molecules of the cold gas in the reverse direction. In addition, another factor operates: when two molecules collide, it is more probable that the high-speed molecule will lose kinetic energy while the low-speed molecule gains kinetic energy than that the reverse will occur. The gases thereby have their temperatures equalized. This assures us that we will *not* find the hot gas getting hotter and the cool gas colder. Although this possibility is not ruled out by the first law of thermodynamics, it is prohibited by the second law of thermodynamics, as we shall see in Section 22-3.

Example 3 One mole of an ideal gas at $0°$ C is heated. The gas expands isothermally to twice its initial volume. What is the amount of heat associated with this isothermal expansion?

In Example 3, Section 20-4, it was shown that the work done by a gas in an isothermal expansion from volume V_1 to V_2 is $nRT \ln (V_2/V_1)$; therefore, $dW = nRT \ln 2$.

Since the temperature of the expanding gas is maintained constant, the internal energy of the gas, $U = \frac{3}{2}nRT$, does not change; that is, during the expansion dU equals zero.

From the first law of thermodynamics,

$$dQ = dU + dW$$

$$dQ = 0 + nRT \ln 2 = (1 \text{ mole})(8.31 \text{ joules/mole-K}°)(273° \text{ K})(\ln 2)$$

$$dQ = 1580 \text{ joules} = 380 \text{ cal}$$

Thus, in this process 1580 joules of disordered, or thermal, energy is transferred from the surroundings to the gas. During this same time the gas does an equal amount of work as it expands.

Example 4   One half of an insulated container holds 1 mole of helium gas at $0°$ C; the other half holds 1 mole of neon gas at $100°$ C. The insulating partition between the two halves is then removed, the gases mix, and thermal equilibrium is achieved. What is the final temperature of the mixture?

Initially the total internal energy of the helium molecules is equal to their total number N_0 multiplied by the initial kinetic energy $\frac{3}{2}kT$ per molecule, or $\frac{3}{2}N_0 kT = \frac{3}{2}RT = \frac{3}{2}R(273° \text{ K})$. Similarly, the total initial internal energy of the neon molecules is $\frac{3}{2}RT = \frac{3}{2}R(373° \text{ K})$. After the molecules are mixed and achieve thermal equilibrium, each of the two types of gas will have an internal energy of $\frac{3}{2}RT_f$, where T_f is the $f$inal temperature. Therefore, by energy conservation,

$$\frac{3}{2}R(273° \text{ K}) + \frac{3}{2}R(373° \text{ K}) = (2)\frac{3}{2}RT_f$$

$$T_f = \frac{273 + 373}{2}° \text{ K} = 323° \text{ K} = 50° \text{ C}$$

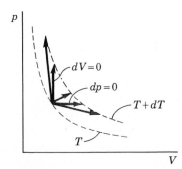

Figure 21-8. Several changes in the state of an ideal gas, leading to an increase in its temperature from T to $T + dT$. The vertical displacement corresponds to isovolumetric heating; the horizontal displacement, to isobaric heating.

21-6   The specific heats of an ideal gas

One simple application of the first law of thermodynamics is in the calculation of the specific heats of an ideal gas. The *specific heat* of any substance is defined as the heat required to raise the temperature of one unit mass of the substance by one degree. For gases, it is more convenient to measure the specific heat in terms of the heat required to increase the temperature of *one mole* by one degree; this is called the *molar specific heat.*

As Figure 21-8 shows, starting from some one state of an ideal gas, there are an infinite number of processes that can lead to a change dT in the gas's temperature. Let us analyze the two common situations:

heating at constant volume, and heating at constant pressure. The molar specific heat at constant *volume* is denoted C_v; the molar specific heat at constant *pressure* is represented by C_p.

We first suppose that an ideal gas is heated at constant volume, its temperature increasing by dT. From the first law of thermodynamics,

$$dQ_v = dU_v + dW_v \qquad\qquad [21\text{-}16]$$

where the subscript v implies that the process takes place at constant *volume*. Since the gas's volume V is constant, $dW_v = p\,dV = 0$. The gas does no work.

By definition, the specific heat at constant volume is

$$C_v = \frac{dQ_v}{n\,dT}$$

or

$$dQ_v = nC_v\,dT$$

Equation 21-16 then gives

$$dU_v = nC_v\,dT \quad \text{(isovolumetric heating)} \qquad\qquad [21\text{-}17]$$

Now suppose that the same gas is heated through the *same* temperature difference dT, but at *constant pressure* rather than at constant volume. As the gas is heated, it must be allowed to expand; otherwise, its pressure will increase. The expanding gas does work in the amount

$$dW_p = p\,dV_p$$

where the subscript p indicates a process at constant *pressure*.

By definition, the molar specific heat at constant pressure is

$$C_p = \frac{dQ_p}{n\,dT}$$

or

$$dQ_p = nC_p\,dT$$

Substituting for dW_p and dQ_p in Equation 21-15 gives

$$nC_p\,dT = dU_p + p\,dV_p \quad \text{(isobaric heating)} \qquad\qquad [21\text{-}18]$$

We recall that the internal energy of an ideal gas depends only on the temperature T, not on p or V singly. Just as we assumed the temperature difference dT to be the *same* for isovolumetric and isobaric heating, we assume the same behavior for the change in the internal energy. Consequently,

$$dU_p = dU_v$$

We may, therefore, eliminate dU between Equations 21-17 and 21-18, to find

$$nC_p \, dT = nC_v \, dT + p \, dV_p$$

We know from the general-gas law that $pV = nRT$ for any process. Thus, in an isobaric process, for which p remains constant, $p \, dV_p = nR \, dT$. Substituting this result in the last equation gives, finally,

$$n(C_p - C_v) \, dT = nR \, dT$$

$$\boxed{C_p - C_v = R} \qquad\qquad [21\text{-}19]$$

Note that Equation 21-19 does *not* give either C_p or C_v separately, but only their difference. Thus, for *any ideal gas*, the molar specific heat C_p exceeds

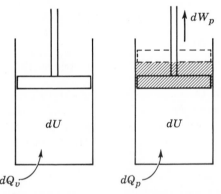

Figure 21-9. (a) Isovolumetric heating: all heat dQ_v entering the gas raises the gas's internal energy dU. (b) Isobaric heating: some of the heat dQ_p entering the system raises the gas's internal energy dU, the remainder corresponds to work dW_p done by the gas.

the molar specific heat C_v by an amount $R = 8.31$ joules/mole-K° $= 1.99$ cal/mole-K°. The physical reason for this difference is that *all* of the thermal energy entering a gas maintained at constant volume goes into raising the gas's temperature. On the other hand, only a fraction of the thermal energy entering a gas maintained at constant pressure changes the gas's temperature; the rest leaves the system as work done by the expanding gas. See Figure 21-9.

Experiment shows that *all* ideal gases, whether monatomic, diatomic, or polyatomic, follow Equation 21-19. Although the values of C_v differ according to the type of gas and its temperature, the respective values of C_p always exceed C_v by R. Compare the values for $C_p - C_v$ for various gases in

Table 21-1. They are all the same: R. We see further that C_v is always close to $\frac{3}{2}R$ for a monatomic gas at *any* temperature, and that C_v is $\frac{3}{2}R$ for a diatomic gas at a sufficiently low temperature. However, for a diatomic gas at higher temperatures, C_v is $\frac{5}{2}R$, and at still higher temperatures it is $\frac{7}{2}R$.

Table 21-1†

Gas	Temp. (°K)	C_v	C_p	$C_p - C_v$
Argon (Ar)	300	1.50 R	2.50 R	1.00 R
Argon (Ar)	600	1.50 R	2.50 R	1.00 R
Argon (Ar)	3000	1.50 R	2.50 R	1.00 R
Helium (He)	300	1.50 R	2.50 R	1.00 R
Hydrogen (H_2)	20	1.50 R	2.50 R	1.00 R
Hydrogen (H_2)	300	2.47 R	3.47 R	1.00 R
Hydrogen (H_2)	600	2.52 R	3.52 R	1.00 R
Hydrogen (H_2)	4000	3.50 R	4.50 R	1.00 R
Oxygen (O_2)	300	2.54 R	3.54 R	1.00 R
Nitrogen (N_2)	300	2.51 R	3.51 R	1.00 R
Ether ($[C_2H_5]_2O$)	300	15.2 R	16.2 R	1.00 R

† At the pressure of 1 atmosphere.

What does the kinetic theory predict? If we consider the internal energy U of an ideal gas to consist *solely* of the *translational* kinetic energy of the molecules, then Equation 21-14 gives

$$U = \tfrac{3}{2}nRT$$

and, therefore,

$$C_v = \left(\frac{1}{n}\right)\frac{dU}{dT} = \left(\frac{3}{2}\right)R$$

This agrees well with the results for monatomic gases at *all* temperatures and with the results for diatomic gases at low enough temperatures. At higher temperatures, however, the diatomic gases must, in view of the larger C_v values, require more heat per degree temperature rise. One must conclude that for nonmonatomic molecules there are additional contributions to the internal energy, having their origin in the complicated structure of molecules. We shall have more about the specific heats of diatomic gases in Section 21-7.

Example 5 Show that, for an adiabatic process of an ideal gas—one in which no thermal energy is transferred into or out of the system—pV^γ is a constant, where $\gamma \equiv C_p/C_v$.

If a gas undergoes an infinitesimal adiabatic expansion, then $dQ = 0$, and the first law becomes

$$dQ = 0 = dU + dW \qquad [21\text{-}20]$$

A gas does positive work $dW = p\,dV$ in expanding; thus, its internal energy *decreases* by $dU = nC_v\,dT$. An adiabatic expansion is accompanied by a *drop* in temperature (see Figure 20-7). Equation 21-20 can be written

$$nC_v\,dT + p\,dV = 0 \qquad [21\text{-}21]$$

This equation relates a change in temperature dT to the volume change dV for an adiabatic expansion. By using the equation of state for an ideal gas, $pV = nRT$, we can eliminate p in Equation 21-21, and then integrate the resulting equation:

$$nC_v\,dT = -\frac{nRT}{V}\,dV$$

$$\int \frac{dT}{T} = -\frac{R}{C_v}\int \frac{dV}{V}$$

$$\ln T = -(R/C_v)\ln V$$

or $\qquad\qquad T\,V^{(R/C_v)} = K_1 \qquad\qquad\qquad [21\text{-}22]$

where K_1 is a constant.

Since $pV \propto T$ for an ideal gas, Equation 21-22 can be written in the form

$$(pV)V^{(R/C_v)} = K$$

where K is another constant.

Using the fact that $R = C_p - C_v$ for any ideal gas, the last equation above becomes

$$\boxed{p\,V^{(C_p/C_v)} = pV^\gamma = K} \qquad [21\text{-}23]$$

where the specific heat ratio γ is defined as $\gamma \equiv C_p/C_v$.

An adiabatic process closely describes the following two physical situations: a gas undergoing a change of state in an insulated container, and a gas expanding or undergoing compression so rapidly that there is not enough time for heat to flow into or out of the system. One important example of the latter situation occurs in the propagation of sound waves through a gas. Here the local variations in pressure occur at so high a rate that no thermal energy is transferred from or into the system.

21-7 The specific heats of diatomic gases The average *translational* kinetic energy of any ideal gas is $\frac{3}{2}RT$ per mole, or $\frac{3}{2}kT$ per molecule. One may consider this energy as being divided equally among the three *translational* degrees of freedom. A translational degree of freedom is defined as one of the independent coordinates needed to specify the position of the molecule's center of mass. Inasmuch as three coordinates (such as x, y, and z) are needed to locate a molecule in space, there are *three* translational degrees of freedom. Consequently, an average energy of $\frac{1}{2}kT$ per molecule may be associated with each of these three degrees of freedom.

A monatomic molecule has only translational degrees of freedom; therefore, a gas of such molecules has $\frac{3}{2}kT$ energy per molecule. On the other hand, a molecule comprised of more than one atom has, in addition to the translational degrees of freedom, internal degrees of freedom. These arise from the internal coordinates required to locate the atoms of the molecule relative to its center of mass. One must associate energy (kinetic and potential) with each of these internal degrees of freedom. If any of these degrees of freedom is active, the total energy per molecule will exceed $\frac{3}{2}kT$.

First, we state (without proof) the classical theorem of the equipartition of energy. In a large collection of molecules at a temperature T, the total energy of the gas is distributed among all the molecules such that, for each molecule, there is an average energy of $\frac{1}{2}kT$ per degree of freedom. Here we apply the equipartition theorem to diatomic molecules.

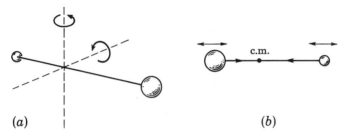

(a)   (b)

Figure 21-10. (a) Molecular rotation of a diatomic molecule about two mutually perpendicular axes. (b) Molecular vibration of a diatomic molecule along the interatomic axis.

A diatomic molecule may be thought of as a dumbbell-like structure, two atoms being at the ends of an "interatomic rod." Such a molecule can rotate about any one of three mutually perpendicular axes passing through the molecule's center of mass, one axis being aligned with, and the other two being perpendicular to, the interatomic axis. We may ignore molecular rotation about the axis coinciding with the interatomic axis, inasmuch as the atomic nuclei, which have most of the atomic mass, lie on the interatomic axis and the moment of inertia about this axis is negligibly small. There remain, then, rotation about two mutually perpendicular axes, both at right angles to the interatomic axis; see Figure 21-10a. There are, then, *two* degrees of freedom associated with rotation for a diatomic molecule. Thus, when molecular rotation is active—that is, when a large fraction of the molecules in a gas are undergoing rotation—the *rotational* energy per molecule is $2 \times \frac{1}{2}kT = kT$.

A diatomic molecule may also have internal energy associated with its vibration. The two atoms may oscillate along the interatomic axis relative to the molecule's center of mass, as shown in Figure 21-10b. For the single vibrational degree of freedom there are *two* contributions to the vibrational energy: one for the kinetic energy and one for the potential energy, each being $\frac{1}{2}kT$. Therefore, when molecular vibration is active, the *vibrational* energy per molecule is $2 \times \frac{1}{2}kT = kT$.

In summary: when a diatomic molecule undergoes translational motion only, its average energy is $\frac{3}{2}kT$; when a diatomic molecule is moving through space and rotating at the same time, its average energy is $\frac{3}{2}kT + kT = \frac{5}{2}kT$; when a diatomic molecule has energy of translation, rotation, and vibration, its average energy is $\frac{3}{2}kT + kT + kT = \frac{7}{2}kT$. The corresponding values for the internal energy U of the gas are $\frac{3}{2}nRT$, $\frac{5}{2}nRT$, and $\frac{7}{2}nRT$, respectively. The molar specific heat at constant volume C_v is computed from U according to the relation $C_v = (1/n)(dU/dT)$. Therefore, the specific heat C_v for a gas consisting of rotating and vibrating molecules is *not* the same as C_v for a gas consisting of single atoms. The values of C_p will also differ, of course; C_p always exceeds C_v by R, following Equation 21-19.

The results given above are summarized in Table 21-2 for the three important classes of diatomic gases. It must be pointed out that, according to the quantum theory, molecular rotation and vibration are not active at relatively low temperatures. Molecular rotation takes place at higher temperatures and, at still higher temperatures, the molecule is active in both rotation and vibration. By comparing the measured values for C_v in Table 21-1 with the theoretical values listed in Table 21-2, one can deduce the state of motion of the molecules

Table 21-2

STATE OF MOTION	ENERGY PER MOLECULE	U	C_v	C_p	γ
Monatomic molecule, or a diatomic molecule undergoing *translation* only	$\frac{3}{2}kT$	$\frac{3}{2}nRT$	$\frac{3}{2}R$	$\frac{5}{2}R$	5/3
Diatomic molecule in *translational* and *rotational* motion	$\frac{3}{2}kT + kT$	$\frac{5}{2}nRT$	$\frac{5}{2}R$	$\frac{7}{2}R$	7/5
Diatomic molecule in *translational, rotational, and vibrational* motion	$\frac{3}{2}kT + kT + kT$	$\frac{7}{2}nRT$	$\frac{7}{2}R$	$\frac{9}{2}R$	9/7

at the temperature given. Thus, helium molecules are always in translational motion only. Oxygen molecules at room temperature, on the other hand, undergo translational and rotational (but not vibrational) motion. The temperatures for hydrogen gas given in Table 21-1 correspond to states of translation only, of translation and rotation, and of translation, rotation, and vibration. Note also that a polyatomic molecule such as ether, $(C_2H_5)_2O$, which has *more* than two rotational degrees of freedom and more than one mode of vibration, has an exceptionally high C_v value.

When the temperature of a *monatomic* gas is raised, all of the added thermal energy appears as energy of *translational* motion. But when a *diatomic* or *polyatomic* gas is heated, only a *fraction* of the additional thermal energy appears as translational energy. For this reason, it is important to speak of the absolute temperature of an ideal gas as a measure of the *translational* kinetic energy, not merely as a measure of the total kinetic energy of the molecules. The internal energy, on the other hand, is a measure of the total thermal-energy content of any ideal gas.

Example 6   An insulated container is divided into two equal volumes by a removable partition. Initially, one side holds 1 mole of helium gas at 0° C; the other holds 1 mole of N_2 at $100°$ C. The partition is then removed, and the mixture of gases is allowed to come to thermal equilibrium. What is the final temperature of the mixture?

This problem is similar to Example 4, Section 21-5, in which equal masses of two *monatomic* gases, one at $0°$ C and the other at $100°$ C, were brought together, and the final temperature of the mixture was found to be $50°$ C. This is *not* the case here.

The initial internal energy of the helium gas is $\frac{3}{2}R(273°$ K); the initial internal energy of the nitrogen (its molecules undergoing translation and rotation at these temperatures) is $\frac{5}{2}R(373°$ K). After mixing and coming to thermal equilibrium, the helium molecules have an internal energy of $\frac{3}{2}RT_f$, where T_f is the final temperature. The nitrogen molecules have final internal energy of $\frac{5}{2}RT_f$. Since no external work is done by the gases and no heat enters the system, the total internal energy of the system is unchanged. Therefore we have

$$\tfrac{3}{2}R(273°\ \text{K}) + \tfrac{5}{2}R(373°\ \text{K}) = \tfrac{3}{2}RT_f + \tfrac{5}{2}RT_f$$

$$T_f = 335°\ \text{K} = 62°\ \text{C}$$

The final temperature is *not* midway between the initial temperatures, because the two gases have *different* specific heats.

21-8 Summary In the kinetic theory of gases it is assumed that molecules of negligible size are in random motion and make perfectly elastic collisions with one another and with the container walls, and that the duration of any one collision is short compared with the time elapsing between collisions. It is also assumed that the molecular collisions are governed by Newtonian mechanics.

An important result of the kinetic theory, relating the pressure p and volume V of an ideal gas to the number N of molecules, the molecular mass m, and the root-mean-square molecular speed v_{rms}, is

[21-9] $$pV = \tfrac{1}{3}Nmv_{\text{rms}}^2$$

The average translational kinetic energy of a molecule in a gas in thermal equilibrium at temperature T is $\frac{3}{2}kT$.

The internal energy U of a monatomic gas of N molecules is

[21-14] $$U = N(\tfrac{3}{2}kT)$$

The first law of thermodynamics can be written

[21-15] $$dQ = dU + dW$$

where dQ is the heat entering the system, dU is the change in the system's internal energy, and dW is the work done by the system on its surroundings. This law is merely the conservation of energy principle generalized to include the transfer of energy into or out of a system by heat, which describes the transfer of disordered energy arising from a temperature difference, in addition to work, which describes energy transfer to ordered energy.

The molar specific heats at constant pressure and constant volume, C_p and C_v, respectively, of *any* ideal gas are always related by

[21-19] $$C_p - C_v = R$$

Gases of polyatomic molecules have higher specific heats than monatomic molecules by virtue of the additional internal energy arising from molecular rotation and vibration.

For an ideal gas, an adiabatic process is given by

[21-23] $$pV^\gamma = \text{constant}, \qquad \text{where } \gamma = C_p/C_v.$$

PROBLEMS

21-1   Given the following data from an electrolysis experiment, compute the value for Avogadro's number: 0.335 gm of silver are electroplated when an electric current of 0.500 amp flows for 10.0 minutes through an electrolytic cell. The atomic weight of silver is 107.9; a silver ion has an electric charge of 1.602×10^{-19} coul. One ampere $= 1$ coul/sec.

21-2   (a) Compute the average separation distance between water molecules when the molecules are in the liquid state. (b) What is the approximate diameter of water molecules? (c) Assuming that water vapor can be considered an ideal gas when its temperature and pressure are at $200°$ C and 0.20 atmospheres, compute the density of the gas. (d) What is the average separation distance between water molecules under the conditions of part (c)? (e) What is ratio of the average separation distance between adjacent water molecules, under the conditions of part (c), to the approximate diameter of a water molecule?

21-3   Gold has an atomic weight of 197.0 and its density in the solid state is 1.93×10^4 kg/m³. (a) How many gold atoms are there in a volume of 1.0 cm³? (b) What is the approximate diameter of a gold atom?

21-4   A certain molecular beam consists of hydrogen molecules (mass, 3.3×10^{-27} kg) all traveling in the same direction at a speed of 1.8 km/sec. The beam is incident normally on a surface, the number of molecules striking the surface per second being 3.0×10^5. (a) What is the average force of the molecular beam on the surface, if it is assumed that all molecules rebound perfectly elastically? (b) What is the average force on the surface if it is assumed that all molecules stick to the surface?

21-5   These are the speeds, in meters per second, of ten molecules: 2, 3, 4, 6, 8, 8, 9, 10, 10, 12. Compute (a) the average speed, and (b) the root-mean-square speed for these ten molecules.

21-6   Consider a vessel of height h containing one molecule moving vertically up and down and making perfectly elastic collisions with the walls. The molecule, of mass m, has a speed v as it moves upward immediately after striking the lower wall, and it is constantly accelerated downward at the rate g. Show that the average force of the molecule on the lower wall exceeds the average force on the upper wall by an amount mg; that is, the average force of the molecule on the container is simply the molecule's weight.

21-7   The weight of a vessel containing gas exceeds the weight of the same vessel evacuated, and a weighing balance indicates a weight for a filled vessel equal to the sum of the weight of the evacuated vessel and weight of the gas alone. Explain why this is so, even though any one molecule of the gas is, according to the kinetic theory, moving freely in space except during collisions of negligible duration. (See Problem 21-6.)

21-8   Derive the following laws from the kinetic theory of gases. (a) Avogadro's law: under the same conditions of temperature and pressure, equal volumes of gas contain equal numbers of molecules. (b) Dalton's law of partial pressures: when two or more gases which do not interact chemically are present together in the same container, the total pressure is the sum of partial pressures contributed independently by each of the several gases.

21-9   The thermal-diffusion method of separating uranium-235 (atomic weight 235) from uranium-238 depends upon the fact that the root-mean-square speeds of the two types of molecules, when the isotopes are in the gas UF_6 (uranium hexafluoride), differ from each other. Compute the ratio of the two rms speeds. The atomic weight of fluorine is 19.

21-10   What is the average translational kinetic energy per molecule (in electron volts) of ammonia (NH_3) gas at 200° C?

21-11   Compute the rms speed of oxygen molecules at 100° C.

21-12   What is the rms speed of electrons in thermal equilibrium at room temperature (300° K)? The mass of an electron is 9.1×10^{-31} kg.

21-13   What is the ratio of the rms speed of oxygen molecules to the rms speed of nitrogen molecules in air at 20° C?

21-14   Compute the average translational kinetic energy per particle, in electron volts, in the interior of the Sun, where the temperature is approximately twenty million degrees Kelvin.

21-15   A thermal neutron is one whose average kinetic energy is equal to that of a molecule of gas at 300° K. What is the rms speed of a thermal neutron (mass, 1.67×10^{-27} kg)?

21-16   A nuclear fusion reaction will occur in a gas of deuterium atoms when the atoms have an average kinetic energy of at least 7.2×10^5 ev. What is the approximate temperature required for nuclear fusion to take place with deuterium?

21-17   The fragments from uranium atoms which have undergone nuclear fission have an average kinetic energy of 70 Mev. What would be the approximate temperature of a gas consisting of such fission fragments?

21-18   The molecules of a certain gas at STP have an rms speed of 1.31 km/sec. What is the gas?

21-19 (a) At what temperature is the rms speed of hydrogen molecules equal to the escape velocity from the Earth's surface? (b) What is the corresponding temperature for escape of hydrogen from the Moon, where the acceleration due to gravity is 1.6 m/sec^2? (c) Why then, is there essentially no hydrogen in the Earth's atmosphere? (d) Why is there essentially no atmosphere on the Moon?

21-20 Show that the rms speed of a gas of molecular weight w at the absolute temperature T is given by $v_{rms} = \sqrt{3RT/w}$.

21-21 The speed of sound through a gas is directly proportional to the rms speed of the gas molecules. What is the ratio of the speed of sound through helium gas to the speed of sound through oxygen gas at the same temperature?

21-22 ★ A container holds 1 mole of helium gas in thermal equilibrium at STP. (a) What is the total translational kinetic energy of the gas molecules? (b) What is the total linear momentum of the gas molecules? (c) Assume now that we observe the gas molecules from a reference frame which travels at a speed of 1.0 km/sec relative to the container; what is the total translational kinetic energy of the gas molecules? (d) What is the total linear momentum of the gas molecules from this reference frame? (e) What fraction of the total translational kinetic energy is disordered kinetic energy as viewed from this reference frame? (f) Suppose now that the container is brought to rest, and that all of the ordered molecular energy becomes disordered; what is the final temperature?

21-23 A *plasma*, called the fourth state of matter, consists of a mixture of neutral atoms, positive ions, and free electrons. The total charge of the plasma is zero. This state can be produced by separating some of the bound electrons from neutral atoms and molecules of a gas. The energy required to ionize a typical atom is of the order of a few electron volts. To what approximate temperature must a gas be heated to produce a plasma?

21-24 (a) What is the total translational kinetic energy for 1 mole of gas in thermal equilibrium at $0°$ C? (b) What is the total linear momentum of the gas molecules? (c) Suppose that the gas is helium and that all helium molecules move with the rms speed corresponding to $0°$ C and in the same direction; what is now the total translational kinetic energy? (d) What is the total linear momentum of the helium molecules under these circumstances?

21-25 What is the total translational kinetic energy of 2 moles of any ideal gas at $300°$ C?

21-26 One mole of helium at standard atmospheric pressure originally fills a volume of 22.4 liters. The gas is compressed isothermally to 11.2 liters. (a) How much work is done in compressing the gas? (b) By how much does the gas's internal energy change? (c) What was the amount of heat extracted from the gas?

21-27 Show that the work done by an ideal gas expanding adiabatically from temperature T_1 to T_2 is $nR(T_1 - T_2)/(\gamma - 1)$.

21-28 Show that, for an adiabatic process, $pT^{[\gamma/(\gamma-1)]}$ is a constant.

21-29 A spring having a force constant of 10 nt/m is stretched 2.0 cm, clamped in position, and then dropped into a vat of acid in which the spring dissolves. By how much is the internal energy of the spring-vat system increased? In this process, ordered potential energy has been converted into disordered potential and kinetic energy.

21-30 A certain gas is compressed when a force of 40 nt displaces a piston on the container a distance of 1.0 cm. No heat leaks into or out of the gas. (a) By how much is the internal energy of the gas changed? (b) Does the temperature of the gas rise or fall?

21-31 One mole of helium gas at STP is contained in a right circular cylinder of cross-sectional area 20 cm². The cylinder is oriented along the vertical and is closed at the top by a freely sliding piston. The gas is heated, the amount of heat being 4.0 joules, and the piston rises 3.0 cm. (a) What is the change in the internal energy of the gas? (b) What is the final temperature of the gas?

21-32 A gas is compressed, the work done in compressing it being 20 joules. (a) If no heat goes into or out of the gas, by what amount is the internal energy increased? (b) As it is compressed, how much thermal energy would have to be removed from the gas to keep its temperature unchanged?

21-33 One mole of argon gas, initially at STP, expands isobarically to twice its initial volume. (a) What is the final temperature of the gas? (b) What is the work done by the gas in expanding? (c) By how much does the internal energy of the gas change? (d) Does thermal energy leave or enter the gas and, if so, how much?

21-34 Repeat the calculations asked for in Problem 21-33, using molecular hydrogen initially at STP rather than argon.

21-35 The *molecular specific heat* of any substance is the amount of heat per *molecule* required to change the temperature by 1 C°. What are (a) the molecular specific heat at constant volume and (b) the molecular specific heat at constant pressure, for hydrogen at room temperature?

21-36 The specific heat at constant pressure for a certain gas is $12.4R$. How much heat is required to change the temperature 10 C° for 2 moles of gas at constant volume?

21-37 Two moles of argon gas at 400° C is mixed with 1 mole of hydrogen gas at 300° C (in a fashion similar to Example 6). What is the final temperature of the mixture?

21-38 Compute the specific heat at constant volume for N_2 at 300° C in units of calories per gram-degree Celsius.

21-39 A container holds a mixture of two gases: n_1 moles of a gas with a constant-volume specific heat C_1, and n_2 moles of a gas with a constant-volume specific heat C_2. Show that the constant-volume specific heat of the mixture is $(n_1 C_1 + n_2 C_2)/(n_1 + n_2)$.

21-40 Two moles of argon gas $(C_v = \frac{3}{2}R)$ are mixed with two moles of hydrogen gas $(C_v = \frac{5}{2}R)$, both gases being originally at 300° K. What is the effective γ for this mixture?

21-41 A gas of molecular hydrogen, H_2, is compressed *adiabatically* when a constant force of 40 nt displaces the piston of the cylinder by 10 cm. By how much would the temperature of the gas increase in this compression for an initial temperature of (a) 20° K, (b) 400° K, and (c) 4000° K? (See Table 21-1.)

21-42 If, in Problem 21-41, the pressure of the gas were to be the same for all three starting temperatures, what would be the ratio of the densities of the gases (a) at 400° and 20° K and (b) at 4000° and 20° K?

21-43 ★ (a) What is the total internal energy of 2 moles of argon at 600° K? (b) What is the total internal energy of molecular hydrogen at 600° K? (c) Both gases next expand adiabatically until they each have a final temperature of 300° K; what fraction of the argon's original internal energy is converted into work? (d) What is the corresponding fraction for hydrogen? (e) If both gases were originally at the same pressure and volume, which gas will have the larger volume after the adiabatic expansion?

TWENTY-TWO

FURTHER ASPECTS OF THE KINETIC THEORY

We first consider the measurement of molecular speeds and the distribution of these speeds for a gas in thermal equilibrium. The distribution of molecular energies is then discussed. We turn next to the fundamental, second law of thermodynamics, as illustrated by the behavior of molecules of an ideal gas. The direct evidence of molecular chaos, given by the phenomenon of Brownian motion, is then treated. We derive relations giving the collision frequency and the mean free path of molecules in a gas. Finally, we discuss deviations from the ideal-gas law.

22-1 Distribution of molecular speeds of gases The kinetic theory of gases predicts average molecular speeds that are measured in kilometers per second, for gases at room temperature. It also identifies the temperature of a gas with the root-mean-square speed of the molecules, through the relation

[21-13] $$\tfrac{3}{2}kT = \tfrac{1}{2}mv_{\text{rms}}^2$$

In this section we wish to take a more detailed look at the distribution of molecular speeds for a gas in thermal equilibrium. We shall find that the experimentally observed speed distribution is in excellent agreement with theoretical prediction.

A simple experimental arrangement for measuring molecular speeds and their distribution is shown in Figure 22-1. The device not only measures the high speeds of molecules by timing their flight over a known distance, but it also counts the number of molecules having a given speed.

The gas to be studied is contained in an oven at temperature T. Molecules of the gas escape from the oven through a small slit and shoot out into an evacuated region, forming themselves into a narrow beam. The beam strikes a rotating disc having a narrow slit. The slit passes across the beam once

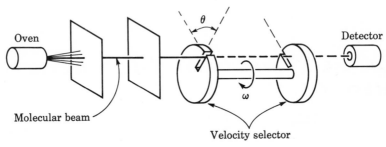

Figure 22-1. Experimental arrangement for measuring molecular speeds.

during each revolution, and at this time a small burst of molecules is allowed to pass through it. These molecules continue in their motion to a second disc, also having a narrow slit and rotating at the same angular velocity as the first. Molecules of all speeds emerge through the first slit; therefore, the molecules arrive at the second slit at various times.

The slit in the second disc does not lie directly behind the slit in the front disc, but maintains a constant angular displacement θ with respect to it, as shown in Figure 22-1. Upon arriving at the second disc, most molecules strike the opaque disc and are stopped. Only those molecules with the proper speed will arrive at just that time at which the slit is in a position to allow them to pass through and be counted in the detector. The speed of the molecules entering the counting detector can be computed if the separation distance between the discs, their common angular velocity, and the angular displacement of the second slit relative to the first, are known.

By varying the common rotational speed of the discs and counting the number of molecules reaching the detector for each speed, one can obtain the distribution of the speeds of the molecules when in thermal equilibrium with the oven at the temperature T. The molecules are observed to have a molecular speed distribution like that shown in Figure 22-2 for nitrogen (N_2) molecules at $T = 0°$ C. Some molecules have very high speeds, others lower speeds, and a few are actually at rest.

It is important to understand clearly the meaning of the velocity-distribution curve of Figure 22-2. If one chooses a small range of speeds dv, extending from the speed v to the speed $v + dv$, then the area of the thin rectangle $N_v \, dv$, compared with the total area N under the curve, gives the fraction of molecules moving at speeds lying between v and $v + dv$. All ideal gases are found to have speed distribution curves similar to that of Figure 22-2. If,

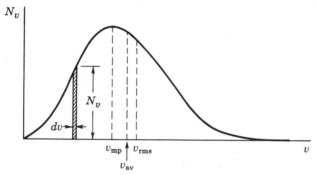

Figure 22-2. Molecular velocity distribution. The most probable speed is v_{mp}, the root-mean-square speed is v_{rms}, and the average speed is v_{av}.

for a given gas, the temperature is increased, the distribution curve shifts to the right and the molecules then have higher speeds than at a lower temperature.

One of the triumphs of the molecular model of the kinetic theory is its ability to describe accurately the observed velocity distribution function N_v. The relation giving the number $N_v \, dv$ of molecules with speeds between v and $v + dv$ for a gas at temperature T was first derived by J. C. Maxwell. This distribution, known as the *Maxwellian distribution* of molecular speeds, is given by

$$N_v \, dv = Av^2 \, e^{-mv^2/2kT} \, dv \qquad\qquad [22\text{-}1]$$

where m is the mass of each molecule, T is the absolute temperature, k is the Boltzmann constant, v is the molecular speed, and A is a constant independent of v but dependent on m, k, and T.†

† The constant A appearing in the right side of Equation 22-1 is so chosen that $\int_0^\infty N_v \, dv = N$, where N is the total number of molecules. Upon integrating, one obtains $A = (4N/\sqrt{\pi})(m/2kT)^{3/2}$.

The Maxwellian distribution is derived by using the basic assumptions of the kinetic theory, including the assumption of complete molecular chaos.† Specifically, all molecules of the gas are assumed to have equal probabilities of occupying any location within the container as well as equal probabilities of having any given linear momentum, with the restriction that the total linear momentum of all the molecules is zero and that the total energy of the gas remains constant. Equation 22-1 is based on the procedures of statistical mechanics; its derivation lies beyond the scope of this book.

Notice that the velocity distribution curve is not symmetrical with respect to the speed corresponding to the peak of the curve. This speed, which represents the *most probable* molecular speed v_{mp}, is to be distinguished from the root-mean-square speed v_{rms}. The rms speed always exceeds the most probable speed; this is so because the high speeds carry great weight when one computes an average depending on the *square* of the speeds. In general, $v_{rms} = 1.22 \, v_{mp}$. The *average* speed v_{av} is intermediate between the most probable speed and the root-mean-square speed; in general, $v_{av} = 1.12 \, v_{mp}$ (see Problems 22-3, 22-4, and 22-5 for the relations between v_{rms}, v_{mp}, and v_{av}).

22-2 Distribution of molecular energies   Since the molecules of a gas in thermal equilibrium are distributed over a range of molecular speeds, they must also be distributed over a range of translational kinetic energies. It is useful to examine the molecular-energy distribution function N_E giving the number of molecules as a function of the molecular translational kinetic energy $E = \frac{1}{2}mv^2$. The quantity $N_E \, dE$ gives the number of molecules having kinetic energies between E and $E + dE$. Inasmuch as $N_E \, dE = N_v \, dv$, the relation for N_E can easily be derived from Equation 22-1. The result is

$$N_E \, dE = C\sqrt{E} \, e^{-E/kT} \, dE \qquad [22\text{-}2]$$

where $C = 2N/(\pi^3 kT)^{3/2}$. A plot of N_E versus E is shown in Figure 22-3.

The average translational kinetic energy per molecule $\bar{E}$ may be computed from Equation 22-2. The result is $\bar{E} = (1/N) \int_0^\infty E N_E \, dE = \frac{3}{2}kT$, in agreement with our earlier result. Note that $\bar{E}$ exceeds the most probable energy, the peak of the N_E versus E curve, which falls at $\frac{1}{2}kT$.

As Equation 22-2 shows, the molecular *energy* distribution does *not* depend on the molecular mass; that is, N_E is not a function of m. This means that, unlike the distribution in molecular speeds, the distribution *in energy* for the

† See, for example, C. Kittel, *Elementary Statistical Physics*, John Wiley & Sons, Inc, 1958, p. 59.

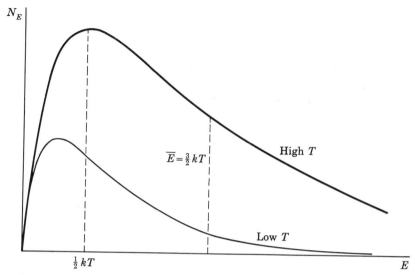

Figure 22-3. Molecular energy distribution for two temperatures. The average energy $\bar{E}$ is $\frac{3}{2}kT$; the most probable energy is $\frac{1}{2}kT$.

molecules of *any* ideal gas in thermal equilibrium at the same temperature T is the *same*. Thus, *all gases* at 300° K have an average translational kinetic energy $\bar{E} = \frac{3}{2}kT = \frac{1}{25}$ ev. In fact, all gases at 300° K have identical energy distribution curves.

The distribution function for molecular energies may be used as a basis of defining the temperature of a gas. We may say that the absolute temperature T is that number in Equation 22-2 which gives a molecular-energy distribution in agreement with the observed distribution in energies. From this point of view, *temperature is that quantity which determines the distribution of particles among the available energies.* One can, however, speak of a temperature only for a large number of molecules in thermal equilibrium and exhibiting the characteristic molecular chaos. It is meaningless to speak of the "temperature" of a single molecule or of a small number of molecules.

22-3 Disorder and the second law of thermodynamics
The first law of thermodynamics is nothing more than the energy conservation principle applied to a macroscopic system comprised of a very large number of molecules. Inasmuch as energy conservation holds for the individual collisions between pairs of molecules, one is not surprised to find that it holds at the macroscopic level. But the first law of thermodynamics alone is *not* sufficient to account for the thermal behavior of gases. For example, when we mix a

hot gas with a cold gas, we know that the final equilibrium temperature lies *between* the two initial temperatures. We do *not* find the hot gas at a higher final temperature and the cold gas at a lower final temperature, although this possibility is not ruled out by energy conservation. An additional fundamental law of physics, the *second law of thermodynamics*, operates here.

One very general formulation of the second law is this: *an isolated system, free of external influence, will, if it is initially in a state of relative order, always pass to states of relative disorder until it eventually reaches the state of maximum disorder.* We will discuss qualitatively the ideas embodied in this statement, as illustrated by the behavior of gas molecules. Further formulations and illustrations of the second law will be given in Chapters 23 and 24 for more complicated systems.

From the microscopic point of view of the kinetic theory, *all* that ever happens in a gas is: molecules collide. In each collision the molecules interchange energy and momentum in such a way that each of these quantities is conserved. *All* general conclusions concerning the behavior of the gas, as reflected in its macroscopic properties, can be drawn from an analysis of the molecular collisions.

Consider the collision shown in Figure 22-4a. Here a molecule with a high speed strikes, and transfers energy and momentum to, a molecule with a low (zero) speed. In this particular collision the energies and speeds of the two molecules have become more nearly equalized. The collision shown in Figure 22-4a is, of course, just one of many possible collisions. Another collision that conserves energy and momentum is shown in Figure 22-4b. Here two molecules, both initially in motion, collide in such a way that one molecule is brought to rest while the other molecule leaves the collision with all of the energy originally shared by the two. To assure ourselves that this is, in fact, a possible collision, one consistent with both momentum and energy conservation, we need merely note that it is simply that of Figure 22-4a run backward in time: if we saw the first collision in a motion picture, the second would be seen by running the film backward, all molecular velocities now being reversed. *On the microscopic scale, all processes*—which is to say, all collisions—*are reversible.*

We have seen that molecular speeds can become more nearly equalized or they can become more *un*equalized, through a collision. That is, in molecular collisions, energy may be transferred from fast to slow particles, or from slow to fast ones. In an ordinary gas there are frequent collisions, and any one molecule will change velocity frequently, moving in a zigzag path. We wish to consider here how the individual molecular kinetic energies of a large number of molecules will change when the particles interact through intermolecular collisions. The detailed analysis of such processes lies in the area of *statistical mechanics*, which combines the laws of Newtonian mechanics with

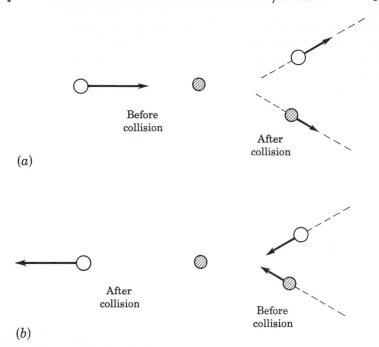

Figure 22-4. Two molecular collisions. In collision (a) the molecular energies become more nearly equal; in collision (b) the molecular energies become more nearly unequal. Collision (b) is merely collision (a) run backward in time.

the rules of statistics to predict the most probable behavior of collections of particles.

Consider a gas of N monatomic molecules confined to a volume V and having a constant total internal energy, thus a constant translational kinetic energy. What shape can we expect for the energy distribution curve? That is, what curve will give the number of molecules N_E as a function of the kinetic energy E per particle? There are, of course, many possibilities consistent with the conservation laws of energy and of momentum; three distributions are shown in Figure 22-5. In Figure 22-5a all molecules have essentially the same kinetic energy; for this distribution all molecules move at the same speed, and the state of the system is a highly ordered one. Figure 22-5b shows another possible energy distribution; in this case there are two peaks in the curve. Finally, Figure 22-5c shows the energy distribution given by the Maxwellian relation, Equation 22-2; this is the experimentally observed distribution for any gas in thermal equilibrium.

Now suppose that we start with the gas molecules in the highly ordered state indicated by Figure 22-4a. If we wait long enough for many collisions to have occurred (typically, 10^{-5} sec), the distribution becomes that of Figure 22-5c. In fact, *any* initial distribution of molecular energies becomes the Maxwellian distribution when the molecules have been allowed to transfer energy in collisions and achieve molecular chaos. The total energy is so distributed that the system achieves the maximum possible state of disorder, namely, the state of thermal equilibrium at temperature T. Indeed, one can define a temperature for a collection of gas molecules *only* when the molecules have achieved thermal equilibrium; then, the average kinetic energy per molecule is, of course, $\frac{3}{2}kT$. One cannot speak of a temperature for nonequilibrium distributions like those in Figures 22-5a and b, even though all three distributions have the same average kinetic energy per molecule.

A collection of molecules achieves thermal equilibrium, whatever the initial distribution of molecular energies, because the equilibrium state represents the *most probable* state. The basic assumption of statistical mechanics in arriving at this result is the following: *all microscopic states are equally probable*, such states being occupied according to pure chance. There is, of course, the additional requirement that the total energy of all molecules be constant and that the total momentum of all molecules be zero.

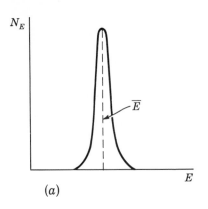

(a)

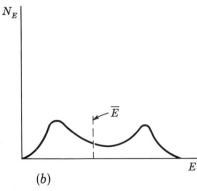

(b)

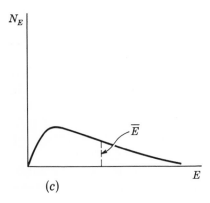

(c)

Figure 22-5. Three possible molecular-energy distributions, all with the same average molecular energy $\bar{E}$. (a) All molecules have nearly the same energy. (b) Two peaks in the energy distribution curve. (c) The Maxwellian energy distribution for a gas in thermal equilibrium.

By a microscopic state is meant a state corresponding to a specific position and momentum for each and every molecule of a gas. There are available so many more microscopic states representing disorder or near disorder than representing order, that the most probable macroscopic state is that of maximum disorder; indeed, it is a near certainty. Similarly, one is not likely to find the cards of a thoroughly shuffled pack in such an ordered state that the first four cards are aces, simply because the number of disordered arrangements greatly exceeds the number of arrangements for which the first four cards are aces. It is *possible* that molecules of a gas initially in equilibrium would, at some later time, all be found moving with exactly the same speed, as in Figure 22-5a, but such a possibility is so overwhelmingly unlikely as to be virtually impossible. When the number of molecules is very large, the macroscopic state is (if the system is not interfered with) almost certain to be the equilibrium state.

This illustrates the second law of thermodynamics, which states that an isolated system will pass from a state of relative order to one of relative disorder because the disordered state is, in fact, the most probable state.

Consider the following example. One mole of oxygen gas is held in the left half of an insulated container, the gas being initially in thermal equilibrium at the temperature T_l. See Figure 22-6a. An equal number of helium molecules is in the right half of the container, separated from the left by a removable partition. The helium gas is initially in thermal equilibrium at the temperature T_h, where $T_h > T_l$. The distributions of the two kinds of molecules, in *space* and in *energy*, are shown in Figure 22-6b and c, respectively. Suppose that we remove the partition and wait until a final equilibrium state is reached. What will the distributions of the molecules in space and energy now be?

Before the partition is removed, there is a certain degree of order in space for the two types of molecules: all oxygen molecules are initially in the left half, all helium molecules are in the right half. There is, moreover, disorder in energy among the oxygen molecules at T_l; similarly, there is disorder in energy among the helium molecules at the temperature T_h. After the partition is removed, the oxygen molecules are free to move into the right half and the helium molecules into the left. Intermolecular collisions occur, the gases become thoroughly mixed, and in a short time we find that both the oxygen and the helium molecules are uniformly distributed throughout the container. Thus, the final distribution of both kinds of molecules is one of maximum disorder, both in space and in energy.

By the second law, the energy distribution will, after the partition is removed, correspond to maximum disorder in energy. Inasmuch as the helium molecules are initially at a higher temperature than the oxygen molecules, the probability that energy will be transferred in a collision from

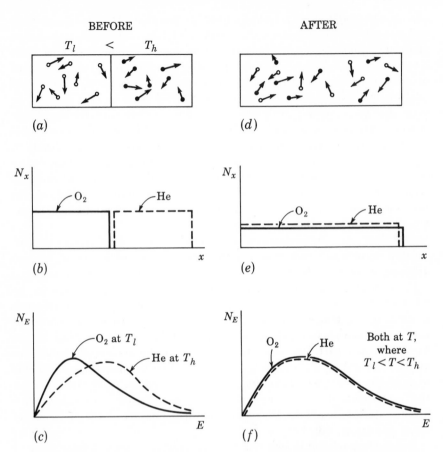

Figure 22-6. Oxygen molecules at a low temperature T_l and helium molecules at a high temperature T_h in a container with a partition. The molecules in the container (a) before, and (d) after, the partition is removed. The spatial distribution of the molecules (b) before, and (e) after, mixing. The molecular energy distribution (c) before, and (f) after, mixing.

a helium molecule to an oxygen molecule is greater than the probability of energy transfer in the reverse sense. Thus, thermal energy will go from the hot helium gas to the cooler oxygen gas until the two reach a common temperature intermediate between T_l and T_h. (See Figure 22-6d.) They will then have common space and energy distributions, as shown in Figures 22-6e and 22-6f.

Is it possible that, at some later time, we will again find the oxygen molecules all on the left side at T_l and the helium molecules all on the right side at temperature T_h? Yes. Is it probable? No. It is extraordinarily improbable because there are very many more microscopic states corresponding to the molecules distributed uniformly in space and having a Maxwellian energy distribution than there are states corresponding to the relatively high degree of order in which the two gases are separated in the container and having different temperatures.

We saw earlier that individual collisions between particles are reversible in time: we cannot tell whether a moving-picture film portraying an intermolecular collision is being run forward or backward. This is *not* the case when one deals with large numbers of particles. On the macroscopic scale, processes are essentially irreversible, since a system moves inexorably from states of relative order to disorder. From our experience, we *can* tell at once when a moving picture of some ordinary large-scale phenomenon, such as an exploding bomb, is run backward. Thus, the second law of thermodynamics implies a directionality of time. At the macroscopic level, time's arrow points to the future. Order turns to disorder; ordered energy is degraded into disordered or thermal energy. So too, the direction of thermal-energy flow—the "direction" of heat, as it were—is from the higher- to the lower-temperature body, it being thereby insured that two isolated bodies, initially at different temperatures, achieve a common final temperature.

In Chapter 24 we shall discuss the second law of thermodynamics in terms of the behavior of heat engines. We shall give alternative statements of the law and arrive at a quantitative measure (called the entropy) of the disorder of a system.

22-4 Brownian motion The discrete random impacts of molecules, which are fundamental in the kinetic theory, can be observed directly in experiment.

Suppose that a very light-weight mirror is suspended from a thin fiber within a container. A beam of light shines on the mirror, is reflected from it, and then enters a distant camera; see Figure 22-7. The film within the camera advances slowly and continuously. Any slight change in the angular position of the mirror causes a deflection of the reflected light beam. This deflection appears on the developed film as a deviation of the trace from the center of the film.

Assume that the pressure of the gas surrounding the mirror suspension is moderate. Then the gas molecules make frequent collisions with both sides of the mirror, the average force over each side is continuous, no resultant torque acts on the mirror, the mirror remains stationary, and a straight line appears on the film. Now suppose that the pressure is decreased until the container is nearly evacuated (say, to 10^{-4} cm Hg), so that the number of collisions per unit time of molecules with the mirror is small. The molecules now arrive at the mirror one by one, each impact imparts an impulsive torque to the mirror, and the recorded trace on the film shows random and measurable deviations from a straight line. The angular deflections of the mirror vary in magnitude because the molecules have a variety of speeds and strike the mirror faces at a variety of angles. The small fluctuations in the angular position of the mirror, which have their origin in the random and discrete impacts of molecules, are one example of *Brownian motion*.

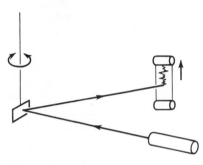

Figure 22-7. Experimental arrangement for observing Brownian motion. Molecules bombard a light-weight mirror suspended by a sensitive fiber. A light beam shines on the mirror, is reflected, and enters a camera. Fluctuations in the mirror's angular position, arising from molecular bombardment, are recorded on the photographic film.

The Brownian motion was discovered by Robert Brown in 1827. Using a microscope he observed small pollen grains floating on water. Brown found that the grains did not remain at rest, but rather underwent abrupt random motion. The erratic motion of an observably large particle is due to the bombardment of water molecules; it merely reflects the chaotic motion of the water molecules, some of which strike a grain with so large a speed as to displace it appreciably.

Brownian motion is also evident when one observes relatively light particles, such as particles of smoke in air, through a moderately high-powered microscope. The smoke particles are occasionally struck by molecules moving with such a high speed that they are displaced by observably large amounts in random directions. One can say that the smoke particles are in thermal equilibrium with the molecules of the gas. Then, just as one can relate the average translational kinetic energy of the molecules of a gas to the absolute temperature, through the relation $\frac{1}{2}mv^2 = \frac{3}{2}kT$, so too one can use the same relation to find the average translational kinetic energy of the smoke particles. Thus, by measuring the average speed of a smoke particle one can compute its mass.

Observations of Brownian motion may be used to determine Avogadro's number. The number of observed displacements depends on the number of molecular impacts, which depends, in turn, on the number of molecules and, hence, on N_0.

In electric circuits Brownian motion has its counterpart in the phenomenon of *Johnson noise*. A random fluctuating voltage appears at the terminals of any electrical resistor at a finite temperature. This random voltage, which is audible as "noise" if amplified, has its origin in the random motions of the electrically charged particles within the resistor. The visual analogue of noise is the "snow" seen on the screen of a television receiver. All signals in electric circuits must exceed in magnitude the ever-present noise if they are to be perceived. By lowering the temperature of the material, Johnson noise and Brownian motion can be reduced, but never eliminated entirely. Thermometers can be constructed which use the magnitude of Johnson noise as a measure of the temperature. One can, for example, measure the temperature of a distant star either by measuring the radio noise from it with a radio telescope or by measuring the emitted visible "noise," or light, with an ordinary telescope.

The random fluctuations occurring at an atomic or molecular level are very small because Avogadro's number is very large, but these fluctuations exist and can be observed because Avogadro's number is not infinite.

22-5 Collision frequency and mean free path   If the molecules of a gas had no finite extension and were truly mass points, they would never collide. Intermolecular collisions occur because molecules have very small, but nonzero, diameters. We use the term "diameter" here as given in Section 21-1, namely, as a measure of that distance between molecular centers at which the intermolecular force becomes strongly repulsive. For simplicity we will regard molecules as hard spheres of diameter d.

The average number of intermolecular collisions made by a molecule per unit time is called the *collision frequency*. A closely related quantity is the *mean free path*, which is defined as the distance traveled by a molecule, on the average, between successive collisions. We wish to derive relations giving the collision frequency f and the mean free path l in terms of the molecular diameter d, the average molecular speed v, and the number of molecules per unit volume n (where $n = N/V = nN_0/V$). We facilitate the derivation by assuming that all molecules within the gas are at rest, except for one molecule which travels at a constant speed v.

Two molecules will collide only if their centers are separated by a distance no greater than d at their closest approach. See Figure 22-8a. We can describe this differently by imagining the moving molecule to have a *radius d*, while all other molecules are regarded as mass points; see Figure 22-8b. The moving molecule sweeps out a right circular cylinder of cross-sectional area πd^2 between collisions, and any stationary molecule whose center lies within this cylinder is struck by the moving molecule. The moving molecule will, of course, change direction upon any collision that is not head on, so that it actually sweeps out a number of cylindrical segments at various angles with one another, as shown in Figure 22-8c.

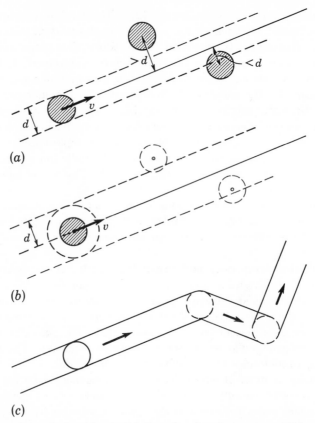

Figure 22-8. (a) A molecule of diameter d undergoes a collision if its center is less than a distance d from the center of a second molecule. (b) Equivalently, a molecule having a *radius* d collides with other molecules represented by mass points. (c) A molecule undergoing collisions sweeps out cylindrical segments.

In the time t the moving molecule has traveled a total distance vt, swept out a volume $(\pi d^2)(vt)$, and collided with all molecules within this volume. Therefore, the total number of collisions occurring in the time t is simply the number of molecules per unit volume, n, multiplied by the volume $\pi d^2 vt$ swept out by the moving molecule:

$$\text{Number of collisions in time } t = n(\pi d^2 vt)$$

By definition, the average collision frequency f is the number of collisions per unit time, or

$$f = \pi d^2 vn$$

The mean free path l is simply the total distance vt, traveled by the moving molecule in the time t, divided by the total number of collisions occurring during this time interval:

$$l = \frac{vt}{\pi nd^2 vt} = \frac{1}{\pi nd^2}$$

The relations for f and l above are not quite correct, inasmuch as we have assumed only one molecule to be in motion and the remaining molecules to be at rest. When we take into account the motion of all molecules, the probability of collision increases and, consequently, the distance traveled between collisions decreases. More detailed analysis shows that f is larger and l is smaller, both by the factor $\sqrt{2}$, than that given in the relations above. The correct expressions are then:

$$f = \sqrt{2}\pi nd^2 v \qquad\qquad [22\text{-}3]$$

$$l = \frac{1}{\sqrt{2}\pi nd^2} \qquad\qquad [22\text{-}4]$$

Table 22-1 gives the collision frequencies and mean free paths of nitrogen molecules at $0°$ C and at three different pressures. The molecular diameter of the N_2 molecule is taken to be 3.5×10^{-10} m $= 3.5$ Å. We see that at

Table 22-1

PRESSURE	f	l
1 atm $= 76$ cm Hg	7.3×10^9/sec	680 Å $\simeq 200$ molecular diameters
10^{-6} atm $= 10^{-4}$ cm Hg	9.5×10^3/sec	5.2 mm
10^{-10} atm $= 10^{-8}$ cm Hg	0.95/sec	0.52 km

STP a typical nitrogen molecule makes nearly 10^{10} collisions per second and travels, on the average, a distance of 200 molecular diameters between successive collisions. For a moderately high vacuum (about one-millionth atmospheric pressure) and a temperature of $0°$ C, there are only about 10^4 collisions per second, and a molecule travels several millimeters between collisions. At a very high vacuum (about 10^{-10} standard atmospheres) a typical molecule makes only about one collision per second, and now travels nearly a kilometer between collisions. Such a large mean free path is possible, of course, only if the container of the gas has dimensions that are large compared with l; otherwise, molecular collisions mainly occur between molecules and the container walls rather than between the molecules themselves.

A fundamental assumption of the kinetic theory is that the time elapsing between successive molecular collisions is very long compared with the duration of any one collision. Let us see whether, in fact, this is the case. The intermolecular force varies with distance (Figure 17-1); it can, however, be replaced approximately by a constant force of about 10^{-13} nt acting over a distance of about 10^{-10} m. A straightforward application of Newton's second law then shows that a colliding molecule, such as N_2, undergoes an acceleration over a time of about 10^{-12} sec. Therefore, the duration of an intermolecular collision is only 10^{-12} sec, whereas the time between collisions $(1/f)$ is 10^{-10} sec. Thus, a typical molecule at STP interacts with other molecules about 1 per cent of the time.

22-6   Deviations from the ideal-gas law and changes in state   Here we consider deviations from the ideal-gas law; these deviations lead to an understanding of the change in state from a gas to a liquid.

We can define an ideal gas *macroscopically* in any one of several equivalent ways: (a) its density is very low; (b) it follows exactly the equation of state $pV = nRT$, isotherms on a p-V diagram being strictly hyperbolic; and (c) the gas's internal energy U depends only on the temperature T.

We can define an ideal gas *microscopically* through either of the equivalent assumptions of the kinetic theory: (a) the volume of any one molecule is negligibly small compared with the volume occupied by all molecules or, in other words, the size of any one molecule is very small compared with the average distance between neighboring molecules; (b) the molecular translational energy is entirely kinetic and no potential energy during molecular interactions need be considered or, another way of putting it, the time elapsing between successive collisions is very large compared with that elapsing during any collision.

When any one of these assertions fails to hold, all fail. Then the gas is not ideal and it may, if the deviations from ideal-gas behavior are large enough, condense into a liquid.

Let us examine the series of isothermal processes on a p-V diagram, shown in Figure 22-9. We imagine a gas to be contained in a cylinder with a movable piston. In each process the gas is maintained at a constant temperature while it is compressed.

Process A occurs at a relatively high temperature. Here the gas is an ideal gas and the isotherm is a hyperbola, pV being constant. Work is done on the gas in compressing it. It follows from the first law of thermodynamics that the internal energy and temperature can remain constant only if thermal

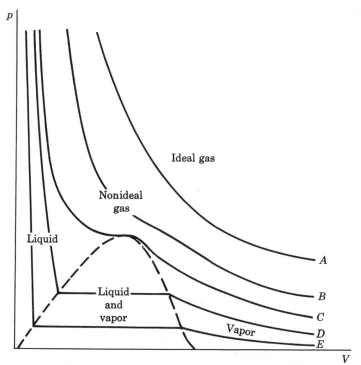

Figure 22-9. Isotherms for a nonideal gas.

energy is extracted from the gas; that is, the container must always be at a very slightly lower temperature than the gas within it, to permit the transfer of energy out of the gas through heat.

Process B takes place at a lower temperature. The isotherm is *not* a hyperbola, and the general-gas law, $pV = nRT$, is *not* the equation of state. Here the molecules are moving at low enough speeds for the intermolecular forces to succeed in slowing the molecules for appreciable time intervals during collisions. The observed behavior of a nonideal gas can be very closely approximated by an equation of state first suggested by J. D. van der Waals and known as the *van der Waals equation*:

$$\left(p + \frac{a}{v^2}\right)(v - b) = RT \qquad [22\text{-}5]$$

The volume per mole, V/n, is represented by v, and a and b are constants chosen to give the best fit to the experimental data.

The constants a and b have a simple interpretation in terms of the departure from ideal-gas behavior. The constant b is proportional to the finite volume occupied by the molecules, so that $v - b$ gives the "free" volume within the container available to the gas molecules. The term a/v^2 takes into account the fact that the average force of the molecules on the container walls, as manifested in the pressure p, is influenced by the nonzero force of other molecules, particularly when the molecules are *not* far separated and when they move at relatively low speeds. Note that Equation 22-5 reduces, as it must, to the general-gas law when a/v^2 and b are very small compared with p and v, respectively.

We shall ignore the process C for the moment, and consider process D. Here the temperature is considerably lower. The isothermal line cannot be given by any simple mathematical relationship. At first, the pressure rises as the gas is compressed. Then, at a point indicated on Figure 22-9 by the dotted line, the gas begins to condense into a liquid. At the right-hand boundary of the dotted line, most of the material within the container is gas. As the gas's volume is reduced, more and more gas is liquefied until, at the left-hand boundary of the dotted line, all of the gas has become liquid. During the condensation process the pressure, as well as the temperature, remains constant. In the region between the two dotted lines one has gas (or what is often called *vapor*) and liquid existing in equilibrium at the same temperature and pressure. This pressure is called the *saturation vapor pressure*.

As one moves horizontally to the left in curve D the liquefaction can proceed only if thermal energy is extracted from the system. That is, the molecules must be slowed if they are to become closely packed in the liquid state. To the left of the dotted-line boundary, where one now has only liquid in the container, the isotherm rises sharply, almost vertically. This abrupt change corresponds to the fact that the container is filled with liquid, which is compressed appreciably only by very large forces.

When the state of the system changes, as is the case when one moves horizontally along a curve such as D, so does the internal energy U of the system. The system does work as liquid becomes vapor and as the volume increases. This evaporation process is possible, however, only if thermal energy is added to the system. In fact, the amount of work dW, done by the gas in expanding, is less than the heat dQ entering the system; consequently, the internal energy must increase by an amount dU, where $dU = dQ - dW$. Therefore, U changes even though the temperature does not. (Recall that for an ideal gas, U remains constant as long as T remains constant.)

The term *latent heat* is used to denote the heat required to transform one unit mass of material from one state to another at a constant temperature. For water at atmospheric pressure, the latent heat of vaporization is found to be 2.26 joules/kg (540 cal/gm). Thus, when 2.26 joules is added to 1 kg of water, 1 kg of water vapor is produced; conversely, the vapor will condense into liquid only if 2.26 joules of thermal energy is extracted from it. More about latent heats in Section 23-5.

Process E also involves the condensation of a vapor into a liquid. The temperature is lower than in process D, and the saturation vapor pressure along the horizontal portion of the isotherm is also lower. In general, the saturation vapor pressure for a liquid and vapor in thermal equilibrium falls as the temperature falls.

Now we consider the very special process labeled C. Here the temperature T_c (to be defined) is such that the isotherm becomes horizontal only at a single point. This point corresponds to the upper boundary of the region enclosed by the dotted lines in Figure 22-9. If the temperature is lower than T_c the gas will condense into a liquid at a sufficiently great pressure; above T_c no pressure, however great, will succeed in condensing the gas into a liquid with a recognizable meniscus. T_c is called the *critical temperature*; the pressure at the horizontal point of curve C is called the *critical pressure*. Thus, to liquefy any gas, one must first cool it to a temperature equal to or below its critical temperature and then compress it until it liquefies. It is conventional to refer to any gas which lies beneath the isotherm C as *vapor*. Only a vapor can be liquefied.

For water, the critical temperature and critical pressure are 647° K and 218 atmospheres, respectively; for helium, they are 7.3° K and 2.3 atmospheres. The temperature of water for which the saturation vapor pressure is 1 atmosphere is 100° C; liquid helium, on the other hand, has a saturation vapor pressure of 1 atmosphere at 4.2° K.

22-7 Summary The molecules of a gas in thermal equilibrium are distributed over a large range of speeds (the Maxwellian distribution), the root-mean-square speed being given by $\frac{1}{2}mv_{\text{rms}}^2 = \frac{3}{2}kT$.

Similarly, the molecules are distributed over a range of energies, the average translational kinetic energy per molecule, $\frac{3}{2}kT$, being the same for all gases at the same temperature T. Furthermore, *all* gases at the same temperature have the *same* molecular energy distribution.

In terms of microscopic molecular behavior, the second law of thermodynamics can be stated as follows: any system free of external influence will always pass from states of relative order to states of relative disorder, until it reaches the state of maximum disorder, thermal equilibrium. The second law and the concept of temperature have meaning only when one deals with very large numbers of particles. Then the state of maximum disorder, consistent with energy and momentum conservation, corresponds to the most probable macroscopic state.

The random nature of molecular behavior is exhibited directly in Brownian motion.

The collision frequency f and the mean free path l are given in terms of the molecular diameter d and the number of molecules per unit volume n by

[22-3] $$f = \sqrt{2}\pi n d^2 v$$

[22-4] $$l = \frac{1}{\sqrt{2}\pi n d^2}$$

PROBLEMS

22-1   Molecular speeds are measured with a device similar to that shown in Figure 22-1. It is found that molecules will pass through a velocity selector, whose discs are separated by 50 cm with an angular displacement between the two slits of 180°, when the discs turn at the rate of 600 rotations/sec. (a) What are the possible speeds (!) of the molecules? (b) At what angular speed must this velocity selector be rotated to allow a beam of light (speed, 3×10^8 m/sec) to pass through both slits?

22-2   By performing the integration indicated in the footnote to Equation 22-1, evaluate the constant A appearing in the Maxwellian speed distribution.

22-3   Show that for the Maxwellian velocity distribution the most probable speed $v_{\mathrm{mp}} = \sqrt{2kT/m}$ is obtained by finding the speed corresponding to the peak in the curve of N_v versus v.

22-4   Show that for the Maxwellian velocity distribution the rms speed is given by $v_{\mathrm{rms}}^2 = \int_0^\infty N_v v^2\, dv / \int_0^\infty N_v\, dv = 3kT/m$.†

22-5   Show that for the Maxwellian velocity distribution the average speed is given by $v_{\mathrm{av}} = \int_0^\infty N_v v\, dv / \int_0^\infty N_v\, dv = \sqrt{8kT/\pi m}$.†

22-6   It is found that, for a certain hydrogen gas in thermal equilibrium, more molecules have the speed 2.1×10^3 m/sec than any other speed. What is the temperature of the gas? (The mass of H_2 is 3.34×10^{-27} kg.)

22-7 ⋆ Helium gas is in thermal equilibrium at 0° C. *Approximately* what fraction of the molecules has speeds lying in the range 2.0 to 2.1 km/sec? (The mass of He is 6.62×10^{-27} kg.)

22-8   Derive the Maxwellian energy distribution fucntion from the Maxwellian speed distribution function by using the fact that $N_E\, dE = N_v\, dv$.

22-9   Show, by finding the energy corresponding to the maximum in the N_E versus E curve, that the most probable translational kinetic energy of a molecule of any gas at the temperature T is $\frac{1}{2}kT$.

† Some useful definite integrals:

$$\int_0^\infty x^2 e^{-ax^2}\, dx = \sqrt{\pi}/4 a^{-3/2} \qquad \int_0^\infty x^4 e^{-ax^2}\, dx = (3\sqrt{\pi}/8)a^{-5/2}$$

$$\int_0^\infty x^3 e^{-ax^2}\, dx = \tfrac{1}{2}a^{-2} \qquad \int_0^\infty x^{3/2} e^{-ax}\, dx = (3\sqrt{\pi}/4)a^{-5/2}$$

22-10 Using the definition of the average kinetic energy, $E_{av} = (1/N) \times \int_0^\infty E N_E \, dE$, and Equation 22-2, show that $E_{av} = \frac{3}{2}kT$.†

22-11 A mixture of helium and oxygen has a temperature of $0°$ C; that is, both gases are in thermal equilibrium at $0°$ C. (a) What is the ratio of the average translational kinetic energy of a helium molecule to the average translational kinetic energy of an oxygen molecule? (b) What is the corresponding ratio for root-mean-square speeds? (c) What is the corresponding ratio for the magnitude of the linear momentum?

22-12 A container with a volume of 1000 cm³ holds 10^6 molecules. (a) What is the probability of finding one molecule located within a certain 1 cm³ region of the container? (b) What is the probability of finding all 10^6 molecules within this region?

22-13 A 1000 cm³ container holds 10^6 molecules. (a) What is the probability of finding a particular molecule to be moving to the right? (b) What is the probability of finding 10^3 molecules moving to the right? (c) What is the probability of finding that 10^3 molecules are located within a 1 cm³ region and moving to the right?

22-14 The Brownian motion of a certain smoke particle in a gas at $300°$ C is observed to have a root-mean-square speed of 2.1 mm/sec. What is the mass of the smoke particle?

22-15 A particle of mass m is immersed in a gas at temperature T. The particle's Brownian motion is observed and its root-mean-square speed is found to be v_{rms}. Derive an expression giving Avogadro's number in terms of m, v_{rms}, T, and R.

22-16 ⋆ A torsion pendulum of the sort shown in Figure 22-7 is an angular simple harmonic oscillator (Section 17-4). Just as a linear harmonic oscillator, such as a diatomic molecule, has an average kinetic energy equal to $\frac{1}{2}kT$, the torsion oscillator has an average kinetic energy $\frac{1}{2}I\overline{\omega^2}$ of $\frac{1}{2}kT$, where I is the moment of inertia of the mirror about its axis of rotation and $\overline{\omega^2} = \omega_{rms}^2$ is the average of the square of the angular velocity of rotation. If ω_{rms} is observed to be 3.2×10^{-2}/sec ($\sim$1 minute of arc per second) and I is known to be 4.1×10^{-17} kg-m², what is the temperature of the gas surrounding the torsion oscillator?

22-17 At STP the molecules of nitrogen make approximately 7×10^9 intermolecular collisions per second. Assume that, contrary to the assumptions of the kinetic theory, the intermolecular collisions are *not* perfectly elastic and that one billionth of the molecular kinetic translational energy is lost in each collision. Approximately how long would it take for the temperature of the gas to fall to $200°$ K?

22-18 Verify the entries for the collision frequency and the mean free path given in Table 22-1.

22-19 The molecular diameter of the molecule H_2 is 1.2×10^{-10} m. Suppose that hydrogen gas at $300°$ C is held in a container whose dimensions

† See footnote to Problem 22-4.

are about 10 cm. At what pressure will collisions between the molecules and the walls become nearly as probable as collisions between gas molecules?

22-20   Show that the molecular collision frequency for a given type of gas in a container of fixed volume varies as the square root of the absolute temperature and that the mean free path is independent of temperature.

22-21   The Explorer X satellite measured the density of matter in the interplanetary space within our solar system and obtained the value 30 hydrogen atoms per cubic centimeter. What is the mean free path of the hydrogen atoms?

22-22   Calculate the mean free path of hydrogen molecules in the space between galaxies, where there are approximately 10^{-6} hydrogen atoms per cubic centimeter. The molecular diameter of hydrogen is 1.1 Å, the molecular weight is 2.

22-23 ★ A narrow beam of electrons travels through a television tube, strikes the screen, and produces fluorescence at the spot of impact. The relative number of collisions of electrons with the molecules of gas contained within the tube must be small if the electron beam is to be maintained narrow and well defined; that is, the mean free path of the electrons with the molecules of gas must be large compared with the length of the tube. Assuming that a collision takes place if an electron comes within 2 Å of a gas molecule and that the temperature of the gas is 300° K, at what pressure (in centimeters of mercury) will the mean free path be equal to the length, say 18 inches, of the TV tube?

22-24   The critical temperature, critical pressure, and critical volume of water are 374° C, 218 atmospheres, and 3.14 cm³/gm, respectively. What would be the pressure corresponding to the temperature and volume given above, if water vapor behaved as an ideal gas?

22-25   Do Problem 22-24, using helium (molecular weight, 4) which has a T_c of 5° K, a p_c of 2.26 atmospheres, and a V_c of 14.4 cm³/gm.

TWENTY-THREE

THERMAL PROPERTIES OF SOLIDS AND LIQUIDS

In this chapter we extend the basic concepts of thermodynamics—temperature, thermal energy, heat, and the first and second laws of thermodynamics—from the simple systems of gas molecules to the more complicated systems of solids and liquids. We consider the fundamental experiments of Joule, which established the first law of thermodynamics, together with specific heats and latent heats. Finally, we treat the modes of thermal-energy transfer: conduction, convection, and radiation.

23-1 Solids and liquids as thermal systems Ideal gases are simple thermal systems. At low densities all gases follow the same equation of state, the general-gas law; the absolute temperature of any ideal gas is merely a measure of the average molecular translational kinetic energy, and one may relate the microscopic molecular behavior to the macroscopic properties of a gas directly through a mechanical model, the kinetic theory. What is the fundamental reason that gases show such relatively simple behavior? It is this: apart from perfectly elastic intermolecular collisions of negligible duration, a molecule in a gas is always in force-free motion, traveling along a straight line at constant speed. Intermolecular collisions serve merely to maintain molecular chaos and thermal equilibrium; otherwise, one need not (for ideal gases) be concerned with interactions between the molecules.

This simple situation does *not* obtain for solids and liquids. In these states, the molecules are *not* separated, on the average, by distances which are large compared with the range of the intermolecular force. Indeed, neighboring molecules interact continuously in the solid and liquid states. As a consequence, the total energy of the particles is *not* merely the sum of the kinetic energies of the particles. One must take into account, in addition, the intermolecular *potential* energies. Let us, then, inquire into the meaning of thermal energy, or what is commonly called heat, for the solid and liquid states.

We first recall that, for a monatomic gas in thermal equilibrium, the only contribution to the thermal energy is the disordered *translational* kinetic energy of the molecules. The total linear momentum of all the molecules is zero. In the case of diatomic or polyatomic molecules, there may be additional contributions. If a molecule rotates, the kinetic energy of rotation is a part of the gas's thermal energy. This *rotational* kinetic energy is disordered because the molecules rotate about axes oriented in all directions; that is, the total angular momentum of all the rotating molecules is zero. Moreover, when the molecules of a polyatomic gas also undergo vibrational motion, the energy associated with the molecular oscillations contributes to the gas's thermal energy. The *vibrational* energy—now a combination of both kinetic energy and potential energy—is disordered because the vibrational axes are randomly oriented; that is, the total linear momentum of all vibrating molecules is zero.

Now consider the contributions to the disordered, or thermal, energy for a solid. A solid may be thought of as a collection of atoms bound together, each atom oscillating about an equilibrium position at any finite temperature. In addition, some of the least tightly bound atomic electrons may wander throughout the solid. Except for extremely low temperatures, the translational kinetic energy of the electrons is usually small compared with the vibrational kinetic energy of the atoms. Therefore, for a solid, the thermal energy consists (almost entirely) of the kinetic and potential energy of atoms vibrating about equilibrium positions.

It is important to distinguish again between *ordered* and *disordered* energy. Suppose that all of the atoms of a solid had the same velocity. Then the solid as a whole would be in motion in the direction of the velocity vectors, and the kinetic energy of the body would be *ordered*. See Figure 23-1a.

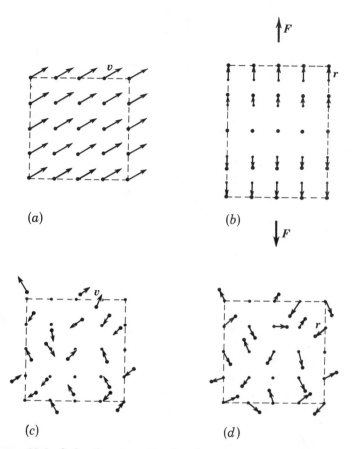

Figure 23-1. Ordered versus disordered energy for the particles of a solid. (a) The body as a whole is in motion and has *ordered kinetic energy*, inasmuch as all atoms have the *same* velocity. (b) The body as a whole is stretched and has *ordered potential energy*, inasmuch as the atoms are displaced along the common direction of the applied forces. (c) *Disordered kinetic energy:* the vectors show the atomic velocities, which are distributed at random in magnitude and direction. (d) *Disordered potential energy:* the vectors show the atomic displacements, which are distributed at random in magnitude and direction.

Likewise, if the body were at rest and a pair of external forces were applied to the solid to stretch it, the atoms would increase their separation distances along the direction of the applied forces and the body as a whole would have *ordered* elastic potential energy. See Figure 23-1b.

The *thermal* energy of a solid is something else. It consists partly of the kinetic energy of atomic vibrations; this *kinetic energy* is *disordered* by virtue of the variety of atomic velocities, both in magnitude and direction, as shown in Figure 23-1c. The resultant linear momentum associated with this disordered energy is zero. Furthermore, there is thermal energy associated with the intermolecular potential energy. This *potential energy* is *disordered* (Figure 23-1d) because the atoms have displacements, from their equilibrium positions, that differ in magnitude and in direction. In short, the random oscillations of atoms in a solid are the origin of the solid's thermal energy (with a relatively minor contribution from the "free" electrons within the solid).

In like fashion, the thermal energy of a liquid is associated with disordered molecular kinetic and potential energy. In this state, however, the molecules are not bound to an equilibrium position, and the disordered translational kinetic energy of the molecules also contributes to the thermal energy.

23-2   The first law of thermodynamics   We wish to apply the first law of thermodynamics to liquids and solids:

$$[21\text{-}15] \qquad \qquad \Delta Q = \Delta U + \Delta W$$

Here ΔU is the change in the internal energy of the system. Both ΔQ and ΔW describe energy-transfer processes. The heat ΔQ measures the disordered energy entering the system by virtue of a temperature difference between the system and its surroundings, whereas the work ΔW represents ordered energy transferred from the system to its surroundings. The first law is then merely the conservation of energy principle expressed in so general a way as to allow for the addition or removal of energy from a system by transfer processes involving either work or heat.

Now let us consider the situation shown in Figure 23-2a, in which a liquid has its internal energy changed by heating. Here an electric generator (with whose details we need not be concerned) is run by a descending weight. The generator sends an electric current through a coil of wire, thereby raising the wire's temperature. When this electric heater is immersed in a liquid (held in an insulated container) it causes the liquid's temperature to rise. We will analyze the changes in the state of the liquid from the first law.

We first choose as our system the *g*enerator and *c*oil (Figure 23-2b). As the weight falls at constant speed, work ΔW_{gc} is done *on* the generator. The magnitude of ΔW_{gc} is equal to the attached weight multiplied by its total vertical displacement. The coil heats the liquid; the heat leaving the coil is ΔQ_{gc}. The internal energy of the generator and coil is unchanged: $\Delta U_{gc} = 0$. Therefore, the first law becomes

$$\Delta Q_{gc} = \Delta W_{gc} \qquad \qquad [23\text{-}1]$$

This relation merely says that, since the internal energy of the generator and coil is unchanged, the energy out, as heat, equals the energy into it as work.

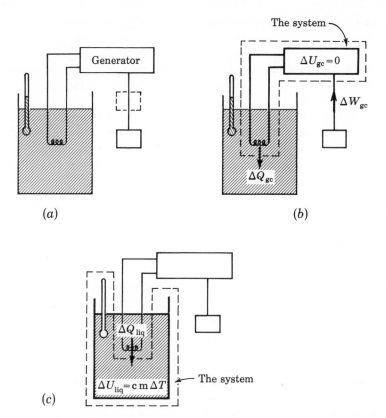

Figure 23-2. (a) A descending weight runs an electric generator, which operates an electric heater, which, in turn, raises the temperature of a liquid. (b) The first law of thermodynamics applied to the system consisting of the generator and coil: the weight does work on the generator, the internal energy is unchanged, and the heater heats the liquid. (c) The first law applied to the system consisting of the liquid: heat enters the liquid, and its internal energy increases.

Now we choose the *liquid* as our system (Figure 23-2c). Heat ΔQ_{liq} enters the liquid. Moreover, the heat *into* the liquid equals the heat *out* of the coil; that is, $\Delta Q_{\text{liq}} = \Delta Q_{\text{gc}}$. The liquid does no work on its surroundings; hence, $\Delta W_{\text{liq}} = 0$. The internal energy of the liquid changes by ΔU_{liq}. Since neither the (macroscopic) kinetic nor potential energy of the liquid changes in the heating process, ΔU_{liq} arises from a change in the thermal-energy content of the liquid and is manifest as a change in the liquid's temperature. Applying the first law of thermodynamics to the system of the liquid gives

$$\Delta Q_{\text{liq}} = \Delta U_{\text{liq}}$$

Using Equation 23-1 together with $\Delta Q_{\text{liq}} = \Delta Q_{\text{gc}}$, we obtain

$$\Delta W_{\text{gc}} = \Delta U_{\text{liq}} \qquad [23\text{-}2]$$

Equation 23-2 implies that one can determine the change in the liquid's thermal energy simply by measuring the work done on the generator (here represented by ΔW_{gc}).

What does experiment show? The increase of the liquid's temperature ΔT is proportional to the work done by the generator. Moreover, for a given ΔW_{gen}, the temperature rise ΔT is found to vary inversely as the mass m of liquid. We may summarize these results by writing

$$\Delta W_{\text{gen}} \propto m \, \Delta T$$

which, by Equation 23-2, is equivalent to

$$\boxed{\Delta U_{\text{liq}} = cm \, \Delta T} \qquad [23\text{-}3]$$

where c is a proportionality constant whose magnitude depends on the chosen units and on the nature of the liquid. Equation 23-3 implies that the change in the thermal energy of a liquid is directly proportional to both the liquid's mass m and the temperature change ΔT. We postpone consideration of the values of c and of the units to the next section.

Let us consider a second situation in which the internal energy and temperature of a liquid rise, but now through work done directly on the liquid rather than through heating.

The experimental arrangement is that shown in Figure 23-3a. Again a weight descends and does work. In this case it turns a stirrer immersed in the liquid. The work done *on* the *st*irrer (Figure 23-3b) by the falling weight equals the work done *on* the *li*quid (Figure 23-3c) by the stirrer; that is, $\Delta W_{\text{st}} = \Delta W_{\text{liq}}$. After the liquid has been set in rotational motion by the stirrer, its internal energy is increased by ΔU_{liq} because it has acquired macroscopic rotational kinetic energy. The liquid soon comes to rest because of internal friction within itself, and its ordered rotational internal energy is converted into disordered thermal energy, not visible as macroscopic kinetic or potential energy. Here $\Delta Q_{\text{liq}} = 0$ and $\Delta W_{\text{st}} = \Delta W_{\text{liq}} = \Delta U_{\text{liq}}$. Again, by experiment we have $\Delta W_{\text{st}} \propto m \, \Delta T$ and, therefore,

[23-3] $$\Delta U_{\text{lip}} = cm \, \Delta T$$

The temperature of a liquid can be changed in any of three ways: by heating it, by doing work on it *without*, however, changing the liquid's macroscopic kinetic and potential energies, and by changing internal ordered kinetic energy or potential energy into internal thermal energy. In all cases

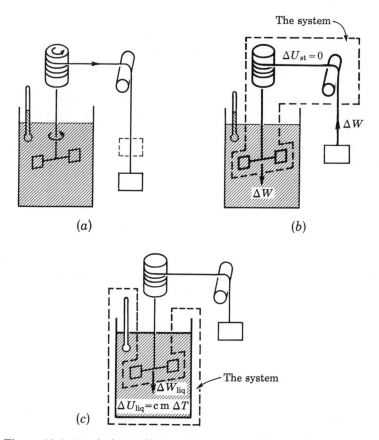

Figure 23-3. (a) A descending weight runs a stirrer, which stirs the liquid. (b) The first law applied to the system consisting of the stirrer: the weight does work on the stirrer, and the stirrer does work on the liquid; the stirrer's internal energy is unchanged. (c) The first law applied to the system consisting of the liquid: the stirrer does work on the liquid, and the liquid's internal energy increases.

in which the temperature changes, the change in thermal energy is proportional to the mass and temperature difference, irrespective of the mode by which energy enters the system.

The same result is found for solids. One may, for example, change the temperature of a metal bar by heating it, by doing work on it in repeatedly flexing it or hammering it, or by bringing it to rest in an inelastic collision. Once again, Equation 23-3 relates the change in internal thermal energy to the solid's mass and temperature rise.

The experiments illustrated in Figures 23-2 and 23-3 are of great historical significance, and were performed with great care by J. Joule (1818–1889). These experiments, together with many others involving the conversion of heat or work into thermal energy, established the validity of the first law of thermodynamics.

23-3 Specific heats and heat units Experiments of the sort described in the last section show that 4.19 joules of work or heat are required to raise the temperature of one gram of water by one Celsius degree. It is convenient to give a special name, the *calorie*, to this amount of energy: by definition,

$$1 \text{ cal} = 4.18605 \text{ joules}$$

Strictly, the amount of energy required to change the temperature of water one Celsius degree differs slightly, according to the initial temperature of the water; therefore, the calorie is, more precisely, the thermal energy that changes the temperature of one gram of water from 14.5° to 15.5° C. This energy unit is sometimes referred to as the *gram-calorie*. The *kilogram-calorie*, also known as the "large" calorie and abbreviated kcal, is 10^3 gm-cal. One kilogram-calorie raises the temperature of one kilogram of water one Celsius degree.

We can also give this result in terms of units of the engineering system. It is found that 778 foot-pounds of work or heat will change the temperature of one pound of water by one Fahrenheit degree. The term *British thermal unit*, abbreviated BTU, is given to this amount of energy:

$$1 \text{ BTU} = 778.26 \text{ ft-lb}$$

Thus, the temperature of one pound of water rises by one Fahrenheit degree when one British thermal unit of thermal energy is added to it. Since $1 \text{ F}° = (5/9)\text{C}°$ (Section 19-2), and 1 pound = 454 gm, 1 BTU is equal to $(5/9)(454) = 252$ cal.

It must be emphasized that the calorie and British thermal unit, although used most often in measuring heat and thermal energy, are merely energy units. One may perfectly well express the kinetic energy of a baseball in calories, or the elastic potential energy of a stretched spring in British thermal units.

By the *specific heat c* of a substance is meant the thermal energy required to change the temperature of a unit mass of material one degree; that is,

$$c = \frac{\Delta U}{m \, \Delta T} \qquad [23\text{-}4]$$

This relation is simply Equation 23-3 solved for the constant c.

By the definition of the calorie, the specific heat of water is 1.00 cal/gm-C°, or 1.00 BTU/ pound-F°. (Unhappily, the pound, which is strictly a *weight* unit in the English engineering system of units, is treated as a *mass* unit for specific heats.) It is found that to raise the temperature of one gram of mercury one Celsius degree requires 0.033 cal; therefore, the specific heat of mercury is 0.033 cal/gm-C° = 0.033 BTU/pound-F°.

Table 23-1 lists the specific heats for a number of materials. We found (Section 21-6) that the molar specific heat C_v of a gas heated at constant volume differed markedly from the specific heat C_p at constant pressure. For

Table 23-1

SUBSTANCE	TEMP. (°C)	SPEC. HEAT (cal/gm-C°)	MOLAR SPEC. HEAT ($\times R$)
Gases†			
Helium	−260 to 3000	1.25	2.49
Water vapor	100 to 120	0.48	4.33
Solids			
Aluminum	20	0.217	2.92
Copper	−263	0.001	0.005
Copper	20	0.093	2.94
Copper	1000	1.10	3.48
Iron	20 to 100	0.113	3.00
Lead	20 to 100	0.031	3.22
Glass	20 to 100	0.199	
Ice	−10 to 0	0.55	
Liquids			
Mercury	0 to 100	0.033	3.35
Water	0	1.009	
	15	1.000	
	100	1.006	

† Specific heats of gases are at constant pressure.

liquids and solids, however, the specific heats at constant volume and at constant pressure are so nearly alike that one need not ordinarily distinguish between them. This is so because liquids and solids are highly incompressible and the work done in expanding is negligible. It should be noted that the specific heat of a liquid or solid is *not* independent of temperature. For example, copper has a specific heat of 0.093 cal/gm-C° at 20° C, but its specific heat at −253° C is only 0.0031 cal/gm-C°. Indeed, the specific heats of all substances approach zero at the absolute zero of temperature. Thus, the specific heat c is not a true constant, and Equation 23-4 applies only when the temperature difference ΔT is small. Nevertheless, the specific heats of most materials at temperatures not very far from room temperature (300° K) may be properly regarded as constants.

The term *heat capacity* (more properly, the *thermal-energy capacity*) is used to denote the thermal energy required to change the temperature of a body by one degree. Thus, the heat capacity of a body of mass m and specific heat c is equal to $\Delta U/\Delta T = cm$.

Example 1   A 40 gm block of copper originally at $20°$ C is dropped into an insulated container holding 200 gm of water originally at $80°$ C. What is the temperature of copper and water after thermal equilibrium has been achieved?

The copper block is heated by the water, which is initially at the higher temperature. Thus, the thermal-energy content of the copper is increased and the thermal-energy content of the water is decreased, both by the same amount, until both substances reach a common temperature. After reaching this common temperature there can be no further heat flow. The increase in the internal energy of copper is, from Equation 23-4,

$$\Delta U_{copper} = cm \, \Delta T_{copper} = (0.093 \text{ cal/gm-C}°)(40 \text{ gm})(t_f - 20° \text{ C})$$

where t_f is the final temperature in Celsius degrees. Similarly, the decrease in the internal energy of the water is

$$\Delta U_{water} = cm \, \Delta T_{water} = (1.00 \text{ cal/gm-C}°)(200 \text{ gm})(80 \text{ C}° - t_f)$$

Since energy is conserved, $\Delta U_{copper} = \Delta U_{water}$ and we have

$$(0.093)(40)(t_f - 20° \text{ C}) = (1.00)(200)(80 - t_f)$$
$$t_f = 79° \text{ C}$$

The temperature of the water decreases by only one Celsius degree, not only because the mass of water exceeds that of the copper but more especially, because the specific heat of water greatly exceeds that of copper. As may be seen from Table 23-1, the specific heat of water is relatively high; as solids or liquids go, water is very hard to heat.

The procedure of this example can be used to measure the specific heat of a substance. The masses, initial temperatures, and final equilibrium temperature are easily measured, and the unknown specific heat can then be computed. This experimental procedure is known as *calorimetry*.

Example 2   A block of copper, originally at $20°$ C and at rest, is dropped from a height of 40 m. The block strikes and comes to rest on an insulated surface. What is the final temperature of the copper, assuming no thermal energy losses?

In Example 1 the internal energy and temperature of the copper were increased because the copper had thermal energy transferred to it through heat. In this example the copper is *not* heated; that is, the copper does *not* change temperature by virtue of being in contact with a hotter material. Here the block (and Earth) lose gravitational potential energy and the block gains macroscopic kinetic energy as it falls. Upon striking the surface, *work* is done on the block. Its internal energy increases as the block becomes deformed, and internal friction changes ordered energy into disordered, or thermal, energy. The original gravitational potential energy $mg \, \Delta y$ has become internal thermal energy $cm \, \Delta T$. Therefore,

$$mg \, \Delta y = cm \, \Delta T$$

$$\Delta T = \frac{g \, \Delta y}{c} = \frac{(9.8 \text{ m/sec}^2)(40 \text{ m})(1 \text{ kg} / 10^3 \text{ gm})}{(0.093 \text{ cal/gm-C}°)(4.19 \text{ joules/cal})} = 1.0 \text{ C}°$$

The copper's final temperature is $21°$ C.

In solving problems of this type, in which thermal energy is expressed in calories or British thermal units and mechanical energy is expressed in joules or foot-pounds, one must be consistent in the use of units. That is, the left and right sides of the equation must both be in the *same units*, as for example, in joules.

23-4 The Dulong-Petit law   The *molar specific heat* of any substance is the thermal energy required to change the temperature of one gram-mole (or 6.02×10^{23} molecules) by one degree. Molar specific heats are customarily given as multiples of the universal gas constant R (Section 21-6), where $R = 8.31$ joules/mole-$C°$ $= 1.99$ cal/mole-$C°$. Since the number of grams per mole is simply the atomic weight of the substance, one can compute the molar specific heat of a material from its ordinary specific heat by multiplying c by the atomic weight.

As Table 23-1 shows, the molar specific heats of many solids at room temperature or greater are very close to $3R \simeq 6$ cal/mole-$C°$. This is no accident. The identical values for the molar specific heats of solids—known as the *law of Dulong and Petit*—can be derived from a simple atomic model of a solid.

A solid can be imagined to consist of N atoms in constant vibration. In Section 21-7 we saw that, for a simple harmonic oscillator, one must associate an energy of $\frac{1}{2}kT$ with the potential energy, as well as with the kinetic energy. Therefore, a total vibrational energy of kT must be associated with oscillation along any direction in space. Since any one atom in a solid oscillates in *three* dimensions, the vibrational energy per atom is $3kT$. Then the total internal thermal energy (arising from atomic vibrations) of a solid of N atoms is $3NkT$:

$$U = 3NkT$$

By definition, the molar specific heat is

$$C = \left(\frac{1}{n}\right) \frac{dU}{dT} = 3\left(\frac{N}{n}\right)k$$

where n is the number of moles. The number of atoms N is related to Avogadro's number N_0 by $N = nN_0$. Therefore,

$$\boxed{C = 3N_0 k = 3R} \qquad [23\text{-}5]$$

Most of the observed values of the molar specific heats of both electrical conductors (such as copper) and insulators (such as diamond) are, at room temperature, in good agreement with Equation 23-5. This can *not* be understood on the basis of classical physics, inasmuch as the free electrons of conductors would be expected to contribute an additional $\frac{3}{2}kT$ of energy per electron. This problem is resolved by a quantum description of specific heats.

23-5   Latent heats   A solid, liquid, or gas changes temperature only if thermal energy is added to or removed from it. The converse is *not* true. If thermal energy enters a substance the temperature of the substance will *not* necessarily change: under such a condition, some of the substance changes its *state*.

Consider Figure 23-4a, a pressure-temperature diagram for water. This diagram shows the conditions under which transformations can take place among the solid, liquid, and gaseous states of water. The diagram is divided by lines into three zones corresponding to the solid, liquid, and gaseous states of water. The line AC gives the saturated vapor pressure (see Section 22-6) of water as a function of temperature. Any point on this line corresponds to a pair of temperature and pressure values at which water in the liquid state can coexist in thermal equilibrium with water in the gaseous state. The line terminates at point C, the critical point (Section 22-6). For temperatures or pressures above the critical temperature (374° C) or above the critical pressure (218 atmospheres), the liquid and gas states of water are indistinguishable.

If one were to begin with water at some state corresponding to a point w in Figure 23-4b, the water would be in the liquid state. This water could be transformed into a gas (or vapor) by reducing the pressure isothermally so as to bring the water to the line AC and then below it into the region of vapor. Thus, one can cause water to boil at some fixed temperature by pumping on the atmosphere surrounding the water. Alternatively, one could, starting at the point w, increase the temperature isobarically until one again takes the substance through the line AC. In this process one causes water to boil by heating it at constant pressure.

When a liquid is vaporized, its volume increases and work is done by the system. In addition, the internal energy of the substance is increased. Thus, one must add an amount of heat L_v, called the *latent heat of vaporization* to each unit mass of liquid to change it to vapor. In such a transformation, the temperature (and pressure) remain constant, even though the internal energy of the system increases. For water at atmospheric pressure, the temperature corresponding to the point on the line AC is 100° C. This is, of course, the boiling temperature of water at standard atmospheric pressure. The latent heat at this temperature is found to be 539 cal/gm.

In general, the heat ΔQ for a mass of substance m undergoing a change in state is given by

$$\Delta Q = mL$$

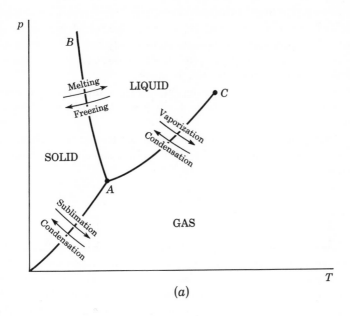

(a)

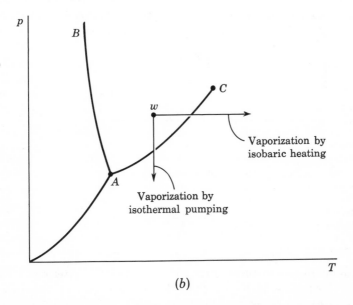

(b)

Figure 23-4. (a) Pressure-temperature diagram giving the states of a substance; point C is the critical point. (b) A liquid (point w) changed into a gas by isobaric heating and by isothermal pumping.

where L is the latent heat of the transformation. The latent heat of vaporization is added to a liquid (a) to allow the molecules, which are bound to one another in the liquid state, to become more nearly free of the attraction of neighboring molecules and (b) to provide the energy required to expand the system. In condensation the reverse happens.

The latent heat of vaporization depends on the temperature: it decreases as the temperature increases. Indeed, the latent heat is zero at the critical temperature (374° C, for water).

Every change in state of a substance is characterized by a change in the volume and a change in internal energy. When we apply the first law of thermodynamics to a change in state, we have

$$\Delta Q = mL = \Delta U + \Delta W \qquad [23\text{-}6]$$

where L is the *latent heat of transformation*, ΔU is the change in the substance's internal energy, and ΔW is the work done by the substance as it changes volume. When a substance undergoes a transformation, or change in phase, between *liquid and gaseous* states, the latent heat is called the *latent heat of vaporization*, L_v; when the transformation is between the *solid and liquid* states, it is called the *latent heat of fusion*, L_f; when the transformation is between the *solid and gaseous* states, it is called the *latent heat of sublimation*, L_s. Table 23-2 lists latent heats for several substances.

Table 23-2

SUBSTANCE	MELT. PT. (°C)	HEAT OF FUSION (CAL/GM)	BOIL. PT. (°C)	HEAT OF VAPORIZ. (CAL/GM)
Water	0	80	100	539
Water			40	574
Water			180	479
Water	−10	68		
Water	−22	56		
Oxygen	−218	3.30	−183	51
Mercury	−39	2.82	357	65
Copper	1083	42	2300	1750
Lead	327	5.86	1620	175

Some interesting features of the phase changes for water and for carbon dioxide can be seen in Figure 23-5. The unique point at which the three lines representing the phase boundaries meet is called the *triple point*. This point gives the pressure and temperature at which the three states of a substance—solid, liquid, and gas—can coexist in thermal equilibrium. For

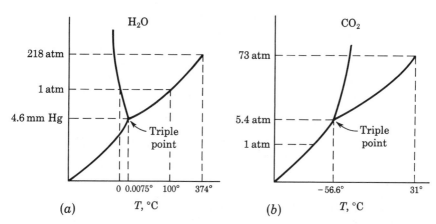

Figure 23-5. Pressure-temperature diagrams (*not* to scale) for (a) water, and (b) carbon dioxide.

water the triple point is at $p = 4.6$ mm Hg and $T = 0.0075°$ C; for carbon dioxide the triple point is at $p = 5.4$ atmospheres and $T = -56.6°$ C. As Figures 23-5a and b show, a pressure of 1 atmosphere lies *above* the triple point for water but *below* the triple point for carbon dioxide. Therefore, as one increases the temperature of ice at a pressure of 1 atmosphere the water changes, in turn, from the solid to the liquid to the gaseous state. On the other hand, solid carbon dioxide at a pressure of 1 atmosphere will, upon an increase in temperature, change directly from the solid to the gaseous state. That is, CO_2 sublimes at atmospheric pressure.

Figure 23-5a also shows that the "freezing line" for water has a negative slope $(dp/dT < 0)$; that is, the temperature of the melting point decreases with an increase in pressure. On the other hand, the freezing line for carbon dioxide (and most other substances) has a positive slope $(dp/dT > 0)$. It can be shown that the sign of the slope is related to the change in volume of the substance as it goes from the solid to the liquid state. For most materials, the freezing-line slope is positive, and such materials always contract upon freezing (expand upon melting). Water, on the other hand, has a negative slope, and it expands upon freezing (water density, 1.0 gm/cm³; ice density, 0.9 gm/cm³).

Example 3   Twenty grams of ice, initially at $-20°$ C, is heated isobarically at standard atmospheric pressure to become water vapor at $100°$ C. (a) What is the total heat ΔQ that must be supplied? (b) What is the total increase in the internal energy of the substance? The specific heats, assumed constant, are 0.50 cal/gm-C° for ice and 1.00 cal/gm-C° for water. The latent heats are 80 cal/gm for fusion and 539 cal/gm for vaporization. The density of water vapor at $100°$ C is 6.0×10^{-4} gm/cm³.

(a) We add up the heats supplied according to the following table.

Process	Heat supplied
Ice, $-20°$ C to $0°$ C	$cm \, \Delta t = (0.50 \text{ cal/gm-C}°)(20 \text{ gm})(20 \text{ C}°) = 0.2 \text{ kcal}$
Ice to water at $0°$ C	$mL_f = (20 \text{ gm})(80 \text{ cal/gm}) = 1.6 \text{ kcal}$
Water, $0°$ C to $100°$ C	$cm \, \Delta t = (1.00 \text{ cal/gm-C}°)(20 \text{ gm})(100 \text{ C}°) = 2.0 \text{ kcal}$
Water to water vapor at $100°$ C	$mL_v = (20 \text{ gm})(539 \text{ cal/gm}) = 10.8 \text{ kcal}$

$$\text{Total } \Delta Q = 14.6 \text{ kcal}$$

(b) The total thermal energy supplied is *not* equal to the total increase in internal energy. This is so because, from the first law of thermodynamics, $\Delta Q = \Delta U + \Delta W$. Thus, part of the heat ΔQ supplied does not change ΔU, but manifests itself as work done on its surroundings by the expanding substance. The work done when ice is heated and melted, and when water is heated to $100°$ C, is negligible, inasmuch as the volume changes are small here. On the other hand, from the liquid (1.0 gm/cm^3) to the gaseous ($6.0 \times 10^{-4} \text{ gm/cm}^3$) state the volume change is ΔV, which is

$$\Delta V = \frac{20 \text{ gm}}{(6.0 \times 10^{-4} \text{ gm/cm}^3)} - \frac{20 \text{ gm}}{(1.0 \text{ gm/cm}^3)}$$
$$= 3.33 \times 10^4 \text{ cm}^3 - 20 \text{ cm}^3 = 33.3 \text{ liters}$$

The work done ΔW then is

$$\Delta W = p \, \Delta V = (1 \text{ atm})(33.3 \text{ l}) = 33.3 \text{ l-atm}$$

We can easily convert this energy into kilocalories by using the fact that $R = 1.99 \times 10^{-3} \text{ kcal/mole-K}° = 0.082 \text{ l-atm/mole-K}°$:

$$\Delta W = (33.3 \text{ l-atm}) \left(\frac{1.99 \times 10^{-3} \text{ kcal/mole-K}°}{0.082 \text{ l-atm/mole-K}°} \right) = 0.8 \text{ kcal}$$

Therefore, the internal energy increase ΔU is

$$\Delta U = \Delta Q - \Delta W = (14.6 - 0.8) \text{ kcal} = 13.8 \text{ kcal}$$

23-6 Thermal conduction

Heat is that energy-transfer process which takes place by virtue of a temperature difference. When a hot body is in contact with a cold body, thermal energy flows from the hot to the cold body. Such a flow can take place within a single body: thermal energy will flow from one region of a body at a high temperature to an adjoining region of the same body at a lower temperature, if the temperature difference is maintained between the two points. This thermal-energy transfer (often termed, redundantly, a "heat transfer process") is *thermal conduction*.

The thermal energy of a solid consists mostly of the vibration of the atoms about their equilibrium positions and, to a lesser extent, of the motion (at room temperature) of "free" electrons throughout the material. By "the atom" is here meant the nucleus together with the tightly bound electrons that surround it. Adjoining atoms in a solid interact. Therefore, as one atom oscillates, it influences the motion of a neighboring atom. Thermal energy can be thus transferred from one atomic oscillator to another. If one region of a solid is at a higher temperature than an adjoining region, the amplitudes (and energies) of the atomic oscillations are greater at the hot regions. Thermal energy is then transferred from the hot to the cold regions by the coupling between neighboring oscillators.

If, in addition to vibrating atoms, a solid also has free electrons, as in the case of metals, these free electrons also contribute to the thermal conduction. That the free electrons play a significant role in thermal conductivity is shown by the fact that good thermal conductors, such as metals, are usually

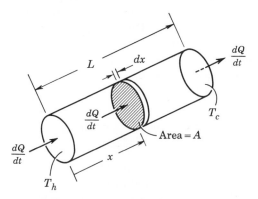

Figure 23-6. Thermal conduction through a rod of length L and cross section A, having its left and right ends at the constant $h$ot and cold temperatures T_h and T_c, respectively. The rate of heat through any cross section is dQ/dt.

also good electrical conductors. The free electrons are the electric-charge carriers whose transport through a material is the origin of electric currents; if the electrons are indeed free, or nearly free, they may then act to transfer thermal energy as well as electric charge.

We now turn to the quantitative aspects of thermal conduction. Consider the situation shown in Figure 23-6. Here a rod of uniform cross section A is surrounded by an insulating material, so that no heat leaks into or out of the rod through its sides. The $h$ot left end is maintained at a constant high temperature T_h while the $c$old right end is maintained at a constant lower temperature T_c. The thermal energy entering the rod per unit time from the hot reservoir (that is, the heat rate into the rod) is dQ/dt. This is also the heat per unit time leaving the right end. In fact, dQ/dt represents the thermal energy crossing the area A per unit time at *any* point along the rod. The *net* heat entering the rod, or entering any small volume of the rod, is *zero*; therefore, the internal energy of the rod remains *constant*. The rod, a thermal conductor, acts merely as a "heat pipe" between the hot and cold reservoirs, degrading thermal energy by sending it to a lower temperature. This behavior continues, of course, only as long as the two ends are maintained at T_h and T_c. When $T_h = T_c$, then $dQ/dt = 0$.

How does the temperature vary along the length of the uniform rod? Measurements show that the temperature drops *uniformly* from the hot to the cold end. The temperature *at any one point* along the rod is unchanged as long as the ends are maintained at constant temperatures.

To obtain the general expression describing thermal conduction, let us concentrate on the temperatue drop dT occurring across a thin section of thickness dx. The quantity dT/dx, called the *temperature gradient*, measures the temperature change per unit displacement along the direction of heat flow. If x is taken as increasing along the direction of dQ/dt, the temperature gradient dT/dx is *negative*; that is, the temperature *drops* as x increases.

Experiment shows that the heat rate $R \equiv dQ/dt$ is related to the temperature gradient dT/dx by

$$\boxed{R = dQ/dt = -KA\,dT/dx}$$ [23-7]

where A is the cross-sectional area through which the thermal energy flows. The quantity K is a positive constant, called the *thermal conductivity*. It is characteristic of the material of the thermal conductor. Equation 23-7 then shows that, for a slice of infinitesimal thickness, the heat rate varies directly as the cross-sectional area and the temperature gradient.

When we integrate Equation 23-7 over the entire rod of length L, extending from $x = 0$ to $x = L$, with the corresponding temperatures T_h and T_c, respectively, we find

$$R = -KA\,dT/dx$$

$$R\int_0^L dx = -KA\int_{T_h}^{T_c} dT$$

Note that R, K, and A are all constants. Then,

$$R = \frac{dQ}{dt} = \frac{KA(T_h - T_c)}{L}$$ [23-8]

The differential form of the thermal-conduction equation given in Equation 23-7 is more general than that given in Equation 23-8. Equation 23-7 can be applied to *all* shapes of conductors, not merely to uniform rods. (One can imagine the conductor to consist of a collection of infinitesimally thin sheets for each of which the differential form holds exactly.)

Measured values of the thermal conductivity K for various materials are given in Table 23-3. A good thermal conductor has a high value of K; a

Table 23-3

SUBSTANCE	TEMP. (°C)	THERMAL CONDUCT. (kcal-m/sec-m²-C°)
Conducting		
Aluminum	−190 to 30	0.050
Copper	−160	0.108
Copper	18	0.092
Copper	100	0.091
Silver	18	0.101
Lead	18	0.0083
Water	20	0.0014
Insulating		
Concrete		0.0002
Cork		0.00001
Glass, wool	50	0.00001
Ice	0	0.0005
Air	0	0.000006

low value of K characterizes a poor thermal conductor, or a good insulator. The units assigned to K depend upon the units used for dQ/dt, $T_h - T_c$, A, and L. For example, if dQ/dt is in kilocalories per second, $T_h - T_c$ in Celsius degrees, A in square meters, and L in meters, then the units for K must be given as (kcal/sec)(m)/m²-C°, to be in accord with Equation 23-8. Still other units, of course, are possible. In engineering practice it is common to give dQ/dt in British thermal units per second, $T_h - T_c$ in Fahrenheit degrees, A in square feet, and L in inches; then the thermal conductivity is written with the units (BTU/sec)(inch)/feet²-F°.

Example 4 An electric heater operating at 200 watts is placed in the interior of a cubical box constructed of insulating material. See Figure 23-7. The edge length of the box is 20 cm and the thickness of each side is 1.0 cm. After the heater has been on for a sufficiently long time, dynamic thermal equilibrium is achieved; the interior surfaces of the box remain at the constant temperature 60° C while the exterior surfaces are at the temperature 20° C. (a) What is the rate of thermal-energy flow out of the box? (b) What is the thermal conductivity of the material of which the box is constructed?

(a) The thermal energy from the electric heater passing into the walls of the box must equal the thermal

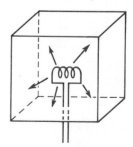

Figure 23-7. An electric heater inside an insulating box.

energy leaving the box. Thus, the rate of thermal-energy flow *out* of the box is

$$dQ/dt = 200 \text{ watts} = (200 \text{ watts})\left(\frac{1 \text{ joule/sec}}{1 \text{ watt}}\right)\left(\frac{1 \text{ cal}}{4.19 \text{ joules}}\right)\left(\frac{1 \text{ kcal}}{10^3 \text{ cal}}\right)$$

$$= 0.048 \text{ kcal/sec}$$

(b) The total area A can be taken as the area of one side, $(0.20 \text{ m})^2$, multiplied by the number of sides (6) of the cube. The thickness L is 0.010 m. Since the edge length of a side is large compared with the thickness of a side, we may properly neglect heat flow along the edges. Thus, Equation 23-8 gives

$$K = \frac{(dQ/dt)L}{A(T_h - T_c)} = \frac{(0.048 \text{ kcal/sec})(0.010 \text{ m})}{6(0.20 \text{ m})^2(40 \text{ C}°)} = 5.0 \times 10^{-5} \text{ (kcal/sec)(m/m}^2\cdot\text{C}°)$$

Good thermal insulators, such as asbestos, have thermal conductivities of this order.

23-7 Convection In thermal conduction, energy is transferred from particle to particle, not because a particle moves through the material but because the atoms are coupled together. The atoms of a fluid (a liquid or gas) do not, however, have to remain localized in position; they can move throughout the material. As a consequence, another thermal-energy transfer process, known as *convection*, can take place.

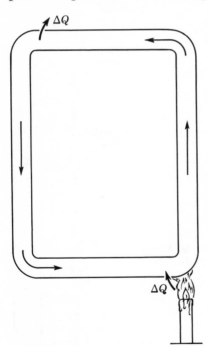

The essential features of convection are shown in Figure 23-8. Here a liquid, held in a closed pipe, is heated at the lower point shown. Assume that the liquid has a positive coefficient of thermal expansion; that is, the density of the liquid decreases with a rise in temperature. Then, as the liquid is heated, its density will be reduced, and it will rise in the pipe. Thermal energy is transferred out of the liquid by conduction at an upper section of the pipe. The temperature of the liquid will then decrease, the liquid's density will increase, and the liquid will readily descend through the return pipe to its starting point. Therefore, in convection, energy is transported from one point in space to another by the bulk displacement of a material.

Figure 23-8. Thermal-energy transfer by convection.

23-8 Thermal-energy transfer through radiation   Suppose that a hot object is placed in a completely evacuated container at a lower temperature. The two bodies, the hot object and the container, are not directly in contact, since they are connected only by a thin thread which acts as an almost perfect thermal insulator; see Figure 23-9. Under these circumstances thermal energy cannot be transferred by conduction. Nor can convection occur, inasmuch as the chamber is completely evacuated. Yet, if one waits for a sufficiently long time, two such bodies are found by experiment to achieve the *same* final temperature. This temperature is intermediate between the two initial temperatures. One must conclude that still another thermal-energy transfer process, distinct from conduction and convection, operates here. This process is the *emission and absorption of electromagnetic radiation.*

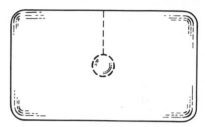

Figure 23-9. A hot object suspended from an insulating thread in the interior of an evacuated enclosure.

Since a thoroughgoing analysis of radiation requires an understanding of the theory of electromagnetism, we can merely summarize the most pertinent properties of electromagnetic radiation as they relate to thermal-energy transfer. Whenever an electrically charged particle accelerates (or decelerates), it loses energy by emitting electromagnetic radiation. This radiation consists of variations in the electric and magnetic fields in space, and these fields represent energy which is propagated through empty space at the unique speed of 3.0×10^8 m/sec, the speed of light.† The reverse process of emission is the absorption of electromagnetic radiation. In absorption the electric and magnetic fields produce forces on electrically charged particles, thereby transferring energy to the particles.

All matter consists of electrically charged particles. Therefore, all materials can and do radiate electromagnetic energy. Conversely, electromagnetic energy impinging on a material can be absorbed when the electric and magnetic fields do work on the charged particles in the material.

Now consider again the situation in Figure 23-9, in which two bodies are at different initial temperatures. The hot body emits *and absorbs* electromagnetic waves. So does the cold body. We find, however, that the hot body loses thermal energy and its temperature falls while the cold body gains

† It is interesting to compare the speeds associated with the three thermal-energy transfer processes. Radiation travels at the speed of light ($\sim 10^8$ m/sec), thermal-conduction energy is propagated at the speed of sound ($\sim 10^4$ m/sec in a typical solid), and convection occurs at a very slow rate, corresponding to the bulk transport of a fluid (~ 1 m/sec).

thermal energy and its temperature rises. Since the hot body has a net loss of energy and the cold body has a net gain of energy, one must conclude that the hot body emits more radiation than it absorbs and that the cold body absorbs more radiation than it emits. One finds from experiment that, although *absorption is temperature-independent, emission is temperature-dependent.* For emission, the higher the temperature of a body the greater the rate at which it emits energy.

The total electromagnetic energy emitted per unit time from a unit area of a black body (defined below) at the absolute temperature T is found to be directly proportional to T^4. This is the *Stefan-Boltzmann law*, which can be written as

$$P = \sigma T^4 \qquad [23\text{-}9]$$

where P is the power radiated per unit area and σ is a universal constant equal to 5.67×10^{-8} watts/m²-(K°)⁴.

An object is black when it absorbs all visible light striking it, reflecting none. An object is white if it reflects all visible light striking it, absorbing none. In thermodynamics a *black body* is defined as an object which absorbs *all* electromagnetic radiation, visible and nonvisible, that impinges on it. Suppose that some body remains at a fixed temperature. Then it must emit at precisely the same rate as it absorbs. Therefore, a black body is a *perfect radiator*, as well as a *perfect absorber*, of electromagnetic waves. By the same token, a poor radiator is a poor absorber.

Paradoxically, a "black body" need not appear black; it may, in fact, appear bright. For example, the Sun can be considered a "black body" because it absorbs essentially all radiation striking it. A still better black body consists of a hole leading to the interior of an enclosure made of *any* material; electromagnetic waves entering through the hole undergo reflections inside until all entering radiation is absorbed. Equation 23-9 gives the total electromagnetic power emitted per unit area for *any* black body at temperature T; the absorbed power per unit area is independent of the temperature of the *absorbing* body.

We return once again to the situation shown in Figure 23-9. Both the suspended hot object and the cold enclosure eventually reach thermal equilibrium at some common final temperature. Until this temperature is reached, the hot body emits more radiant energy than it absorbs, and the cold body absorbs more radiant energy than it emits. Recalling that one must associate energy with an electromagnetic disturbance in space, we see that there are *three* contributions to the total thermal energy for this system: from the suspended object, from the enclosure, and from the electromagnetic radiation which fills the space between them. The radiation of the electromagnetic field represents energy which has been emitted, but not yet absorbed. The electromagnetic radiation within an enclosure which acts as a black body at a temperature T may be said to be in thermal equilibrium with the body. Such radiation is known as *thermal radiation* at the temperature T.

23-9 Summary The thermal energy for solids consists mainly of the disordered kinetic and potential energy of atomic oscillations. For liquids, there is, in addition, disordered translational kinetic energy.

When a solid or liquid undergoes a temperature change ΔT, its internal energy changes by

[23-3] $$\Delta U = cm\,\Delta T$$

where m is the mass and c is a constant, characteristic of the material, called the specific heat. Water has a specific heat of 1 cal/gm-C° = 1 BTU/pound-F°.

When the thermal energy of a solid is due entirely to atomic vibrations, the molar specific heat C is the same for all materials (the Dulong-Petit law) and has the magnitude

[23-5] $$C = 3R$$

The heat required to change the state of a substance with no temperature change is given by

[23-6] $$\Delta Q = mL = \Delta U + \Delta W$$

where L is the latent heat of transformation (vaporization, fusion, or sublimation).

The heat rate dQ/dt through a sheet of cross-sectional area A is given by

[23-7] $$dQ/dt = -KA\,dT/dx$$

where dT is the temperature change across a sheet of thickness dx and the thermal conductivity K is a constant characteristic of the material.

Convection is the mode of thermal-energy transfer arising from the bulk transport of a fluid.

Thermal energy may be transferred by the emission or absorption of electromagnetic radiation. The absorption process is temperature-independent, but the emission of radiation from a black body, a perfect radiator (and absorber) is governed by the Stefan-Boltzmann relation,

[23-9] $$P = \sigma T^4$$

where P is the power radiated from a unit surface area of the black body at the temperature T and σ is a universal constant.

PROBLEMS

23-1   In a Joule experiment, of the sort shown in Figure 23-2, a mass of 50 kg falls through a distance of 1.5 m twenty times. The heated liquid is water and its temperature rises 10 C°. What is the mass of the water?

23-2   A 2000-pound automobile, moving initially at 30 miles/hour, is brought to rest. What is the increase of thermal energy of the automobile, assuming that the dissipated energy appears in the automobile alone?

23-3   An electric heater, when immersed in a liquid of mass 2000 gm and specific heat 0.42 cal/gm-C°, raises the temperature of the liquid 10 C° in 15 minutes. What is the power rating of the heater?

23-4   How much copper, initially at 300° C, must be dropped into 400 gm of oil, with specific heat 0.65 cal/gm-C° and initial temperature of 30° C, to bring the mixture to a final temperature of 40° C?

23-5   A bullet of lead strikes and comes to rest at an insulating wall. With what initial speed must the bullet move so that its temperature will rise by 40 C°, assuming that all of the energy dissipated goes into raising the temperature of the bullet?

23-6   A thermometer, having a heat capacity of 8.0 cal/C° and initially at 25.00° C, is immersed in a liquid with a heat capacity of 1000 cal/C° at a temperature of 40.00° C. After reaching thermal equilibrium, what temperature does the thermometer register?

23-7   A 1.0 kg copper block slides at constant speed down a rough inclined plane of 30° for a distance of 8.0 m. Assuming that the inclined plane is a perfect insulator, by how much does the temperature of the block rise?

23-8   What is the atomic specific heat (the heat required to raise the temperature of one atom one Celsius degree) in units of electron volts per Celsius degrees for a solid that obeys the Dulong-Petit law?

23-9 ★ A copper block 1.0 kg in mass, moving initially with a speed of 0.20 m/sec, strikes a 1.0 kg aluminum block initially at rest. The two blocks stick together in a perfectly inelastic collision. Assuming that all of the energy dissipated goes into raising the temperature of the two blocks, what is this temperature rise? Assume that both blocks have the same initial temperature and the same final temperature.

23-10   How many grams of water vapor at 100° C must be mixed with 100 gm of water initially at 20° C to bring the temperature of the system to 60° C?

23-11   One gram of water vapor at 100° C is brought to thermal equilibrium with 1 gm of ice at 0° C. (a) What is the final state (or states)? (b) How much liquid is there finally?

23-12   Twenty grams of lead initially at 180° C are dropped into a 100 gm block of ice initially at −20° C. What is the final temperature?

23-13   What is the latent heat of vaporization of water in British thermal units per pound?

23-14   Compute from water's latent heat of vaporization the approximate binding energy per molecule, in electron volts, between the molecules of water.

23-15   At standard atmospheric pressure liquid helium boils at a temperature of $4.2°$ K. Its latent heat of vaporization is 4 cal/gm. What constant power must be absorbed to boil 1.0 kg of liquid helium per hour?

23-16   Air conditioners are sometimes rated in "tons." A 1 ton unit, when operated continuously for 1 day, extracts an amount of energy which is equivalent to the thermal energy extracted by 1 ton of ice melting into water. What is the (thermal) power rating of a 1-ton air conditioner expressed in (a) horsepower, (b) kilowatts, and (c) British thermal units per hour?

23-17   Confirm the Dulong-Petit law by computing the molar specific heats from the mass specific heats, in calories per gram-degrees (Celsius), listed in Table 23-1.

23-18   What radius of an aluminum rod 10 cm long must be used to conduct 10 cal/sec from a $400°$ C reservoir to a $100°$ C reservoir?

23-19   Confirm the conversion factor between the thermal conductivity units: 1 (kcal/sec)m/m^2-C$°$ = 8.05(BTU/sec)inches/feet^2-F$°$.

23-20   A long cylindrical copper bar with a radius of 1.0 cm conducts heat along its length at the rate of 4.0 watts. What is the temperature gradient along the bar?

23-21   Water is contained in an aluminum pot on a stove's heating element. The water, at $100.00°$ C, is boiling away at the rate of 20 gm/min. (a) What is the rate of heat flow into the water? (b) If the bottom of the aluminum pot has a surface area of 80 cm^2 and a thickness of 1.0 mm, what is the temperature at the lower surface of the pot?

23-22   Two thermal conductors, having the same lengths and cross-sectional areas and made of the same material, are first connected end to end between two reservoirs of constant, but different, temperatures. Then the conductors are both individually connected directly between the reservoirs at the same temperatures. What is the ratio of the rate of heat flow in the second case to the first?

23-23 ★   A cylindrical pipe of length L and inner and outer radii r_1 and r_2 conducts heat radially outward at the constant rate $R = dQ/dt$, both the inner and outer cylindrical surfaces being maintained at constant temperatures. Show that the temperature difference between the inner and outer surfaces is given by $(R/2LK)$ ln (r_2/r_1), where K is the thermal conductivity of the material of the pipe. (*Hint:* Apply Equation 23-7 to a cylindrical shell of thickness dr and integrate from r_1 to r_2.)

23-24 ★   A hollow sphere with inner and outer radii r_1 and r_2 conducts heat radially outward at the rate R, both the inner and outer spherical surfaces being maintained at constant temperatures. Show that the temperature difference between the inner and outer surfaces is given by $(R/4K)(1/r_1 - 1/r_2)$. (*Hint:* Apply Equation 23-7 to a spherical shell of thickness dr, and integrate from r_1 to r_2.)

23-25 ★ A cube is comprised of two parallel slabs of materials having different thermal conductivities, as shown in Figure 23-10. The cube is to be used as a heat pipe between two reservoirs at different temperatures, the reservoirs being in thermal contact with the cube over two opposite

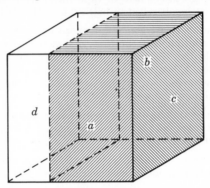

Figure 23-10.

faces. Which faces, the front and back (a and b) or the right and left (c and d), should be placed in contact with the reservoirs to give the greatest rate of heat flow? (*Hint:* Imagine that one of the materials first has a very high thermal conductivity and then a very low thermal conductivity compared with the second material.)

23-26 A certain black body with a surface area of 0.20 m² has a constant temperature of 1000° K. (a) What is the *total* power radiated by the black body? (b) If the black body absorbs radiation at the rate of 5000 watts, what is the *net* power radiated by the black body?

23-27 The temperature of the filament of an incandescent lamp bulb is 2400° K. The filament may be regarded as a black body. (a) If the power of the lamp bulb is 100 watts, what is the surface area of the filament? (b) If the same lamp is operated at 200 watts, what is then the temperature of the filament?

23-28 (a) Show, from the Stefan-Boltzmann law, that the power radiated from a 1 cm² surface of a black body at the Kelvin temperature T is $(T/645)^4$ watts. (b) At what temperature will a black body radiate 1.0 watt/cm²?

23-29 A spherical shell 10 cm in radius acts as a black body and absorbs all of the 2.0-megawatt radiation falling continuously on it. The shell's temperature remains constant. What is this temperature?

23-30 A copper spherical shell having a total surface area of 0.25 m² and a thickness of 1.0 mm encloses an electric heater. The temperature difference between the inside and outside surfaces of the container is 0.040 C°. At what power is the electric heater operating?

23-31 The Sun may be regarded as a black body with a temperature of about 6000° K. The Sun's radius is 1.4×10^6 km. (a) What is the total power radiated by the Sun? (b) Assuming that the radiated power passing through a unit area placed at right angles to the direction of propagation of the radiation varies inversely as the square of the distance from the Sun, what is the power through a 1 cm² area, at a distance of 1.5×10^8 km, the distance of the Earth from the Sun? (c) The observed radiation intensity at the Earths' surface is 0.13 watt/cm². What fraction of the radiation emitted from the Sun and incident on the Earth's atmosphere arrives at the Earth's surface?

TWENTY-FOUR

THE SECOND LAW OF THERMODYNAMICS AND HEAT ENGINES

The kinetic theory, treating of the mechanical details of particle motion, is basically a microscopic approach to thermal behavior. Formal thermodynamics, on the other hand, deals with the macroscopic behavior of sytems and takes no account of the details of the system's microscopic behavior. Therein lies its power.

In this chapter we shall consider the most general properties of heat engines and heat pumps, not so much because of their practical importance but rather because we shall thereby be led to a formulation of the second law of thermodynamics. Using the properties of heat engines we shall then see that it is possible to define a temperature scale which is altogether independent of the nature of the thermometric substance. Finally, we shall discuss the thermodynamic concept of entropy, as a quantitative measure of a system's disorder. The entropy concept then leads to still another formulation of the second law.

24-1   Energy convertibility   The systems of which we shall speak in this chapter may consist of *any* well-defined collection of objects. The system may be a single spring, or a magnet, or a complicated machine with many internal moving parts, or it may consist simply of an ideal gas in a container. We shall use the ideal gas to illustrate the processes which follow, because the behavior of such a system is well known, the equation of state being merely the general-gas law.

A system is said to be in thermodynamic equilibrium when (a) the resultant force on it, or on any part of it, is always zero, (b) it is in chemical equilibrium, no chemical reactions taking place, and (c) it is in thermal equilibrium, all its parts and its environment being at the same temperature. It is the third requirement on which we shall concentrate.

A process is a change in the state of a system (Section 20-2). Two types of processes must be distinguished: reversible processes and irreversible processes. A *reversible* process can be made to run backward *merely by reversing* the direction in which the thermodynamic variables change; an *irreversible* process can *not*. For example, if the pressure of a gas in a container of fixed volume is increased by an infinitesimally small amount dp, the temperature will rise by dT. If one wishes, the gas can be returned to its original state simply by lowering the pressure by dp, the temperature then falling by the amount dT. Such a process is reversible. On the other hand, if a gas is allowed to expand freely and suddenly, to fill a container of larger size, and no work or heat enters or leaves the gas, the expansion process is irreversible. That is, the gas will not return to its original state by spontaneously contracting. In general, a reversible process must consist of a succession of infinitesimal changes taking place slowly, so that at each stage the system is in thermodynamic equilibrium. Then, and only then, can a temperature be defined for all intermediate stages.

All isothermal processes are reversible. Since the temperature throughout the system remains constant, the system is always in thermal equilibrium as its state changes. Nonisothermal processes, on the other hand, may or may not be reversible. Consider, for example, an adiabatic process. If a process is to be both adiabatic and reversible, the process must take place fast enough that no thermal energy enters or leaves the system, but slowly enough that the system is at all times in thermal equilibrium. Such conditions can be achieved when the system is inside a good thermal insulator. There are, of course, many examples of irreversible processes: a bursting balloon, a dropped egg, an overstretched spring, a magnetic material suddenly demagnetized by the turning off of an external magnetic field. Indeed, a perfectly reversible process is virtually unattainable; in the macroscopic world all transformations are, to some degree, irreversible.

Consider a system consisting of an ideal gas undergoing a reversible process

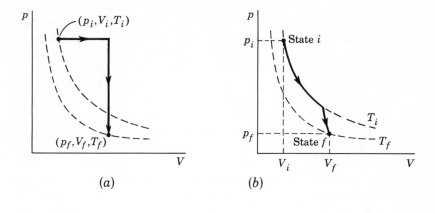

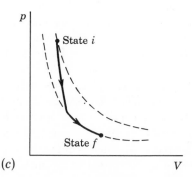

Figure 24-1. Three reversible paths leading from state i to state f at a lower temperature: (a) isobaric expansion followed by isovolumetric cooling, (b) adiabatic expansion followed by isothermal expansion, and (c) isothermal expansion followed by adiabatic expansion.

from some initial state (p_i, V_i, T_i) to some final state (p_f, V_f, T_f). According to the first law of thermodynamics, the heat ΔQ_{if} supplied to the system, the work ΔW_{if} done by the system, and the change in the system's internal energy ΔU_{if} in going from i to f, are related by

[21-15] $$\Delta Q_{if} = \Delta U_{if} + \Delta W_{if}$$

Both ΔQ_{if} and ΔW_{if} depend on the path leading from i to f, but $\Delta U_{if} = U_f - U_i$ does *not*. The internal energy of a system is a function of the *state* of the system, not of its history.

Figure 24-1 shows three possible reversible paths on a p-V diagram between the same pair of initial and final states. In (a) the gas expands at first isobarically and then isovolumetrically, in (b) at first isothermally and then adiabatically, and in (c) at first adiabatically and then isothermally. The internal-energy change is the same for all three processes, since i and f are the same for all three. The temperature falls, and therefore ΔU_{if} is negative. The work done by the gas in going from i to f, which is represented by the area under the curve, differs for (a), (b), and (c). So does the total heat into the system for the three processes. Inasmuch as ΔU_{if} is negative, the first law of thermodynamics requires that the work done in all three processes exceed the net heat added. This is to say, disordered thermal energy from the surroundings (ΔQ_{if}) and internal energy from the system itself (ΔU_{if}) have been converted into ordered energy in the form of work (ΔW_{if}).

The three processes shown in Figure 24-1 were assumed to be reversible. Indeed, a process can be represented by a continuous line on a p-V diagram only if it is reversible, for only then does the system progress through a succession of states of thermal equilibrium with a well-defined temperature at each stage. For an irreversible process, one may show the end points on a p-V diagram, but one can *not* draw *any* line connecting them.

Suppose now that the three processes of Figure 24-1 are exactly reversed, the system now undergoing compression, rather than expansion. In going from state f to i the internal energy change is positive, heat is removed from the system, and work is done on it. That is, ordered energy has been converted into disordered, or thermal, energy which leaves the system as heat or remains in the system to raise its internal energy. In general, when a system undergoes a reversible process in which heat is converted into work, one may rerun the process to return the system to its initial state, work then being converted into heat. The over-all change in the internal energy over the cycle is then zero. Moreover, since such a cycle is represented by a single line on a p-V diagram, not a loop, the heat into the system over the entire cycle is zero and the work done by the system over the entire cycle is also zero.

24-2   Heat engines, heat pumps, and the second law of thermo-dynamics   To utilize the energy stored in chemical or nuclear fuels, such as coal, oil, natural gas, or uranium, one must first convert the fuel's potential energy into thermal energy and then convert some of the thermal energy into work. The chemical or nuclear potential energy stored in fuels can be converted into thermal energy with 100 per cent efficiency (for example, by oxidation or nuclear fission), but the second process, that in which heat is converted into work through the use of a heat engine operating through a cycle, can never, we shall see, have 100 per cent efficiency. Before studying the circumstances under which one achieves the maximum efficiency for heat engines, let us first observe some general properties of all heat engines and heat pumps.

A *heat engine* is any device which, operating *through a cycle, converts* (*some*) *heat into work*. A heat engine is always returned to its initial state after undergoing certain processes in a cycle. Most ordinary heat engines contain a gas as the *working substance*. (This need not be the case. Although it would be awkward to use, an ordinary elastic spring can act as a heat engine: one may heat or cool a spring, and the spring may do work, or have work done on it, as it expands and contracts.) In what follows we shall assume that heat engines have no friction. But even if no energy were dissipated in friction, the efficiency of any engine would be less than 100 per cent—for much more fundamental reasons.

A *heat pump* is a heat engine run backwards. Thus, a heat pump is a device which, operating *through a cycle, converts work into heat* and at the same time *transfers heat* from a low- to a high-temperature reservoir. One simple example of a heat pump is a refrigerator.

The most general type of heat engine is shown schematically in Figure 24-2. We will not be concerned with any mechanical details of construction. The engine, which is represented by a circle, is simply a system

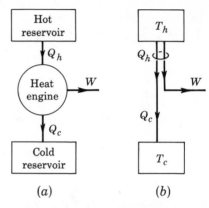

Figure 24-2. (a) Generalized form of a heat engine. (b) Energy flow for a heat engine operating between the temperatures T_h and T_c.

into and out of which heat can flow, and which, when taken through a complete cycle, does net work on its surroundings. The engine may be connected to one heat reservoir which is always at some *hot* temperature T_h. This reservoir contains so large an amount of thermal energy that, even if it loses or gains heat from the engine, the temperature T_h of the reservoir remains unchanged. A second heat reservoir, also of large thermal-energy capacity, remains at the cold temperature T_c.

The following steps take place as an engine is run through one complete cycle. The engine is brought in thermal contact with the hot reservoir, and heat in the amount Q_h enters the engine. The engine converts this thermal energy partly into mechanical energy, or work W, leaving the system, and partly into thermal energy Q_c passing from the engine to the low-temperature reservoir. Having returned to its initial state, the engine has then completed the cycle. The heat Q_c discarded to the low-temperature reservoir, or exhaust, is here represented as a positive quantity. We shall, for convenience, use Q_h, Q_c, and W_c to represent merely the *magnitudes* of heat and work; whether energy is going into or out of the system will be indicated by the directions of arrows in diagrams, rather than by plus and minus signs.

The ratio, of useful work done by any heat engine over a complete cycle to heat supplied to the engine, is called the engine's *the*rmal efficiency e_{th}:

$$e_{th} = \frac{\text{work out}}{\text{heat in}} = \frac{W}{Q_{in}} \qquad [24\text{-}1]$$

where W is the work out per cycle and Q_{in} is the heat in per cycle. If all of the heat enters at the same high temperature T_h, we write $Q_{in} = Q_h$. Applying the first law of thermodynamics to one cycle we have

$$\Delta Q = \Delta U + \Delta W$$
$$Q_h - Q_c = 0 + W$$

Since the system returns to its initial state in completing a cycle, $\Delta U = 0$. Using the equation above in Equation 24-1, we have

$$e_{th} = \frac{Q_h - Q_c}{Q_h} = 1 - \frac{Q_c}{Q_h} \qquad [24\text{-}2]$$

An engine has a 100 per cent thermal efficiency only if $Q_c = 0$, that is, only if no thermal energy is exhausted to the cold reservoir. A perfectly efficient heat engine would convert *all* of the thermal energy entering it into work output when operated over a complete cycle, discarding none. According to the *second law of thermodynamics*, this is impossible!

We earlier stated (Section 22-3) the second law of thermodynamics in terms of the microscopic behavior of a system in passing from states of relative order to states of relative disorder. In macroscopic terms and in the formal language of thermodynamics, the second law of thermodynamics may be given as follows: *no heat engine, reversible or irreversible, operating in a cycle, can take in thermal energy from its surroundings and convert all of this thermal energy into work.* Thus, for any cyclic engine, $Q_c > 0$ and $e_{th} < 100$ per cent. This statement of the second law, first propounded by Lord Kelvin in 1851, is a fundamental law of physics. No exceptions to it have ever been found.

Now consider a heat engine run in reverse as a heat pump. During each cycle, work W is done *on* the system, heat in the amount Q_c is extracted *from* the low-temperature reservoir, and heat in the amount Q_h is exhausted *to* the high-temperature reservoir. See Figure 24-3. Heat is pumped from the low- to the high-temperature reservoir. Note that the thermal energy Q_h given to the hot reservoir is *greater* than the thermal energy Q_c taken from the cold reservoir. This follows from the first law of thermodynamics, with $\Delta U = 0$;

$$Q_h = Q_c + W$$

The heat pump acts as a refrigerator in removing thermal energy from the cold reservoir. If this reservoir has a noninfinite heat capacity, its temperature will fall.

An equivalent statement of the second law of thermodynamics in terms of a heat pump, given by R. Clausius in 1850, is this: *no heat pump, reversible or irreversible, operating over a cycle, can transfer thermal energy from a low-temperature reservoir to a higher-temperature reservoir without external work being done on it.* Thus, for any cyclic heat pump, $W_{in} > 0$. This statement of the second law tells us that, if a hot body and a cold body are placed in thermal contact, it is impossible for the hot body to get hotter while the cold body gets colder.

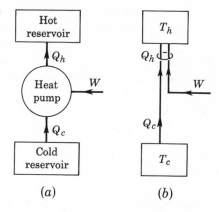

Figure 24-3. (a) Generalized form of a heat pump. (b) Energy flow for a heat pump operating between the temperatures T_h and T_c.

Example 1 (a) Over each cycle, a heat engine removes 1000 calories of heat from a hot reservoir and exhausts 400 calories to a cold reservoir. What is the thermal efficiency of this engine? (b) When the same engine is run in reverse, with the same reservoirs, it is found that to pump 1000 calories of heat per cycle to the hot reservoir requires that 2000 joules of work be done on the pump. Is this engine a reversible or an irreversible engine?

(a) We have $Q_h = 1000$ cal, and $Q_c = 400$ cal. Therefore, $W = Q_h - Q_c = 600$ cal. From Equation 24-2,

$$e_{th} = 1 - (Q_c/Q_h) = 1 - (400/1000) = 60\%$$

(b) If the engine were reversible, then, when it was operated as a heat pump, we would again have $Q_h = 1000$ cal, $Q_c = 400$ cal, and $W = 600$ cal. But the work W is actually 2000 cal. The engine is clearly irreversible.

24-3 Reversible and irreversible heat engines Quite apart from frictional losses, which we will assume to be zero, no heat engine can be perfectly efficient. What, then, is the least inefficient cycle for the conversion of heat into work? In 1824 (before the validity of the first law of thermodynamics had been accepted!), the engineer S. Carnot (1796–1832) studied this question from a theoretical viewpoint and arrived at the following results, all consistent with the first and second laws of thermodynamics.

Of all possible heat engines operating cyclically between any two extremes of temperature T_h and T_c,

(1) a reversible engine taking in heat Q_h at a fixed temperature T_h and rejecting heat Q_c at a fixed temperature T_c is always more efficient than any irreversible engine operating between the same temperatures,

(2) the efficiency of a reversible Carnot engine is independent of the working substance of the engine, and

(3) of all reversible engines operating between the two temperature extremes, the most efficient is the Carnot cycle, which takes in all its heat at a common high temperature and discharges all its heat at a common low temperature.

The first two statements can be proved directly by using the first and second laws of thermodynamics, and we shall do so here. The third statement will be proved in the next section.

Proof of Statement 1. We first recall that a reversible engine can be run forward or backward with no change in the magnitudes of Q_h, Q_c, or W. One need merely change their "directions." Now, if we assume that an irreversible engine actually has a greater efficiency than a reversible engine, we will find that we have a violation of the second law.

We can see this result by considering the two engines R (for *r*eversible) and I (for *i*rreversible) of Figure 24-4 operating between the same two reservoirs. In Figure 24-4a, we see the engine R operating with $Q_h = 10$, $Q_c = 8$, and $W = 2$. (We choose specific values for Q_h, Q_c, and W to avoid an abstract argument.) The engine I in Figure 24-4c is assumed to have the same $Q_h = 10$, but $Q_c = 6$ and $W = 4$. Thus, the irreversible engine I would have a thermal efficiency of 40 per cent; this exceeds that of the reversible engine R, which is only 20 per cent. Figure 24-4b shows the reversible engine R run backwards as a heat pump and, for convenience, Q_h, Q_c, and W all doubled with respect to their magnitudes in Figure 24-4a. If we now imagine the heat pump R of Figure 24-4b to be coupled to the engine I of Figure 24-4c, the work output of I is the work input of R. The work into the composite engine-pump system comprised of I and R together is zero. Therefore, the net result is the pumping of thermal energy from the low-temperature reservoir to the high-temperature *without* work having been done on the system. This is not, of course, a violation of the first law of thermodynamics, but it is an obvious violation of the second law. It is impossible because it is never found to occur in nature.

The hypothetical device shown in Figure 24-4d is known as a *perpetual-motion machine of the "second kind."* This is a device that pumps heat to higher temperatures without having work done on it. If such a device could

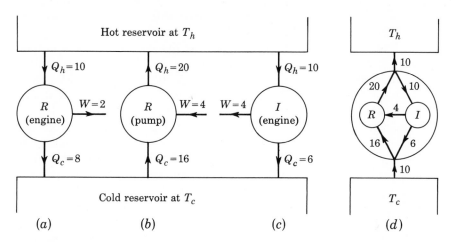

Figure 24-4. (a) and (b) A reversible engine, R, (and pump) and (c) an irreversible engine, I, operating between the same hot and cold reservoirs. (d) A hypothetical combined reversible pump and irreversible engine operating together between T_h and T_c.

be made to work, it would be possible to convert all the thermal energy in the universe into ordered energy, or work. For example, one could run an engine by using the thermal energy in the ocean. An alternative statement of the second law of thermodynamics is this: *it is impossible to construct a perpetual-motion machine of the second kind.*

A perpetual-motion machine of the *first* kind is one in which the mechanical energy remains constant. It is a device that continues in motion indefinitely because it is free of frictional, or other dissipative, losses. This device, which would not involve heat reservoirs, would be basically a toy, rather than a useful machine.

Proof of Statement 2. The efficiency of a reversible Carnot engine is independent of the engine's working substance.

Consider two engines operating in the same reversible cycle, but having different working substances (a steam engine and a diesel engine, for example). Assume that the efficiency of one engine is greater than that of the other. Then we can run the lower-efficiency engine in reverse as a heat pump, couple it to the higher-efficiency engine, and have a net result like that of Figure 24-4d—a transfer of heat from a low- to a high-temperature reservoir without any work being done. By the second law of thermodynamics, this is impossible. Therefore, *the efficiency of a reversible engine is completely independent of the nature of the working substance.*

24-4   The Carnot cycle and the thermodynamic scale of temperature

Carnot recognized that, of all possible heat engines operating between two temperature extremes, the most efficient is the reversible one, which (a) receives thermal energy from some hot reservoir at the constant temperature T_h in an isothermal process, (b) rejects thermal energy to a cold reservoir at the constant temperature T_c, again in an isothermal process, and (c) during any change in the temperature of the engine, has no heat entering or leaving it, the temperature changes taking place in reversible adiabatic processes.

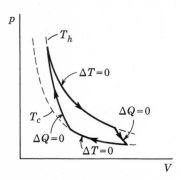

Such a reversible cycle, comprised of two isothermal processes bounded by two reversible adiabatic processes, is known as a *Carnot cycle*. See Figure 24-5.

We proved in the last section that the thermal efficiency of any reversible cycle, such as the Carnot cycle, is independent of the working substance. From Equation 24-2, we have

[24-2] $e_{th} = 1 - (Q_c/Q_h)$

Figure 24-5. A Carnot cycle, consisting of two reversible adiabatic and two isothermal transformations, operating between T_h and T_c.

The ratio Q_c/Q_h does *not* depend on the working substance. If the engine's cycle is a Carnot cycle, the ratio Q_c/Q_h can depend *only on the temperatures T_h and T_c* at which the heat enters and leaves the system. It is possible, therefore, to use the Carnot cycle to define an *absolute thermodynamic temperature scale*, altogether independent of the thermometric substance, in terms of the heat, Q_h and Q_c, entering and leaving during a Carnot cycle. This was first done by Lord Kelvin in 1848, and the thermodynamic temperature scale is sometimes called the Kelvin temperature scale. *By definition*, for a reversible Carnot cycle,

$$T_h/T_c \equiv Q_h/Q_c$$ [24-3]

The size of the unit of the temperature scale is still arbitrary. To be consistent with the size of the Celsius unit (defined in Chapter 19), we assign to the triple point of water the temperature of $273.16°$ K.

Then, the temperature of *any* substance (a solid or liquid, as well as a gas) can be found by (a) cycling the substance through a Carnot cycle, (b) measuring the heat Q entering (or leaving) the system at the unknown temperature T, (c) measuring the heat Q_{tp} leaving (or entering) the system when the system is in thermal equilibrium with water at its *triple point*, and

(d) using the relation

$$T = 273.16° \text{ K} \left(\frac{Q}{Q_{tp}} \right)$$

By combining Equations 24-2 and 24-3, we can write the thermal efficiency of a Carnot cycle as

Carnot cycle: $e_{th} = 1 - \left(\dfrac{T_c}{T_h} \right)$ [24-4]

Equation 24-4 gives the maximum thermal efficiency attainable for any engine operating between the temperatures T_h and T_c. The thermal efficiency

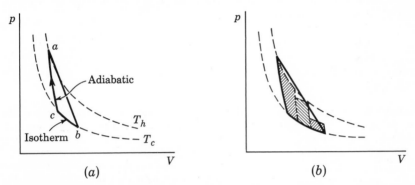

Figure 24-6. (a) A non-Carnot cycle operating between T_h and T_c. (b) The reversible expansion can be approximated closely by a series of adiabatic and isothermal expansions.

is 100 per cent only if the engine exhausts heat to a cold reservoir at the absolute zero of temperature—an impossibility. Typical heat engines have very low efficiencies. For example, if an engine takes in heat at a high temperature of 200° C and exhausts heat at a room temperature of 30° C ($T_h = 473°$ K, $T_c = 303°$ K), its efficiency can never exceed

$$e_{th} = 1 - (303/473) = 36\%.$$

In actual engines friction is present, the processes are not perfectly reversible, and the operating cycle is not a Carnot cycle; consequently, the actual efficiency is even less.

It is not difficult to show that the Carnot cycle is the most efficient of all reversible cycles operating between two fixed temperatures extremes. For example, consider the cycle shown in Figure 24-6a. Starting at point a the system expands reversibly along the line ab (which is *not* an adiabatic or an isothermal path), the temperature decreasing from T_h to T_c. This is followed by an isothermal compression to point c and then an adiabatic compression which returns the system to point a. How does the efficiency of this reversible cycle compare with that of a Carnot cycle between the same temperature extremes? As shown in Figure 24-6b, the reversible expansion can be approximated as closely as we wish by a series of isothermal and adiabatic steps. Thus, we can replace the reversible cycle of Figure 24-6a by a large number of small, adjacent Carnot cycles, as shown in Figure 24-6b. The efficiency of any one of these small Carnot cycles depends on its upper and lower temperatures. In Figure 24-6b, the upper temperature of any small Carnot cycle is not, in general, as great as T_h (similarly, the lower temperature need not be as low as T_c). Therefore, the over-all efficiency of the whole reversible cycle must be less than that of a Carnot cycle between T_h and T_c. Thus, we can write

$$\text{Any non-Carnot reversible engine:} \quad e_{\text{th}} < 1 - \left(\frac{T_c}{T_h}\right)$$

where T_c and T_h are the temperature extremes of the working substance in the engine.

Example 2 Show that the absolute temperature scale defined on the basis of the general-gas law for an ideal gas is equivalent to the absolute thermodynamic temperature scale (which holds, of course, for *any* thermometric substance, ideal gas or otherwise).

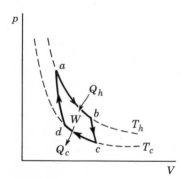

Figure 24-7. Energy transfers in a Carnot cycle between temperatures T_h and T_c.

Let us take an ideal gas around a closed Carnot cycle, as shown in Figure 24-7. We wish to show that $Q_h/Q_c = T_h/T_c$, where T_c and T_h are now the temperatures defined by the general-gas law.

For the isothermal processes,

$$pV = \text{constant}$$

and the work done in expansion (see Example 3, Section 20-4) is

$$[20\text{-}11] \qquad W_{i \to f} = nRT \ln (V_f/V_i) \qquad [24\text{-}5]$$

For the adiabatic processes,

$$[21\text{-}23] \qquad pV^{\gamma} = K_1$$

or, equivalently,

$$[21\text{-}22] \qquad TV^{(\gamma-1)} = K \qquad [24\text{-}6]$$

Note that the T appearing in Equations 24-5 and 24-6 is the absolute temperature defined by the general-gas law.

The internal energy of an ideal gas does not change in an isothermal process. Therefore, during the isothermal expansion, the heat Q_h entering the system at the high temperature must equal the work done by the gas in expanding from a to b:

$$Q_h = W_{a \to b} = nRT_h \ln (V_b/V_a) \qquad [24\text{-}7]$$

where we have used the results of Equation 24-5. In similar fashion, the heat Q_c leaving the system is

$$Q_c = -W_{d \to c} = nRT_c \ln (V_c/V_d) \qquad [24\text{-}8]$$

We wish to show that $V_b/V_a = V_c/V_d$. For any adiabatic expansion of an ideal gas between the *same* two isotherms, the ratio of the final volume to the initial volume depends only on the two fixed temperatures T_h and T_c. This follows from Equation 24-6. Thus, the ratio of final to initial volumes is constant:

$$V_d/V_a = V_c/V_b$$
$$V_b/V_a = V_c/V_d \qquad [24\text{-}9]$$

Using Equation 24-9 in Equations 24-7 and 24-8 to find the ratio of Q_h to Q_c, we find

$$Q_h/Q_c = T_h/T_c$$

This is identical with Equation 24-3, which gives the Kelvin definition of the absolute temperature scale. Therefore, ideal-gas thermometers register the absolute thermodynamic temperature.

Example 3 One mole of helium gas is taken through the reversible closed cycle shown in Figure 24-8a. (a) Calculate the thermal efficiency of an engine operating

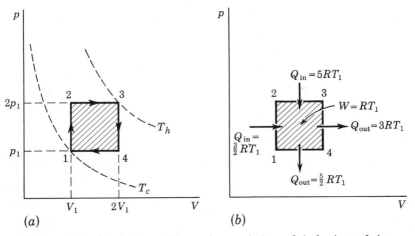

Figure 24-8. (a) A reversible cycle consisting of isobaric and iso-volumetric transformations operating between the temperature extremes T_h and T_c. (b) The energy transfers occurring in this cycle.

in this reversible cycle. (b) What would be the efficiency of an engine operating in a Carnot cycle between the temperature extremes given by part (a)?

(a) The thermal efficiency of any heat engine is given by

[24-1] $e_{\text{th}} = W/Q_{\text{in}}$

The work W done per cycle by the gas is just the shaded area in the figure,

$$W = p_1 V_1$$

or, using the general-gas law $pV = nRT$, with $n = 1$,

$$W = RT_1$$

The calculation of Q_{in}, the net heat entering the system over one cycle, is a little more complicated. We first use the general-gas law to find the temperatures at points 2, 3, and 4, noting that $p_2 = 2p_1$ with $V_2 = V_1$, that $p_3 = 2p_1$ with $V_3 = 2V_1$, and that $p_4 = p_1$ with $V_4 = 2V_1$. Therefore,

$$T_2 = 2T_1, \qquad T_3 = 4T_1, \qquad \text{and} \quad T_4 = 2T_1$$

We find the internal energy at the four points by using Equation 21-14, $U = \frac{3}{2}nRT = \frac{3}{2}RT$:

$$U_1 = \tfrac{3}{2}RT_1,$$
$$U_2 = 2U_1 = 3RT_1$$
$$U_3 = 4U_1 = 6RT_1$$
$$U_4 = 2U_1 = 3RT_1$$

Finally, we find the heat into the system in each of the four processes by applying the first law of thermodynamics:

$$\Delta Q = \Delta U + \Delta W$$
$$Q_{1\to2} = (U_2 - U_1) + W_{1\to2} = \tfrac{3}{2}RT_1 + 0 = \tfrac{3}{2}RT_1$$
$$Q_{2\to3} = (U_3 - U_2) + W_{2\to3} = 3RT_1 + 2RT_1 = 5RT_1$$
$$Q_{3\to4} = (U_4 - U_3) + W_{3\to4} = -3RT_1 + 0 = -3RT_1$$
$$Q_{4\to1} = (U_1 - U_4) + W_{4\to1} = -\tfrac{3}{2}RT_1 - RT_1 = -\tfrac{5}{2}RT_1$$

The total heat Q_{in} *into* the system per cycle is (see Figure 24-8b):

$$Q_{in} = Q_{1\to2} + Q_{2\to3} = \tfrac{3}{2}RT_1 + 5RT_1 = \tfrac{13}{2}RT_1$$

Similarly,

$$Q_{out} = Q_{3\to4} + Q_{4\to1} = 3RT_1 + \tfrac{5}{2}RT_1 = \tfrac{11}{2}RT_1 \qquad \text{(in magnitude)}$$

We saw earlier that the work done per cycle is $W = RT_1$. This also follows from applying the first law of thermodynamics to the *entire cycle*; $\Delta U = 0$, and therefore $\Delta Q = \Delta W$, or

$$W = \Delta W = \Delta Q = Q_{in} - Q_{out} = \tfrac{13}{2}RT_1 - \tfrac{11}{2}RT_1 = RT_1$$

Therefore,

$$e_{th} = \frac{W}{Q_{in}} = \frac{RT_1}{\tfrac{13}{2}RT_1} = \frac{2}{13} \simeq 15\%$$

(b) For a Carnot engine operating between $T_h = T_3 = 4T_1$ and $T_c = T_1$ the thermal efficiency is

[24-4]   Carnot engine: $e_{th} = 1 - \dfrac{T_c}{T_h} = 1 - \dfrac{1}{4} = 75\%$

24-5 Entropy We saw in Section 22-3 that the second law of thermo-dynamics is strictly a macroscopic principle. It has meaning only when we deal with large numbers of particles. The second law, as formulated in

Section 22-3, required that any isolated system always proceed toward states of greater disorder. We wish to find that quantity, called the entropy, which gives a quantitative measure of the disorder of the system. Indeed, we shall see, through the concept of entropy, that the two formulations of the second law of thermodynamics—one in terms of the behavior of heat engines and the other in terms of the passage of an isolated system to states of greater disorder—are, in fact, equivalent.

The absolute thermodynamic temperature was defined for a reversible Carnot cycle in such a way that the ratio of heat to temperature was the same for both the isothermal expansion and the isothermal compression. That is, from Equation 24-3, $Q_h/T_h = Q_c/T_c$ for a *Carnot* cycle, where Q_h and Q_c represent, respectively, the *magnitudes* of the heat in and the heat out. In the analysis that follows it will be important to adhere to the sign convention used originally in developing the first law of thermodynamics: heat *entering* the system is *positive;* heat *leaving* is *negative.* Using this convention, we then have for the Carnot cycle

$$\frac{Q_h}{T_h} = -\frac{Q_c}{T_c}$$

or,
$$\frac{Q_h}{T_h} + \frac{Q_c}{T_c} = 0 \qquad [24\text{-}10]$$

Thus, for a *Carnot* cycle, the sum of the quantities Q/T around a closed cycle is zero. This rule is more general, holding for *any* reversible cycle, as we shall now show.

Consider the reversible cycle shown in Figure 24-9. Any reversible cycle can be approximated as closely as we wish by a series of isothermal and adiabatic processes; that is, a reversible cycle is equivalent to a series of Carnot cycles. For example, we can approximate the cycle in Figure 24-9 by three adjacent Carnot cycles. Equation 24-10 holds for each of the Carnot cycles. Adding together the equations for the three Carnot cycles which approximate the original reversible cycle, we have

$$\left(\frac{Q_1}{T_1} + \frac{Q_1'}{T_3}\right) + \left(\frac{Q_2}{T_2} + \frac{Q_2'}{T_4}\right) + \left(\frac{Q_3}{T_3} + \frac{Q_3'}{T_4}\right) = 0$$

No heat enters or leaves the system during the adiabatic processes (portion within dotted lines in Figure 24-9). Therefore, we can write the last equation more simply as

$$\Sigma\,(Q/T) = 0$$

where the summation is taken around the periphery of the original cycle.

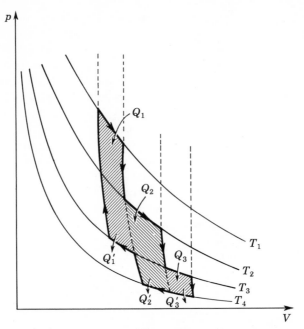

Figure 24-9. A reversible cycle approximated by a number of Carnot cycles.

In general, we can approximate any actual reversible cycle by a series of isothermal and adiabatic segments. In the limit, we can then write

$$\oint \frac{dQ}{T} = 0 \qquad \text{(for } any \text{ } reversible \text{ cycle)} \qquad \text{[24-11]}$$

The circle about the integral sign indicates that the integration is to be taken around a closed path.

In words, Equation 24-11 says that, for *any reversible cycle*, the sum of the quantities giving the ratio dQ/T, of the heat dQ entering the system to the temperature T at which the heat enters, is *zero* around the cycle. This is equivalent to saying that the integral of dQ/T between any initial state i and any final state f is the same for *all reversible* paths from i to f. As Figure 24-10 shows, $\int_i^f dQ/T$ along the path P_1 equals $\int_i^f dQ/T$ along the path P_2.

In Section 12-2 it was shown that if a particle is subject to a conservative force F, then $\oint F \cdot ds = 0$; that is, when the particle is taken around a closed loop the work done on a particle by a conservative force is zero. Consequently, we were able to define a quantity called the potential energy U, such that $U_f - U_i = -\int_i^f F \cdot ds$, the difference in potential energy depending on the end points i and f but not on the route from i to f. In like fashion we can define a thermodynamic quantity called the *entropy*, S, whose difference depends only on the end points. By definition,

$$S_f - S_i \equiv \int_i^f \frac{dQ}{T} \qquad\qquad [24\text{-}12]$$

Note that the integration may be carried out along *any reversible* path leading from i to f. Equation 24-12 reduces, of course, to Equation 24-11 when $i = f$.

Suppose that an actual system proceeds *irreversibly* from state i to state f. We can *not* represent any irreversible process by a path on a p-V diagram. Nevertheless we *can* determine the entropy difference between the states i and f. We simply imagine the system to pass from i to f along a *reversible* path and compute the change in entropy, using Equation 24-12. This is allowed, inasmuch as the entropy difference depends on the end points and not on the path. (Analogously, in mechanics we can evaluate the potential-energy difference between two points, even when a nonconservative dissipative force acts and the system is not able to pass reversibly between the end points.)

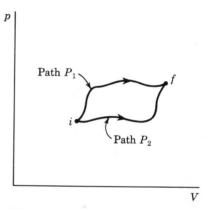

Figure 24-10. Two reversible paths, P_1 and P_2, leading from state i to state f.

In general, when a system is taken around a complete *reversible* cycle and returned to its initial state i, the net change in the internal energy is zero ($\Delta U = 0$), the net change in the entropy is zero ($\Delta S = 0$), the work done (ΔW) by the system is equal to the area enclosed by the loop on the p-V diagram and, by the first law of thermodynamics, the net heat ΔQ entering the system is $\Delta Q = \Delta W$. Moreover, when a system is taken through an *irreversible* cycle and returned to its initial state i, the change in the internal energy again is zero ($\Delta U = 0$), the change in entropy is also zero ($\Delta S = 0$), the system has done work in the amount ΔW, *not* representable by any area on a p-V diagram, and net heat entering the system is again $\Delta Q = \Delta W$.

Example 4 One mole of an ideal gas is initially in the state (p_1, V_1, T_1). Find the change in entropy of the system when the gas expands to twice its initial volume (a) along a reversible adiabatic path, (b) along a reversible isothermal path, and (c) along a reversible isobaric path.

(a) The three processes are shown in Figure 24-11a. Using Equation 24-12 we have, for the adiabatic path from 1 to 4,

$$S_4 - S_1 = \int_1^4 dQ/T = 0$$

since dQ is zero for an adiabatic process. Therefore, $S_4 = S_1$. The entropy is the same at all points along a *reversible adiabatic path*; therefore, a reversible adiabatic process is often referred to as an *isentropic* process.

(b) For the isothermal path from 1 to 3,

$$S_3 - S_1 = \int_1^3 dQ/T = Q_{1\to3}/T_1$$

Inasmuch as the temperature is constant along an isothermal path, T_1 was taken outside the integral sign. We recall that the change in the internal energy of the

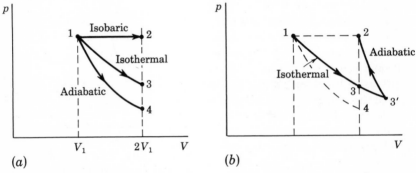

(a)   (b)

Figure 24-11. (a) Three reversible expansions. (b) The entropy change in the expansion from 1 to 2 is most easily computed by considering an isothermal expansion from 1 to 3 to 3′ followed by an adiabatic compression to 2.

gas is zero along an isothermal path. Therefore, the first law of thermodynamics gives

$$Q_{1\to3} = W_{1\to3} = RT_1 \ln (V_3/V_1)$$

where we have used the result found in Example 3, Section 20-4. Combining the last two equations and using the fact that $V_3 = 2V_1$, we have

$$S_3 - S_1 = R \ln 2$$

(c) The entropy change $(S_2 - S_1)$ for the isobaric process is independent of the reversible path we choose between points 1 and 2. Therefore, let us, to simplify the computation, first proceed along the isothermal path to point 3′ and then along the adiabatic path from 3′ to 2, as shown in Figure 24-11b.

From part (a), there is no entropy change along the adiabatic compression from 3′ to 2. We have, then, using the results of part (b),

$$S_2 - S_1 = S_{3'} - S_1 = R \ln (V_{3'}/V_1) \qquad [24\text{-}13]$$

For the adiabatic path between 3′ and 2, we have, from Equation 21-22,

$$T_1 V_{3'}{}^{\gamma-1} = T_2 V_2{}^{\gamma-1} \qquad [24\text{-}14]$$

The ideal-gas law relates points 1 and 2:

$$p_1 V_1/T_1 = p_2 V_2/T_2$$

and, since $p_2 = p_1$ and $V_2 = 2V_1$, we have $T_2 = 2T_1$. Using these relations in Equation 24-14 yields

$$V_{3'}/V_1 = 2 V_{3'}/V_2 = 2 \times 2^{1/(\gamma-1)} = 2^{\gamma/(\gamma-1)}$$

and Equation 24-13 becomes

$$S_2 - S_1 = R \ln 2^{\gamma/(\gamma-1)} = R\left(\frac{\gamma}{\gamma-1}\right)\ln 2$$

The results above show that the entropy at point 2 is greater than that at point 3, which is, in turn, greater than that at point 4.

24-6   Entropy and the second law of thermodynamics

We now state the second law of thermodynamics in terms of the concept of entropy and show that this formulation of the second law is equivalent to that given in Section 24-2 in terms of heat engines.

The *second law of thermodynamics:* for an *isolated* system the *total entropy* remains *constant* in time if *all* processes occurring within the system are *reversible*; on the other hand, the *total entropy* of an isolated system increases with time if *any* process within the system is *irreversible*. Inasmuch as all actual macroscopic systems undergo irreversible processes, the *total entropy* of any real system always increases with time.

The equivalence between this statement of the second law and that given in Section 24-2 can easily be shown. Consider a system composed of a hot reservoir at temperature T_h, a cold reservoir at temperature T_c, and a heat engine operating between the two heat reservoirs, as shown in Figure 24-12. The engine may be either reversible or irreversible.

For each complete cycle of the heat engine, the total change in the entropy of the entire system—the heat engine and its surroundings—is described as follows.

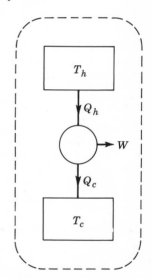

Figure 24-12. The system, consisting of the heat engine together with the hot and cold reservoirs, chosen in applying the second law of thermodynamics to heat engines and in computing entropy changes.

(1) The hot reservoir *loses* entropy because heat Q_h *leaves* the reservoir: ΔS (hot reservoir) $= -Q_h/T_h$.

(2) The cold reservoir *gains* entropy because heat Q_c *enters* the reservoir: ΔS (cold reservoir) $= Q_c/T_c$.

(3) The heat engine alone undergoes *no change* in entropy, since it is returned to the same entropy state after completing a cycle, whether the engine is reversible or not.

(4) As work is done by the engine, energy leaves the system, but *no* entropy thereby leaves or enters the system inasmuch as *ordered* energy has no entropy content.

Adding together these contributions, we find for the total entropy change ΔS of the system:

$$\Delta S = \frac{Q_c}{T_c} - \frac{Q_h}{T_h} \qquad [24\text{-}15]$$

We recall the definition of the thermal efficiency of a heat engine:

$$[24\text{-}2] \qquad \textit{Any} \text{ engine}: \qquad e_{\text{th}} = 1 - \frac{Q_c}{Q_h}$$

Our earlier statement of the second law was that no engine operating between the two fixed temperatures T_h and T_c can be more efficient than a reversible Carnot engine, whose efficiency is

$$[24\text{-}4] \qquad \textit{Carnot} \text{ engine}: \qquad e_{\text{th}} = 1 - \frac{T_c}{T_h}$$

Therefore,

$$\textit{Any} \text{ engine}: \qquad e_{\text{th}} = 1 - \frac{Q_c}{Q_h} \leq 1 - \frac{T_c}{T_h}$$

or, rewriting,

$$\frac{Q_c}{T_c} \geq \frac{Q_h}{T_h}$$

Equation 24-15 then gives

$$\text{Entire system}: \qquad \Delta S \geq 0$$

The equality sign applies for reversible processes; the inequality sign, for irreversible processes.

Example 5 What is the entropy change arising in the free expansion of an ideal gas from volume V_i to V_f?

No heat enters or leaves the system in this irreversible process ($\Delta Q = 0$), and the gas does no work when it expands freely ($\Delta W = 0$). Therefore, from the first law, $\Delta U = \Delta Q - \Delta W = 0$. Since the temperature is directly proportional to the internal energy for an ideal gas, the free expansion represents an *irreversible* adiabatic expansion in which the temperature in the final equilibrium state is the same as that in the initial state. (This free expansion should not be described as an isothermal expansion, even though the initial and final temperatures are the same. The expansion proceeds irreversibly, and during this expansion thermal equilibrium does not exist and a temperature cannot be defined for the system.) The initial and final states are shown in Figure 24-13.

We can find the entropy change of the gas between the states i and f by recalling that ΔS depends only on the end points, not on the path. For the purpose of computing ΔS, it is most simple to imagine the gas as proceeding from i to f via an isothermal path:

$$S_{i \rightarrow f} = \int_i^f dQ/T = (1/T) \int_i^f dQ$$
$$= (1/T) \int_i^f dW$$

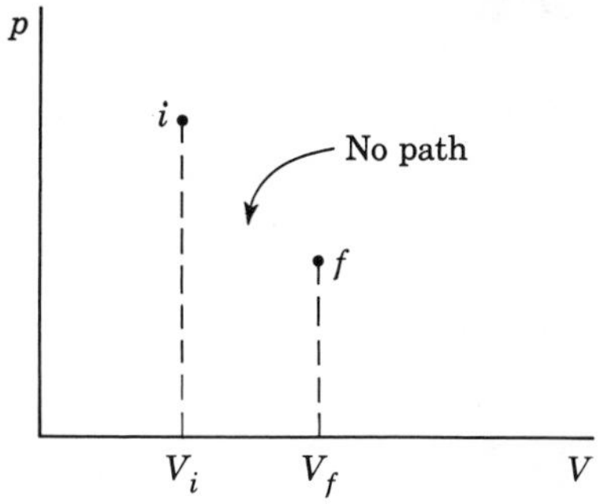

It was shown in Example 3, Section 20-4, that $dW = nRT \ln (V_f/V_i)$ in an isothermal expansion. This being so,

$$\Delta S(\text{gas}) = nR \ln (V_f/V_i)$$

Figure 24-13. The initial and final states for a free (irreversible) expansion. Note that *no* path can be drawn from i to f.

This is the entropy change whenever an ideal gas expands from (V_i, T_i) to (V_f, T_i), whether it expands reversibly *or* irreversibly. Inasmuch as the gas does not interact with its surroundings in the irreversible free expansion, the total entropy change of the system (gas and surroundings) is that of the gas itself. Thus,

$$\Delta S(\text{system}) = nR \ln (V_f/V_i)$$

The entropy change is greater than zero and independent of the temperature.

It was shown in the above example that a freely expanding ideal gas increases its entropy and shows no change in its final equilibrium temperature. This process was discussed in Section 22-3 in terms of the microscopic behavior of the gas molecules. We saw there that when a gas expands freely to fill a larger volume, the *spatial disorder* of the system of molecules increases. No change occurs, however, in the disorder of the molecules as measured by their kinetic energies, inasmuch as the temperature is unchanged. Example 6 below shows that *disorder in energy* increases for an irreversible process, even though the spatial disorder is unchanged.

The entropy of a system is a quantitative measure of the disorder (in space, in energy, or in both) of a system. This is proved in detail through the arguments of statistical mechanics. Thus, when the second law of thermodynamics asserts that the total entropy of an isolated system must increase in time, it implies that any isolated system undergoing a change proceeds to states of greater disorder. The simplest example of a system whose entropy (and disorder) increases is that of two bodies, initially at different temperatures, that are brought together and reach a final thermal equilibrium at a temperature intermediate between the two initial temperatures. Example 6, which uses ideal gases, for simplicity, shows that in all such irreversible processes the entropy of the system increases.

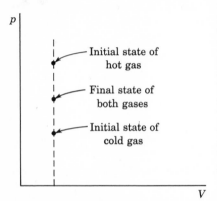

Figure 24-14. Changes in the states of a hot and cold gas brought into thermal equilibrium.

Example 6 One mole of an ideal monatomic gas is held in each of two halves of a container. The gas in one half has an initial temperature T; the other gas is initially at the temperature $T/2$. No heat leaves or enters through the walls. We now imagine that the partition separating the two gases has become a thermal conductor, so that thermal energy flows from the hot to the cold gas until both gases arrive at thermal equilibrium at the common final temperature $\frac{3}{4}T$. What is the total entropy change for the system?

The initial and final states are shown in Figure 24-14. Since neither gas changes volume, the change in entropy of the system does not arise from an increase in spatial disorder. The change in entropy for the hot gas is $\int_{T}^{\frac{3}{4}T} dQ/T$ and for the cold gas it is $\int_{\frac{1}{2}T}^{\frac{3}{4}T} dQ/T$. The total entropy change for the system is then

$$\Delta S = \int_{T}^{\frac{3}{4}T} dQ/T + \int_{\frac{1}{2}T}^{\frac{3}{4}T} dQ/T$$

Neither gas does work: $\Delta W = 0$. From the first law,

$$\Delta Q = \Delta U = \tfrac{3}{2}R\,\Delta T$$

Therefore,

$$\Delta S = \tfrac{3}{2}R \int_{T}^{\frac{3}{4}T} dT/T + \tfrac{3}{2}R \int_{\frac{1}{2}T}^{\frac{3}{4}T} dT/T$$

$$\Delta S = \tfrac{3}{2}R(\ln \tfrac{3}{4} + \ln \tfrac{3}{2}) = \tfrac{3}{2}R \ln \tfrac{9}{8}$$

The entropy of the system *increases* in this irreversible process.

The first law of thermodynamics states that the total energy of a completely isolated system remains constant in time; the second law states that the total entropy of such a system increases with time. Whereas the first law is concerned with the *quantity* of energy in an isolated system, which remains unchanged, the second law is, so to speak, concerned with the *quality* of energy in an isolated system, which becomes degraded as the disorder of the system increases.

The conservation of energy principle applies at both the macroscopic and microscopic levels. Energy is conserved both in atomic collisions and in large-body collisions. But such thermodynamic terms as "temperature" and "entropy" have meaning only at the macroscopic level, where one deals with systems containing many particles. Microscopic transformations, such as atomic collisions, are completely reversible in time. On the other hand, macroscopic systems proceed irreversibly to states of greater disorder and greater entropy. The impression that there are violations of this rule, in the remarkable order and organization of living materials, arises only when one fails to recognize that the obviously decreasing entropy of a living organism is more than compensated for by the increasing entropy of its environment.

24-7 Summary One must distinguish between two general classes of thermodynamic processes, the reversible and the irreversible.

A heat engine operates through a cycle to convert heat to work. A heat pump operates through a cycle to convert work to heat, at the same time transferring heat from a low- to a high-temperature reservoir.

The thermal efficiency of a heat engine, defined as the work W out of the engine divided by the net heat Q_{in} into the engine over a cycle, is equal to

[24-1]
$$e_{th} = \frac{W}{Q_{in}} = 1 - \frac{Q_c}{Q_h}$$

where Q_c is the heat exhausted to the cold reservoir and Q_h is the heat entering from the hot reservoir.

Three general properties of heat engines are these: (a) a reversible engine is always more efficient than an irreversible engine, the two operating between the same temperatures, (b) a Carnot engine (one comprised of two isothermal and two adiabatic processes) has an efficiency that is independent of the working substance, and (c) a Carnot engine is more efficient than any other engine operating between the same two temperature extremes, and its thermal efficiency is given by

[24-4]
$$\text{Carnot engine:} \quad e_{th} = 1 - \frac{T_c}{T_h}$$

where T_c and T_h are the temperatures of the cold and hot reservoirs, respectively.

The absolute thermodynamic temperature scale is defined, in terms of the heats Q_h and Q_c respectively, that enter and leave, any thermometric substance carried through a reversible Carnot cycle, by the following relation:

[24-3]
$$\frac{T_h}{T_c} = \frac{Q_h}{Q_c}$$

The entropy change between states i and f is defined as

$$[24\text{-}12] \qquad\qquad S_f - S_i = \int_i^f \frac{dQ}{T}$$

this difference being independent of the path between states i and f. Entropy is a quantitative measure of disorder.

For any isolated system, the entropy change $\Delta S = 0$ if the system undergoes only reversible processes, but $\Delta S > 0$ for irreversible systems.

The following are equivalent statements of the second law of thermodynamics:

(1) No heat engine, reversible or irreversible, operating over a cycle, can take in thermal energy from its surroundings and convert all of this thermal energy into work.

(2) No heat pump, reversible or irreversible, operating over a cycle, can transfer thermal energy from a low-temperature reservoir to a high-temperature reservoir without external work being done on it. It is impossible to construct a perpetual-motion machine of the "second kind."

(3) The total entropy of any isolated system increases with time.

(4) Any isolated system always passes from states of relative order to states of relative disorder (Chapter 22).

PROBLEMS

24-1 Two moles of an ideal monatomic gas are initially at $600°$ K and 2.0 atm. The gas expands along an isothermal path to twice its original volume. (a) Calculate the work done by the gas. (b) How much heat enters the gas during this expansion? (c) What is the change in internal energy of the gas?

24-2 As in Problem 24-1, 2 moles of an ideal monatomic gas are initially at $600°$ K and 2.0 atm. Assume that the gas now expands reversibly along an adiabatic path to twice its original volume. (a) Calculate the work done by the gas. (b) How much heat enters the gas in this expansion? (c) What is the change in internal energy of the gas?

24-3 What is the maximum possible thermal efficiency of an engine extracting heat at $400°$ F and rejecting heat at $100°$ F?

24-4 A reversible heat pump acts as a refrigerator, work being done on the heat pump at the rate of 1.00 kw. If heat is taken from the low-temperature reservoir at the rate of 0.40 kw, what is the rate at which heat is given to the high-temperature reservoir?

24-5 A heat engine operates between the temperatures of $300°$ and $30°$ C. What is the maximum thermal efficiency possible for this heat engine? (b) If this engine were to be operated in reverse as a heat pump, what would be the maximum ratio (called the *coefficient of performance of a* *refrigerator*) of the heat extracted from the lower-temperature reservoir to the work into the heat pump? (c) What would be the maximum ratio (called the *coefficient of performance of a heat engine*) of the heat added to the higher-temperature reservoir to the work into the heat engine?

24-6 ⋆ Consider the two-cycle reversible processes shown in Figure 24-15 for an ideal monatomic gas: an expansion along a straight-line path from the initial state (p_1, V_1, T_1) to the state $(\frac{1}{2}p_1, 2V_1, T_1)$, followed by an isothermal compression back to the initial state. (a) What is the

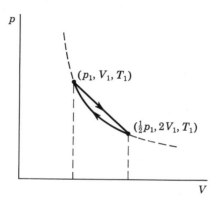

Figure 24-15.

highest temperature the gas reaches during this closed cycle? (b) Through what part of the straight-line path is heat entering the gas? (c) What is the thermal efficiency of this reversible cycle? (d) What would be the thermal efficiency of a Carnot engine operating between the same temperature extremes?

24-7 An ordinary helical spring is taken through a Carnot cycle by having it undergo, in turn, an expansion at constant temperature, an expansion with no loss or gain of heat, an isothermal compression, and an adiabatic compression which returns the spring to its original state. The isothermal expansion takes place at the temperature of the triple point of water, 200 joules of heat entering the spring in this process. In the isothermal compression 150 joules of heat leave the spring. (a) What is the temperature of the spring in the isothermal compression? (b) What is the thermal efficiency of the spring as a heat engine?

24-8 One mole of an ideal monatomic gas, initially at 1.0 atmosphere and 127° C, is taken through the following reversible Carnot cycle: isothermal expansion to twice its initial volume, adiabatic expansion to 27° C, isothermal compression, and an adiabatic compression which returns the gas to its initial state. Find (a) the heat entering the gas per cycle, (b) the heat leaving the gas per cycle, and (c) the work done per cycle.

24-9 Two Carnot engines, one with a monatomic ideal gas and the second with a diatomic ideal gas, operate between the same hot- and cold-temperature reservoirs. Assume that both gases undergo the *same isothermal expansion*. (a) Do the two engines necessarily have the same thermal efficiency? (b) Which engine takes in the greater heat during the isothermal expansion?

24-10 Consider Example 4c, Section 24-5. Evaluate the entropy change $S_2 - S_1$ along the reversible isobaric path, using Equation 24-12, and show that one again obtains $R\gamma \ln 2/(\gamma - 1)$.

24-11 ★ Show that *all irreversible* adiabatic expansions of an ideal gas must end in final states which lie on a p-V diagram between the two lines defining a *reversible* adiabatic expansion and a *reversible* isothermal expansion, respectively.

24-12 One hundred grams of copper (specific heat, 0.093 cal/gm-C°) at 100° C are dropped into 150 gm of water initially at 10° C. Assume that no thermal energy leaves the system composed of the copper and water. (a) What is the final equilibrium temperature? (b) What is the change in thermal energy of the system? (c) What is the change in entropy of the system? (d) Is this a reversible or irreversible process?

24-13 Assume the conditions given in Problem 24-1. (a) What is the change in entropy of the gas in the expansion process? (b) What is the change in the total entropy of the gas and its surroundings?

24-14 See Problem 24-8. Compute (a) the change in entropy of the gas per cycle and (b) the change in the total entropy of the gas and its surroundings per cycle.

24-15 For an ideal gas a reversible adiabatic path can cross a reversible isothermal path on a p-V diagram once only. Suppose that the system is *not* an ideal gas and that the relation for an adiabatic transformation is *not* $pV^\gamma = K$. Show that, *in general*, a reversible adiabatic path on a p-V diagram can cross an isothermal path only once, since two crossings would be a violation of the second law of thermodynamics. (*Hint*: What would be the temperatures at the two points where the isothermal and adiabatic paths cross? What would be the entropy change over one cycle?)

appendix I

FUNDAMENTAL CONSTANTS

The values listed below are taken from the *American Institute of Physics Handbook* (1957). The last significant figure may in some instances be indefinite.

NAME OF QUANTITY	COMMON SYMBOL	VALUE
Acceleration due to gravity (standard value)	g	9.80665 m/sec^2 = 32.1740 ft/sec^2
Universal gravitational constant	G	6.673×10^{-11} nt-m^2/kg^2
Speed of light (in vacuum)	c	2.99793×10^8 m/sec
Earth's mass	m_E	5.975×10^{24} kg
Earth's mean radius	r_E	6.371×10^6 m = 3959 mi
Earth–moon mean distance	r_{EM}	$3.84 \times 10^8 \simeq 60$ Earth radii
Earth–sun mean distance (1 astronomical unit)	1 AU	1.49×10^{11} m = 92.9×10^6 mi
Sun's mass	m_S	1.99×10^{30} kg
Electron mass	m_e	9.1083×10^{-31} kg
Proton mass	m_p	1.67239×10^{-27} kg
Density of water (at $3.98°$ C)		0.999973 gm/cm^3
Standard atmospheric pressure	1 atm	1.013×10^5 nt/m^2 = 76 cm Hg
Universal gas constant	R	8.317 joules/mole-K$°$ = 0.0821 liter-atm/mole-K$°$
Volume of 1 mole ideal gas at STP		22.415 liters
Absolute zero of temperature		$-273.15°$ C
Triple point of water		$273.16°$ K
Avogadro's number	N_0	6.025×10^{23}/gm-mole
Boltzmann's constant	k	1.3804×10^{-23} joule/K$°$
"Mechanical equivalent of heat"	J	4.1855 joules/gm-cal
Stefan-Boltzmann constant	σ	5.669×10^{-8} joule/m^2-sec-(K$°$)^4

appendix II

CONVERSION FACTORS

Length

	M	CM	KM
1 meter	1	10^2	10^{-3}
1 centimeter	10^{-2}	1	10^{-5}
1 kilometer	10^3	10^5	1
1 inch	2.540×10^{-2}	2.540	2.540×10^{-5}
1 foot	0.3048	30.48	3.048×10^{-4}
1 mile	1609	1.609×10^5	1.609

	IN.	FT	MI
1 meter	39.37	3.281	6.214×10^{-4}
1 centimeter	0.3937	3.281×10^{-2}	6.214×10^{-6}
1 kilometer	3.937×10^4	3.281×10^3	0.6214
1 inch	1	8.333×10^{-2}	1.578×10^{-5}
1 foot	12	1	1.894×10^{-4}
1 mile	6.336×10^4	5280	1

1 foot $= \frac{1200}{3937}$ m

1 mile $= 10^{-3}$ in.

1 light-year $= 9.4600 \times 10^{12}$ km

1 parsec $= 3.084 \times 10^{13}$ km

1 astronomical unit (mean Earth–Sun distance) $= 1$ AU $= 1.49 \times 10^{11}$ m

1 micron $= 1\ \mu = 10^{-6}$ m

1 millimicron $= 1\ m\mu = 10^{-9}$ m

1 Ångstrom $= 1$ Å $= 10^{-10}$ m

1 X-unit $= 1$ XU $= 10^{-13}$ m

Plane Angle

$$1 \text{ rev} = 2\pi \text{ radian} = 360°$$

Mass

	KG	GM	SLUG	AMU
1 kilogram	1	10^3	6.852×10^{-2}	6.024×10^{26}
1 gram	10^{-3}	1	6.852×10^{-5}	6.024×10^{23}
1 slug	14.59	1.459×10^4	1	8.789×10^{27}
1 atomic mass unit	1.660×10^{-27}	1.660×10^{-24}	1.137×10^{-28}	1

Time

	SEC	MIN	HR	DAY	YR
1 second	1	1.667×10^{-2}	2.778×10^{-4}	1.157×10^{-5}	3.169×10^{-8}
1 minute	60	1	1.667×10^{-2}	6.994×10^{-4}	1.901×10^{-6}
1 hour	3600	60	1	4.167×10^{-2}	1.141×10^{-4}
1 day	8.640×10^4	1440	24	1	2.738×10^{-3}
1 year	3.156×10^7	5.259×10^5	8.766×10^3	365.2	1

Speed

	M/SEC	CM/SEC	FT/SEC	MI/HR
1 meter/second	1	10^2	3.281	2.237
1 centimeter/second	10^{-2}	1	3.281×10^{-2}	2.237×10^{-2}
1 foot/second	0.3048	30.48	1	0.6818
1 mile/hour	0.4470	44.70	1.467	1

$$1 \text{ mi/min} = 60 \text{ mi/hr} = 88 \text{ ft/sec}$$

Force

	NT	DYNE	LB
1 newton	1	10^5	0.2248
1 dyne	10^{-5}	1	2.248×10^{-6}
1 pound	4.448	4.448×10^5	1

Work, Energy, Heat

	JOULE	ERG	FT-LB
1 joule	1	10^7	0.7376
1 erg	10^{-7}	1	7.376×10^{-8}
1 ft-lb	1.356	1.356×10^7	1
1 ev	1.602×10^{-19}	1.602×10^{-12}	1.182×10^{-19}
1 gm-cal	4.186	4.186×10^7	3.087
1 BTU	1.055×10^3	1.055×10^{10}	7.779×10^2
1 kw-hr	3.600×10^6	3.600×10^{13}	2.655×10^6

	EV	CAL	BTU	KW-HR
1 joule	6.242×10^{18}	0.2389	9.481×10^{-4}	2.778×10^{-7}
1 erg	6.242×10^{11}	2.389×10^{-8}	9.481×10^{-11}	2.778×10^{-14}
1 ft-lb	8.464×10^{18}	0.3239	1.285×10^{-3}	3.766×10^{-7}
1 ev	1	3.827×10^{-20}	1.519×10^{-22}	4.450×10^{-26}
1 gm-cal	2.613×10^{19}	1	3.968×10^{-3}	1.163×10^{-6}
1 BTU	6.585×10^{21}	2.520×10^2	1	2.930×10^{-4}
1 kw-hr	2.247×10^{25}	8.601×10^5	3.413×10^2	1

Pressure

	NT/M²	DYNE/CM²	ATM
1 newton/meter²	1	10	9.869×10^{-6}
1 dyne/centimeter²	10^{-1}	1	9.869×10^{-7}
1 atmosphere	1.013×10^5	1.013×10^6	1
1 centimeter mercury†	1.333×10^3	1.333×10^4	1.316×10^{-2}
1 pound/inch²	6.895×10^3	6.895×10^4	6.805×10^{-2}
1 pound/foot²	47.88	4.788×10^2	4.725×10^{-4}

	CM Hg	LB/IN.²	LB/FT²
1 newton/meter²	7.501×10^{-4}	1.450×10^{-4}	2.089×10^{-2}
1 dyne/centimeter²	7.501×10^{-5}	1.450×10^{-5}	2.089×10^{-3}
1 atmosphere	76	14.70	2.116×10^3
1 centimeter mercury†	1	0.1943	27.85
1 pound/inch²	5.171	1	144
1 pound/foot²	3.591×10^{-2}	6.944×10^{-3}	1

† At 0° C and at a location where the acceleration due to gravity has its "standard" value, 9.80665 m/sec².

Power

1 horsepower = 550 ft-lb/sec = 0.7457 kilowatt

appendix III

MATHEMATICAL RELATIONS

Series Expansions

$$(a + b)^n = a^n + \frac{n}{1!} a^{n-1} b + \frac{n(n - 1)}{2!} a^{n-2} b^2 + \cdots$$

$$\lim_{n \to \infty} \left(1 + \frac{x}{n}\right)^n \equiv e^x = 1 + x + \frac{x^2}{2!} + \frac{x^3}{3!} + \cdots$$

$$\sin x = x - \frac{x^3}{3!} + \frac{x^5}{5!} - \cdots$$

$$\cos x = 1 - \frac{x^2}{2!} + \frac{x^4}{4!} - \cdots$$

$$\tan x = x + \frac{x^3}{3} + \frac{2x^5}{15} + \cdots \qquad \left(\text{for } -\frac{\pi}{2} < x < \frac{\pi}{2}\right)$$

Trigonometric Identities

$$\sin^2 a + \cos^2 a = 1$$

$$\sin (a \pm b) = \sin a \cos b \pm \cos a \sin b$$

$$\cos (a \pm b) = \cos a \cos b \mp \sin a \sin b$$

Numerical Constants

$$\pi = 3.14159$$
$$e = 2.71828$$
$$\sqrt{2} = 1.414$$
$$\sqrt{3} = 1.732$$

Numerical Constants (*cont.*)

$$1 \text{ radian} = 57.3°$$

$$\sin 30° = \cos 60° = \tfrac{1}{2} = 0.500$$

$$\cos 30° = \sin 60° = \frac{\sqrt{3}}{2} = 0.866$$

$$\sin 45° = \cos 45° = \frac{\sqrt{2}}{2} = 0.707$$

For small θ (in radians), $\sin \theta \simeq \theta$, $\tan \theta \simeq \theta$.

a p p e n d i x   I V

CHRONOLOGY OF IMPORTANT
ADVANCES IN CLASSICAL
MECHANICS AND HEAT

Listed below are the dates of first publication or announcement of important advances in classical mechanics and heat, together with the scientist responsible. This brief chronology does not list significant advances in mathematics or in the philosophy of science, nor does it list the contributions of the scientists to other branches of physics (see Appendix IV, Volume II).

The following books give excerpts (in English) from original papers:

Magie, W. F., *A Source Book of Physics*, New York: McGraw-Hill Book Company, Inc., 1935.

M. H. Shamos, *Great Experiments in Physics*, New York: Holt, Rinehart and Winston, Inc., 1960.

Elementary physics textbooks giving more emphasis to the history of classical physics are:

Taylor, L. M., *Physics, the Pioneer Science*, New York: Dover Publications, 1959.
Holton, G. J., and D. H. D. Roller, *Foundations of Modern Physical Science*, Reading, Mass.: Addison-Wesley Publishing Company, 1958.
Rogers, E. M., *Physics for the Inquiring Mind*, Princeton, N.J.: Princeton University Press, 1960.

Publication date	Scientist or Group	Discovery or Accomplishment
ca. 240 B.C.	Archimedes (287?–212 B.C.)	Buoyancy; the lever
A.D. 1506	da Vinci, Leonardo (1452–1519)	First statement of law of inertia; mechanics; levers; hydrostatics

Publication date		*Scientist or Group*	*Discovery or Accomplishment*
A.D.	1530	Copernicus, Nicolaus (1473–1543)	Reference frames
	1586	Stevinus, Simon (1548–1620)	Statics of a particle; vector addition of forces
	1619	Kepler, Johannes (1571–1630)	Laws of planetary motion
	1632	Galilei, Galileo (1564–1642)	Foundations of mechanics
	1637	Descartes, René (1596–1650)	Linear momentum as a measure of the "quantity of motion"
	1641	Torricelli, Evangelista (1608–1647)	Hydrodynamics
	1653	Pascal, Blaise (1623–1662)	Hydrostatics
	1662	Boyle, Robert (1627–1691)	Pressure–volume relationship for gases at constant temperature
	1673	Huygens, Christian (1629–1695)	Oscillations; pendulum; work and energy
	1678	Hooke, Robert (1635–1703)	Elasticity
	1686	Newton, Sir Isaac (1642–1727)	*Principia Mathematica Philosophiae Naturalis;* laws of motion; universal gravitation; equality of inertial and gravitational mass
	1686	Leibnitz, Gottfried (1646–1716)	Kinetic energy as a measure of the "quantity of motion"
	1687	Varignon, Pierre (1654–1722)	Torques
	1738	Bernoulli, Daniel (1700–1782)	Hydrodynamics
	1743	d'Alembert, Jean (1717?–1783)	Demonstration that both linear momentum and kinetic energy are proper measures of the "quantity of motion"; inertial forces
	1779	Coulomb, Charles (1736–1806)	Torsional elasticity; friction
	1789	Lavoisier, Antoine (1743–1794)	Mass conservation in chemical reactions
	1798	Cavendish, Henry (1731–1810)	Gravitational experiments
	1798	Thompson, Benjamin (1753–1814)	Demonstration that thermal energy is produced in unlimited quantity by friction
	1799	Davy, Sir Humphry (1778–1829)	Heat produced by friction
	1799	Laplace, Pierre (1749–1827)	Molecular forces; adiabatic processes; celestial mechanics

Publication date	*Scientist or Group*	*Discovery or Accomplishment*
A.D. 1802	Gay-Lussac, Joseph (1778–1850)	Thermal expansion of gases
1803	Black, Joseph (1728–1799)	Specific heat; latent heat; change of state; distinction between heat and temperature
1807	Young, Thomas (1773–1829)	Concept of kinetic energy; elasticity
1808	Dalton, John (1766–1844)	Atomic hypothesis confirmed in chemical reactions
1813	Avogadro, Amedeo (1776–1856)	Equal gas volumes contain equal numbers of molecules
1819	Dulong, Pierre (1785–1838) and Petit, Alexis (1791–1820)	Atomic specific heats
1820	French National Assembly	Adoption of the metric system
1822	Fourier, Jean (1768–1830)	Theory of mass, length, and time as fundamental dimensions
1824	Carnot, Nicolas (1796–1832)	Engines; theoretical foundations of thermodynamics
1827	Brown, Robert (1773–1858)	Direct observation of molecular chaos
1834	Poinsot, Louis (1777–1859)	Rotational dynamics
1842	Mayer, Julius (1814–1878)	Equivalence of heat and work
1843	Joule, James (1818–1889)	Experimental verification of energy conservation (through the constancy of the "mechanical equivalent of heat"—4.19 joules/calorie); free expansion of gases
1847	von Helmholtz, Hermann (1821–1894)	Energy conservation and conservative forces
1850	Clausius, Rudolph (1822–1888)	Kinetic theory of gases; thermodynamics
1851	Foucault, Jean (1819–1868)	Demonstration of the Earth's rotation through a pendulum; the gyroscope
1851	Kelvin, Baron (William Thomson) (1824–1907)	Absolute scale of temperature; second law of thermodynamics
1860	Maxwell, James (1831–1879)	Molecular velocity distribution; kinetic theory
1877	Boltzmann, Ludwig (1844–1906)	Entropy and probability; black-body radiation
1880	van der Waals, Johannes (1837–1923)	Equation of state of a nonideal gas
1915	Einstein, Albert (1879–1955)	Principle of equivalence; relativity theory

appendix V

NATURAL TRIGONOMETRIC FUNCTIONS

ANGLE		SINE	COSINE	TANGENT	ANGLE		SINE	COSINE	TANGENT
DEGREES	RADIANS				DEGREES	RADIANS			
0°	0.000	0.000	1.000	0.000					
1°	0.018	0.018	1.000	0.018	46°	0.803	0.719	0.695	1.036
2°	0.035	0.035	0.999	0.035	47°	0.820	0.731	0.682	1.072
3°	0.052	0.052	0.999	0.052	48°	0.838	0.743	0.669	1.111
4°	0.070	0.070	0.998	0.070	49°	0.855	0.755	0.656	1.150
5°	0.087	0.087	0.996	0.087	50°	0.873	0.766	0.643	1.192
6°	0.105	0.105	0.995	0.105	51°	0.890	0.777	0.629	1.235
7°	0.122	0.122	0.993	0.123	52°	0.908	0.788	0.616	1.280
8°	0.140	0.139	0.990	0.141	53°	0.925	0.799	0.602	1.327
9°	0.157	0.156	0.988	0.158	54°	0.942	0.809	0.588	1.376
10°	0.175	0.174	0.985	0.176	55°	0.960	0.819	0.574	1.428
11°	0.192	0.191	0.982	0.194	56°	0.977	0.829	0.559	1.483
12°	0.209	0.208	0.978	0.213	57°	0.995	0.839	0.545	1.540
13°	0.227	0.225	0.974	0.231	58°	1.012	0.848	0.530	1.600
14°	0.244	0.242	0.970	0.249	59°	1.030	0.857	0.515	1.664
15°	0.262	0.259	0.966	0.268	60°	1.047	0.866	0.500	1.732
16°	0.279	0.276	0.961	0.287	61°	1.065	0.875	0.485	1.804
17°	0.297	0.292	0.956	0.306	62°	1.082	0.883	0.470	1.881
18°	0.314	0.309	0.951	0.325	63°	1.100	0.891	0.454	1.963
19°	0.332	0.326	0.946	0.344	64°	1.117	0.899	0.438	2.050
20°	0.349	0.342	0.940	0.364	65°	1.134	0.906	0.423	2.145
21°	0.367	0.358	0.934	0.384	66°	1.152	0.914	0.407	2.246
22°	0.384	0.375	0.927	0.404	67°	1.169	0.921	0.391	2.356
23°	0.401	0.391	0.921	0.425	68°	1.187	0.927	0.375	2.475
24°	0.419	0.407	0.914	0.445	69°	1.204	0.934	0.358	2.605
25°	0.436	0.423	0.906	0.466	70°	1.222	0.940	0.342	2.747
26°	0.454	0.438	0.899	0.488	71°	1.239	0.946	0.326	2.904
27°	0.471	0.454	0.891	0.510	72°	1.257	0.951	0.309	3.078
28°	0.489	0.470	0.883	0.532	73°	1.274	0.956	0.292	3.271
29°	0.506	0.485	0.875	0.554	74°	1.292	0.961	0.276	3.487
30°	0.524	0.500	0.866	0.577	75°	1.309	0.966	0.259	3.732
31°	0.541	0.515	0.857	0.601	76°	1.327	0.970	0.242	4.011
32°	0.559	0.530	0.848	0.625	77°	1.344	0.974	0.225	4.331
33°	0.576	0.545	0.839	0.649	78°	1.361	0.978	0.208	4.705
34°	0.593	0.559	0.829	0.675	79°	1.379	0.982	0.191	5.145
35°	0.611	0.574	0.819	0.700	80°	1.396	0.985	0.174	5.671
36°	0.628	0.588	0.809	0.727	81°	1.414	0.988	0.156	6.314
37°	0.646	0.602	0.799	0.754	82°	1.431	0.990	0.139	7.115
38°	0.663	0.616	0.788	0.781	83°	1.449	0.993	0.122	8.144
39°	0.681	0.629	0.777	0.810	84°	1.466	0.995	0.105	9.514
40°	0.698	0.643	0.766	0.839	85°	1.484	0.996	0.087	11.43
41°	0.716	0.656	0.755	0.869	86°	1.501	0.998	0.070	14.30
42°	0.733	0.669	0.743	0.900	87°	1.518	0.999	0.052	19.08
43°	0.751	0.682	0.731	0.933	88°	1.536	0.999	0.035	28.64
44°	0.768	0.695	0.719	0.966	89°	1.553	1.000	0.018	57.29
45°	0.785	0.707	0.707	1.000	90°	1.571	1.000	0.000	∞

appendix VI

THE GREEK ALPHABET

Alpha	α	A
Beta	β	B
Gamma	γ	Γ
Delta	δ	Δ
Epsilon	ϵ	E
Zeta	ζ	Z
Eta	η	H
Theta	θ, ϑ	Θ
Iota	ι	I
Kappa	κ	K
Lambda	λ	Λ
Mu	μ	M
Nu	ν	N
Xi	ξ	Ξ
Omicron	o	O
Pi	π	Π
Rho	ρ	P
Sigma	σ, ς	Σ
Tau	τ	T
Upsilon	υ	Υ
Phi	ϕ, φ	Φ
Chi	χ	X
Psi	ψ	Ψ
Omega	ω	Ω

ANSWERS

to odd-numbered numerical problems

CHAPTER 2

2-1   6

2-3   (a) ~7920 mi in direction N.Y. to Mel.;   (b) 12,400 mi;   (c) 390 mi/hr;
(d) 246 mi/hr in direction N.Y. to Mel.

2-7   (a) 78.0 m/sec;   (b) 72.1 m/sec;   (c) 72.0 m/sec;   (d) 72.0 m/sec

2-9   (a) $v = 3At^2$, $a = 6At$, $A:(L/T^3)$;   (b) $v = CB \cos Ct$, $a = -C^2B \sin Ct$,
$B:(L)$, $C:(1/T)$;   (c) $v = -kD\,e^{-kt}$, $a = k^2D\,e^{-kt}$, $D:(L)$, $k:(1/T)$;
(d) $v = E + 2Ft + 3Gt^2$, $a = 2F + 6Gt$, $E:(L/T)$, $F:(L/T^2)$, $G:(L/T^3)$

2-13 $(1.1 \times 10^3 \text{ m/sec})/n$, where $n = 1, 2, 3, \ldots$

2-15   (a) 12.6 sec;   (b) 554 ft

2-17   (a) 13 m, 7.5 m/sec;   (b) 31 m, 1.5 m/sec

2-19   Dusenberg

2-21   (a) yes, twice;   (b) truck passes car at 1.3 sec and 0.62 m from light;   car
passes truck at 49 sec and 950 m from light

2-23   (a) 405 ft;   (b) 4.6 sec;   (c) 62 mi/hr east   *32.4 sec*

2-25   (a) left plate;   (b) 4.0×10^{-9} sec

2-27   (a) 64 ft/sec;   (b) 64 ft

2-29   1130 ft/sec

2-31   Yes

2-33   21 ft/sec

2-35   (a) 44.8 ft/sec;   (b) 15.4 ft

2-37   170 sec

2-39   (a) 4.6 sec;   (b) 120 ft/sec

2-41   90 ft

2-43 $a \propto \sin \theta$

CHAPTER 3

3-1   1.6 mi, 70° east of south

3-3   (a) +25.0 ft, −43.3 ft;   (b) −2.5 ft, 4.33 ft;   (c) −10.0 ft, 17.3 ft

3-5   (a) −17 ft, +10 ft;   (b) 0 ft, −30 ft;   (c) +30 ft, −40 ft

3-7   (a) 8 ft;   (b) 6 ft

3-9   0.9 m south

3-13   Any vector perpendicular to A

3-21   (a) parallel;   (b) antiparallel;   (c) at angle of 139°;   (d) at angle of 99°

CHAPTER 4

4-1 $x = -104$ ft, $y = -72$ ft, $v_x = -30.4$ ft/sec, $v_y = -7.2$ ft/sec

4-3   (a) 18 m/sec, 56° above negative X-axis;   (b) 72 m/sec², 34° below
positive X-axis

4-5   (a) reversed in direction;   (b) same;   (c) reversed in direction

4-7   5.7 ft

4-9   98 m

4–11 (a) $\dfrac{v_0{}^2 \sin^2 \theta_0}{2g}$; (b) $\dfrac{2v_0 \sin \theta_0}{g}$

4–13 (a) 0.21 m; (b) 0.23 m

4–15 1500 ft

4–17 (a) 33 ft; (b) 39 ft/sec

4–19 72 ft/sec, 66° above the horizontal

4–21 140 ft/sec, 53° above horizontal

4–23 29,000 m, 160 sec, 104,000 m

4–25 Strikes ceiling 15 ft horizontally from point thrown

4–27 (a) 30 ft/sec; (b) 17 ft

4–29 (a) 4 ft; (b) 13 ft/sec

4–31 4.5×10^{13} m/sec^2

4–33 6.7×10^{-12} cm

CHAPTER 5

5–1 60 ft

5–3 4.5×10^{16} m/sec^2

5–7 (a) 31.9 ft/sec^2 upward; (b) 31.9 ft/sec^2 downward; (c) nearly "weightless"

5–9 (a) 52 m/sec; (b) 5.2×10^9 m/sec

5–11 (a) 0.11 ft/sec^2; (b) 0.078 ft/sec^2; (c) zero

5–13 $6.1 \times 10^{-4} g$

5–17 26 ft/sec^2, 19 ft/sec^2

5–19 (a) 16 ft/sec^2; (b) -28 ft/sec^2

5–21 (a) $\pi^2 r/8$; (b) $r/2$

5–23 (a) 3.0 ft; (b) 12 sec; (c) 1.6 ft/sec; (d) 0.82 ft/sec^2; (e) 1.5 ft, -1.4 ft/sec, -0.41 ft/sec^2

5–25 0.90 rad/sec

5–27 $x = 6.0 \cos 13t$, $y = -6.0 \sin 13t$, $v_x = -78 \sin 13t$, $v_y = -78 \cos 13t$, $a_x = -1100 \cos 13t$, $a_y = 1100 \sin 13t$

5–31 (a) 0.75 ft; (b) 16 rad/sec

5–37 160 cm/sec^2

5–39 (a) 0.388 cm above equilibrium position; (b) 2.4 cm

5–41 7.06 vib/sec

5–43 (a) 100 cm/sec horizontally; (b) 210 cm/sec, 62° to horizontal

CHAPTER 6

6–3 (a) 80 mi/hr east; (b) 100 mi/hr 37° south of east

6–5 (a) 260 mi/hr; (b) 82° north of east

6–7 29 mi/hr

6–9 20 ft/sec

6–11 (a) 23 ft/sec, 32 ft/sec^2; (b) 33 ft/sec, 32 ft/sec^2

6–13 (a) 12 m/sec up; (b) 28 m/sec at 26° above horizontal

6–15 (a) directly below; (b) 62 ft/sec; (c) 65 ft/sec, 72° below horizontal; (d) 39 ft

6–17 14 ft/sec at 88.5° below forward horizontal direction

6–19 (a) 3960 mi, 1030 mi/hr, 0.107 ft/sec^2; (b) 3960 mi, 0, 0

6–21 (a) 50 mi/hr; (b) 0; (c) 100 mi/hr forward; (d) 71 mi/hr at 45° to the horizontal

6–23 330 ft/sec

CHAPTER 7

7–3 1.6×10^3 kg/m³
7–5 $\sim 3 \times 10^{-10}$ m
7–7 2.39×10^{-3} amu

CHAPTER 8

8–1 $p = mgt$
8–3   1.8 m/sec
8–5   1.88 kg
8–7   2 m/sec
8–9   (a) 40 ft; (b) 43 ft
8–11   0.32 m/sec northward
8–13   (a) 180 kg; (b) 6000 m/sec forward
8–15   (a) $v = v_e$; (b) 0.368
8–17 $3/5v$
8–19   1050 m/sec north
8–21 $\tan^{-1}\dfrac{v'}{v}$
8–23   72 mi/hr, 34° east of north; 72 mi/hr, 34° west of north
8–25   1, 2, 3, 4
8–27   (a) 6.1×10^5 m/sec; (b) 1.6×10^5 m/sec
8–29   (a) Cl³⁵ at 1.82×10^{-10} m; I¹²⁷ at 0.50×10^{-10} m; (b) 3.6
8–31   In opposite direction
8–33 $\bar{x} = -1.77$ m, $\bar{y} = -2.07$ m
8–35   0.22 mi/hr
8–37   On the axis of symmetry, $h/4$ above base
8–39 $\bar{x} = 0.067R$, $\bar{y} = -0.067R$
8–41   (a) 50 kg-m/sec to the right; (b) 1.7 m/sec to the right; (c) 20-kg mass, 13.3 m/sec to the right; 10-kg mass, 26.7 m/sec to the left; (d) 20-kg mass, 267 kg-m/sec to the right; 10-kg mass, 267 kg-m/sec to the left

CHAPTER 9

9–1   1720 lb at 53° W of N
9–3   (a) 31 lb; (c) zero
9–5   180 lb
9–7   (a) 1000 dynes; (b) 15,000 dynes
9–9 $2mv \sin \theta$ perpendicular to cushion
9–11   (a) 2000 lb toward batter; (b) 2000 lb away from batter
9–13   2.00 nt
9–15   3.4 nt/m²
9–17   (b) zero
9–19   (a) 5.0 slugs; (b) 26 lb
9–21 $(41 + 2.7t)$ nt

CHAPTER 10

10–1   (a) 40 ft/sec²; (b) 80 ft; (c) 80 ft/sec, all 53° below horizontal
10–3   (a) 0.38 slug-ft/sec; (b) 1.60 slug-ft/sec
10–5   64.4 lb, 19.6 nt, 1.96×10^6 dynes
10–7 1.9×10^3 m/sec²

10–9   (a) 7.6×10^{-19} kg-m/sec; (b) 4.2×10^{-19} kg-m/sec; (c) 3.8×10^{-14} nt

10–11   9.4 lb

10–13   30°

10–15   (a) 1.1 lb; (b) 1.9 lb; (c) 1.2 lb

10–17   0.8 m

10–19   (a) 2.0 m/sec^2; (b) 6.0 nt to the left; (c) 6.0 nt to the right

10–21   (a) 1.0 m/sec to the right; (b) 500 nt

10–23   (a) 0.82 kg; (b) masses to 4 significant figures, acceleration to 3

10–25   (a) 13 ft/sec^2; (b) 1.2 lb; (c) 4.0 in.; (d) 2.0 lb

10–27   95 gm

10–29   (a) 1.1 lb, 8.0 ft/sec^2 down incline; (b) 0.85 lb, 19 ft/sec^2 down incline; (c) zero, 58 ft/sec^2 at 34° below horizontal

10–31   (a) Tension in both strings 20 nt, acceleration zero; (b) 25 nt and 21 nt, 1.6 m/sec^2

10–33   In all three cases the center of mass accelerates to the right at 150 m/sec^2

10–35   A circle

10–37   (a) $N_a = 800$ lb, $N_b = 3600$ lb, $N_c = 2000$ lb; (b) It would leave the road at a!

10–39   (a) 0.48; (b) 73 lb; (c) 26°

10–41   12 in.

10–43   (b) $(m_0 g/v_e)\, e^{-gt/v_e}$; (c) both zero; (d) $(m_0 g)\, e^{-gt/v_e}$; (e) $(m_0 a/v_e)\, e^{-at/v_e}$

CHAPTER 11

11–1   (a) 60 ft-lb; (b) zero; (c) zero

11–3   (a) 0.98×10^6 m/sec; (b) 2.3×10^4 m/sec

11–5   20 ft-lb

11–7   (a) 40 nt-sec, 400 joules; (b) 40 nt-sec, -200 joules

11–9   16 lb

11–11   2.7 ft-lb

11–13   (a) $\frac{1}{2}(k_1 + k_2)x^2$; (b) $(k_1 + k_2)x$

11–15   (a) 25; (b) 2.9

11–19   (a) 5.2 cm/sec; (b) zero

11–21   (a) $x\sqrt{2k/m}$; (b) $x\sqrt{k/m}$

11–23   (a) $\frac{1}{8}$ joule; (b) $\frac{3}{8}$ joule; (c) $\frac{1}{8}$ watt; (d) $\frac{3}{8}$ watt

11–27   1.2 hp

11–29   9.6 kw

CHAPTER 12

12–1 $\sqrt{2gL}$

12–3   (a) 3.5 ft; (b) 12.5 ft-lb; 22 ft/sec

12–5   1.0 joule

12–7   (a) 48,000 lb; 2.9 hp

12–9 $r/2$

12–11   6.9 m/sec

12–13   (a) 4.1 ft/sec; (b) 6.5 in.

12–15   (a) 1.9 ft/sec; (b) 2 in.

12–17   0.19 m/sec and 0.09 m/sec

12–21 $-\left(\dfrac{A}{r}\right) e^{-(r/a)} \left(\dfrac{1}{a} + \dfrac{1}{r}\right)$

12–23   (a) 98 lb; (b) 4.4 hp; (c) the frictional force of the road surface on the wheels
12–25   0.88 ft-lb
12–27   3.3 ft
12–29   (a) 2.29 m/sec; (b) 7.6 m; (c) 6.9 m/sec
12–31   180 in.
12–33 -8.3 m/sec and 26.7 m/sec
12–35   (a) 1.0 joule; (b) $\frac{1}{2}$ joule; (c) 50%; (a′) 1.0 joule; (b′) zero; (c′) 100%
12–37   290 m/sec

CHAPTER 13
13–1 -130 rad/sec^2
13–3   2900 rad
13–5   1.0 rad/sec^2
13–11   (a) 67 rad/sec; (b) 13.5 rad/sec^2
13–13   (a) 4.4 rad/sec; (b) 3.1 rad/sec
13–15 $\frac{1}{60}$
13–19   (a) 5 rad/sec^2 south; (b) zero; (c) 50 rad/sec south

CHAPTER 14
14–1   (a) 21 down; (b) 21 up
14–3   Vectors are in a plane perpendicular to A and of magnitude 48; each vector is also perpendicular to B.
14–5   (a) 2.5 m; (b) 340 kg-m^2; (c) 4.4 m; (d) 240 kg-m^2; (e) 3.8 m; (f) zero
14–7   (a) $8mL^2$; (b) $4mL^2$; (c) $4mL^2$
14–9   (a) $\frac{1}{4}MR^2$; (b) $\frac{5}{4}MR^2$
14–11 $5ML^2/64$
14–13   (a) 5.6 slug-ft^2; (b) 15 ft-lb; (c) 2.7 sec^{-2}; (d) 8.0 sec^{-2}; (e) 40 ft-lb; (f) 40 ft-lb
14–17   0.20
14–19 $\sqrt{4g(R-r)/3}$
14–21   The loop
14–23   (a) 0.37 m-nt; (b) 7.4 m/sec^2
14–25   (a) 21.3 ft/sec^2; (b) $Mg/6$
14–27 $(17/21)H$
14–29   41°
14–33   Center of mass
14–35   (a) 2500 lb; (b) 54 in.
14–37   All the way
14–41   (a) 74° above the horizontal; (b) 0.29
14–43   (a) 190 lb at 72° above horizontal; (b) 133 ft-lb

CHAPTER 15
15–1   (a) 2×10^4 kg-m^2, 500 kg-m/sec north, 0.25 rad/sec north; (b) 5×10^3 kg-m^2, 500 kg-m/sec north, 0.10 rad/sec north
15–3 1.06×10^{-34} joule-sec
15–5   (a) mvd; (b) $m(v + V)d$
15–7   (a) $M/(M + 2m)$; (b) mv
15–13   (a) $\sqrt{Mgr/m}$; (b) $\sqrt{Mmgr^3}$; (c) $\sqrt{Mgr^3/m}(r - y)$; (d) $Mgry/2(r - y)^2[2r - y] - Mgy$

15–15   (a) 63 rpm; (b) 59 ft-lb
15–17 4ω
15–19   (a) $v/3$; (b) $mvL/3$; (c) v/L; (d) $\frac{2}{3}$
15–21 $2mvd/3I$

15–23 $v = \dfrac{2}{R}\left[\dfrac{mg}{M+2m}\left(\dfrac{2mh}{M+2m}+R\right)\right]^{1/2}$

15–25   10 parts in 10^5
15–27 $\omega_p = Mgd/I\omega$

CHAPTER 16
16–1   (a) 600 ft; (b) 12 sec
16–3 6.2×10^{-10} m-nt
16–5   (a) 0.42 m from 1-kg mass, 0.58 m from 2-kg mass; (b) 7.6×10^{-10} nt
16–7   27,000 mi
16–9   320
16–11 6.1×10^{-6}
16–13   (a) 6.8×10^{-3}; (b) 3.4×10^{-3}

16–15   (a) $mg\left[1 - \left(2 - \dfrac{r\omega^2}{g}\right)\dfrac{r\omega^2}{g}\cos^2\theta\right]^{1/2}$; (b) $\tan\varphi = \left(\dfrac{1}{1-\dfrac{r\omega^2}{g}}\right)\tan\theta$

16–17   (a) 0.998 mg, 0.16° with the 45° line; (b) 2.2 hr
16–19   (a) 11 km/sec; (b) few hundred hours
16–21 10^{-5}
16–23 1.62×10^5 mi from Earth; (b) 1.63×10^5 mi from Earth; (c) 3.1×10^7 joules
16–25   (a) $v_1/v_2 = 2$, velocities in opposite directions; (b) Gm^2/d
16–27   (a) 6.6×10^9 joules; (b) same
16–29   Oxygen: (a) no, (b) no; hydrogen: (a) no, (b) yes; xenon: (a) no, (b) no
16–31 6.2×10^9 joule
16–35   (a) $0.38r$; (b) $2.62r$; (c) $6\pi\sqrt{r^3/Gm_e}$
16–37   (a) 3490 mi; (b) 8.2×10^3 m/sec; (c) 1.1×10^8 joules
16–41   (a) out of paper; (b) down
16–43   (a) $\tan^{-1}(r\omega^2/g)$ from the vertical; (b) $(g^2 + \omega^4 r^2)^{1/2}$
16–45   (a) oscillation about a line which is 71.6° below the horizontal; (b) 36.8°

CHAPTER 17
17–1   (a) $2k$; (b) $4k$
17–3   7.4 lb
17–5   (a) 5.5×10^{-7} cm; (b) 5.5×10^{-6} cm
17–13   (a) 2.30×10^{-8} cm; (b) 9.2×10^{-11} cm; (c) 2.0×10^3 nt; (d) 9.4×10^9 atoms; (e) 2.1×10^{-7} nt; (f) 2.3×10^3 nt/m
17–15   (a) $0.050 \cos 40t$; (b) 2.0 joules; (c) 0.76 joules; (d) 1.24 joules
17–17   1.1 sec
17–19   (a) 84.6 sec; (b) the same
17–21 $2f$
17–23   0.31 sec
17–27   (a) $G = \kappa\theta r^2/Mml$; (b) $\kappa = 2\pi^2 ml^2/T^2$
17–29 4.1×10^{-5} kg-m^2
17–31   (a) 1.6 sec; (b) $T = 2\pi[2(l^2 + 3y^2)/3g(l + 2y)]^{1/2}$

17–33   (a) an edge; (b) $2\pi(\frac{2}{3}g)^{1/2}(l^2 + w^2)^{1/4}$; (c) at the center; (d) infinite
17–35   (a) $\pi\sqrt{6R/g}$; (b) $3R/2$

CHAPTER 18
18–1   (a) 0.01 kg; (b) 1.9 $\times$ 10⁵ nt/m²
18–3   1.2 $\times$ 10¹⁹ lb
18–5   17 ergs
18–7   (b) 0.149 mm
18–9   (a) 7.8 lb/in.²; (b) 4.3 lb/in.²; (c) 32 ft/sec at all three points; (d) 0.44 lb/ft³
18–11   0.44 in.
18–13   2.3 lb/in.²
18–15   (a) 0.088 ft³/sec; (b) 0.17 slug/sec
18–17   (a) $A = A_u\sqrt{h/(y + h)}$; (b) $A_u\sqrt{2gh}$
18–19   (a) 16 ft; (b) 32 ft
18–21   75.4 cm Hg
18–23   (a) 27 cm; (b) $\sim$10⁻⁴ cm
18–25   160 lb
18–27   1.8 cm
18–29   1.1 $\times$ 10³ nt; (b) 1.1 $\times$ 10² joules
18–31   (a) 0.92; (b) same
18–33   13 nt
18–35   2.2 slugs
18–37   3.6 gm/cm³; (b) 0.70 gm/cm³
18–39   1.0 sec

CHAPTER 19
19–1   (a) 4.17° K; (b) 90.28° K; (c) 600.5° K; (d) 1945.4° F; (e) 6116° F
19–3   (2.73 $\times$ 10⁵)°
19–5   271° C
19–9   0.4 in.
19–11   13 nt
19–15   (a) 93° C; (b) 240° C; (c) 170° C
19–17 $(\alpha_l + \alpha_w)$
19–19   (a) 6.9 $\times$ 10⁻³ mm³; (b) 20 mm
19–21   Three
19–23   1.2 $\times$ 10⁸ nt/m²

CHAPTER 20
20–1   510° C
20–3   95 cm
20–7   (b) no
20–9   2.5 liters
20–11   Helium
20–13   (a) 2.1 mole; (b) 0.83 gm/liter; (c) 13 gm/liter
20–15   3.0 atm
20–17   (a) 5.4 kg; (b) 1.3 kg/cm³; (c) 7.2 atm
20–21   (a) zero; (b) 136.5° K; (c) 1.12 $\times$ 10³ joules; (d) 273° K; (e) 1.54 $\times$ 10³ joules
20–23   (a) isovolumetric to zero pressure, isobaric to V_2, isovolumetric to p_2; (b) 0° K

CHAPTER 21

21–1 6.02×10^{23}
21–3   (a) 5.90×10^{22}; (b) 3.2 Å
21–5   (a) 7.2 m/sec; (b) 7.8 m/sec
21–9 1.004
21–11 538 m/sec
21–13 0.93
21–15 2.73×10^3 m/sec
21–17 $(5 \times 10^{11})^\circ$ K
21–19 (a) $(1.01 \times 10^4)^\circ$ K; (b) 1650° K
21–21 2.83
21–23 $(\sim10^4)^\circ$ K
21–25 $14,700$ joules
21–29 2×10^{-3} joule
21–31 (a) -2.1 joules; (b) -0.17° C
21–33 (a) 546° K; (b) 2.26×10^3 joules; (c) thermal energy enters gas, 1140 joules
21–35 (a) 3.5×10^{-23} joule/molecule-C°; (b) 4.8×10^{-23} joule/molecule-C°
21–37 354° C
21–41 (a) 3.2° K; (b) 1.9° K; (c) 1.4° K
21–43 (a) $15,000$ joules; (b) $25,000$ joules; (c) 0.50; (d) 0.50; (e) hydrogen

CHAPTER 22

22–1   (a) $[600/(2n + 1)]$m/sec with $n = 0, 1, 2, 3, \ldots$;
          (b) 3×10^8 rot/sec
22–7 $\sim2.2\%$
22–11 (a) 1.0; (b) 2.8; (c) 0.35
22–13 (a) $\frac{1}{2}$; (b) $(\frac{1}{2})^{10^3}$; (c) $(1/2000)^{10^3}$
22–15 $3RT/mv_{\mathrm{rms}}^2$
22–17 0.04 sec
22–19 1.2×10^{-5} atm
22–21 7.5×10^{14} cm $\simeq 5 \times 10^8$ mi!
22–23 1.27×10^{-6} atm
22–25 3.9×10^{-5} cm Hg

CHAPTER 23

23–1 350 gm
23–3 39 watt
23–5 320 m/sec
23–7 0.42 C°
23–9 7.7×10^{-6} C°
23–11 (a) 100° C; (b) $\frac{4}{3}$ gm
23–13 973 BTU/lb
23–15 4.6 watt
23–21 (a) 750 watt; (b) 101.34° C
23–25 ab
23–27 (a) 0.53 cm²; (b) 2860° K
23–29 4100° K
23–31 (a) 1.8×10^{27} watt; (b) 0.64 watt/cm²; (c) 20 percent

CHAPTER 24
24–1 (a) 6900 joules; (b) 6900 joules; (c) zero
24–3 34%
24–5 (a) 47%; (b) 1.1; (c) 2.1
24–7 (a) 205° K; (b) 25%
24–9 (a) yes; (b) the diatomic gas
24–13 (a) 12 joules/K°; (b) zero

INDEX